Handbook of linear integrated
electronics for research

Handbook of linear integrated electronics for research

T. D. S. Hamilton
Senior Lecturer in Physics
University of Manchester

McGRAW-HILL Book Company (UK) Limited

London · New York · St Louis · San Francisco · Auckland · Bogotá
Düsseldorf · Johannesburg · Madrid · Mexico · Montreal · New Delhi
Panama · Paris · São Paulo · Singapore · Sydney · Tokyo · Toronto

Published by
McGRAW-HILL Book Company (UK) Limited
MAIDENHEAD · BERKSHIRE · ENGLAND

British Library Cataloguing in Publication Data
Hamilton, T D S
  Handbook of linear integrated electronics for research.
  1. Linear integrated circuits
  I. Title
  621.381′73   TK7874   77–30037
  ISBN 0–07–084483–6

Copyright © 1977 McGraw-Hill Book Company (UK) Limited. All rights reserved. No part of this publication may be reproduced, stored in a retrieval system, or transmitted, in any form or by any means, electronic, mechanical, photocopying, recording, or otherwise, without the prior permission of McGraw-Hill Book Company (UK) Limited, or of the original copyright holder.

12345 WC&S 7987

PRINTED AND BOUND IN GREAT BRITAIN

To Laura, Ross and Dougal

Contents

Preface   xi

Notation   xv

1   Review of basic circuit theory   1

1.1   Ohm's law and all that   1
1.2   Network theorems   9
1.3   Phase and frequency response   14
1.4   Time constants, bandwidth, and pulse response   18
1.5   Impedance matching   23
1.6   Feedback   26
1.7   Grounding, loops, and guards   28
1.8   Noise   31
1.9   Basic diode and transistor characteristics   36
1.10   Some IC arrangements   47
1.11   Laplace transforms   51

2   Operational amplifiers   68

2.1   Introduction   68
2.2   The ideal amplifier and the virtual ground   70
2.3   Classes of operational amplifier   75
2.4   Frequency response and stability   81
2.5   Inverting, summing, non-inverting, and differential amplifiers   82
2.6   Operational integrator   87
2.7   Operational differentiator   94
2.8   Charge amplifier   100
2.9   IC amplifier characteristics   102

3   Stability of feedback systems   120

3.1   Introduction   120
3.2   The root-locus   120
3.3   The Nyquist diagram   123
3.4   The Bode plot   125

3.5	Phase compensation	128
3.6	12 dB/octave operational amplifiers	136
3.7	Transient response	138

4 Amplifiers — 143

4.1	Low noise amplifiers	143
4.2	Differential and instrumentation amplifiers	150
4.3	Logarithmic amplifiers	153
4.4	Active filters	158
4.5	Servo amplifiers and systems	173
4.6	High input impedance and electrometer amplifiers	181
4.7	Audio and servo power amplifiers	188
4.8	Miscellaneous amplifiers	

5 Oscillators — 229

5.1	Sinusoidal *RC* oscillators	229
5.2	Function generators	232
5.3	Relaxation and negative resistance oscillators	239
5.4	Crystal oscillators	249

6 Circuit functions — 260

6.1	Comparators and discriminators	260
6.2	Multipliers	268
6.3	Modulators	274
6.4	Phase-locked loop	278
6.5	Sample-hold	283

7 Power supplies — 297

7.1	Rectifiers	297
7.2	Voltage regulators	302
7.3	Current regulators	305
7.4	Constant voltage, constant current regulators	308
7.5	Series and parallel operation	309
7.6	Protection and ancillary circuits	313
7.7	IC regulators	316
7.8	Switching regulators	319
7.9	Cells and batteries	322
7.10	Voltage and current regulator diodes	325

8 Circuit devices — 342

8.1	Field-effect transistors	342
8.2	Voltage-controlled resistors and switches	349
8.3	Thyristors	355

9	**Optoelectronics**	375
9.1	Light units and measurement	375
9.2	Photodiodes and phototransistors	378
9.3	Photoresistors	383
9.4	Photomultipliers	385
9.5	Lamps and light-emitting diodes	394
9.6	Optoelectronic couplers	399
9.7	Miscellaneous opto devices	402
10	**Signal detection**	419
10.1	Signals and noise	419
10.2	Lock-in or coherent detection	420
10.3	Signal averaging	424
10.4	Correlation	427
11	**Applications**	436
Bibliography		445
Appendix: Complex numbers		447
Index		451

Preface

> 'Experience is the name everyone gives to their mistakes.'
> *Oscar Wilde*

This book is intended for people in a wide range of fields who use electronics in their experimental work. It is not particularly intended as a textbook or for professional engineers, though it could be of substantial use in both cases. Electronics is a vast subject and one cannot hope either to cover all of it in one volume, or even to know much about many aspects of it, so a severe restriction on topics must be accepted. I have chosen to omit both communication and digital applications. The former is not commonly of interest to experimenters, and the latter requires several volumes to even begin to do it justice.

The development of low cost integrated circuits constitutes, in my view, a revolution in electronics, possibly of greater magnitude than the advent of the transistor itself. It is now possible to think largely in terms of building blocks which can be assembled to form the required system, without necessarily knowing too much about the more detailed techniques of circuit design. Some knowledge of the mode of operation, however, can lead to more effective use of any device. The ready availability of many circuit functions, therefore, has been taken as the unifying feature of much of the present book.

The choice of topic and level of treatment has been strongly influenced by personal experience and by discussions with colleagues and students. As a physicist rather than an electronic engineer, one possibly sees things somewhat differently and this influences the way one understands and describes them. I have tried to concentrate on an understanding of how things work rather than on specific applications—the latter are covered by a fairly extensive collection of references to the literature and to the many excellent application notes produced by manufacturers. Though their efforts in this direction may not always be entirely altruistic, they and their authors deserve our commendation for this very substantial contribution of really useful information and guidance.

A rather larger number of references than is usual have been included and, though some of them may effectively duplicate one another, this makes it more likely that you will have access to a suitable one. More general references to a wide range of applications are given in chapter 11, followed by a bibliography of useful books. The references have been prepared directly from a computer print-out which allows them to be more up to date than would otherwise be possible. It should be noted that by no means all the references are referred to in the text, so it is worth scanning through the appropriate list to see if any others may be of use. Full titles are given in every case, so it is easier to decide whether they are worth looking up. Nowadays data sheets often contain extensive application information, so reference to these is not only an indication of the origin of the various devices.

The level of treatment poses a delicate problem—at what level does one start and how far should the development go? There is a tendency to eschew all but the most elementary mathematical ideas, but it seems to me too great a loss not to make use of some of the powerful and instructive tools available. In particular, the Laplace transform is so useful in circuit theory, and provides such a convenient description of many important situations, that it has been used wherever necessary. A short description is given of its use and application, at least to the level where a table of transform pairs can be used as readily as a set of log tables. Time spent in studying this section (1.11) will, I feel, be amply rewarded in understanding circuits, and in time saved in debugging poorly designed systems.

Chapter 1 is a resumé of useful basic circuit theory—the sort of mental furniture it is useful to have readily available. If the material is not familiar it may well repay the effort of reading this before consulting other sections. Chapter 2 begins the consideration of integrated circuits, with coverage of the forerunner of most linear devices (and still the cornerstone of systems)—the operational amplifier. This device has gone through several generations of development (now said by the admen to be in the third or is it the fourth?) and has now reached a very advanced level, with a multitude of models to suit practically every need. The introduction of negative feedback, upon which operational amplifiers depend, must rank as one of the great landmarks in the history of electronics. However effective, use of feedback requires a good understanding if disaster is to be avoided. Chapter 3 covers this topic in some detail in a form suitable for practical application.

The most common system element is probably the amplifier, operational or otherwise. Chapter 4 covers a range of the more commonly encountered types, from low-level to power and d.c. to wideband, with some discussion of servo theory *en passant*. Chapter 5 deals with oscillators, both sinusoidal and function generators. Also included are other positive feedback applications, such as the various forms of multivibrator, and the commonly used negative resistance unijunction transistor. A number of linear circuit functions are used frequently enough to warrant development of a range of IC realizations. Chapter 6 covers a number of the commonly used functions—comparators, multipliers, modulators, phase-locked loops, and sample-holds.

In every electronic circuit there is always the often somewhat neglected power supply. The whole of chapter 7 is devoted to this and related topics, covering rectification, regulation including regulator diodes, and the increasingly popular switching regulator. In recent years there has also been considerable progress in IC regulators, so that for most purposes, the provision of regulated supplies is now quite simple and in many situations more effective than before. The treatment of regulators as power operational amplifiers enables the theory of the latter, developed in chapters 2 and 3, to be used directly here.

Chapter 8 treats a number of useful discrete devices: field-effect transistors and their derivatives voltage-controlled resistors and switches, and the range of thyristor devices. Though a wide range of optical detectors has long been available, the field of optoelectronics has been somewhat limited because of the lack of convenient and fast light sources. The discovery of the light-emitting diode, in particular, has led to considerable development in the field of optoelectronics, and chapter 9 treats the more commonly used devices.

It is in the nature of research that one is frequently looking for signals hidden by noise. For this reason, particular attention has been paid to the characteristics of noise (Sec. 1.8), the performance of low-noise amplifiers (Sec. 4.1) and optical detectors (Sec. 9.3, 9.4) and, in chapter 10, the extraction of signals from noise. Though this represents by no means a comprehensive coverage, it is hoped that it will provide at least the realization of the importance of noise and of designing to minimize it. It is often no more difficult or expensive to produce a low noise rather than a noisy system.

I should like to thank my colleagues and all the correspondents who kindly answered my queries, and the semiconductor and other manufacturers who willingly supplied information, literature, and permission to copy diagrams. Also I must thank the members of the computer group of Daresbury laboratory for their assistance with my problems in setting up the reference data, Clara Nicholls for her most careful typing, and finally my family for their tolerance and understanding over the several years this book has been in the making.

The Physical Laboratories   21 September 1976
University of Manchester
Manchester M13 9PL, England

Notation

a	prefix atto, 10^{-18}
A	ampere, unit of current
B	susceptance
$\mathscr{B}$	bandwidth
$\mathscr{B}_N$	noise bandwidth
C	capacitance
C	coulomb, unit of charge
C_J	junction capacity
CMRR	common-mode rejection ratio
dB	decibel
D	FET drain
E_C	capacitor voltage
E_P	peak voltage
E_T	transformer voltage
e_{os}	offset voltage
F	farad, unit of capacitance
F	noise figure
f	frequency
f	prefix femto, 10^{-15}
f_T	transition frequency
g_{fs}	transconductance
g_m	transconductance
g_{os}	output conductance
G	prefix giga, 10^{12}
G	conductance
G	FET gate
G	gain
G_{bp}	band-pass gain
G_{bs}	band-stop gain
G_d	differential gain
G_{hp}	high-pass gain
G_{lp}	low-pass gain
G_n	noise gain
G_P	power gain
$G(s)$	gain at frequency s
$G(0)$	gain at zero frequency
G_0	gain at zero frequency

$G(\infty)$	gain at infinite frequency
G_∞	gain at infinite frequency
H	henry, unit of inductance
Hz	hertz, unit of frequency
h_{FE}	transistor d.c. current gain
I_B	base current
I_C	collector current
I_D	FET drain current
I_{DSS}	FET drain current at zero bias
I_{DZ}	FET drain current for zero temperature coefficient
I_E	emitter current
I_G	gate current
I_H	holding current in thyristor
I_S	P–N junction reverse saturation current
i_b	bias current
i_{NC}	collector noise current
i_{ND}	drain noise current
i_{NE}	emitter noise current
i_{NG}	gate noise current
i_{NS}	shot-noise current
J	joule, unit of energy
K	kelvin, unit of absolute temperature
k	Boltzmann's constant, 1.38×10^{-23} J/K
k	prefix kilo, 10^3
L	inductance
L	load
M	prefix mega, 10^6
m	prefix milli, 10^{-3}
m	metre, unit of length
N	turns
n	prefix nano, 10^{-9}
P	power
p	prefix pico, 10^{-12}
Q	quality factor
Q	charge
Q	transistor
q	electronic charge, 1.602×10^{-19} C
R_{cm}	common-mode resistance
R_d	differential input resistance
R_f	feedback resistor
R_i	input resistor
R_{id}	input differential resistance
R_L	load resistance
R_{NI}	equivalent noise current resistance
R_{NV}	equivalent noise voltage resistance
R_{SV}	voltage source resistance
$R_{S(opt)}$	optimum source resistance
R_{SI}	current source resistance

R_S	source resistance	
r_b	transistor base resistance	
$r_{bb'}$	base spreading resistance	
r_{be}	base–emitter resistance	
r_e	transitor emitter resistance	
r_e	diode incremental resistance	
S	source	
S	FET source	
S	signal	
s	second, unit of time	
s	complex frequency	
T	time constant	
T	time interval or delay	
T	prefix tera, 10^9	
t_p	pulse width	
t_r	risetime	
t_{rr}	reverse recovery time	
V	volt, unit of potential	
V_{BE}	base–emitter voltage	
V_{CC}	supply voltage	
V_{CE}	collector–emitter voltage	
V_{DS}	drain–source voltage	
V_{GS}	gate–source voltage	
V_J	P–N junction voltage	
V_{oc}	open-circuit voltage	
V_P	pinch-off voltage	
V_{SS}	FET supply voltage	
V_{th}	threshold voltage	
V_+	positive supply voltage	
V_-	negative supply voltage	
v_{NA}	amplifier noise voltage	
v_{NB}	base noise voltage	
v_{NO}	output noise voltage	
v_{NR}	resistor noise voltage	
v_S	signal voltage	
W	watt, unit of power	
X	reactance	
Y	admittance	
Z	impedance	
$(+)$	non-inverting input terminal	
$(-)$	inverting input terminal	
α	alpha, collector to emitter current ratio	
β	beta, feedback factor	
β_0	d.c. current gain	
δ	delta, secondary electron emission ratio	
ε	epsilon, permittivity	
ε_0	permittivity of free space, 8.854×10^{-12} F/m	
ζ	zeta, damping factor	

η	eta, quantum efficiency
λ	lambda, wavelength
μ	mu, permeability
μ_0	permeability of free space, $1{\cdot}257 \times 10^{-6}$ H/m
μ	prefix micro, 10^{-6}
τ	tau, time constant
ω	omega, angular frequency
ω_T	transition frequency

Mathematical symbols

$>$	greater than
$\gg$	much greater than
$<$	less than
$\ll$	much less than
$=$	equals
$\doteq$	approximately or very nearly equals
$\approx$	of the order of
$\Rightarrow$	tends to, becomes
$\langle \, \rangle$	the average value of
$\overline{}$	negation, in logic signals
$|\,|$	modulus or absolute value of
∂	partial differential
δ	a small increment
Δ	a small change or increment
exp	exponential
j	square root of -1
$\mathcal{I}m$	imaginary part of a complex number
$\mathcal{R}e$	real part of a complex number

1 Review of basic circuit theory

1.1 Ohm's law and all that

The basic circuit relation is Ohm's law which states that the current, I, in a conductor is proportional to the voltage, V, between its terminals:

$$V = IR \quad (\text{volts} = \text{amps} \times \text{ohms}) \qquad (1.1.1)$$

with the proviso that the constant of proportionality R, the resistance, is not dependent on factors such as temperature, time or, more directly, voltage or current. These conditions are often not met, so that although a resistance can be determined for a particular V and I, a different value will be found if either or both are changed. In normal circumstances, most commonly used conductors and resistors are assumed to have constant resistance (i.e., to be linear) for the sake of circuit analysis, but in critical situations these factors must be considered. Notwithstanding its apparent simplicity, Ohm's law is often all that is needed to analyse the quiescent conditions in circuits.

The current flowing in a resistor dissipates energy, the rate of dissipation or power being given by:

$$P = IV = I^2 R = V^2/R \text{ watt} \qquad (1.1.2)$$

If there are reactive elements in the circuit and V and I are varying with time, then this relation must be modified (see Eq. (1.1.14)), or I and V more particularly defined. The energy dissipated in this way heats up the resistor, and is largely lost to the system since a resistor cannot store electrical energy as can a reactive element. There is a small usually undesirable return in that the noise power is increased by the increased temperature (see Sec. 1.8). The random signal due to this noise is not of significance in terms of the circuit analysis, although it is of course of considerable importance in other respects (chapter 3 and Sec. 4.1).

In measuring the efficiency or amplification of a system the ratio of two powers is taken. These ratios often span a large range and arise from several stages of gain. It is then convenient to use a logarithmic scale to compress the range, and to allow gains of individual stages to be added rather than multiplied to give the overall value. The logarithm to base 10 of the power ratio is measured in a unit called after Bell although, in practice, one-tenth of this, the decibel (dB), is used:

$$\text{Power gain or ratio} \quad G_P = 10 \log_{10} (P_1/P_2) \text{ dB} \qquad (1.1.3)$$

so that if we have a series of amplifiers with power gains G_{P1}, G_{P2}, etc., then the overall gain is:

$$G = G_{P1} \times G_{P2} \times \cdots \times G_{Pn}$$

or
$$G_P = G_{P1} (\text{dB}) + G_{P2} (\text{dB}) + \cdots + G_{Pn} (\text{dB}) \qquad (1.1.4)$$

If the input and output resistances are specified then Eq. (1.1.3) can be written in terms of V and R using Eq. (1.1.2). For equal resistances:

$$G_P = 10 \log (V_1^2/V_2^2) = 20 \log (V_1/V_2) \qquad (1.1.5)$$

The convenience of the logarithmic scale has led to its use for voltage or current ratios, as in Eq. (1.1.5), which is legitimate enough, but the unit used is still the dB,

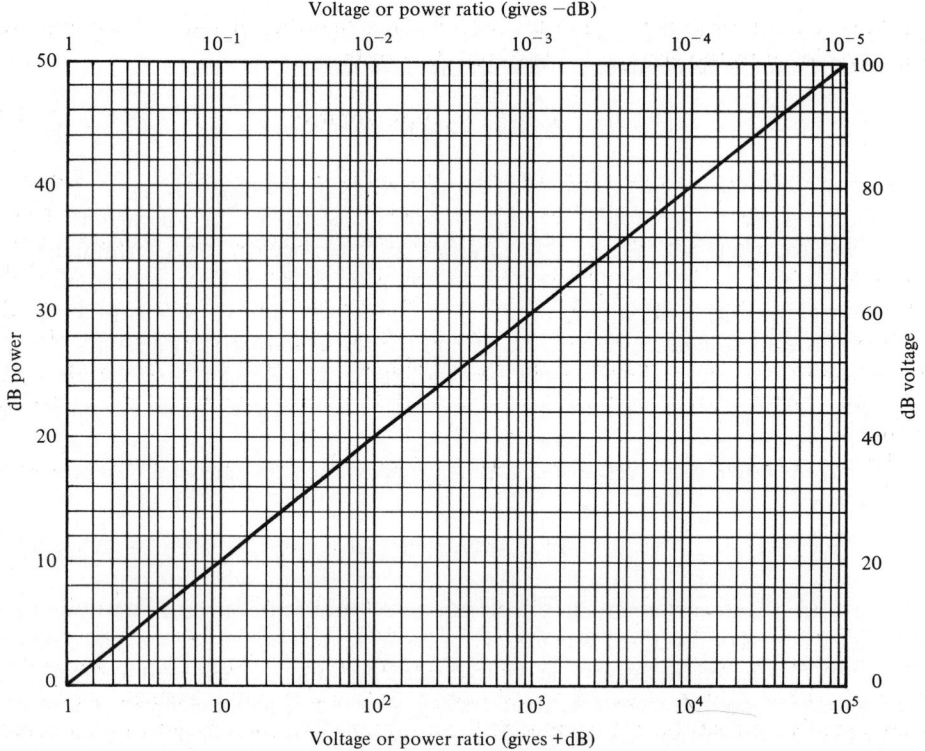

Fig. 1.1.1 Conversion of voltage and power ratios to dB

which is strictly not correct [n1, o1]. However, so long as we specify voltage or power gain there should be no confusion. For example a gain of 60 dB means a power ratio of 10^6 (1.1.3) but a voltage ratio of only 10^3 (1.1.5). Since $\log (P_1/P_2) = \log (P_1) - \log (P_2)$, then if $P_1 > P_2$ (i.e., gain) we get $+X$ dB say, while if $P_1 < P_2$ (i.e., loss or attenuation) we get $-Y$ dB say. The latter is stated as a 'gain' of $-Y$ dB, a loss of Y dB, or the output is said to be Y dB down on the input. For example, the most frequently quoted value is ± 3 dB which corresponds to a voltage gain of $\sqrt{2} = 1.414$ or an attenuation of $1/\sqrt{2} = 0.707$. Conversions may readily be made using Table 1.1.1 or Fig. 1.1.1.

Table 1.1.1 Conversion of power and voltage ratios to dB

Gives −dB		dB	Gives +dB		Gives −dB		dB	Gives +dB	
Voltage ratio	Power ratio		Voltage ratio	Power ratio	Voltage ratio	Power ratio		Voltage ratio	Power ratio
1	1	0	1	1	0·519	0·269	5·7	1·928	3·715
0·989	0·977	0·1	1·012	1·023	0·513	0·263	5·8	1·95	3·802
0·977	0·955	0·2	1·023	1·047	0·507	0·257	5·9	1·972	3·89
0·966	0·933	0·3	1·035	1·072	0·501	0·251	6	1·995	3·981
0·955	0·912	0·4	1·047	1·096	0·495	0·245	6·1	2·018	4·074
0·944	0·891	0·5	1·059	1·122	0·49	0·24	6·2	2·042	4·169
0·933	0·871	0·6	1·072	1·148	0·484	0·234	6·3	2·065	4·266
0·923	0·851	0·7	1·084	1·175	0·479	0·229	6·4	2·089	4·365
0·912	0·832	0·8	1·096	1·202	0·473	0·224	6·5	2·113	4·467
0·902	0·813	0·9	1·109	1·23	0·468	0·219	6·6	2·138	4·571
0·891	0·794	1	1·122	1·259	0·462	0·214	6·7	2·163	4·677
0·881	0·776	1·1	1·135	1·288	0·457	0·209	6·8	2·188	4·786
0·871	0·759	1·2	1·148	1·318	0·452	0·204	6·9	2·213	4·898
0·861	0·741	1·3	1·161	1·349	0·447	0·2	7	2·239	5·012
0·851	0·724	1·4	1·175	1·38	0·442	0·195	7·1	2·265	5·128
0·841	0·708	1·5	1·188	1·413	0·437	0·191	7·2	2·291	5·248
0·832	0·692	1·6	1·202	1·445	0·432	0·186	7·3	2·317	5·37
0·822	0·676	1·7	1·216	1·479	0·427	0·182	7·4	2·344	5·495
0·813	0·661	1·8	1·23	1·514	0·422	0·178	7·5	2·371	5·623
0·804	0·646	1·9	1·245	1·549	0·417	0·174	7·6	2·399	5·754
0·794	0·631	2	1·259	1·585	0·412	0·17	7·7	2·427	5·888
0·785	0·617	2·1	1·273	1·622	0·407	0·166	7·8	2·455	6·025
0·776	0·603	2·2	1·288	1·66	0·403	0·162	7·9	2·483	6·166
0·767	0·589	2·3	1·303	1·698	0·398	0·158	8	2·512	6·309
0·759	0·575	2·4	1·318	1·738	0·394	0·155	8·1	2·541	6·456
0·75	0·562	2·5	1·334	1·778	0·389	0·151	8·2	2·57	6·607
0·741	0·55	2·6	1·349	1·82	0·385	0·148	8·3	2·6	6·761
0·733	0·537	2·7	1·365	1·862	0·38	0·145	8·4	2·63	6·918
0·724	0·525	2·8	1·38	1·905	0·376	0·141	8·5	2·661	7·079
0·716	0·513	2·9	1·396	1·95	0·372	0·138	8·6	2·691	7·244
0·708	0·501	3	1·413	1·995	0·367	0·135	8·7	2·723	7·413
0·7	0·49	3·1	1·429	2·042	0·363	0·132	8·8	2·754	7·586
0·692	0·479	3·2	1·445	2·089	0·359	0·129	8·9	2·786	7·762
0·684	0·468	3·3	1·462	2·138	0·355	0·126	9	2·818	7·943
0·676	0·457	3·4	1·479	2·188	0·351	0·123	9·1	2·851	8·128
0·668	0·447	3·5	1·496	2·239	0·347	0·12	9·2	2·884	8·317
0·661	0·437	3·6	1·514	2·291	0·343	0·117	9·3	2·917	8·511
0·653	0·427	3·7	1·531	2·344	0·339	0·115	9·4	2·951	8·709
0·646	0·417	3·8	1·549	2·399	0·335	0·112	9·5	2·985	8·912
0·638	0·407	3·9	1·567	2·455	0·331	0·11	9·6	3·02	9·12
0·631	0·398	4	1·585	2·512	0·327	0·107	9·7	3·055	9·332
0·624	0·389	4·1	1·603	2·57	0·324	0·105	9·8	3·09	9·55
0·617	0·38	4·2	1·622	2·63	0·32	0·102	9·9	3·126	9·772
0·61	0·372	4·3	1·641	2·691	0·316	0·1	10	3·162	10
0·603	0·363	4·4	1·66	2·754	0·313	0·098	10·1	3·199	10·232
0·596	0·355	4·5	1·679	2·818	0·309	0·096	10·2	3·236	10·471
0·589	0·347	4·6	1·698	2·884	0·305	0·093	10·3	3·273	10·715
0·582	0·339	4·7	1·718	2·951	0·302	0·091	10·4	3·311	10·964
0·575	0·331	4·8	1·738	3·02	0·299	0·089	10·5	3·35	11·22
0·569	0·324	4·9	1·758	3·09	0·295	0·087	10·6	3·388	11·481
0·562	0·316	5	1·778	3·162	0·292	0·085	10·7	3·428	11·748
0·556	0·309	5·1	1·799	3·236	0·288	0·083	10·8	3·467	12·022
0·55	0·302	5·2	1·82	3·311	0·285	0·081	10·9	3·507	12·302
0·543	0·295	5·3	1·841	3·388	0·282	0·079	11	3·548	12·589
0·537	0·288	5·4	1·862	3·467	0·279	0·078	11·1	3·589	12·882
0·531	0·282	5·5	1·884	3·548	0·275	0·076	11·2	3·631	13·182
0·525	0·275	5·6	1·905	3·631	0·272	0·074	11·3	3·673	13·489

Table 1.1.1, continued

Gives −dB		dB	Gives +dB		Gives −dB		dB	Gives +dB	
Voltage ratio	Power ratio		Voltage ratio	Power ratio	Voltage ratio	Power ratio		Voltage ratio	Power ratio
0·269	0·072	11·4	3·715	13·803	0·162	0·026	15·8	6·166	38·016
0·266	0·071	11·5	3·758	14·125	0·16	0·026	15·9	6·237	38·901
0·263	0·069	11·6	3·802	14·454	0·158	0·025	16	6·309	39·807
0·26	0·068	11·7	3·846	14·79	0·157	0·025	16·1	6·382	40·735
0·257	0·066	11·8	3·89	15·135	0·155	0·024	16·2	6·456	41·683
0·254	0·065	11·9	3·935	15·487	0·153	0·023	16·3	6·531	42·654
0·251	0·063	12	3·981	15·848	0·151	0·023	16·4	6·607	43·648
0·248	0·062	12·1	4·027	16·217	0·15	0·022	16·5	6·683	44·665
0·245	0·06	12·2	4·074	16·595	0·148	0·022	16·6	6·761	45·705
0·243	0·059	12·3	4·121	16·981	0·146	0·021	16·7	6·839	46·769
0·24	0·058	12·4	4·169	17·377	0·145	0·021	16·8	6·918	47·859
0·237	0·056	12·5	4·217	17·782	0·143	0·02	16·9	6·998	48·974
0·234	0·055	12·6	4·266	18·196	0·141	0·02	17	7·079	50·114
0·232	0·054	12·7	4·315	18·62	0·14	0·02	17·1	7·161	51·282
0·229	0·052	12·8	4·365	19·053	0·138	0·019	17·2	7·244	52·476
0·226	0·051	12·9	4·416	19·497	0·136	0·019	17·3	7·328	53·698
0·224	0·05	13	4·467	19·951	0·135	0·018	17·4	7·413	54·949
0·221	0·049	13·1	4·518	20·416	0·133	0·018	17·5	7·499	56·229
0·219	0·048	13·2	4·571	20·892	0·132	0·017	17·6	7·585	57·539
0·216	0·047	13·3	4·624	21·378	0·13	0·017	17·7	7·673	58·879
0·214	0·046	13·4	4·677	21·876	0·129	0·017	17·8	7·762	60·25
0·211	0·045	13·5	4·731	22·386	0·127	0·016	17·9	7·852	61·654
0·209	0·044	13·6	4·786	22·907	0·126	0·016	18	7·943	63·09
0·207	0·043	13·7	4·842	23·441	0·124	0·015	18·1	8·035	64·559
0·204	0·042	13·8	4·898	23·987	0·123	0·015	18·2	8·128	66·063
0·202	0·041	13·9	4·954	24·545	0·122	0·015	18·3	8·222	67·602
0·2	0·04	14	5·012	25·117	0·12	0·014	18·4	8·317	69·176
0·197	0·039	14·1	5·07	25·702	0·119	0·014	18·5	8·414	70·788
0·195	0·038	14·2	5·128	26·301	0·117	0·014	18·6	8·511	72·436
0·193	0·037	14·3	5·188	26·913	0·116	0·013	18·7	8·61	74·124
0·191	0·036	14·4	5·248	27·54	0·115	0·013	18·8	8·709	75·85
0·188	0·035	14·5	5·309	28·182	0·114	0·013	18·9	8·81	77·617
0·186	0·035	14·6	5·37	28·838	0·112	0·013	19	8·912	79·425
0·184	0·034	14·7	5·432	29·51	0·111	0·012	19·1	9·015	81·275
0·182	0·033	14·8	5·495	30·197	0·11	0·012	19·2	9·12	83·168
0·18	0·032	14·9	5·559	30·901	0·108	0·012	19·3	9·225	85·105
0·178	0·032	15	5·623	31·62	0·107	0·011	19·4	9·332	87·087
0·176	0·031	15·1	5·688	32·357	0·106	0·011	19·5	9·44	89·116
0·174	0·03	15·2	5·754	33·111	0·105	0·011	19·6	9·549	91·191
0·172	0·03	15·3	5·821	33·882	0·104	0·011	19·7	9·66	93·316
0·17	0·029	15·4	5·888	34·671	0·102	0·01	19·8	9·772	95·489
0·168	0·028	15·5	5·956	35·479	0·101	0·01	19·9	9·885	97·713
0·166	0·028	15·6	6·025	36·305	0·100	0·01	20·0	10·0	100·0
0·164	0·027	15·7	6·095	37·151					

If voltage and current are varying with time then Ohm's law must be interpreted more carefully. The instantaneous ratio of voltage to current is not constant but varies over an infinite range, unless the circuit contains purely resistive elements. If inductance or capacity is included energy may be stored, so that the current depends not only on the instantaneous voltage but also on all that happened before. In terms of alternating or sinusoidal voltages there will be a phase difference between the voltage and current, and it is only the averages over a cycle (r.m.s. values), or the peak values that will satisfy Ohm's law, although the effective 'resistance' may not be a purely real number [a1].

Sinusoidally varying quantities are most conveniently written in complex representation; see appendix, Eq. (A.8):

$$v = v_0 \exp(j\omega t) = v_0 \cos(\omega t) + jv_0 \sin(\omega t) \tag{1.1.6}$$

ω is the angular frequency; the frequency $f = \omega/2\pi$, and the period $T = 1/f = 2\pi/\omega$. The resulting current is not necessarily in phase so that:

$$i = i_0 \exp j(\omega t - \theta) = i_0[\cos(\omega t - \theta) + j\sin(\omega t - \theta)] \tag{1.1.7}$$

The relation between v and i is now defined by the complex form of Ohm's law with a complex impedance Z (ohms):

$$\text{Modulus } Z = |Z| = \left[\frac{v_0^2}{i_0^2}(\cos^2\theta + \sin^2\theta)\right]^{1/2} = \frac{v_0}{i_0} \tag{1.1.8}$$

$$\text{Argument } Z = \phi = \tan^{-1}\left(\frac{\sin\theta}{\cos\theta}\right) = \tan^{-1}(\tan\theta) = \theta$$

The real part of Z is called the resistance, R, and the imaginary part the reactance, X:

$$Z = R + jX, \quad R = \frac{v_0 \cos\theta}{i_0}, \quad X = \frac{v_0 \sin\theta}{i_0} \tag{1.1.9}$$

Note that R does not necessarily arise only from the real resistances in the circuit. The magnitude of the impedance is given by:

$$|Z| = [(R+jX)(R-jX)]^{1/2} = (R^2 + X^2)^{1/2} \tag{1.1.10}$$

and the phase difference between v and i by:

$$\phi = \tan^{-1}(X/R) \tag{1.1.11}$$

Measuring instruments are usually calibrated to read r.m.s. values where:

$$v_{\text{r.m.s.}} = \langle v^2 \rangle^{1/2} \tag{1.1.12}$$
$$= v_0/\sqrt{2} = 0.707\, v_0 \quad \text{for sinusoidal signals}$$

The numerical value is only true for an undistorted sine wave. If harmonics are present, or if the wave is of other forms, e.g., square, triangular, etc., then considerable error may be introduced in using an r.m.s. calibrated instrument. An oscilloscope is usually safer.

The power dissipated in an a.c. circuit will vary throughout the cycle so we must average over the cycle to get the mean value. The instantaneous value is given by:

$$P_i = vi = v_0 \cos(\omega t) \cdot i_0 \cos(\omega t - \theta)$$
$$= \tfrac{1}{2} v_0 i_0 [\cos(2\omega t - \theta) + \cos\theta] \tag{1.1.13}$$

(The second line makes use of a standard trigonometrical identity [i1, p. 19].) The first term $\cos(2\omega t - \theta)$ is oscillatory and averages to zero over a cycle so that the average power dissipated is given by:

$$P = \tfrac{1}{2} v_0 i_0 \cos\theta = v_{\text{r.m.s.}} i_{\text{r.m.s.}} \cos\theta \quad (\text{watts})$$

or
$$P = \tfrac{1}{2} \mathcal{R}e(v^*i) = \tfrac{1}{2} \mathcal{R}e(vi^*) = \tfrac{1}{2} vv^* \mathcal{R}e(Y) = \tfrac{1}{2} ii^* \mathcal{R}e(Z) \tag{1.1.14}$$

The impedance of a capacitor C for a sinusoidal voltage $v = v_0 \cos \omega t$ is readily found from the capacitor equation:

$$i = C\, dv/dt$$
$$= -\omega C v_0 \sin(\omega t) \quad \text{or} \quad = \mathscr{R}e\, j\omega C v_0\, e^{j\omega t}$$
$$= -i_0 \sin(\omega t) = \mathscr{R}e\, i_0\, e^{j\omega t}$$

$$Z_C = \frac{v_0}{i_0} = \frac{1}{j\omega C} = \frac{-j}{\omega C} \text{ ohms} \tag{1.1.15}$$

These equations show that the current through the capacitor leads the voltage by 90°, and that the impedance is a pure reactance. In practice, all capacitors will depart from pure reactance at high frequencies, the deviation being measured by the loss tangent. Electrolytic capacitors depart from the ideal at comparatively low frequencies.

The energy stored in a capacitor charged to a voltage v is given by:

$$W_C = \tfrac{1}{2} C v^2 \text{ joules} \tag{1.1.16}$$

For an inductor we can find in a similar manner as above ($i = i_0 \cos(\omega t) = \mathscr{R}e\, i_0\, e^{j\omega t}$):

$$v = L\, di/dt \qquad Z_L = j\omega L \text{ ohms}$$
$$= -\omega L i_0 \sin \omega t$$
$$= \mathscr{R}e\, j\omega L i_0\, e^{j\omega t}, \qquad W_L = \tfrac{1}{2} L i^2 \text{ joules} \tag{1.1.17}$$

The current now lags the voltage by 90° and the impedance is again a pure reactance. In practice, inductors will always be less than ideal since they must be constructed of imperfect conductors. Thus, there will always be resistance in the inductor except in the special case of superconductors at very low temperatures. The closeness to the ideal is measured by the Q or quality factor; see Eq. (1.1.23).

The impedance of any circuit can now be written down in the same way as for d.c. circuits, using the values R, Z_C, and Z_L. For example, for the three elements in series, Figure 1.1.2(a):

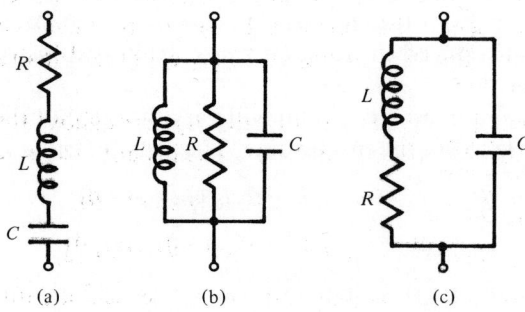

Fig. 1.1.2 Series and parallel resonant circuits

$$Z = R + j\omega L + 1/j\omega C = R + j(\omega L - 1/\omega C)$$
$$|Z| = [R^2 + (\omega L - 1/\omega C)^2]^{1/2}, \qquad \tan \theta = (\omega L - 1/\omega C)/R \tag{1.1.18}$$

For impedances in parallel the reciprocals must be added together. In many instances it is more convenient to work directly with the reciprocals:

$$1/Z = Y = G + jB \text{ mho} \qquad (1.1.19)$$

where Y is the admittance which has a real part G, the conductance, and an imaginary part B, the susceptance. For Fig. 1.1.2(b):

$$Y = \frac{1}{R} + \frac{1}{j\omega L} + j\omega C = \frac{1}{R} + j\left(\omega C - \frac{1}{\omega L}\right) \qquad (1.1.20)$$

For the series or parallel circuit there will be some frequency, ω_0, where $\omega_0 L = 1/\omega_0 C$:

$$\omega_0 = (LC)^{-1/2} \qquad (1.1.21)$$

when the series impedance (1.1.18) is a minimum $Z = R$, and the parallel admittance (1.1.20) is a minimum $Y = 1/R$. This condition is referred to as resonance. The variation of phase and magnitude as a function of frequency is shown in Fig. 1.1.3.

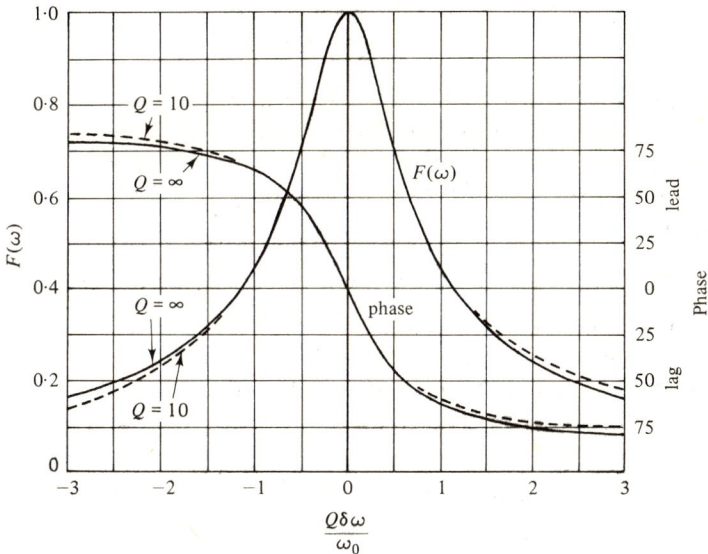

Fig. 1.1.3 Universal resonance curves

For the series circuit at resonance the current flowing will be simply $i = v/R$. This flows through L and C giving voltages across these:

$$v_L = \frac{v}{R}(j\omega_0 L), \qquad v_C = \frac{v}{R}\left(\frac{-j}{\omega_0 C}\right) = \frac{-v}{R}(j\omega_0 L) \qquad (1.1.22)$$

Thus v_C and v_L are equal in magnitude, $\mp 90°$ out of phase with the current i and the applied voltage v, and 180° out of phase with one another to cancel exactly. The dimensionless factor relating v_C and v_L to the applied voltage v is called the Q of the circuit:

$$Q = \frac{\omega_0 L}{R} = \frac{1}{\omega_0 CR} = \frac{1}{R}\left(\frac{L}{C}\right)^{1/2} \qquad (1.1.23)$$

If R is small, Q may be a large number, in which case $v_C = v_L = Qv$ are correspondingly greater than v. In practice, even if there is no specific resistance included the inherent resistance of the inductor will ensure that Q will not be infinite.

The Q value is also a measure of the sharpness of the resonance, a high Q corresponding to a narrow resonance. We may rewrite Eq. (1.1.18), using (1.1.23) and (1.1.21), as:

$$Z = R\left[1 + jQ\left(\frac{C}{L}\right)^{1/2}\left(\omega L - \frac{1}{\omega C}\right)\right]$$
$$= R\left[1 + jQ\left(\frac{\omega}{\omega_0} - \frac{\omega_0}{\omega}\right)\right] \quad (1.1.24)$$

In the region close to resonance we may put $\omega = \omega_0 \pm \delta\omega$, so that the inner bracket of Eq. (1.1.24) is $\doteq 2\delta\omega/\omega_0$. Then:

$$Z = R(1 + 2jQ\,\delta\omega/\omega_0) = R/F(\omega)$$
$$|Z| = R(1 + 4Q^2\,\delta\omega^2/\omega_0^2)^{1/2} = R/|F(\omega)| \quad (1.1.25)$$
$$|F(\omega)| = (1 + 4Q^2\,\delta\omega^2/\omega_0^2)^{-1/2}, \quad \arg F(\omega) = \tan^{-1}(-2Q\,\delta\omega/\omega_0)$$

The function $F(\omega)$ is known as a Lorentzian function and is the one plotted in Fig. 1.1.3. At a frequency deviation $\delta\omega = \omega_0/2Q$ (or frequency $\omega = \omega_0(1 + 1/2Q)$), $|F(\omega)|$ will have decreased to $1/\sqrt{2} = 0.707$ (or -3dB) of its value at $\omega = \omega_0$, and the phase shift will be $\pm 45°$. Thus if the width $\Delta\omega$ of a resonance is measured between the -3dB points then:

$$Q = \omega_0/\Delta\omega \quad (1.1.26)$$

A similar treatment may be given for the three elements in parallel in Fig. 1.1.2(b), but it is more useful to consider the case of L and C in parallel but with a resistor R in series with L to represent the resistance of the inductor; Fig. 1.1.2(c). The admittance of the circuit is:

$$Y = \left[\frac{R}{R^2 + \omega^2 L^2}\right] = j\left[\omega C - \frac{\omega L}{R^2 + \omega^2 L^2}\right]$$
$$\doteq \frac{R}{\omega^2 L^2} + j\left[\omega C - \frac{1}{\omega L}\right] \quad (1.1.27)$$

where the approximation is for the case $R \ll \omega L$, i.e., reasonable Q, say > 10. At the resonance frequency, ω_0, the susceptance is zero, the admittance (and impedance) real and a minimum:

$$\omega_0 = (LC)^{-1/2}, \quad i_0 = vY_0 = vR/\omega_0^2 L^2 \quad \text{(a minimum)}$$
$$Y_0 = |Y| = R/\omega_0^2 L^2 = 1/RQ^2 \quad \text{(a minimum)}$$
$$Z_0 = |Z| = \omega_0^2 L^2/R = Q^2 R \quad \text{(a maximum)} \quad (1.1.28)$$
$$Z_0 = RQ(1 + Q^2)^{1/2} \quad \text{(with no approximation)}$$

The width and phase shifts are similar to the series resonant circuit and are also shown in Fig. 1.1.3. While in the series resonant circuit the voltages are increased by

Q times, in the parallel circuit the currents are increased by the same quantity. The circulating current in the LCR circuit, i_{L0} or i_{C0}, will be Q times the generator current i_0, and 90° out of phase:

$$\frac{i_{L0}}{i_0} = \frac{v}{j\omega_0 L} \cdot \frac{\omega_0^2 L^2}{vR}, \quad \text{or} \quad i_{L0} = jQi_0 \tag{1.1.29}$$

For low values of Q the approximation $R \ll \omega L$ is no longer valid. The resonant frequency is no longer given by (1.1.28) and the response is no longer symmetrical, Z tending to R at low frequency. Typical curves are shown in [i1, pp. 145–148].

The Q of a system may also be defined in terms of energy. Using Eq. (1.1.16) and Eq. (1.1.17) it is readily shown that:

$$Q = \frac{2\pi \,(\text{energy stored})}{\text{energy dissipated per cycle}}$$

$$= \frac{\text{energy stored}}{\text{energy dissipated per radian}}$$

$$= \frac{2\pi W}{-\Delta W}$$

or
$$\frac{\Delta W}{\Delta t} = \frac{-2\pi W}{Q \Delta t} = \frac{-\omega_0 W}{Q}, \quad (\omega_0 = 2\pi f = 2\pi/\Delta t) \tag{1.1.30}$$

Thus the energy has a decay time (Sec. 1.4) of Q/ω_0, while the amplitude has twice the decay time, $2Q/\omega_0$ (the energy is proportional to the square of the amplitude).

It is worth noting that a parallel circuit similar to Fig. 1.1.2(c), but with a resistor R in series with C equal to that in series with L and having a value $R = (L/C)^{1/2}$, will present a resistive impedance equal to R at all frequencies (see Sec. 1.11(c)).

1.2 Network theorems

There are several useful network theorems that are often helpful when analysing circuits. They are dealt with in many places and so will be only briefly noted here [c1, d1, e1].

1.2(a) Superposition theorem

In a linear bilateral network the current at any point is the algebraic sum of the currents due to each generator considered separately, with all other independent generators replaced by their internal impedance. It must be emphasized that this

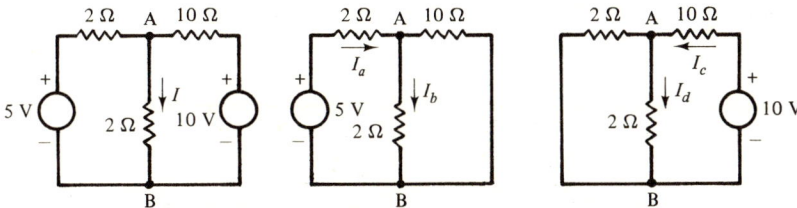

Fig. 1.2.1 Superposition theorem

will not necessarily be applicable to circuits containing non-linear or unilateral elements. However, in many cases it may be applied for small incremental changes.

Figure 1.2.1 illustrates a simple application of this theorem. The current I is to be found. The 10 volt source is first replaced by its internal impedance (zero) and the current I_b determined. I_d is found in similar fashion. Then according to the theorem $I = I_b + I_d$.

$$I_a = \frac{5}{2+1\cdot 67} = 1\cdot 36 \text{ A}, \qquad I_b = \frac{10 \times 1\cdot 36}{12} = 1\cdot 13 \text{ A}$$

$$I_c = \frac{10}{10+1} = 0\cdot 91 \text{ A}, \qquad I_d = \frac{2 \times 0\cdot 91}{4} = 0\cdot 46 \text{ A} \qquad (1.2.1)$$

$$I = I_b + I_d = 1\cdot 59 \text{ A}$$

The theorem applies equally well, whether the generators are d.c. or a.c.

1.2(b) *Thévenin's theorem*

Any linear network of generators and impedances viewed from any two points in the network can be replaced by an equivalent ideal voltage source (i.e., zero internal impedance) V_{oc} in series with an impedance Z_t equal to that seen at this port (Fig. 1.2.2).

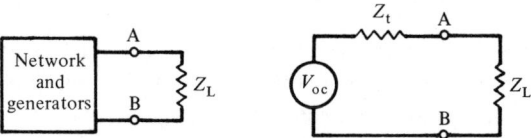

Fig. 1.2.2 Thévenin equivalent circuit

The values of V_{oc} and Z_t are determined as follows. The voltage between terminals A and B with the load impedance Z_L removed is the Thévenin equivalent voltage V_{oc}, i.e., it is the open circuit voltage. If A and B are short circuited a current I_{sc} will flow. Then $Z_t = V_{oc}/I_{sc}$. Alternatively, Z_t is the impedance measured between A and B if all the internal voltage generators are replaced by short circuits and all the current generators by open circuits. For simple networks V_{oc} and Z_t may be calculated if all the parameters are known. For more complex networks measurement may be a much simpler technique.

1.2(c) *Norton's theorem*

Any linear network of generators and impedances viewed from any two points in the network can be replaced by an equivalent current source I_{sc} in parallel with an impedance Z_t (Fig. 1.2.3).

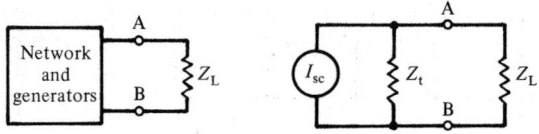

Fig. 1.2.3 Norton equivalent circuit

The value of the current generator I_{sc} is the current that would flow if A and B were short circuited. From Thévenin's theorem this current is $I_{sc}=V_{oc}/Z_t$. The parallel Norton impedance is just Z_t, since this leads to an open circuit voltage at A, B of $V=I_{sc}Z_t=V_{oc}$. This theorem is just a simple corollary of Thévenin's.

1.2(d) *Millman's theorem*

If V_o is the open circuit voltage, I_s the short circuit current, and $Z(Y)$ the impedance (admittance) between two terminals of a network then:

$$V_o = I_s Z = I_s/Y \qquad (1.2.2)$$

This may be illustrated by application to Fig. 1.2.1. The current through a short circuit across AB is:

$$I_s = \frac{5}{2} + \frac{10}{10} = 3 \cdot 5 \text{ A}$$

The admittance between A and B is given by the three resistors in parallel, the generators being of zero impedance (infinite admittance). It is convenient to choose admittance here since we are dealing with impedances in parallel. Thus:

$$Y_{AB} = \frac{1}{2} + \frac{1}{2} + \frac{1}{10} = \frac{11}{10} \text{ mho}$$

From Eq. (1.2.2) we now have:

$$V_{AB} = V_o = \frac{I_s}{Y_{AB}} = 3 \cdot 5 \times \frac{10}{11} = 3 \cdot 18 \text{ V}$$

$$I = \frac{V_{AB}}{R_{AB}} = \frac{3 \cdot 18}{2} = 1 \cdot 59 \text{ A}$$

1.2(e) *Kirchoff's laws*

(i) The algebraic sum of all voltage sources and voltage drops around a loop, or mesh, must be zero.
(ii) The sum of all currents towards a node must be zero.

These two laws, in contrast to those previously discussed, are valid even for networks containing non-linear elements. They allow us to write either mesh or nodal equations for complex networks. The mesh equations allow the determination of the currents in the network, and are useful in cases where the current in each branch is different. Irrespective of the source of the branch currents the total mesh voltage must be zero. Nodal equations give the voltages at the nodes. The choice between the two approaches will depend on the parameter of interest or the number of equations involved. For example, in the network of Fig. 1.2.4 only two nodal equations are required for solution, as compared with three mesh equations.

The mesh equations for Fig. 1.2.4(a) are:

$$I_1(R_1+R_4) - I_2 R_4 = V_1 \quad \text{(mesh 1)}$$
$$-I_1 R_4 + I_2(R_3+R_4+R_5) + I_3 R_5 = 0 \quad \text{(mesh 2)} \qquad (1.2.3)$$
$$I_2 R_5 + I_3(R_2+R_5) = V_2 \quad \text{(mesh 3)}$$

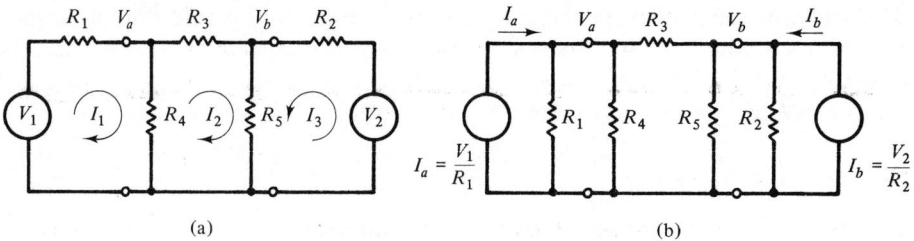

(a)   (b)

Fig. 1.2.4 Kirchoff's laws (a) mesh (b) node

i.e., three equations for three unknowns I_1, I_2, I_3. The nodal equations are obtained from Fig. 1.2.4(b) where the voltage sources have been replaced by the Norton equivalent current generators (Sec. 1.2(c)). There are two nodes giving the equations:

$$I_a - V_a(Y_3 + Y_4 + Y_1) + V_b Y_3 = 0 \quad (\text{node } a)$$
$$I_b + V_a Y_3 - V_b(Y_3 + Y_2 + Y_5) = 0 \quad (\text{node } b)$$
(1.2.4)

i.e., two equations for two unknowns V_a, V_b. From personal observation, most people use mesh analysis as this somehow seems more natural or straightforward. This apparently arises from a psychological preference for the Thévenin rather than the Norton picture of the driving source, i.e., that voltages are somehow more basic than currents. However, nodal analysis can be used with equal ease once familiar with it and is often more direct.

It is worth noting that Kirchoff's laws are valid only in conditions of equilibrium where we can assume the currents to be uniform along the length of a conductor. On a short enough time scale where propagation times are significant, e.g., on a transmission line, these laws must be used with discretion.

1.2(f) *Star–delta or tee–pi transformations*

A star–delta or tee–pi (depending on whether you are a power or an electronic engineer) transformation is often a useful way of simplifying the analysis of some networks. The circuit representations are shown in Fig. 1.2.5.

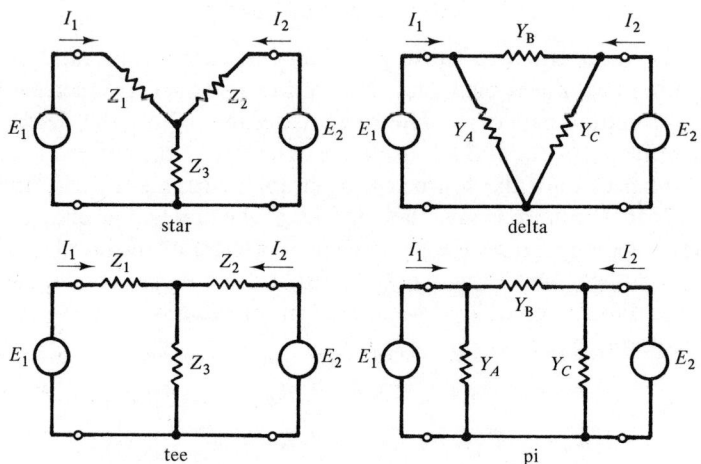

Fig. 1.2.5 Star–delta or tee–pi transformation

12

For the circuits to be equivalent, the same currents I_1, I_2 must flow when the same voltages E_1, E_2 are applied. Using superposition we can write down the equations for the pi circuit:

$$I_1 = E_1(Y_A + Y_B) - E_2 Y_B$$

$$I_2 = -E_1 Y_B + E_2(Y_B + Y_C)$$

or

$$E_2 = \frac{Y_B}{Y^2} I_1 + \frac{(Y_A + Y_B)}{Y^2} I_2$$

$$E_1 = \frac{(Y_B + Y_C)}{Y^2} I_1 + \frac{Y_B}{Y^2} I_2$$

where

$$Y^2 = Y_A Y_B + Y_B Y_C + Y_C Y_A \qquad (1.2.5)$$

The corresponding equations for the tee circuit are:

$$E_2 = Z_3 I_1 + (Z_2 + Z_3) I_2$$

$$E_1 = (Z_1 + Z_3) I_1 + Z_3 I_2$$

Since the equations must be equivalent for all values of current, the coefficients of corresponding terms must be equal. Hence:

$$Z_1 = \frac{Y_C}{Y^2}, \qquad Z_2 = \frac{Y_A}{Y^2}, \qquad Z_3 = \frac{Y_B}{Y^2} \qquad (1.2.6)$$

which are the equations for obtaining the tee from the pi configuration.

To make the transformation from the tee to the pi we note that using Eq. (1.2.5) and Eq. (1.2.6):

$$Y^2 = Y^4(Z_2 Z_3 + Z_3 Z_1 + Z_1 Z_2)$$

or

$$Z^2 = (Z_1 Z_2 + Z_2 Z_3 + Z_3 Z_1) = 1/Y^2$$

and hence:

$$Y_A = \frac{Z_2}{Z^2}, \qquad Y_B = \frac{Z_3}{Z^2}, \qquad Y_C = \frac{Z_1}{Z^2} \qquad (1.2.7)$$

An example of the application of this transformation is the design of a variable attenuator for a differential amplifier stage; Fig. 1.2.6(a). A convenient and effective means of introducing attenuation is the insertion of an emitter resistor on each side as shown in Fig. 1.2.6(b). To make the attenuation variable then requires a closely

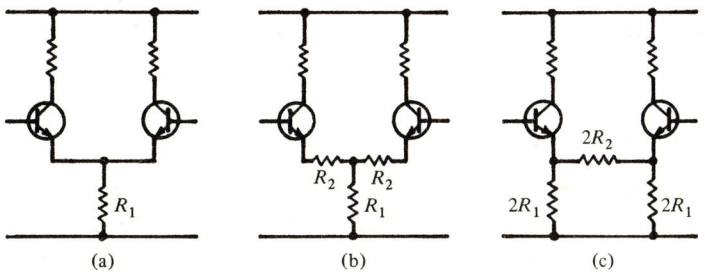

Fig. 1.2.6 Example of tee–pi transformation

matched ganged potentiometer. However, by transforming from the tee network to the equivalent pi, as in Fig. 1.2.6(c) it is evident that only a single potentiometer is required. As $R_1 \gg R_2$ the values of the pi resistors are as indicated.

1.2(g) *Series–parallel equivalent circuits*

It is sometimes easier to appreciate the effect or operation of a circuit if it is transformed from series form to parallel, or vice versa (see, for example, Sec. 1.4). For reactive circuits the equivalence is only exact at a specified frequency, but it is still a useful technique. We will consider the equivalence of two *RC* circuits shown in Fig. 1.2.7.

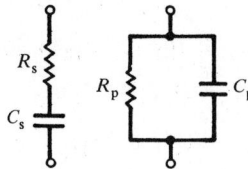

Fig. 1.2.7 Series–parallel equivalent circuits

The impedances of the series and parallel circuits are:

$$Z_s = R_s - \frac{j}{\omega C_s}, \qquad Z_p = \frac{R_p - j\omega C_p R_p^2}{1 + (\omega C_p R_p)^2}$$

Equating real parts and imaginary parts and putting $H = \omega C_p R_p$ gives:

or
$$R_s = \frac{R_p}{1 + (\omega C_p R_p)^2}, \qquad C_s = \frac{1 + (\omega C_p R_p)^2}{\omega^2 C_p R_p^2}$$

$$\frac{R_p}{R_s} = 1 + H^2, \qquad \frac{C_p}{C_s} = \frac{H^2}{1 + H^2} \qquad (1.2.8)$$

$$H = \omega C_p R_p = \frac{1}{\omega C_s R_s}$$

These equations allow transformation in either direction. Since H contains ω, the values of the equivalent circuit are frequency dependent. More complex circuits can be transformed from first principles, or by successive applications of the above relations.

1.3 Phase and frequency response

The phase and frequency response of networks and circuits will frequently be of interest in later sections. Although these may be quite complex they can often be determined as the sum of a number of simpler responses. We will consider here the response of several simple *RC* networks, as well as convenient representations and approximations.

The most commonly occurring network is the lag or low-pass circuit shown in Fig. 1.3.1:

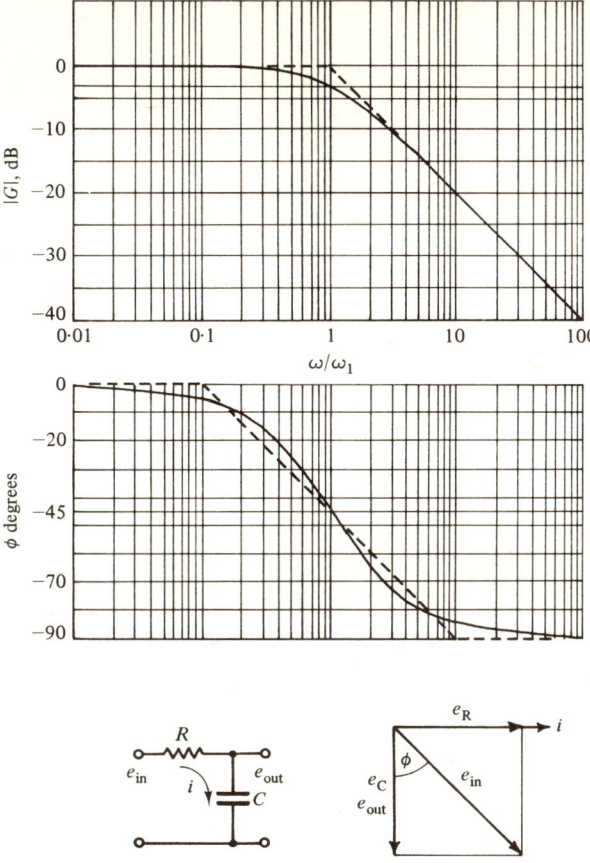

Fig. 1.3.1 Lag, low-pass, or single pole response

The gain and phase shift for this circuit is given by:

$$G = \frac{e_{out}}{e_{in}} = \frac{1/j\omega C}{R + 1/j\omega C} = \frac{1}{1 + j\omega RC} = \frac{1}{1 + j\omega/\omega_1}, \quad \text{where} \quad \omega_1 = 1/RC$$

$$|G| = [1 + (\omega/\omega_1)^2]^{-1/2}, \quad |G| \text{ dB} = -10 \log [1 + (\omega/\omega_1)^2] \quad (1.3.1)$$

$$\phi = \tan^{-1}(-\omega/\omega_1) = -\tan^{-1}(\omega/\omega_1)$$

At low frequencies the gain is unity (0 dB), and above frequencies of the order of ω_1 the gain falls off steadily. The phase shift varies from zero at low frequencies, through $-45°$ at ω_1, to $-90°$ at high frequencies. The representation of gain and phase shown in Fig. 1.3.1 is called a Bode plot [c1], the frequency being on a logarithmic scale, the gain on a linear dB (and thus also on a log) scale, and the phase on a linear scale. These choices are convenient since cascaded gains are simply added in dB while phases are added linearly (see appendix). Log scales also encompass a large range of variable, and make the phase curve symmetrical. At the characteristic frequency ω_1:

$$|G| = G_0/2^{1/2} \qquad \phi = -\tan^{-1}(1)$$
$$= 0.707 \, G_0 \qquad \qquad = -45°$$
or
$$= -10 \log 2 \text{ dB}$$
$$= -3 \text{ dB} \qquad \qquad (1.3.2)$$

The asymptotic slope of the gain curve at high frequencies, $\omega \gg \omega_1$, is of interest. Here unity may be neglected relative to ω/ω_1, and taking two frequencies either a factor 2 (octave) or a factor 10 (decade) apart, Eq. (1.3.1) gives:

$$|G_{2\omega}| - |G_\omega| = -20[\log (2\omega/\omega_1) - \log (\omega/\omega_1)]$$
$$= -20 \log [(2\omega/\omega_1)(\omega_1/\omega)]$$
$$= -6 \text{ dB/octave} \quad (\text{or } -20 \text{ dB/decade}) \qquad (1.3.3)$$

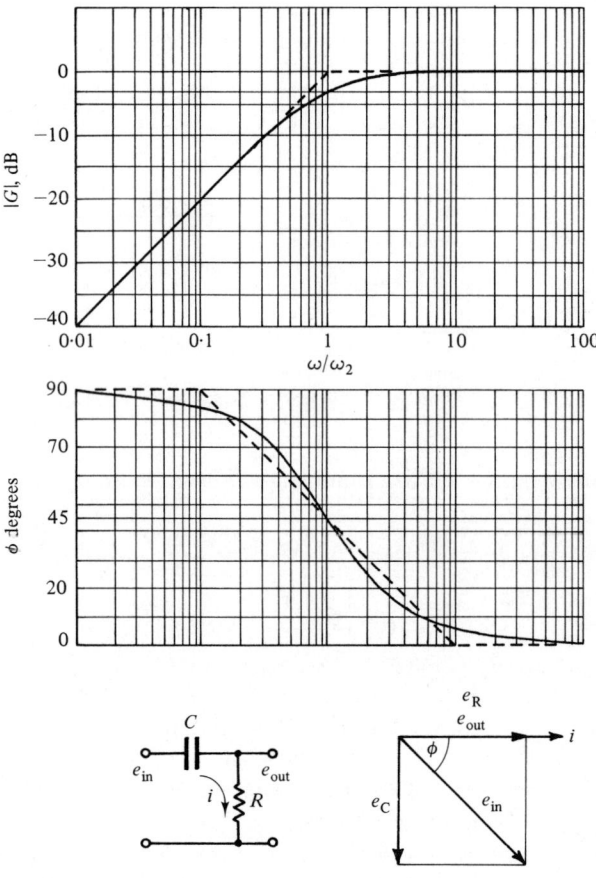

Fig. 1.3.2 Lead or high-pass response (1 pole, 1 zero at the origin)

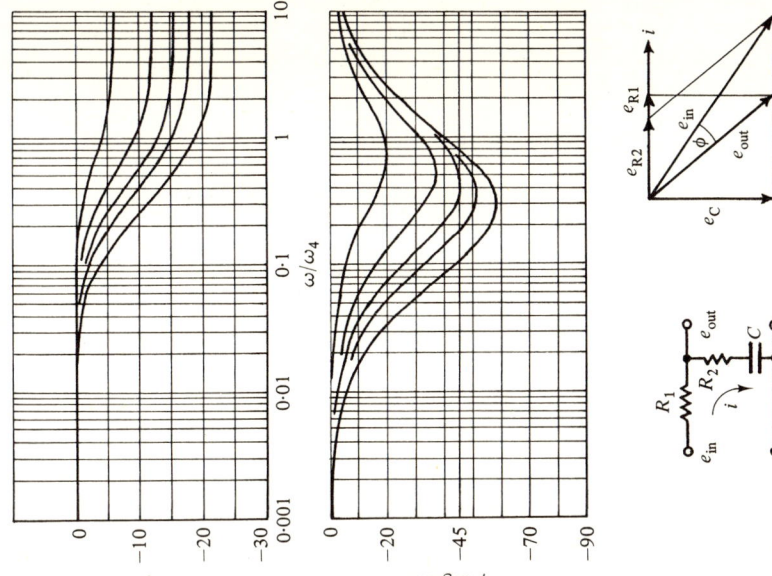

Fig. 1.3.3 Lead–lag or transitional response (1 zero, 1 pole)

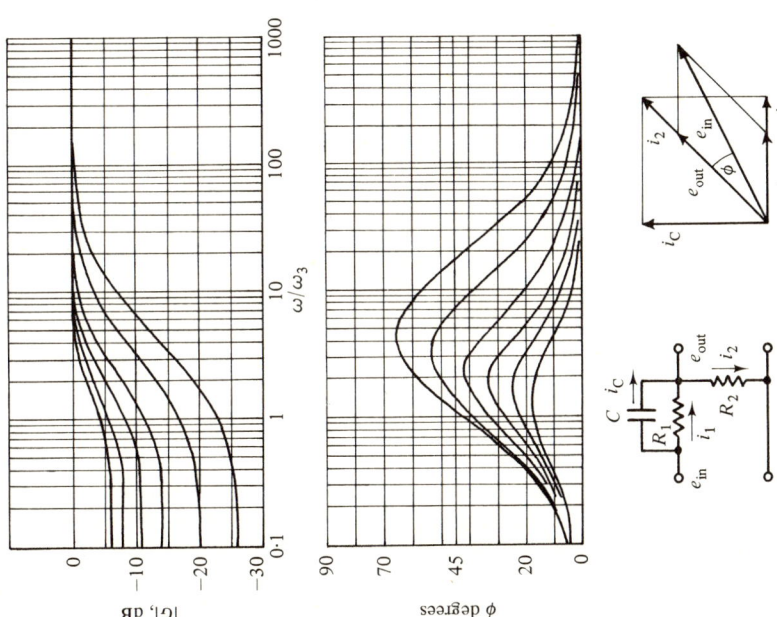

Fig. 1.3.4 Lag–lead or transitional response (1 pole, 1 zero)

The asymptotic slope is thus -6 dB/octave or -20 dB/decade. This cuts the low frequency asymptote G_0 (0 dB here) when $\log(\omega/\omega_1) = 0$ or $\omega = \omega_1$. The two asymptotes give a good approximation to the gain curve, the maximum error being 3 dB at ω_1. Table 1.3.1 lists the errors for several frequencies. The straight line approximation is much easier to draw, and is accurate enough for most purposes.

Table 1.3.1 Phase and amplitude errors for straight line approximations

Frequency relative to ω_1	Corrections	
	Gain ($-$dB)	Phase (degree)
0·05	0·01	-3
0·1	0·04	-6
0·33	0·46	$+5$
0·5	1	$+5$
1	3	0
2	1	-5
3	0·46	-5
10	0·04	$+6$
20	0·01	$+3$

The phase shift takes place mainly between frequencies $0.1\,\omega_1$ to $10\,\omega_1$, the residual values at these frequencies being only 6° (Table 1.3.1). A straight line approximation to this curve, therefore, is made by joining the points $\phi = 0°$, $\omega = 0.1\,\omega_1$ and $\phi = 90°$, $\omega = 10\,\omega_1$, the line passing through $\phi = 45°$ at $\omega = \omega_1$. The maximum error is 6° and occurs at the two end points. As will be discussed in Sec. 1.11 this network has a single pole at ω_1. The pole–zero classification will be attached to the following circuits for later convenience.

There are a number of other simple RC networks that are of interest and which we will make use of later. These are shown in Figs. 1.3.2, 1.3.3, and 1.3.4, together with the appropriate equations.

1.4 Time constants, bandwidth, and pulse response

The form of a sinusoidal wave is not altered by passage through any linear circuit—only the phase and amplitude will be changed. This form is unique in this respect, and is an important reason for its widespread use. Any other waveform will be more or less altered depending on the waveshape, repetition frequency, and circuit constants.

The response of circuits or systems is often characterized in terms of risetime or bandwidth, the former being used when considering pulses and the latter for sinusoids. The values of these quantities give a quick indication of the range of signals for which the circuits may usefully be used. The bandwidth $\mathscr{B}$ of a circuit is normally defined as the range of frequency between the points at which the response has fallen by 3 dB relative to the midband value. This assumes that the midband response is reasonably flat. There will usually be a low-frequency as well as a high-frequency -3 dB point, although many of the circuits we will consider later operate down to zero frequency, and so do not have a lower -3 dB point. In this case, the bandwidth is measured from zero frequency. At the -3 dB points the amplitude will have fallen to 0·707 of the midband value, and the phase shift will be $\pm 45°$ (Sec. 1.3). $\mathscr{B}$ is often a conservative indication of the usable bandwidth, and significant gain is often available at considerably higher frequencies (see, for example, Fig. 1.3.1). This should be remembered in using an oscilloscope, for example, with a given $\mathscr{B}$.

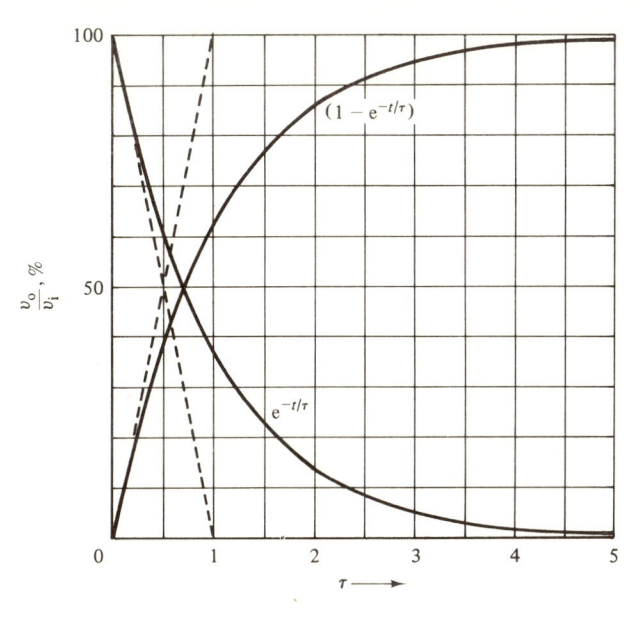

Fig. 1.4.1 Response of *RC* and *CR* networks to step input

When considering the response of a system to pulse waveforms the bandwidth does not provide an immediate guide to performance. For pulses two qualities are of interest: the ability to follow rapid changes in level and the ability to maintain steady levels. The first is determined by the high frequency response and the second by the low. To show this dependency we must consider the response of low-pass *RC* and high-pass *CR* circuits (Sec. 1.3) to step and pulse inputs.

For the low-pass *RC* circuit, the response to an input step v_i is given by:

$$v_0 = v_i(1-e^{-t/RC}) = v_i(1-e^{-t/\tau}) \qquad (1.4.1)$$

where $\tau = RC$ is called the time constant. The response is shown in Fig. 1.4.1.

The output is effectively complete after 5τ, the remaining 0·7 per cent being negligible for most purposes. However, for high resolution measurements, for example in a digital voltmeter, considerably longer times must be allowed. A commonly used measure of the rise of a pulse or step is defined as the time taken to go from 10 to 90 per cent. This risetime, t_r, is seen from the figure to be given by:

$$t_r = 2·2\, RC = 2·2/\omega_1 = 2·2/2\pi f_1 = 0·35/f_1 \qquad (1.4.2)$$

Thus, for systems that can be approximated to a single low-pass circuit there is a simple relationship between the risetime and the upper -3 dB frequency f_1. If the lower corner frequency is zero or low, compared with f_1, then we can use $t_r = 0·35/\mathscr{B}$.

A '100 MHz' oscilloscope, for example, will have a risetime of 3·5 nanoseconds (ns). Curves for several cascaded but non-interacting *RC* time-constants are given in [k1, pp. 47, 136–139]. Note that if the input step has a risetime t_1 and the oscilloscope or other instrument a risetime t_2, then the displayed risetime will be approximately [g1]:

$$t_r = (t_1^2 + t_2^2)^{1/2} \qquad (1.4.3)$$

The response of the low-pass *RC* circuit to a pulse, is easily determined as the response to two opposite step voltages, i.e., an exponential rise and fall. The nett effect will depend on the relative values of pulse width, t_p, and time constant, τ. The response for several values of time constant is shown in Fig. 1.4.2.

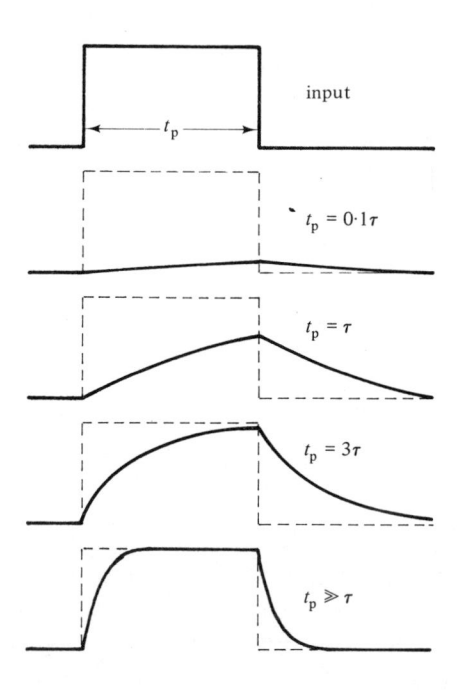

Fig. 1.4.2 Response of low-pass *RC* circuit to pulse input

If the corner frequency $f_1 = 1/$(pulse width t_p) then the risetime is $t_r = 0.35\, t_p$, from Eq. (1.4.2), and the pulse shape will not be too seriously distorted. Thus, to pass a 100 ns pulse, an f_1 of at least 10 MHz is required. If the frequency response extends to zero frequency then there is no further distortion of the pulse. However, if this is not so, then the d.c. and low frequency components will be removed and the flat upper and lower levels of the input pulse will be distorted in the output pulse.

The output of a high-pass *CR* circuit for a step input will just be the difference between the *RC* response shown in Fig. 1.4.1 and the input pulse, since $v_{in} = v_C + v_R = v_C + v_{out}$. This is shown as the curve $e^{-t/\tau}$ in Fig. 1.4.1. Initially, $v_C = 0$ and, since this cannot change instantaneously, v_{out} will equal v_{in} immediately after the step. Then, with constant v_{in}, *C* will charge up exponentially through *R*, and the voltage across *R* fall correspondingly. Note that current flows *through* a capacitor rather than *into* it.

A given amount of positive charge entering one terminal will result in an equal amount of positive charge leaving the other terminal.

The response to a pulse is again dependent on the relative values of time constant and pulse width, a number of typical cases being illustrated in Fig. 1.4.3.

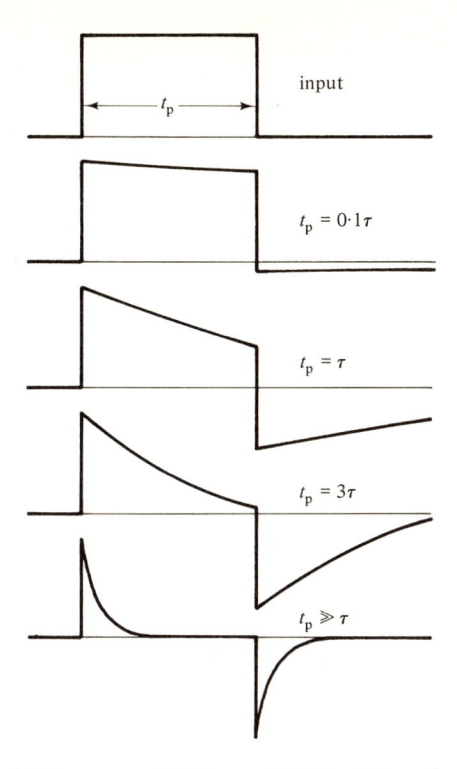

Fig. 1.4.3 Response of high-pass CR circuit to pulse input

If the droop is not too large ($t_p \leqslant \tau/3$) then the exponential decay $v_0 = v_i \exp(-t/\tau)$ may be approximated by $v_0 = v_i(1 - t/\tau)$. Then the fractional droop D:

$$D = \frac{v_i - v_0}{v_i} = \frac{t_p}{\tau} = \omega_1 t_p = 2\pi f_1 t_p \qquad (1.4.4)$$

where $f_1 = 1/2\pi CR$ is the corner frequency. Thus the lower f_1 the less the droop. For example, for $f_1 = 1/(100\, t_p)$ the droop is 6 per cent [h1, i1].

The elimination of the d.c. path between input and output has a further important effect. Since no d.c. level is transmitted, the output d.c. level must be zero, i.e., the pulse and undershoot will always be such that the average level is zero. This means that the areas above and below zero will be equal. For a repetitive waveform there will be an effective bias on the output, so that the pulses will appear to rise from a level other than zero (Fig. 1.4.4).

The new baseline will depend on the pulse repetition rate and the mark–space ratio. This could cause difficulties, as for example when the pulses must trigger some subsequent circuit at a fixed voltage level. For random pulses the situation is even more difficult. Various types of clamping circuit can be used in some cases [k1, p. 262] but these are often unsatisfactory. For many applications it is necessary to use d.c. coupling throughout, or to convert the pulses to bipolar form with equal positive and negative areas so that there is no variation of output baseline [k1, p. 95].

A commonly encountered case where the pulse response of a network is of importance is met in oscilloscope measurements [d1, e1]. The input impedance of most oscilloscopes is $R_2 = 1$ MΩ in parallel with $C_2 = 15$ to 30 pF; Figure 1.4.5(d). To this must be added the capacity of the cable connecting the oscilloscope to the point of measurement, which for standard coaxial cables is about 100 pF/m. Even though the input resistance R_2 may be large enough not to load the circuit under test, the large capacity together with the source impedance will cause attenuation at high frequency

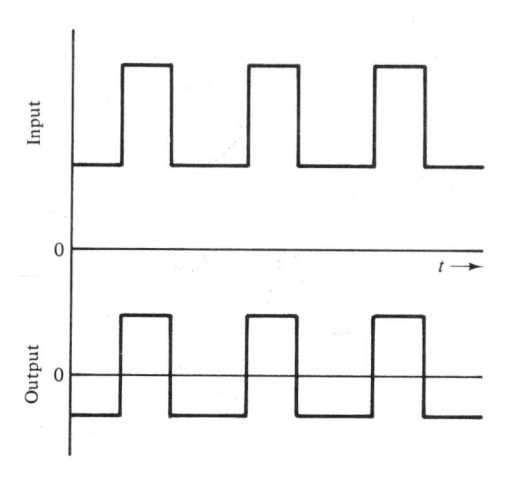

Fig. 1.4.4 Response of high-pass CR circuit to repetitive pulse train

and poor pulse response. To reduce the loading effect a high impedance probe is generally used; Fig. 1.4.5(d). This is essentially a compensated attenuator in which $R_1 = 9$ MΩ and $C_1 \doteq 13$ pF; Fig. 1.4.5(a). This gives a low frequency input resistance of 10 MΩ, and attenuation of 10 times. The shunting capacity would be about 12 pF. The loading on the circuit under test is reduced from 1 MΩ in parallel with 115 pF, to 10 MΩ in parallel with 12 pF. The penalty is the times 10 attenuation.

Practical oscilloscope probes differ slightly from this simple arrangement, a typical equivalent circuit being shown in Fig. 1.4.5(d) [a1, b1, c1]. Capacitor C_1 is of concentric tubular sleeve form, and can be varied for optimum compensation by rotating part of the probe body. The connecting cable has a fine sinuous resistive inner conductor with a distributed capacity $C_s \doteq 30$ pF/m. Since the cable is severely mismatched at both ends this resistive conductor is chosen to give optimum pulse waveshape for fast pulses, the resistance being $R_s \doteq 650$ ohms. The cable, therefore, must never be replaced or extended in any way or the performance will be seriously impaired. There will also be a small stray input capacity $C_t \doteq 3$ pF.

The bandwidth when operating from a low impedance source will be about 100 MHz, equivalent to a risetime of about 3 ns. This is appropriate to pulse waveforms where low impedances are usual. However, the resistive and reactive components of the input impedance of the probe fall off with frequency (10 pF has an impedance of 10 kΩ at 1·6 MHz) and this will have significant effects on high impedances as may be found, for example, in tuned circuits. Thus, for these cases more care must be exercised. At 10 MHz the equivalent circuit of the probe can be approximated by Fig. 1.4.5(b).

Using Eqs. (1.2.8) C_1 and R_s can be transformed into the equivalent $C_p = 3$ pF and $R_p = 43$ kΩ ($H = 8·1$ for this particular frequency). Thus, the equivalent input resistance is only 43 kΩ rather than the nominal 10 MΩ. For a typical 10 MHz resonant circuit ($\omega_0 = 6·3 \times 10^7$, $C = 100$ pF, $L = 2·5$ μH, $Q = 100$) the impedance at resonance is, from Eq. (1.1.28), $Z = Q\omega_0 L = 15·8$ kΩ. Applying the probe to this circuit will shift the resonant frequency by two per cent and the Q by 25 per cent. The effect, therefore, is quite significant, and it would be better to connect with a single wire and a $C_2/10$

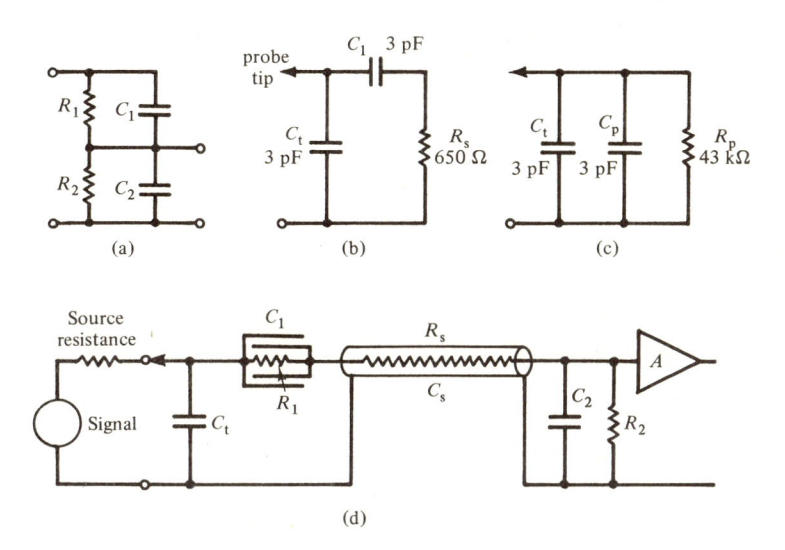

Fig. 1.4.5 Compensated attenuator and probe

capacitor. Note also that the phase shift is dependent on the $C_2 R_2$ load, so that if probes are used in measuring phase shifts these loads must be equal. The Y and X inputs of oscilloscopes often have unequal input impedances so that X–Y displays may be misleading [b1].

In more recent model probes extra compensation is included in a small housing at the plug end of the cable to improve high frequency response. All probes have a maximum voltage rating (d.c. plus peak a.c. value) which holds only up to some specified maximum frequency (≈ 20 MHz). Above this derating must be applied otherwise the probe may be damaged. However, it is unlikely that these conditions will arise in integrated circuit systems.

1.5 Impedance matching

Impedance matching is generally concerned with providing the necessary conditions to achieve maximum power transfer from generator to load. Consider a generator with output resistance R_0 connected to a load resistor R_L; Fig. 1.5.1(a).

The power P dissipated in R_L is given by:

$$P = i^2 R_L = \frac{e^2 R_L}{(R_0 + R_L)^2}, \quad \text{since} \quad i = \frac{e}{R_0 + R_L}$$

$$\frac{\partial P}{\partial R_L} = \frac{(R_0 + R_L)^2 e^2 - 2 R_L e^2 (R_0 + R_L)}{(R_0 + R_L)^4} = 0 \quad \text{for maximum}$$

so $\quad R_0 = R_L \quad \text{for} \quad P_{\max} = e^2/4R_L$ (1.5.1)

Thus, for maximum power transfer the load resistor must be equal to the generator output resistance. Half the power is then dissipated in R_L and half in R_0.

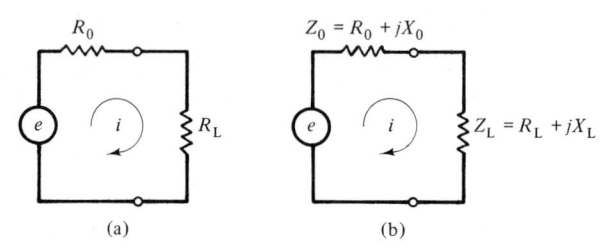

Fig. 1.5.1 Impedance matching for maximum power transfer

When the output impedance Z_0 is complex, as in Fig. 1.5.1(b), the matching condition is slightly modified. One may expect that maximum power transfer will be achieved when the current is in phase with the voltage. This would occur when the reactance of the circuit is zero, i.e., $X_0 = -X_L$. This can be shown in a similar manner to that above. Using Eq. (1.1.14):

$$P = \tfrac{1}{2} ii^* \mathcal{R}e(Z), \quad i = \frac{e}{(R_0 + R_L) + j(X_0 + X_L)} = \frac{e}{R + jX}$$

$$= \frac{e^2 R_L}{2(R^2 + X^2)}$$

$$\frac{\partial P}{\partial X} = \frac{e^2 R_L (0 - 2X)}{2(R^2 + X^2)} = 0 \text{ for maximum}$$

so $\quad X = 0 \quad \text{or} \quad X_L = -X_0$ (1.5.2)

$\partial P/\partial R$ then follows identically to Eq. (1.5.1). Thus the load to match an output impedance $(R + jX)$ is $(R - jX)$.

The above form of matching is not always convenient or possible. For various reasons the load may have to be some given impedance (e.g., a loudspeaker with a few ohms resistance) while the generator may have a quite different value. Some means of transforming the impedances to achieve a match is then required. This is possible using a transformer consisting of two inductively coupled coils usually wound on a core of magnetic material; Fig. 1.5.2(a):

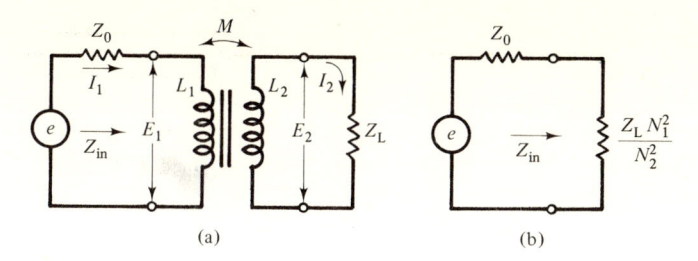

Fig. 1.5.2 (a) Impedance matching by transformer, (b) equivalent circuit

Assuming a perfect transformer, i.e., one in which the two coils are perfectly coupled with no leakage flux so the mutual inductance $M = (L_1 L_2)^{1/2}$, and that $Z_{L1} \gg Z_0$, $Z_{L2} \gg Z_L$, then we can write the standard relations [h1, i1]:

$$\frac{E_1}{E_2} = \frac{N_1}{N_2} = \frac{I_2}{I_1}, \quad P_1 = E_1 I_1 = E_2 I_2 = P_2$$

$$Z_{in} = \frac{Z_L N_1^2}{N_2^2}, \quad \frac{Z_L}{Z_0} = \frac{N_2^2}{N_1^2} \quad \text{for matching} \tag{1.5.3}$$

This provides only one parameter, the turns ratio N_2/N_1, so that resistive and reactive matching cannot be achieved independently. However, it is usually the resistive component of the load that is of importance, so that extra reactive components may be added to the load (or generator) to achieve a match.

The type of magnetic material used for the transformer core depends particularly on the frequency region of interest. At low frequencies, up to ≈ 20 kHz, the common laminated cores, or 'C' cores are used. Above this, up to ≈ 100 kHz, toroidal cores wound with very thin strip material and covered with a thin layer of insulation are popular for higher power applications. For frequencies from 10 kHz up to hundreds of megahertz ferrite cores of various shapes, particularly the various sizes and grades of pot core, are used [j1].

A further application of matching is in connection with high frequency transmission lines such as coaxial cables. These have a resistive characteristic impedance Z_0, most commonly 50 ohm, but also 75 or 100 ohm, dependent on the geometric cross-section. A line of any length terminated in this resistance will be matched, and all the power flowing along the line will be dissipated in the terminating resistor. An equally important consequence is that there will be no reflected wave travelling back towards the generator, since all the incident power is absorbed. In signal handling situations this is the important consideration, rather than power transfer, especially when dealing with fast pulses.

If L and C are the inductance and capacitance per unit length, then $Z_0 = (L/C)^{1/2}$, but the product LC is independent of geometry and is equal to the product of the magnetic permeability, $\mu\mu_0$, and the electric permittivity, $\varepsilon\varepsilon_0$, of the medium between the conductors. The velocity of the wave on the line is $u = (LC)^{-1/2}$ m/s, $\mu_0 = 4\pi \times 10^{-7}$ H/m, $\varepsilon_0 = (36\pi \times 10^9)^{-1}$ F/m, and for air dielectric $\mu = \varepsilon = 1$, so that the velocity $u = 3 \times 10^8$ m/s equivalent to a time delay $T = 3 \cdot 3$ ns/m. This is the same as the velocity in free space. For a coaxial cable $\mu = 1$, $\varepsilon \doteq 2 \cdot 3$ for the commonly used dielectrics, so $u = 2 \times 10^8$ m/s ($T = 5$ ns/m).

The question sometimes arises, when is a coaxial cable a transmission line and when is it just a lumped inductance and capacity? The answer depends on whether we are considering a sine wave or a pulse signal. For a sine wave the electrical length uT of the line must be substantially less than $\lambda/4$ before it may be considered a lumped impedance. For pulses, T must be substantially less than the risetime τ_R (say $T<\tau_R/4$). Thus, for a risetime of 5 ns a cable longer than about 25 cm should be considered a transmission line. If lines are not correctly terminated in the characteristic impedance there will be reflections giving standing waves or distorted pulses [k1, p. 90; g1; f1].

At high frequencies, lengths of transmission line may be used as series or shunt transformers to match resistive and reactive components, but they are frequency sensitive as they depend on the ratio of the length of cable to signal wavelength. Some rather ingenious *wound transmission line* broad band transformers particularly suitable for pulses are discussed in [k1, p. 106; a1; b1; c1].

1.6 Feedback

Feedback is one of the most important techniques used in electronics and is essential in any control system of whatever nature [b1]. We shall be specially concerned later (chapter 2) with one particular form of feedback, but it is desirable to point out some of the other forms and the differences between them. Feedback can be either negative or positive. In the former, the feedback signal opposes the input signal, while in the latter it assists it. As may be expected the effects will be quite different.

Feedback is commonly considered in two applications:

(i) The modification or stabilization of some parameter of an overall open-loop system, e.g., the modification of the input impedance or the stabilization of the gain of an amplifier.
(ii) In a closed-loop or servo system used to control some external parameter, e.g., temperature control of an oven or provision of a stable voltage supply.

The principles and problems are essentially identical and it is only in usage that they appear to differ.

In (i) the gain of the amplifier may depend on many factors such as temperature or ageing with time. If a reduced dependency is needed better components or circuits may be used, or the gain may be made to depend on the properties of components with more stable characteristics rather than the active gain components. Although circuits and components can improve performance directly, e.g., differential amplifiers with matched silicon transistors as against single-ended amplifiers with germanium transistors, it is the use of negative feedback that provides the most dramatic, flexible, and convenient means of achieving our ends. The gain can then be made dependent on high stability passive components, with the gain of the transistors being of minor significance. Of course, there is a price to be paid and the skill of the designer lies in reducing this to a minimum while satisfying the requirements.

In some cases it is not so much improvement of performance of some basic system that is required, but modification to give some quite different response. Examples of this are the production of a logarithmic or exponential response (Sec. 4.3) or the provision of snap-action switching, this latter being achieved by means of positive feedback (Secs. 5.3(a), 6.1).

The application of feedback is achieved by passing part of the output signal, via a feedback network, to the input where it is *added* to the actual input signal. The feedback may be proportional to output current or voltage and added to the input again as a current or voltage. This provides four different configurations which are discussed in some detail by Gray and Searle [a1, pp. 630–665] who identify them in terms of node or loop output sampling, and node or loop input comparison. The particular choice of sampling and comparison topology determines the characteristics of the resultant system. For example, node comparison lowers the input impedance while loop sampling increases it relative to the unfedback system. The corresponding choice of sampling has a corresponding effect on the output impedance. Thus, statements made in chapter 2 of the present work regarding the effects of negative feedback, only necessarily apply to that particular topology, which is node–node. See Table 1.6.1.

Table 1.6.1 Feedback configurations

	Input comparison topology	
	Node	Loop
Source representation	Norton	Thévenin
Input impedance	decreased by $(1 - A\beta)$	increased by $(1 - A\beta)$
	Output sampling topology	
	Node	Loop
Feedback stabilizes	voltage	current
Output impedance	decreased by $(1 - A\beta)$	increased by $(1 - A\beta)$

Although negative feedback is most commonly encountered, positive feedback also has its uses. The most important is in the realization of oscillators. These are systems with sufficient power gain to be able to supply their own input and so be self-sustaining (chapter 5). For this the feedback must reinforce the existing input sufficiently to compensate for the inevitable losses in the system. Since it is virtually impossible to maintain an exact balance, an excess must be fed back which means that the oscillations grow until some inherent internal limitation occurs. Although this may be satisfactory in some instances, it is often required to stabilize the amplitude at some value or to minimize distortion, in which case some amplitude-dependent negative feedback must be applied (Sec. 5.1). Thus, positive and negative feedback may be found together in the same system.

Servo feedback is used in closed-loop systems to control some external parameter by reference to a preset demand value. The emphasis is on control modified by the deviation of the actual output from the desired output [c1]. In the example above, we might specify the temperature of the oven in terms of the resistance of some resistance thermometer or the output voltage from a thermocouple. Any change in the temperature, from whatever source, will cause a change in the resistance (or voltage). The magnitude and sense of the deviation from the preset value provides the information that can be used to control the power supplied to the oven.

The servant- or servomechanism is dedicated to carrying out its specified task to the best of its ability. This depends not only on the quality of the tools it is given, but also on its agility and on how harmoniously the various parts work together. The harmony affects the efficiency of the system and the agility the time response. The time or frequency response is of the greatest importance, since a delayed response can lead to the feedback assisting the undesired changes rather than opposing them. The system then becomes unstable and oscillates uncontrollably, i.e., the feedback has become positive.

All systems will have some feedback even if none has been deliberately applied. This arises for example from stray capacities between the terminals of a transistor or bulk resistance in a semiconductor junction. The stray capacity between collector and base of a transistor leads to what is known as the Miller effect (Fig. 1.6.1).

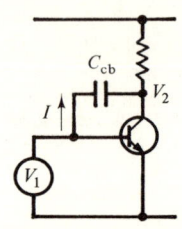

Fig. 1.6.1 Miller effect

If the gain of the transistor $V_2/V_1 = -K$, and the impedance of C_{cb} is Z_{cb}, the current I flowing through C_{cb} is given by [d1]:

$$I = \frac{V_1 - V_2}{Z_{cb}} = \frac{V_1(1+K)}{Z_{cb}} \tag{1.6.1}$$

so that the effective value of C_{cb} has been increased by $(1+K)$ times. This increased capacity will have an important effect on the frequency response and phase shift of the amplifier.

7 Grounding, loops, and guards

Correct grounding is of great importance in most circuits and vital in many. Incorrect grounding can lead to pickup of spurious signals, undesired feedback leading to unstable operation or oscillation, and ground loops with large induced circulating currents. The fallacy is that all points on a good conductor are at the same potential. For an ordinary conductor (as against a superconductor) this is unfortunately not true enough. For example, 10 cm of 20 SWG copper wire has a resistance of 2·6 mΩ. The same length of 2·5 mm wide *1 oz* (0·035 mm) printed circuit conductor, has a resistance of 18·4 mΩ. The inductances of the two conductors are 0·15 and 0·18 µH, giving a resultant impedance at 10 kHz of 9·3 and 21·4 mΩ. (Note that the impedance of a conductor increases with frequency as a result of both skin effect and inductance [l1].) These impedances may appear negligible, but a current of 1 A, not uncommon in a supply bus, gives voltage drops of 2·6 or 18·4 mV at d.c., and larger at higher frequencies.

Consider the simple amplifier circuit shown in Fig. 1.7.1.

Current I_1 in the ground bus will produce a voltage between points a and b. Since this appears between base and emitter it will be amplified. When a signal source is connected, as shown, then the voltage due to I_1 between b and c will be effective. If I_1 is due to later or output stages of the amplifier, the feedback may be sufficient to

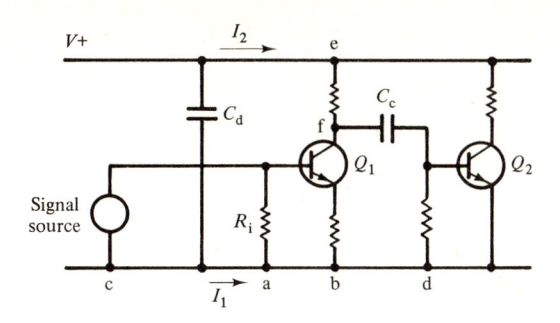

Fig. 1.7.1 Effects of currents in supply lines

cause oscillation. The effect of this form of coupling can be removed by joining the power supply to the output rather than the input end of the buses. The heavy output stage currents then circulate between output stage and power supply and do not affect the input, except for any common-mode effects (see Fig. 4.7.2). Another desirable practice is to make a, b and c one physical point so they will be at the same potential whatever is the value of I_1. Varying voltages at e, due for example to current I_2 in the bus, can feed via f and C_c to Q_2, and hence be amplified. The decoupling capacitor C_d, therefore, should be connected between e and d, but it is better, as for the ground bus, to keep large currents away from low level stages.

It is frequently necessary to connect one unit to another, usually by two leads or a coaxial cable, as shown in Fig. 1.7.2.

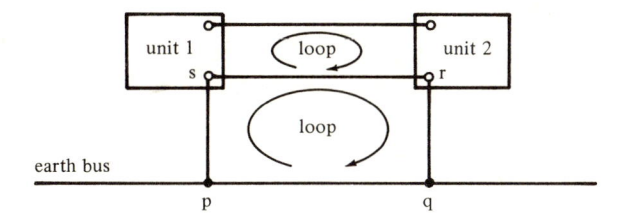

Fig. 1.7.2 Ground loops

If both units are powered from the mains they will be connected separately to earth via the power sockets, which may be electrically separated as shown at p and q. Large currents may flow in the earth bus as a result of other equipment further up the line. These currents will flow partly in pq and partly in rs depending on the relative impedances, producing spurious signals between r and s. Low impedance loops such as pqrs can carry electromagnetically induced currents from fluctuating magnetic fields. If the impedance is low enough these currents can be surprisingly large. It is not ordinarily possible to measure currents in such low impedance circuits, since the resistance of any current meter inserted in the circuit will substantially increase the resistance and reduce the induced current. They can be measured, however, by various forms of clip-on ammeter, which detect the magnetic field surrounding the conductor without introducing significant impedance into the circuit [g1, j1, A1].

It is a personal practice to construct all units completely isolated from the chassis, the latter being earthed for safety and screening. A collection of units can then be earthed (or not) at any convenient or most effective point. This practice requires some care as circuits may be earthed inadvertently. This may happen for example in bolting the circuit board to chassis, fixing a signal socket to the panel, or mounting an electrolytic capacitor can to the chassis with a metal clamp. The final product should be directly tested to check isolation. Circuit boards for sensitive applications preferably should be double-sided with a ground plane on one side joined to the 0 V bus at one point only. For high frequency circuits it may be preferable to use the ground plane as the 0 V (zero volt) bus to obtain the lowest possible impedance. Connections between board and panel should be carefully considered to avoid loops and the proximity of low and high level signals. Twisted pairs are an effective way of reducing loops and miniature coaxial cables are also useful, but watch out for loops formed by interconnecting screens. Supply line bypassing *on board* is most desirable, but remember the poor high frequency performance of electrolytic capacitors and the comments above regarding inductance.

All capacitors will have some equivalent series inductance, so that above a certain frequency the impedance will increase rather than decrease. For large value aluminium electrolytic capacitors the minimum impedance can occur at a frequency as low as a few hundred Hz, but this can range up to about 100 kHz depending on value, size, construction, etc. Tantalum electrolytics may be used up to about 1 MHz, but are rather more expensive. Small size ceramic capacitors are good up to about 100 MHz and are adequate for most applications, but they must be connected by the shortest leads as close as possible to the device to be bypassed.

In high impedance circuits electrostatic pickup and leakage, due to imperfect insulation may be problems. A field-effect transistor (FET) may have an input resistance of say 10^{10} ohm. Thus, if the circuit board has even this high resistance between a supply bus and the FET gate terminal, half the supply voltage will appear at the gate! Similarly, a capacity of only 1 pF, which could arise from two conductors 2 cm long spaced by 2·5 mm, has an impedance of 10^{10} ohm at only 16 Hz. The electrostatic pickup can be reduced by effective conductive screening, and this and leakage can be overcome effectively by the use of guard circuits. If a conductor is interposed between the input and the rest of the circuit and maintained at the same potential as the input, then there can be no coupling to the input resistively or capacitively. The guard must thus be actively driven via an effectively unity-gain amplifier. An example of this is illustrated in Fig. 7.3.2.

In many situations, particularly with low level signals or long leads, the problem of common-mode interference becomes critical. Two methods of improving the rejection of these effects, are the use of differential techniques and of passive guard circuits. The principles of differential measurements are simple enough but, in practice, there are many difficulties in realizing the maximum advantage. Basic differential amplifiers are discussed in Secs. 2.5 and 4.2 and an extensive discussion by Demrow is given in [d1]. Here we will only consider the effects of guard circuits [b1, c1, h1]. Consider the circuit of Fig. 1.7.3(a), which shows a differential amplifier being used to measure a normal-mode voltage e_s and subject to a common-mode voltage e_c.

If the resistance of the cable screen R_b is substantially greater than that of the earth bus R_c, then we can neglect R_b. The common-mode voltage e_c will cause a current to flow via R_u (where subscript u refers to unbalance) and C_1 and, since $Z_1 \gg R_u$, it will cause a much smaller current to flow via Z_1 and C_1, which can be neglected. To show the effect of the common-mode voltage we will use the values shown in Fig. 1.7.3 [a1]. The value $R_u = 1\,k\Omega$ should be explained. In order to allow comparisons between the effectiveness of different systems this standard value has been chosen, and is used by most manufacturers in specifying the common-mode rejection ratio (CMRR). This is defined as the signal gain/common-mode gain, or the ratio of the common-mode voltage to the normal-mode voltage that gives the same output [d1]. It is usually given in decibels. The current flowing at 50 Hz will be 3·3 µA, and the voltage across R_u will be 3·3 mV, and this is added to e_s.

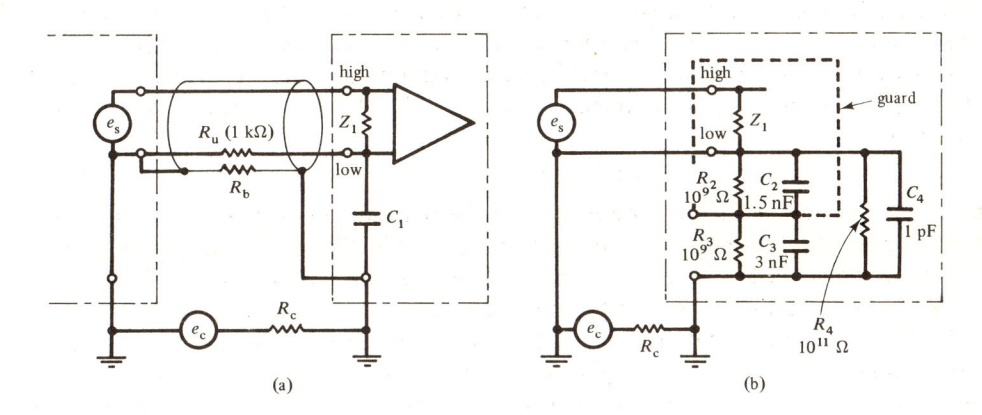

Fig. 1.7.3 Guard circuits

The addition of a conducting guard shield enclosing the input circuit can reduce these common-mode effects considerably; Fig. 1.7.3(b). The guard is isolated from ground, and the various impedances may typically have the values shown. The guard is connected so that it is driven by the common-mode voltage, and so it is effectively at the same voltage as the *low* terminal. Thus, no current flows through R_2, C_2, and the only current through R_u is that due to R_4, C_4. The impedance of C_4 at 50 Hz is $3 \times 10^9\,\Omega$, giving a current of 3·3 nA and a voltage across R_u of 3·3 µV.

1.8 Noise

The ultimate sensitivity of any measurement will be limited by spontaneous fluctuations or noise. This will be present both in the signal itself and in the measuring system. We are not concerned here with noise on the signal, assuming that there is nothing to be done about this, but one should always be concerned about adding any extra noise due to the measuring system. There are several forms of noise as follows.

1.8(a) *Johnson noise*

An electrical or electromechanical system will exhibit random fluctuations in the variables or parameters which specify its state, for example voltage, current, energy, etc. If the system is in thermal equilibrium with its surroundings, then the thermal fluctuations can be derived from thermodynamic arguments without in any way considering the actual nature of electricity, such as that it is due to discrete electrons of charge q. This thermal noise was first investigated experimentally by Johnson and a theoretical relation was derived by Nyquist [e1, p. 141–153; d1; f1; g1; l1].

By considering the equilibrium at temperature T between thermal (black body) radiation and resistors terminating a transmission line, Nyquist showed that the mean squared Johnson noise voltage, appearing across a resistor R, in any frequency interval Δf, is given by:

$$\langle v_{NR}^2 \rangle = 4kTR\, \Delta f \text{ volt}^2 \qquad (1.8.1)$$

or $\qquad v_{NR} = 0{\cdot}13[R\,.\,\Delta f]^{1/2}\ \mu\text{V r.m.s. at 300 K}$

where R is in kilohms, Δf is in kilohertz, and k is Boltzman's constant $1{\cdot}38 \times 10^{-23}$ joule/deg K. This spectral distribution is said to be *white*, in that it is independent of frequency, i.e., it is only the frequency interval Δf that matters. The description *white* arises from the similar situation in white light. Maximum noise power will be delivered by a resistor when it feeds a matched load (Sec. 1.5). The power into the load is then given by:

$$P_{NR} = \langle v_{NR}^2 \rangle / 4R = kT\, \Delta f \qquad (1.8.2)$$

For a complex impedance, the Johnson noise depends on the real or resistive part, a pure reactance generating no noise (but see [L1]). Since the real part will be a function of frequency it is more appropriate to work in terms of a spectral density, $J = 4kTR(f)$, and integrate over the frequency interval of interest [d1, p. 591].

It should be noted that Eq. (1.8.1) is derived on the basis of the low frequency approximation of Planck's law (the Rayleigh–Jeans approximation) which is valid up to submillimetre wavelengths at ordinary temperatures. For higher frequencies or very low temperatures the full expression must be used:

$$\langle v_{NR}^2 \rangle = \frac{4hfR\, \Delta f}{\exp(hf/kT) - 1} \qquad (1.8.3)$$

where h is Planck's constant ($6{\cdot}625 \times 10^{-34}$ joule s).

v_{NR} as a function of resistance and bandwidth for room temperature, Eq. (1.8.1), is shown in Fig. 1.8.1.

1.8(b) *Shot noise*

The fact that an electrical current does consist of a stream of individual electrons gives rise to a second source of random fluctuation called shot noise, appropriately enough first investigated by Schottky. The charges are assumed to pass or arrive quite randomly in which case Poissonian statistics will apply. Then, if an average number $\langle n \rangle$ are counted in a given interval of time t, the variance $\langle \Delta n^2 \rangle$ in this number will be given by $\langle n \rangle$. The average current $\langle I \rangle$ and variance $\langle i_{NS}^2 \rangle$ are:

$$\langle I \rangle = \langle n \rangle q/t, \qquad \langle i_{NS}^2 \rangle = \langle \Delta n^2 \rangle q^2/t^2 = \langle n \rangle q^2/t^2$$

so $\qquad \langle i_{NS}^2 \rangle = \langle I \rangle q/t = 2q\langle I \rangle\, \Delta f \qquad (1.8.4)$

or $\qquad i_{NS} = 5{\cdot}7 \times 10^{-4}[I\,.\,\Delta f]\ \mu\text{A r.m.s.}$

where I is in milliamperes and Δf is in kilohertz.

The final step introducing Δf does not follow immediately but requires some mathematical consideration [d1, f1, E1]. The arrival of the charges corresponds to a sharp impulse whose effect will be felt for some time after, depending on the response function of the system (Sec. 1.11). A measure of this effect requires integration over a convolution of random pulses with the response function [E1]. The final result given in Eq. (1.8.4) is the same as assuming that the bandwidth Δf associated with a

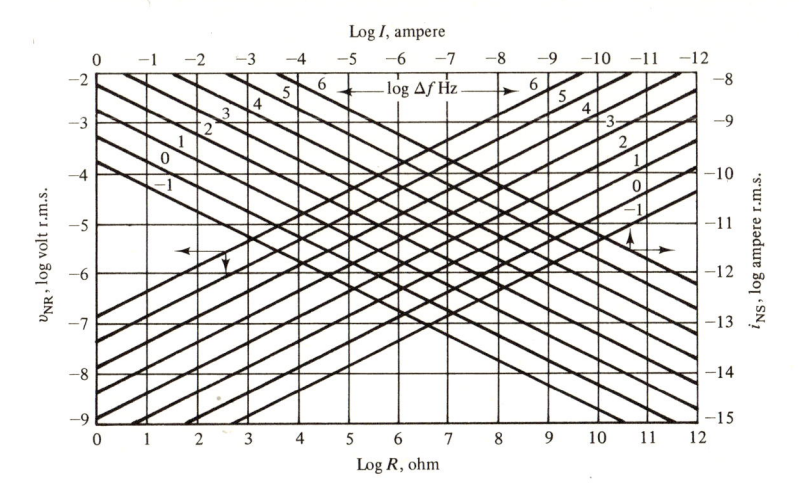

Fig. 1.8.1 Johnson and shot noise as a function of resistance and bandwidth at 300 K

time interval t is $1/2t$, which is quite plausible. As shot noise is again dependent only on frequency interval rather than frequency, its spectral distribution is also white. The variation of i_{NS} as a function of $\langle I \rangle$ for given values of Δf is shown in Fig. 1.8.1.

1.8(c) *Flicker or $1/f$ noise*

The origin of flicker noise is not well understood but it generally exhibits a 1/frequency dependence, and hence is most significant at low frequencies [f1, g1, j1, d1]. As a consequence of its low frequency weighting, it is sometimes referred to as pink noise in contrast to the previous white. Above some corner frequency, ω_L, the flicker noise will be negligible compared with the white noise sources, but below this it will generally be the major noise source. The value of ω_L depends on the particular device and the operating conditions, and ranges from about 1 Hz to 1 kHz [F1]. This is, in most senses, a technical source of noise rather than a fundamental one like Johnson and shot noise. Improved techniques and devices have considerably reduced it, and further improvement may be expected.

We may also mention here another excess low frequency noise, which is more prevalent in IC circuits than ordinary devices. This is the so-called burst or popcorn noise, consisting of sudden large and random jumps in output level possibly due to some form of intermittent breakdown, or to jitter between different values of current gain in a transistor. If this presents a problem special selected units are available (e.g., CA6741T low popcorn, and $1/f$ version of type 741) [I1, J1].

1.8(d) *Noise figure and signal-to-noise ratio*

Any amplifying system will contribute extra noise to an input, which will itself have some noise content. The point of concern is how much worse will the signal-to-noise ratio be after amplification, compared with the original input. We use signal here to mean the actual useful or desired part of the input.

Consider an amplifier of gain A with an equivalent input noise v_{NA} or output noise $v_{NO} = A v_{NA}$. If the applied input consists of a signal v_S plus noise v_{NR} then the noise figure F is given by:

$$F = \frac{\text{signal-to-noise ratio of input}}{\text{signal-to-noise ratio of output}}$$

$$= \frac{\langle v_S^2 \rangle / \langle v_{NR}^2 \rangle}{A^2 \langle v_S^2 \rangle / (A^2 \langle v_{NR}^2 \rangle + \langle v_{NO}^2 \rangle)}$$

$$= 1 + \frac{\langle v_{NO}^2 \rangle}{A^2 \langle v_{NR}^2 \rangle}$$

$$= 1 + \frac{\langle v_{NO}^2 \rangle}{4 A^2 k T R_S \Delta f} \quad \text{from Eq. (1.8.1)} \tag{1.8.5}$$

where R_S is the effective signal source Johnson noise resistance. F can thus never be less than unity, or 0 dB, which represents a perfect noiseless amplifier. A value less than 2 (3 dB) is regarded as a low-noise system. A noisy amplifier may be represented by a noiseless amplifier together with appropriate input noise generators, e.g., in Eq. (1.8.5) this would be a series generator of amplitude v_{NA}. This technique is very convenient and, in considering it further, we will follow the excellent discussion of Faulkner [b1, L1]. This should be read carefully as he points out several serious misconceptions in many other treatments. The following is a brief outline of some of the points in this paper.

To represent the most general noisy amplifier a voltage and a current noise generator are required (Fig. 1.8.2). These generators are usually specified by their noise resistances:

$$R_{NV} = \langle v_{NA}^2 \rangle / 4kT \Delta f, \qquad R_{NI} = 4kT \Delta f / \langle i_{NA}^2 \rangle \tag{1.8.6}$$

or $\qquad v_{NA} = 4 R_{NV}^{1/2} \text{ nV}/(\text{Hz})^{1/2}, \qquad i_{NA} = 4/R_{NI}^{1/2} \text{ pA}/(\text{Hz})^{1/2}$

where R_{NV} and R_{NI} are in kilohms.

Note that in general R_{NV} and R_{NI} will be functions of frequency.

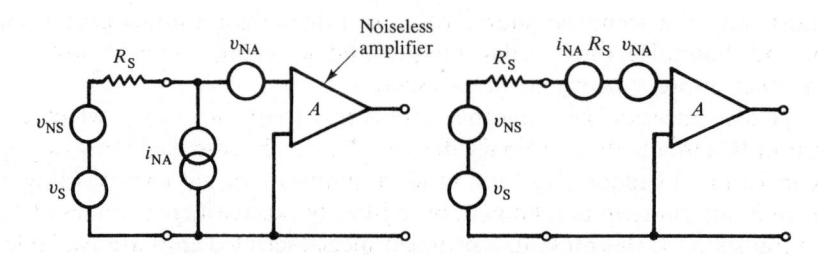

Fig. 1.8.2 Equivalent circuits for noisy amplifier

The noise figure is most easily found by transforming the current noise generator, i_{NA}, to an equivalent series generator, $i_{NA} R_S$. Then, ignoring any correlation effects between the generators:

$$F = \frac{\langle v_S^2 \rangle}{NR_S} \cdot \frac{NR_S + (NR_S^2/R_{NI}) + NR_{NV}}{\langle v_S^2 \rangle} \quad (N \equiv 4kT\Delta f)$$

$$= 1 + \frac{R_S}{R_{NI}} + \frac{R_{NV}}{R_S} \tag{1.8.7}$$

Several useful results follow from the form of Eq. (1.8.7). Resistance in series with the input (R_{NV}) should be small, and that in parallel (R_{NI}) large, relative to R_S to achieve a low noise figure. On the other hand a noiseless resistance connected in parallel with the input will not affect F. Thus, when the input resistance is determined by feedback, for example, it is possible to make it much less than R_S without degrading F.

By differentiating Eq. (1.8.7) with respect to R_S the optimum source resistance $R_{S(opt)}$, for a given amplifier, can be determined.

$$\frac{\delta F}{\delta R_S} = 0 + \frac{1}{R_{NI}} - \frac{R_{NV}}{R_S^2} = 0 \quad \text{for minimum } F,$$

therefore
$$R_{S(opt)} = (R_{NV} R_{NI})^{1/2} \tag{1.8.8}$$

Using this in Eq. (1.8.7) gives the minimum noise figure:

$$F_{min} = 1 + 2(R_{NV}/R_{NI})^{1/2} \tag{1.8.9}$$

Thus, a good noise figure is possible if $R_{NV} \ll R_{NI}$. R_S is then chosen such that:

$$R_{NI} \gg R_S \gg R_{NV} \tag{1.8.10}$$

and the noise resistances will have minimal effect. The noise figure at a given frequency can now be completely specified by F_{min} and $R_{S(opt)}$ using Eqs. (1.8.7) and (1.8.8):

$$F - 1 = \tfrac{1}{2}(F_{min} - 1)\left[\frac{R_{S(opt)}}{R_S} + \frac{R_S}{R_{S(opt)}}\right] \tag{1.8.11}$$

Thus, the noise capabilities of a system in a given frequency range should be assessed in terms of F_{min}, and not on the basis of some arbitrary source resistance R_S, a low value series noise resistance R_{NV} or, for that matter, on parameters quoted for a transistor and measured at some convenient collector current. This will be considered further in Sec. 4.1.

Since negative feedback is such an important and useful technique some comments on its effect on noise are necessary. Application of negative feedback to a given system cannot improve the noise figure [K1]. In the common case the bandwidth is increased by feedback (Sec. 2.4) which leads to a correspondingly increased noise figure. However, this does not mean that a lower noise system cannot be designed using feedback compared with not using it. On the contrary, when all the performance parameters are considered, it is often possible to achieve a considerably better noise figure with a feedback amplifier than with a straight amplifier that can otherwise provide the same performance. An appropriate example is an amplifier which is required to have an input resistance of 1 Ω and to operate from a source resistance of

1 kΩ [b1, p. 27]. Connection of a 1 Ω resistor across the input of a simple amplifier would give the required input resistance, but the noise figure would be very large. Using the operational amplifier feedback configuration (chapter 2) the required input resistance may be obtained with insignificant effect on the noise figure.

It is useful to have a measure of the equivalent white noise bandwidth of a simple low-pass RC filter. This is the bandwidth of the ideal low-pass filter which will pass the same noise power as the actual filter. The transfer function of the RC filter is given by Eq. (1.3.1) and since we are interested in power ($\propto \text{voltage}^2$) we have (see appendix, Eq. (A.10)) [C1]:

$$|G(f)^2| = G(f)G(f)^* = \frac{1}{1+(2\pi fRC)^2} \qquad (1.8.12)$$

This must be integrated over the range of f from zero to infinity and divided by the d.c. gain. Since $G(0)=1$ for the RC filter, we have for the noise bandwidth $\mathscr{B}_N$:

$$\begin{aligned}\mathscr{B}_N &= \int_0^\infty \frac{df}{1+(2\pi fRC)^2} = \frac{1}{2\pi RC}\int_0^\infty \frac{dx}{1+x^2} \quad (x \equiv 2\pi fRC) \\ &= \frac{1}{2\pi RC}[\tan^{-1} x]_0^\infty \\ &= \frac{1}{4RC} \end{aligned} \qquad (1.8.13)$$

which is a little larger than the normal signal bandwidth $1/2\pi RC = (1/6\cdot3)RC$.

1.9 Basic diode and transistor characteristics

We review here some of the basic semiconductor diode and transistor characteristics, in particular those that may be referred to in later sections.

1.9(a) *P–N junction diode*

The *P–N* junction diode has a theoretical current–voltage relationship given by [a2, N1, h2, i2]:

$$I = I_S\left[\exp\left(\frac{qV}{mkT}\right) - 1\right] \qquad (1.9.1)$$

or $V = V_J \ln(I/I_S)$ for $V \gg V_J$

where q = electron charge = $1\cdot602 \times 10^{-19}$ coulomb
 k = Boltzmann's constant = $1\cdot38 \times 10^{-23}$ joule/K
 T = absolute temperature, degrees K

and m is a correction factor to the ideal relation that depends on the recombination of carriers in the junction region. m may vary between 1 for germanium and 2 for small currents in silicon. The value depends on the type and structure of the junction and can be even greater in some devices [a2, N1, p1]. The characteristic voltage of the junction:

$$V_J = \frac{kT}{q} = \frac{T}{11\,600} = 25 \text{ mV at 293 K (20°C)} \qquad (1.9.2)$$

I_S is the reverse saturation current and, for reverse voltages $\gg V_J$, is practically constant. In real junctions there is also some leakage current, due to surface effects for example, which means that I_S increases slowly with voltage. If the reverse voltage is too high various breakdown processes are initiated and I_S increases rapidly, and unless the current is limited to a low value the junction will be destroyed. Typical characteristic curves for several types of diode are shown in Fig. 1.9.1. Figure

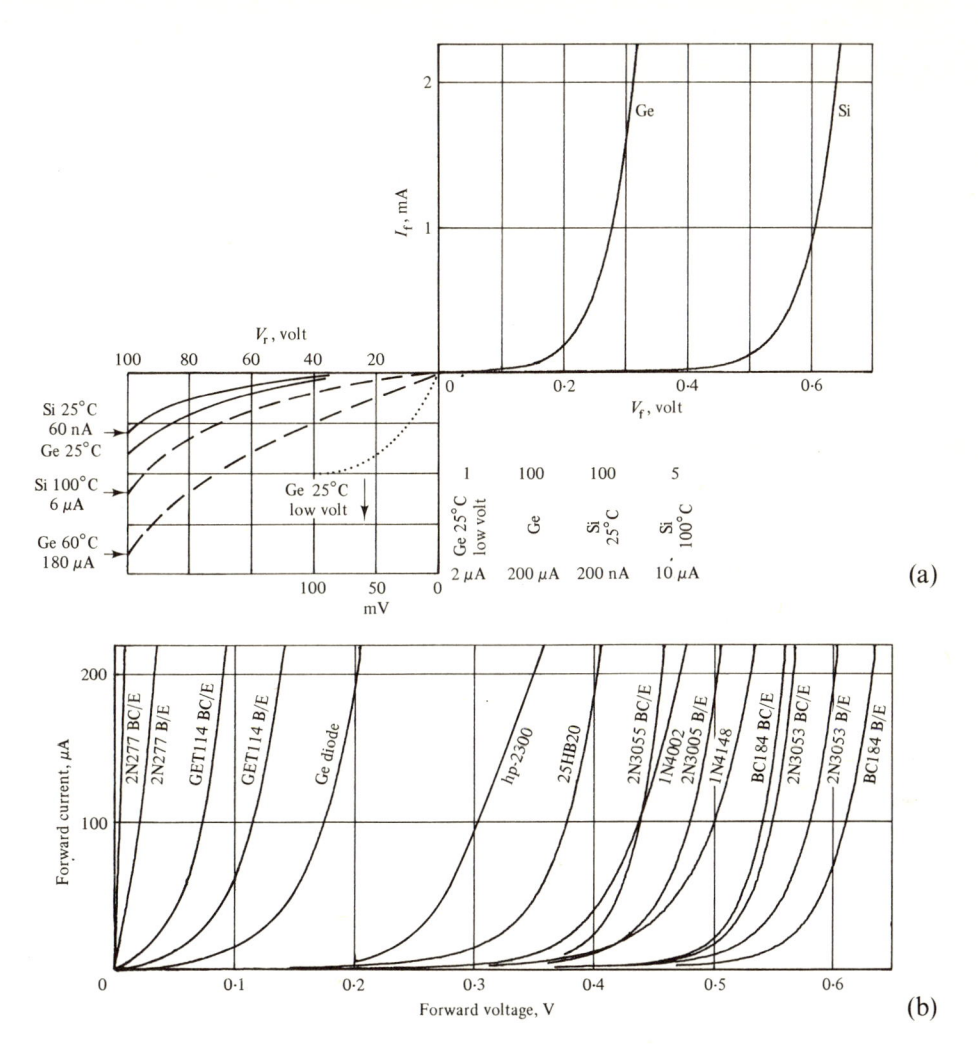

Fig. 1.9.1 *P–N* **junction characteristic curves**

1.9.1(a) shows the forward conductance for larger currents together with the reverse currents on various scales (much expanded) and different temperatures. The dotted curve shows the form of the reverse characteristic for voltages up to 100 mV. Figure 1.9.1(b) shows the forward conduction, on an expanded scale, of a number of *junctions*, illustrating the wide range that may be encountered.

For silicon diodes in particular the reverse current is quite negligible for most applications. If it is critical, as for example in long term sample-and-hold systems, diodes with I_s less than 1 pA at 45 V are available [J1]. Although small, I_S increases rapidly with temperature at a rate of about 7%/K, or alternatively doubles for every 10 K rise in temperature. The forward voltage, V_f, is also temperature sensitive and, for a given current, decreases with rise in temperature. Theoretically, the coefficient is -1.7 mV/K for silicon or -1.8 mV/K for germanium, while in practice it may be greater, say -2 to -2.5 mV/K [N1, 11].

Note that, on the characteristic curves, in the forward direction there is an effective cut in voltage, 0·2 V for germanium, 0·6 V for silicon, below which the current is small (say <1 mA) and above which it rises very rapidly. Thus, when a diode is conducting or a transistor base-emitter junction forward biased, these are the voltages one would expect to find across the junctions. For very large currents, as in power rectifiers, these voltages will be exceeded as a result of ohmic bulk resistance in the device.

For forward conduction a quantity of interest is the incremental or dynamic resistance r_e, which is the slope of the characteristic at the point of interest. Using Eq. (1.9.1) in the region above cut-in where unity may be neglected relative to the exponential:

$$r_e = \frac{dV}{dI} = \left[\frac{qI_s}{mkT} \exp\left(\frac{qV}{kT}\right)\right]^{-1} = \frac{mkT}{qI} = \frac{26\,m}{I} \text{ ohm at } 27°C \quad (1.9.3)$$

where I is in milliamperes.

Note that r_e is the incremental and not the actual resistance of the diode. The latter is given by the slope of the line from the origin to the point of interest.

Two factors are of importance in considering the high frequency performance of a diode: the capacity and the reverse recovery time t_{rr}. In any diode there is of course the capacity of the package, but there is also the capacity of the junction itself. This is not usually of concern for forward conduction, but in reverse bias the junction acts like a small parallel plate capacitor, the *separation* of the plates increasing with reverse bias. Thus, the junction capacity C_J decreases with increasing reverse bias. For fast signal diodes C_J may be a few picofarads at zero bias and will change by a factor ≈ 2 for a bias of 20 V.

When a diode is conducting there will be a high density of minority carriers in the junction region. If a reverse bias is suddenly applied the reverse current will not immediately drop to zero (or at least its reverse saturation current I_s) until all these excess carriers have been removed. Thus, there will be a transient reverse current, independently of that through C_J, lasting for the reverse recovery time t_{rr}. For fast signal diodes this is of the order of a few nanoseconds.

There are many thousands of different diodes so which one do you use? This, of course, depends on the application and requirements such as forward current, reverse voltage, recovery time, and cost. A number of semiconductor devices have become very popular since they meet a wide range of requirements, and as used in large quantities the cost is low. For small signal diodes such a device is the 1N914/1N4148 series for which $I_{f(max)} = 75$ mA, $V_{r(max)} = 75$ V, $t_{rr} = 4$ ns, $C_{J0} = 2$ to 4 pF. For small power rectifiers the 1N4001/7 covering a range $V_{r(max)} = 50$ to 1000 V at $I_{f(max)} = 1$A are popular.

Very fast response times of the order of tens of picoseconds are possible with metal–semiconductor, hot-carrier, or Schottky diodes. A typical characteristic is shown in Fig. 1.9.1(b) and is similar to normal *P–N* diodes [N1, b2, c2, G1, g2]. The cut-in voltage can be varied by selection of a particular metal [E1, h1], and they can have a near perfect logarithmic characteristic in the forward direction.

The exponential or logarithmic characteristic of a *P–N* junction is used in a number of computing applications such as multipliers and dividers (Sec. 6.2) and logarithmic circuits (Sec. 4.3). For these it is of the utmost importance that the relationship be accurately exponential over large ranges of current, i.e., *m* constant, and since matched devices are usually required for temperature compensation, the value of *m* must be well defined. It is found that transistors connected as diodes are much superior in both respects and have an *m* value almost exactly equal to 1 [p1, I.32 and II.22]. The so-called trans-diode connection can give an accurate response over a current range of the order of $10^{10}:1$! [b1, c1].

1.9(b) *Transistors*

The general characteristics and usage of transistors are covered in so many places that no repetition is necessary here [m1, l1, M1, N1, d1, e1, k1, s1, B1]. However, we will consider briefly several of the more important parameters and limiting values.

Both diodes of a transistor will break down at some reverse voltage in the same way as an ordinary diode. Thus, the transistor specification will give absolute maximum values for these voltages. Exceeding these is likely to result in instant destruction of the junction, although if the current is limited to low enough values a stable zener breakdown may be obtained; see Sec. 7.10(a). However, in this mode the current gain of the transistor is likely to be degraded. It is important to appreciate that these are not design maxima since, as a result of faults, transients, inductive spikes, etc., the limit may easily be exceeded. In deciding on design maxima some latitude must be allowed to cover any possible excursions.

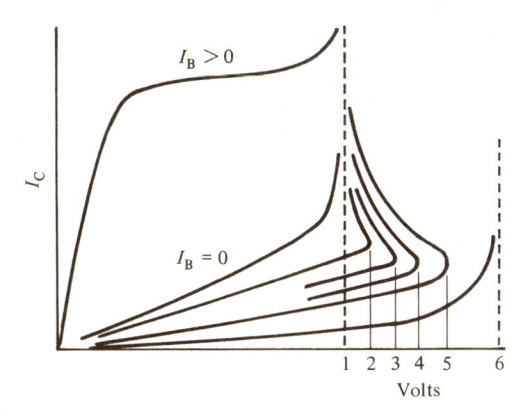

Breakdown voltages:

(1) BV_{CEO}: Collector–emitter, base open circuit ($I_B = 0$)
(2) BV_{CER}: Collector–emitter, resistor *R* from base to emitter
(3) BV_{CES}: Collector–emitter, base shorted to emitter
(4) BV_{CEX}: Collector–emitter, base reverse biased
(5) BV_{CEX}: Collector–emitter, base reverse biased (>4)
(6) BV_{CBO}: Collector–base, emitter open circuit

Fig. 1.9.2 Transistor breakdown voltages

The main difficulty with voltage limits is that they depend on circuit conditions, e.g., resistance between terminals, voltage across the other pair of terminals, or currents flowing. There are thus several breakdown limits commonly used in device specifications, the critical one depending on the particular circuit. Those usually defined are shown in Fig. 1.9.2 [l1, N1, g1, V1].

These breakdown conditions are avalanche effects and are sometimes referred to as first breakdown, as there is a further breakdown process. The so-called second breakdown is a function of I_C and time, for a given V_{CE}. It arises from a current hogging effect due to the large positive temperature coefficient of I_C at a given V_{BE}. As a result of local variations, one small area of the transistor can hog most of the current leading to excessive localized heating and destruction of the junction in this region. The junctions are shorted and V_{CE} drops to a low value. Since heating is involved, time is a factor (Fig. 1.9.3) [g1, Q1, R1].

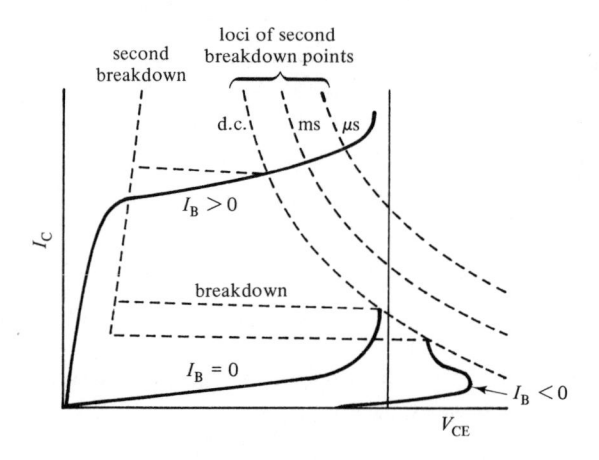

Fig. 1.9.3 Transistor second breakdown

To specify the allowable operating conditions, for power transistors in particular, a maximum area of operation is often specified as shown in Fig. 1.9.4 [g1, u1, D1, I1, P1, Q1, R1, W1, T1, j1, n1].

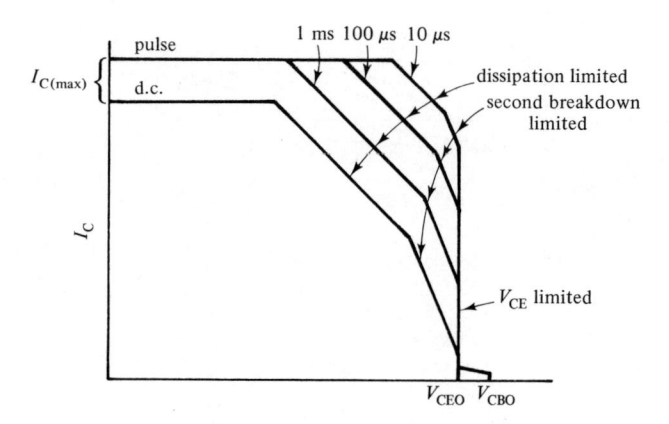

Fig. 1.9.4 Transistor safe operating areas

The various pulse ratings are for single non-repetitive pulses. If they are repetitive, proper allowance must be made. The power dissipated will lead to higher junction and case temperatures, depending on thermal resistances and time constants. The second breakdown locus varies only slightly with temperature so the main concern is with the dissipation limited region [g1]. The power dissipation thermal rating falls linearly to zero at 200°C case temperature, while the second breakdown derating falls to a limiting value of about 70 per cent of the 25°C value at 200°C.

In normal operation the base–emitter junction will be forward biased with $V_{BE} \doteq 0{\cdot}6$ V for silicon, while the collector–base junction is reverse biased. If the base

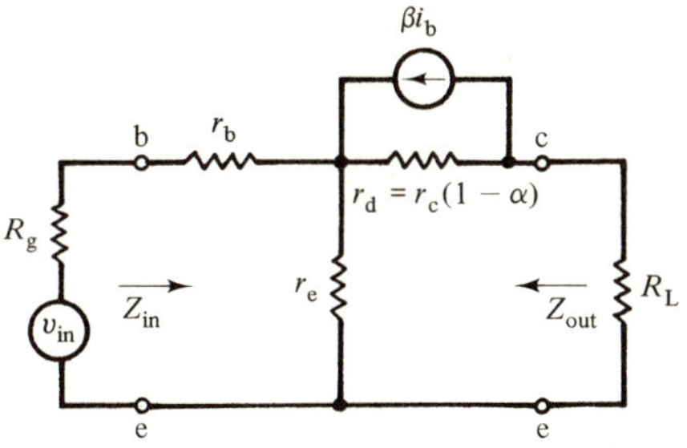

Input impedance
$$z_{in} = r_b + \frac{r_e(r_c + R_L)}{R_L + r_e + r_c/(1+\beta)} \doteq \beta r_e$$

Output impedance
$$z_{out} = r_e + r_c(1-\alpha) - \frac{r_e(r_e - \alpha r_c)}{R_g + r_b + r_e}$$

Voltage gain
$$a_v = \frac{-R_L}{r_e + r_b/\beta} \quad \text{for} \quad R_L \ll r_c(1-\alpha), \quad R_g = 0$$

$$a_v = \frac{r_e - \alpha r_c}{R_g + r_b + r_e} \quad \text{for} \quad R_L \to \infty$$

Current gain
$$a_i = \frac{r_e - \alpha r_c}{R_L + r_e + r_c(1-\alpha)}$$

$$= \frac{r_e - \alpha r_c}{R_L + r_e + r_c(1+\beta)} \doteq \beta \quad \text{for} \quad R_L \ll r_c(1-\alpha)$$

If emitter resistor R_E is present, this must be added to r_e. Typical values at 1 mA collector current:

$$r_b = h_{ie} - \frac{h_{re}(1 + h_{fe})}{h_{oe}} \approx 200\,\Omega$$

$$r_e = \frac{h_{re}}{h_{oe}} \approx 26\,\Omega$$

$$r_c = \frac{1 + h_{fe}}{h_{oe}} \approx 10\,\text{M}\Omega$$

$$\alpha = \frac{\beta}{1+\beta} \approx 0{\cdot}996$$

$$\beta = \frac{\alpha}{1-\alpha} \approx 250$$

Fig. 1.9.5 Transistor tee equivalent circuit

current is increased substantially $I_C = h_{FE} I_B$ increases rapidly, so that if there is a collector load V_{CE} drops to a very low value. If $I_B \geq I_C/h_{FE}$ the transistor is in saturation and V_{CE} will be rather less than V_{BE}, say 0·3 to 0·7 V, i.e., the collector–base junction will be forward biased. The excess minority carrier density in this condition has significant effects on the switching times of the transistor [N1].

The most commonly specified signal parameter (and often the only one) is the current gain. This may be the d.c. value β_0 or $h_{FE} = I_C/I_B$, or the small signal common emitter gain β or $h_{fe} = \partial I_C/\partial I_B$. These values will be specified at a particular value of collector current I_C. For several reasons such as power dissipation, input impedance, or low noise operation, it is often necessary to operate at quite different values of I_C. The current gain of modern planar transistors does not vary drastically over large variations in I_C. Transistor parameters are usually specified at relatively large collector currents, for ease of measurement. Those transistors specified at low currents are generally quite expensive, while others specified at much higher currents may be quite as good at the same low current and cost very much less [f1, q1, O1]. There is no reason at all for accepting the specification value as an optimum determined by the manufacturer.

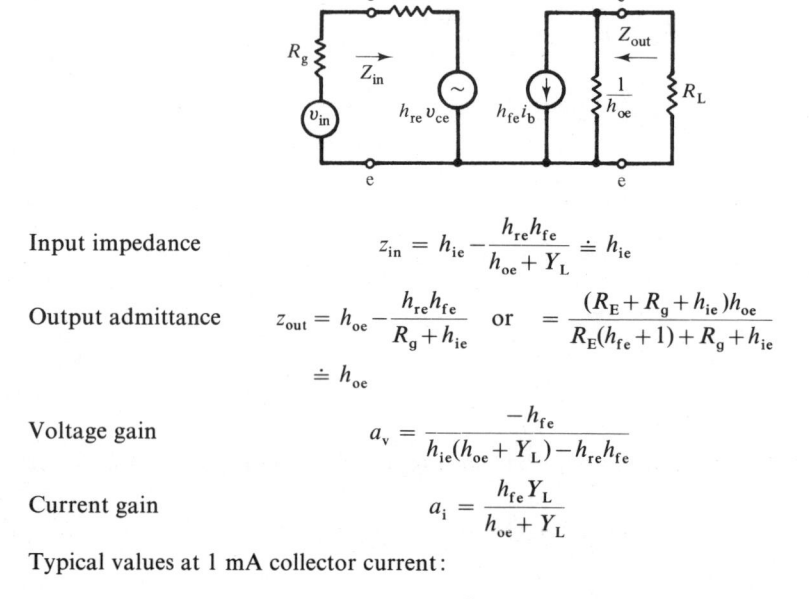

Input impedance
$$z_{in} = h_{ie} - \frac{h_{re} h_{fe}}{h_{oe} + Y_L} \doteq h_{ie}$$

Output admittance
$$z_{out} = h_{oe} - \frac{h_{re} h_{fe}}{R_g + h_{ie}} \quad \text{or} \quad = \frac{(R_E + R_g + h_{ie}) h_{oe}}{R_E(h_{fe} + 1) + R_g + h_{ie}}$$
$$\doteq h_{oe}$$

Voltage gain
$$a_v = \frac{-h_{fe}}{h_{ie}(h_{oe} + Y_L) - h_{re} h_{fe}}$$

Current gain
$$a_i = \frac{h_{fe} Y_L}{h_{oe} + Y_L}$$

Typical values at 1 mA collector current:

$$h_{ie} = r_b + \frac{r_e}{(1-\alpha)} \approx 6{\cdot}7 \text{ k}\Omega$$

$$h_{re} = \frac{r_e}{(1-\alpha)r_e} \approx 6{\cdot}5 \times 10^{-4}$$

$$h_{fe} = \frac{\alpha}{1-\alpha} \approx 250$$

$$h_{oe} = \frac{1}{(1-\alpha)r_c} \approx 2{\cdot}5 \times 10^{-5} \text{ mho}$$

Fig. 1.9.6 Transistor hybrid equivalent circuit

Current gain h_{fe} decreases at large I_C and at high frequencies. The frequency at which it has decreased by 3 dB ($\times 0.7$) from its low frequency value h_{feo} being called f_{hfe}. In many cases the transition frequency f_T is given instead where:

$$f_T = h_{feo} f_{hfe} = f_{hfb} \qquad (1.9.4)$$

where f_{hfb} refers to the common base configuration. Thus, for a 6 dB/octave roll-off f_T is also the gain–bandwidth product (Sec. 1.3). f_T is a function of I_C [l1, q1].

For circuit analysis, transistors are represented by an equivalent circuit of impedances and generators from which the small signal or incremental performance may be determined. The parameters of the equivalent circuit are dependent on the d.c. operating point, but the equivalent circuit says nothing about the d.c. conditions. There are a number of equivalent circuits in use but we will consider only the three most commonly encountered. The first, shown in Fig. 1.9.5 is the tee circuit. Included in the figure are the derived quantities—gain, and input and output impedance—together with typical values of the parameters and their relations with those of the hybrid circuit [m1, l1, k1].

The hybrid circuit is shown in Fig. 1.9.6, together with its various relationships. The reason for the name is that the h parameters have mixed or hybrid units, ohms, mhos, and dimensionless. These are the parameters most commonly specified for transistors, and their variation with d.c. operating point is shown graphically in the data sheets.

The variation of the most important parameters with I_C can be predicted quite well for low frequencies (say < 1 MHz), and for I_C between a few mA and 100 nA in the case of small-signal silicon planar transistors. If the values at some I_C are known, the values at any other current in the range can be calculated [f1, O1].

(i) Transconductance

$$g_m = y_{feo} = i_c/v_{be} = \partial I_C/\partial V_{BE} = qI_C/kT = 38 I_C \text{ milliamps/volt}$$

where $I_C \doteq I_E$ is in milliamps.

(ii) Small-signal low frequency current gain

$$h_{feo} = \partial I_C/\partial I_B = i_c/i_b \propto I_C^{(1-M)}$$

(iii) D.C. current gain

$$h_{FE} = \beta_0 = I_C/I_B = M h_{feo} \propto I_C^{(1-M)}$$

assuming that $M \neq$ function of I_C

(iv) Input resistance

$$h_{ieo} = \partial V_{BE}/\partial I_B = v_{be}/i_b = h_{feo}/y_{feo} \propto I_c^{-M}$$

M is a coefficient characteristic of the individual transistor and its value typically lies between 0.7 and 0.9. For low-level devices it is about 0.85, and for high speed devices about 0.7. To determine M find h_{FE} at I_C and $10 I_C$. If h_{FE} increases by a factor P then $M = (1 - \log_{10} P)$. To assist in using these relations the curves of Fig. 1.9.7 may be used.

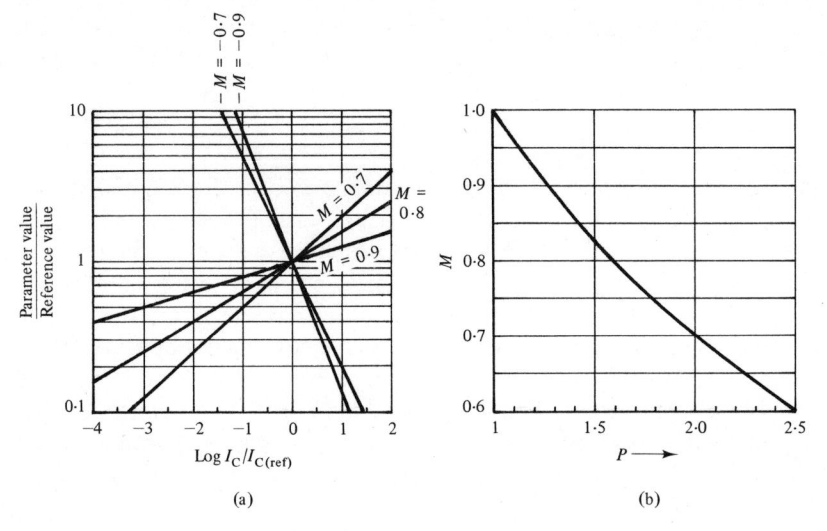

Fig. 1.9.7 (a) Parameter ratio as a function of M value, (b) M value as a function of P

At high frequencies the hybrid-pi equivalent circuit is often used (Fig. 1.9.8). The point b′ represents the *real* base, whereas b represents the *external* base connection. $r_{bb'}$ then represents the bulk or base spreading resistance.

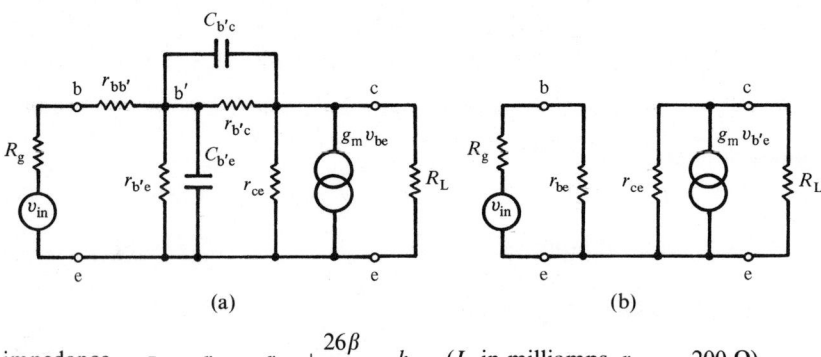

Input impedance $\quad z_{in} = r_{be} = r_{bb'} + \dfrac{26\beta}{I_C} = h_{ie} \quad$ (I_C in milliamps, $r_{bb'} = 200\ \Omega$)

Output impedance $\quad z_{out} = r_{ce} = \dfrac{1}{h_{oe}}$

Voltage gain $\quad a_v = \dfrac{g_m R_L r_{ce}}{R_L + r_{ce}} = g_m R_L \quad (r_{ce} \gg R_L)$

Current gain $\quad a_i = \beta$

Typical values at 1 mA collector current:

$$r_{ce} = 1/h_{oe} \approx 4 \times 10^4\ \Omega$$

$$r_{be} = h_{ie} \approx 6\cdot 7\ k\Omega$$

$$g_m = \dfrac{\beta}{r_{bb'} + 26\beta/I_C} \approx 38\ mA/V$$

Fig. 1.9.8 Transistor hybrid-pi equivalent circuit

This is a rather complex circuit so we will only consider the low frequency equivalent, Fig. 1.9.8(b), which ignores the capacities and the feedback impedance $r_{b'c}$ since this is very large. The resulting circuit is then the same as the hybrid (Fig. 1.9.6) if the feedback there is neglected, i.e., h_{re} small. This simplified circuit now looks like many other active device representations [l1, m1, k1]. In Fig. 1.9.9 are shown the variation of g_m and r_{be} with I_E. This is plotted for typical values, $\beta = 200$, $r_{bb'} = 200$ ohm.

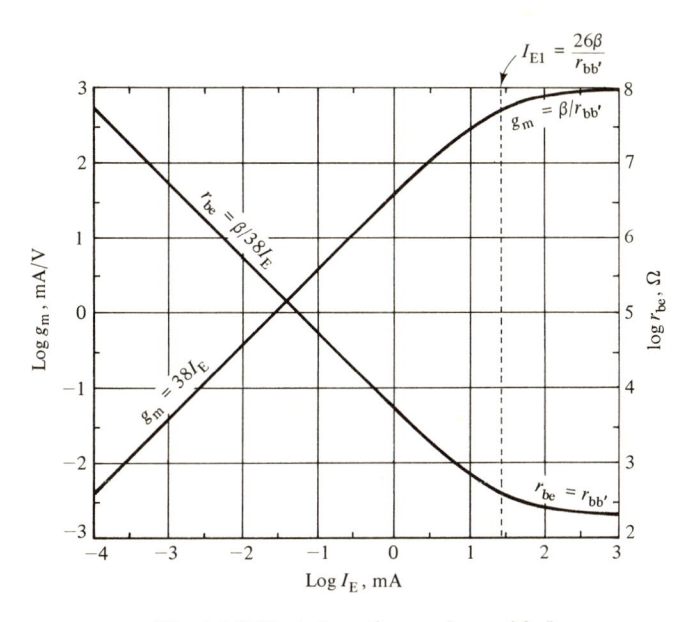

Fig. 1.9.9 Variation of g_m and r_{be} with I_E

The region of operation for low level signal transistors is below I_{E1}, while power transistors operate in the region above this. Thus, for the latter, the transconductance and input resistance are approximately constant. However, at large currents, $r_{bb'}$ increases and β decreases, so that g_m decreases and r_{be} increases. The typical values shown in Fig. 1.9.9 are not representative of power transistors, because of the larger size and different methods of fabrication. Values of $\beta = 50$ at $I_E = 10$ amperes, and $r_{bb'} = 1$ to 10 ohm, would be more appropriate [n1, f2].

The input resistance r_{be} can be very large at low I_E, and if driven from a source impedance substantially less than this, the transistor acts as a voltage-operated device. This contradicts the common acceptance of the transistor as a low input impedance current-operated device. Also, since g_m is well defined, while h_{fe} is rather variable in a batch of devices, the voltage operated mode provides predictable gain. The noise performance can also be excellent [o1, f1, S1].

Power transistors are made using several different processes, each with particular advantages and disadvantages. In choosing a power transistor for a particular application these should be kept in mind. Table 1.9.1 classifies the four different types, where 3 indicates superior and 0 markedly inferior performance [A1]. Alternative names for the different types are also included [v1].

Table 1.9.1 Comparison of power transistor types (Texas Instruments, with permission)

Performance	Triple diffused	Single diffused (unibase)	Single diffused epitaxial base (epibase)	Planar (double diffused)
Voltage	3	0	1	1
Current	2	2	2	2
Gain linearity	2	0	1	3
V_{sat}	1	1	1	3
Switching	2	0	2	3
Complements	0	2	3	2
Forward biased second breakdown	2	3	2	0
Reverse second breakdown	2	2	1	0
Leakage	1	0	1	3
Frequency	2	0	1	3
Dissipation	1	2	1	1
Cost advantage	2	3	3	0

A number of conclusions may be drawn from the table and are quoted here [A1]:

(i) Triple diffused devices, while having the best performance in high voltage applications, where robustness is important, do not easily yield complementary devices. *PNP* high voltage devices (>400 V) are extremely difficult to manufacture.

(ii) Single diffused devices are very robust, yield complements, are simple and inexpensive to manufacture, but are slow switches and can suffer from high leakage current, particularly at elevated temperature.

(iii) Single diffused epitaxial base transistors are manufactured for ease of generating complementary products, and at the same time have most of the advantages of true single diffused devices with the exception of safe operating area, which is marginally worse.

(iv) Planar power devices offer the circuit designer several benefits in particular applications—notably high speed, low saturation voltage, accepted reliability, linear $h_{FE} I_C$ characteristics and low leakage currents (due to passivation). This type of product makes an excellent high-speed switch where quality and low losses are important. Planar power devices are expensive, however, and are not robust by accepted standards.

These varied properties suit differing applications as shown in Table 1.9.2 [v1].

Table 1.9.2 Applications of power transistor types (Courtesy Motorola Semiconductors and Texas Instruments)

Application	Triple diffused	Unibase (single diffused)	Epibase (single diffused expitaxial base)	Double diffused (planar)
Audio			✓	✓
Series regulator		✓	✓	
Inverter	✓		✓	
Inductive loads			✓	✓
Power switch (fast)	✓		✓	✓
Power switch (slow)		✓		

1.10 Some IC arrangements

In the design of integrated circuits a number of circuit configurations recur frequently. As these techniques are interesting and common to a number of different IC classes they will be discussed here. Though these circuits often rely on the special conditions existing in IC's, i.e., close electrical matching and thermal tracking, they can be used in discrete circuits by using the various IC transistor arrays [g1, h1, i1, f1].

1.10(a) *Constant current source*

An ideal constant current source has infinite source impedance. To approach this using a simple resistor would evidently require excessive voltages for any usable current, and high value resistors are in any case not economic in IC's. An alternative arrangement is to use the high differential output impedance at the collector of a transistor with an emitter resistor [f1, j1]; Fig. 1.10.1(a).

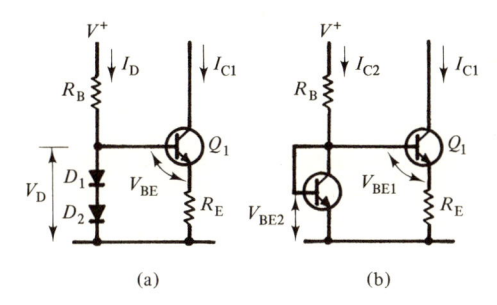

Fig. 1.10.1 IC constant current sources

Assuming Q_1 has a large current gain, the current I_D flowing through R_B flows mainly through $D_{1,2}$, to produce a voltage $V_D = 1 \cdot 2$ volts. Allowing for the V_{BE} of Q_1, the voltage across R_E is $\frac{1}{2}V_D = 0 \cdot 6$ volts which fixes I_{C1} for a given value of R_E. The output impedance of Q_1 is increased substantially by the presence of R_E. To calculate the value the h parameters are required. These are not generally quoted for IC transistors, but we can find approximate values by using the h parameters for an IC array (CA3045). The values are dependent on collector current:

$$I_C = 100 \text{ μA} \qquad I_C = 10 \text{ μA}$$
$$h_{fe} = 80 \qquad\qquad 13$$
$$h_{oe} = 5 \times 10^{-6} \qquad 3 \cdot 7 \times 10^{-6} \text{ mho}$$
$$h_{re} = 9 \times 10^{-4} \qquad 2 \cdot 2 \times 10^{-3}$$
$$h_{ie} = 2 \cdot 1 \times 10^4 \qquad 6 \cdot 3 \times 10^4 \text{ ohm}$$

For $I_{C1} = 100$ μA, $R_E = 6$ kΩ, and the output impedance is [k1]:

$$Z_0 = \frac{1}{h_{oe}}\left[1 + \frac{h_{fe}}{1 + (h_{ie}/R_E)}\right]$$

$$= 3 \cdot 8 \text{ MΩ}$$

The voltage required for an equivalent resistor constant current source would be 380 volts compared with the few volts at the collector of Q_1. As the circuit stands it is not temperature compensated. This can be achieved directly, or in conjunction with the elements for which the circuit supplies the constant current [h1, p. 44].

If lower constant currents are required a rather large R_E would be necessary. To avoid this the circuit of Fig. 1.10.1(b) is used [h1, g1, j1]. Since the two transistors will be closely matched in an IC and close together, which gives good thermal tracking, the emitter–base voltage differential ΔV_{BE} will be highly predictable for differing collector currents. From Eq. (1.9.1) (in the region where unity may be neglected):

$$\Delta V_{BE} = V_{BE2} - V_{BE1} = V_J \left[\ln\left(\frac{I_{C2}}{I_{C1}}\right) + \ln\left(\frac{I_{S1}}{I_{S2}}\right) \right]$$

$$= V_J \ln\left(\frac{I_{C2}}{I_{C1}}\right), \text{ or } 60 \text{ mV/decade } (I_{C2}/I_{C1}) \qquad (1.10.1)$$

where we have assumed transistors of identical geometry so that $I_{S1} = I_{S2}$ (ln 1 = 0). Thus, for a current $I_{C1} = 10$ µA and, say, $I_{C2} = 1$ mA (ratio = 2 decades), the voltage across R_E must be $\Delta V_{BE} = 120$ mV. This means $R_E = 120$ mV/10 µA = 12 kΩ compared with an equivalent simple resistor source of 1 MΩ. It is worth noting that although I_{C2} depends directly on V^+, I_{C1} depends only on the ln of this. For example, reducing V^+ by 50 per cent changes I_{C1} by only 14 per cent in the above case.

If $R_E = 0$ then the base–emitter voltages are equal, so $\Delta V_{BE} = 0$ and $I_{C1} = I_{C2}$. Thus I_{C1} is a *reflection* of I_{C2}, and the circuit has been named a current mirror [h1 p. 179; a1; d1]. The circuit is then as shown in Fig. 1.10.2(a).

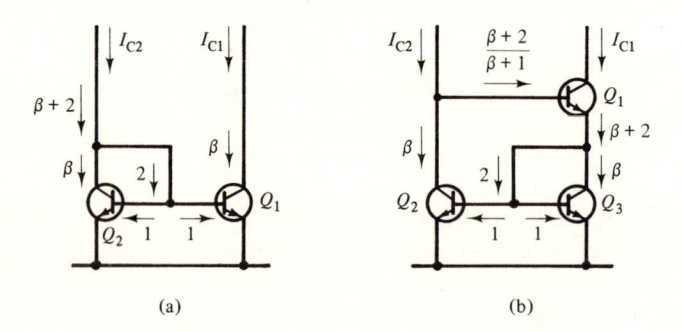

Fig. 1.10.2 Current mirrors, (a) basic, (b) improved

Taking the base currents as unity and the two current gains equal at β, then the various currents will have the proportions shown and $I_{C1}/I_{C2} = \beta/(\beta+2)$. To improve the matching, and the output resistance of Q_1, the modified circuit shown in Fig. 1.10.2(b) is used. Taking the base currents of Q_2, Q_3 equal to unity as before, the various currents are in the proportions shown. The current mirror ratio is then:

$$\frac{I_{C1}}{I_{C2}} = \beta\left(\frac{\beta+2}{\beta+1}\right)\frac{(\beta+1)}{(\beta^2+2\beta+2)} = \frac{\beta^2+2\beta}{\beta^2+2\beta+2} \qquad (1.10.2)$$

The appearance of the β^2 term means that the matching is almost exact even for β as low as 10 [a1]. In some applications, multiple collectors are used on Q_1. The total current will then be fixed by I_{C2} and the relative proportions by the geometry of the collectors.

Many other more complex arrangements are possible which can give improved performance in particular respects. Several of these are discussed in [g1 section 10; h1].

1.10(b) *Active loads, and differential to single-ended converter*

Active loads are essentially high impedance constant current sources used to replace the usual resistive load. This technique achieves much higher gain per stage (≈ 5000) thus allowing a reduction in the number of stages. It also reduces power consumption, improves frequency response, allows operation over a much wider range of supply voltage, and gives large linear voltage swings [g1, l1, j1].

A basic active load circuit would be the same as discussed above in Sec. 1.10(a) and, at the same time would serve to convert the output from a differential amplifier to a single-ended or ground referred signal (Fig. 1.10.3).

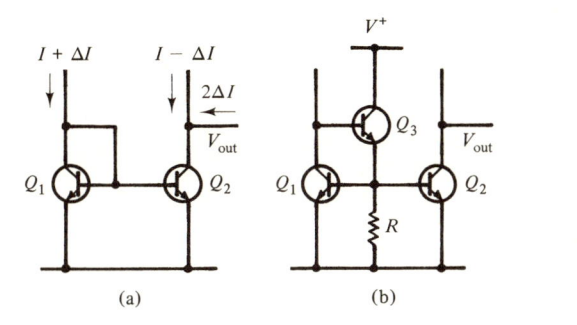

Fig. 1.10.3 IC active load, and differential to single-ended converter

The output currents $I + \Delta I$ and $I - \Delta I$ from the collectors of a differential amplifier (in this case consisting of *PNP* transistors; see, for example, Fig. 2.3.1) flow towards the collectors of Q_1 and Q_2. As explained in Sec. 1.10(a), the currents through Q_1 and Q_2 must be equal so the difference of the input currents, $2\Delta I$, must flow in the output lead as shown. The circuit is unbalanced, in that two base currents must be fed from the collector of Q_1. The balance is improved by the addition of Q_3 and R to supply these currents, Q_1 now only supplying the very small base current to Q_3; Fig. 1.10.3(b). Even this can be balanced, as could the simpler circuit, by arranging that the base of the transistor fed by V_{out} draws the appropriate current. Imbalance due to large variations of collector–base voltage of Q_2 can be alleviated by the addition of emitter resistors to both Q_1 and Q_2: this gives the configuration used in the 741 amplifier, Fig. 2.3.1.

1.10(c) *Variable zener*

In an IC a fixed voltage zener, typically 5 to 8 volts, can be obtained from a reverse biased base–emitter junction. A more versatile variable zener can be produced with the circuit of Fig. 1.10.4.

From the figure and Eq. (1.9.1):

$$I_B \doteq 0, \quad I = \frac{V_{CE}}{R_1 + R_2}, \quad V_{BE} = IR_2 = \frac{V_{CE} R_2}{R_1 + R_2}$$

or
$$V_{CE} = \left(\frac{R_1 + R_2}{R_2}\right) \cdot V_{BE} = \left(\frac{R_1 + R_2}{R_2}\right) \cdot V_J \ln\left(\frac{I_C}{I_S}\right) \quad (1.10.3)$$

$$= \left(\frac{R_1 + R_2}{R_2}\right) \cdot 60 \text{ mV/decade } (I_C/I_S)$$

The logarithmic term is only a slowly varying function of I_C so that, for ordinary variations of I_C, V_{BE} and hence V_{CE} are effectively constant. The choice of R_1 and R_2 fixes the *zener* voltage. In a discrete circuit a potentiometer may be used to provide a

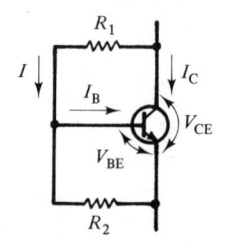

Fig. 1.10.4 Variable zener

continuously variable zener. A useful application of this is in setting the quiescent current in power amplifier output stages (Fig. 4.7.2).

1.10(d) *PNP transistors*

In normal IC production it is difficult to produce good *PNP* transistors with the standard processing steps. However, the performance that can be achieved can still be of considerable use in circuit design [g1, i1, b1, f1, h1]. The lateral *PNP* structure is formed parallel to the silicon wafer surface and has a rather broad base region. This results in low current gain but also in high breakdown voltages. The transistor can be isolated and so can be used in any circuit location. The low current gain is not a drawback in many applications, e.g., d.c. level shifting, but *PNP* transistors must generally be used with care as the high frequency performance is poor. In some cases, feedforward techniques can be used to overcome this; Sec. 3.5(c). The high breakdown voltage can be used to advantage in input stages (Sec. 2.3). In some of the most recent IC amplifiers high gain lateral *PNP*'s have been realized, giving improved system performance, but these amplifiers are rather more expensive.

An alternative *PNP* structure having good performance, is possible. The *vertical PNP* is formed normal to the wafer surface just like the *NPN* transistors, but has the substrate (i.e., the original starting semiconductor material) as collector. Since the substrate must be connected to the negative supply voltage for correct operation of all the IC components, this type of transistor can be used only in certain circuit locations, e.g., in a complementary symmetry output stage (Fig. 2.3.1, Q_{20}).

1.11 Laplace transforms

1.11(a) *Transformations and transfer functions*

Many problems are more readily solved by transferring them into a different guise or representation. One very common case is the transformation from ordinary numbers to logarithms, which considerably simplifies such operations as multiplication, division, roots, raising to powers, etc. By learning the rules, logarithms may be used effectively without considering the underlying theory in detail. Since we do not have space here the following treatment will be in this vein.

In the present circumstance we have the problem of an electrical network, which may contain passive and active elements, to which is applied an input or excitation function. The network modifies the input according to its transfer function to give an output or response function (Fig. 1.11.1).

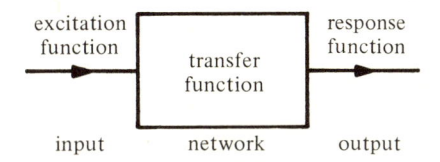

Fig. 1.11.1 Transfer function

This may be written algebraically as:

$$\text{Response function} = \text{transfer function} \times \text{excitation function} \quad (1.11.1)$$

If this problem is approached in the usual way the functions in Eq. (1.11.1) usually contain combinations of integrals, derivatives, trigonometric terms, etc., which are very awkward to deal with. The attraction of the Laplace transform is that all these are transformed into algebraic forms which can be easily manipulated. Once this is done the problem then arises of transforming from the Laplace to the original representation, as we would do with logarithms by looking up the antilogarithms. To enable Laplace transforms to be used with the same facility a very large number have been worked out and tabulated, and we will not need to work any out [b1, d1, e1, k1, l1, g1].

The technique for writing down the impedance of components of a circuit for sinusoidal waveforms is familiar (Sec. 1.1). For a wave of frequency $f = \omega/2\pi$, the impedances of a resistor R, capacitor C, or inductor L are given by (see Sec. 1.1):

$$Z_R = R; \qquad Z_C = \frac{1}{j\omega C} = \frac{-j}{\omega C}; \qquad Z_L = j\omega L \quad (1.11.2)$$

where j is the imaginary quantity $\sqrt{-1}$. We may look upon $j\omega$ as a sort of operator, that operates on the magnitude of the component to give its impedance. The inclusion of j describes the phase shifts introduced between voltage and current, which may be illustrated by phasor diagrams (Fig. 1.11.2).

In writing Eq. (1.11.2) we have used a simple operator that is applicable to sinusoidal waves, and very useful it is too. The particular form arises because of the property of sinusoidal functions that differentiation and integration do not change the form—only the phase and amplitude of the function. However, in many cases we are not dealing with the simple sinusoidal form, but with more complex forms such as square, triangular, sawtooth, pulses, etc. For these the $j\omega$ operator is only applicable in the Fourier sense, in that it could be applied to each frequency component and the resultants added up. This is a cumbersome process, and what is needed is a more general operator that would be applicable in all cases. (Even sinusoidal waves have

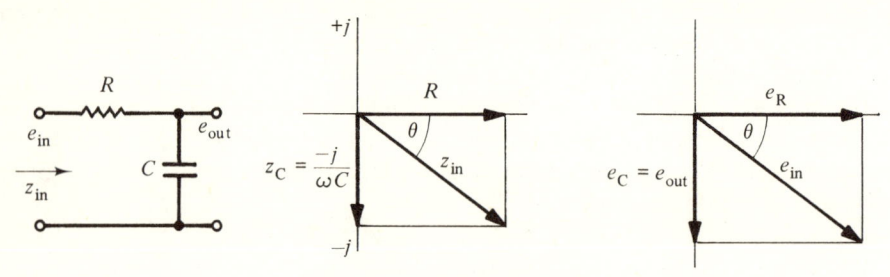

Fig. 1.11.2 Phasor diagrams

to be switched on.) It turns out that the operator to use includes $j\omega$ but is symmetrical (in the complex number sense) in that it has a real as well as imaginary part:

$$s = \sigma + j\omega \qquad (1.11.3)$$

The $j\omega$ operator involves a transformation between the time (t) and the frequency (ω) domains, the connection between the two being the Fourier transform. For the s operator the transformation is between the time (t) and the complex frequency (s) domains, the connection being the Laplace transform. The idea of a complex frequency may seem strange at first, but with a little experience and familiarity one soon gets used to it. In practice, we usually refer to s as simply a frequency, *complex* being understood.

The Laplace transform $F(s)$ of some function $f(t)$ is defined by:

$$\mathscr{L} f(t) = F(s) = \int_0^\infty f(t)\, e^{-st}\, dt \qquad (1.11.4)$$

and the inverse transform $\mathscr{L}^{-1}$ by:

$$\mathscr{L}^{-1} F(s) = f(t) = \frac{1}{2\pi j} \oint F(s)\, e^{ts}\, ds \qquad (1.11.5)$$

the integral being a line integral around all the poles of $F(s)$, see Sec. 1.11(b). These look rather formidable and we cannot justify any of it here (see, e.g. [b1, e1, f1, i1]), but as mentioned above the answers are known for all the common cases. Some of the commonest pairs are listed in Table 1.11.1. A comment on the unit step function $u(t)$ and the unit impulse function $\delta(t)$ is necessary. $u(t)$ represents a step of unit amplitude, the rise of the step taking place in an infinitesimally short time. $\delta(t)$ represents a spike of infinitesimal time duration, but of infinite amplitude, in such a way that the impulse (time × amplitude) is unity. These are of course mathematical ideals, as is a pure sine wave, but they can be realized with the desired accuracy in any particular situation, or allowance made for their deviation from the ideal.

Table 1.11.1 Laplace transform pairs

$f(t)$	$F(s)$
1. $\delta(t)$	1 (impulse function)
2. $Au(t)$	A/s (step function, A = constant)
3. t	$1/s^2$ (ramp function)
4. $\exp(-\alpha t)$	$1/(s+\alpha)$
5. $\exp(\alpha t)$	$1/(s-\alpha)$
6. $\cos(\omega t)$	$s/(s^2+\omega^2)$
7. $\sin(\omega t)$	$\omega/(s^2+\omega^2)$
8. $\exp(-\alpha t)\sin(\omega t)$	$\omega/[(s+\alpha)^2+\omega^2]$
9. $\exp(-\alpha t)\cos(\omega t)$	$(s+\alpha)/[(s+\alpha)^2+\omega^2]$
10. $\exp(\alpha+j\omega)t$	$1/(s-\alpha-j\omega)$
11. $\exp(\alpha-j\omega)t$	$1/(s-\alpha+j\omega)$
12. $e^{-\alpha t}(1-\alpha t)$	$s/(s+\alpha)^2$
13. $t^{n-1}\exp(-\alpha t)/(n-1)!$	$1/(s+\alpha)^n$
14. $(e^{-\alpha t}-e^{-\beta t})/(\beta-\alpha)$	$1/(s+\alpha)(s+\beta)$
15. $(\alpha e^{-\alpha t}-\beta e^{-\beta t})/(\alpha-\beta)$	$s/(s-\alpha)(s-\beta)$
16. $[(a_0-\alpha)e^{-\alpha t}+(\beta-a_0)e^{-\beta t}]/(\beta-\alpha)$	$(s+a_0)/(s+\alpha)(s+\beta)$ ($\alpha \neq \beta$, see 12)
17. $[(1/\alpha\beta)+(\beta e^{-\alpha t}-\alpha e^{-\beta t})]/[\alpha\beta(\alpha-\beta)]$	$1/[s(s+\alpha)(s+\beta)]$

Note: $A, \alpha, \beta, \omega, a_0$ are constants. $(n-1)! = (n-1)(n-2)(n-3)\ldots 1$.

Consider now the simple circuit elements R, L, C. We have the basic relationships:

$$e(t) = Ri(t), \qquad e(t) = \frac{L\,di(t)}{dt}, \qquad e(t) = \frac{1}{C}\int i(t)\,dt \qquad (1.11.6)$$

which give when Laplace transformed (we use capitals to represent transformed quantities, e.g., $\mathscr{L}\,e(t) = E(s)$):

$$E(s) = RI(s), \qquad E(s) = sLI(s), \qquad E(s) = \frac{I(s)}{sC}$$

or

$$Z_R(s) = \frac{E(s)}{I(s)} = R, \qquad Z_L(s) = sL, \qquad Z_C(s) = \frac{1}{sC} \qquad (1.11.7)$$

Thus, the impedances in the s representation look just like those in Eqs. (1.11.2), so they will be as easy to use. In fact, Eqs. (1.11.2) are for the special case $\sigma = 0$.

For the networks that we will be concerned with, the relationship between input x and output y can be expressed in the form of a linear differential equation with constant coefficients:

$$a_0 y + a_1 \frac{dy}{dt} + a_2 \frac{d^2 y}{dt^2} + \cdots = b_0 x + b_1 \frac{dx}{dt} + b_2 \frac{d^2 x}{dt^2} \cdots \qquad (1.11.8)$$

In these cases the transfer function, $Z_T(s)$, of Eq. (1.11.1) can be written as a rational function of s with coefficients obtained directly from the differential equation:

$$Z_T(s) = \frac{Y}{X} = \frac{a_0 + a_1 s + a_2 s^2 + \cdots + a_m s^m}{b_0 + b_1 s + b_2 s^2 + \cdots + b_n s^n} \qquad (1.11.9)$$

The order of a polynomial is given by the highest power of the variable; the variable in Eq. (1.11.9) is s. The order, n, of the denominator is usually greater than that of the numerator, *m*, since the output usually falls to zero for infinite values of the frequency *s*. As an example, consider the simple circuit of Fig. 1.11.3.

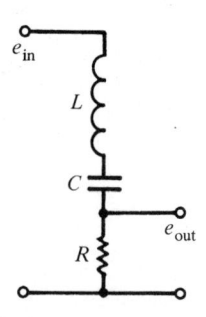

Fig. 1.11.3 *LCR* **circuit**

Here the input, *x*, is now the voltage, e_{in}, and the output, *y*, is e_{out}. We can write down the basic equations for e_{in} and e_{out}, take the Laplace transforms and find the transfer function Z_T.

$$e_{in}(t) = L\frac{di(t)}{dt} + \frac{1}{C}\int i(t)\,dt + Ri(t)$$

$$E_{in}(s) = sLI(s) + \frac{I(s)}{sC} + RI(s)$$

$$e_{out}(t) = Ri(t), \qquad E_{out}(s) = RI(s) \qquad (1.11.10)$$

and
$$Z_T = \frac{E_{out}(s)}{E_{in}(s)} = \frac{R}{sL + 1/sC + R} = \frac{R}{L} \cdot \frac{s}{s^2 + sR/L + 1/LC}$$

Note that Z_T is not an impedance. We can also see that Z_T could just as easily have been written down using the complex impedances of Eq. (1.11.7). The response of the network for any given input can now be determined. As an example, consider a delta function impulse input:

$$e_{in}(t) = \delta(t), \qquad E_{in}(s) = 1$$

$$E_{out}(s) = \frac{R}{L} \cdot \frac{s}{s^2 + sR/L + 1/LC} \qquad \text{from Eq. (1.11.10)}$$

$$e_{out}(t) = \frac{R}{L} \cdot \frac{\beta e^{-\beta t} - \alpha e^{-\alpha t}}{\beta - \alpha} \qquad (\alpha \neq \beta) \qquad (1.11.11)$$

where
$$\alpha + \beta = \frac{R}{L}, \qquad \alpha\beta = \frac{1}{LC}$$

Solving for α and β we get:

$$\alpha = \frac{R}{2L} + \frac{1}{2}\left[\frac{R^2}{L^2} - \frac{4}{LC}\right]^{1/2}, \qquad \beta = \frac{R}{2L} - \frac{1}{2}\left[\frac{R^2}{L^2} - \frac{4}{LC}\right]^{1/2} \qquad (1.11.12)$$

The actual form of the response, Eq. (1.11.11), depends primarily on the values of the exponential exponents α and β. If these are real we get simple exponential decays according to $e^{-\alpha t}$ and $e^{-\beta t}$. If they are complex, however, we then get an oscillatory response, since (see appendix):

$$e^{-(a+jb)t} = e^{-at}[\cos(bt) - j\sin(bt)] \qquad (1.11.13)$$

Thus, from Eq. (1.11.12) if:

(i) $\dfrac{4}{LC} < \dfrac{R^2}{L^2}$, α, β are real, giving exponential response

(ii) $\dfrac{4}{LC} > \dfrac{R^2}{L^2}$, α, β are complex giving oscillatory response $\qquad (1.11.14)$

(iii) $\dfrac{4}{LC} = \dfrac{R^2}{L^2}$, $\alpha = \beta$, a special case (critical damping) with response no. 12, Table 1.11.1

We have not used all the information yet, as there is still the e^{-at} term, as in Eq. (1.11.13), in the oscillatory case (ii). If a is positive, then this term indicates an

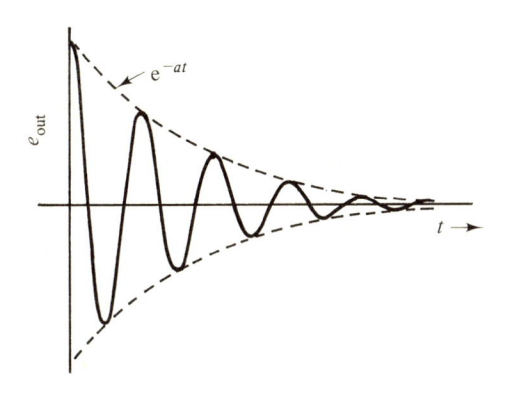

Fig. 1.11.4 Damped oscillatory response

exponentially decaying amplitude, so the response e_{out} will eventually tend to zero (Fig. 1.11.4). If a were negative we would have an exponentially increasing wave. This cannot happen in passive networks as a source of energy would be needed.

The response found above is the natural or free response, i.e., free of any driving function except for the initial impulse. If the excitation continues after $t=0$, then the response will be a combination of the free and the continuing forced response. Examples of this are considered in later chapters (e.g., Sec. 2.7).

There are a number of operational theorems which are useful in working out transforms and some of these are listed in Table 1.11.2. Note that multiplying by s (no. 8) is equivalent to differentiation in the time domain, and division by s is equivalent to integration (no. 4). Number 5 is known as the initial value theorem and no. 6 as the final value theorem. Both require that $f(t)$ and its first derivative are Laplace transformable, the former that the derivative of $F(s)$ exists as $s \to \infty$, and the latter that $sF(s)$ does not have poles on the $j\omega$ axis or in the right half-plane; see Sec. 1.11(b). Examples of the use of the final value theorem will be found in Sec. 4.5.

Table 1.11.2 Operational theorems

$f(t)$	$F(s)$	Theorem
1. $af(t)$	$aF(s)$	
2. $e^{at}f(t)$	$F(s-a)$	shifting
3. $f(t/a)$	$aF(s-a)$	
4. $\int_0^t f(t)\,dt$	$F(s)/s$	
5. $\lim_{t\to 0} f(t)$	$\lim_{s\to\infty} sF(s)$	initial value
6. $\lim_{t\to\infty} f(t)$	$\lim_{s\to 0} sF(s)$	final value
7. $\int_0^t f_1(t-\tau)f_2(\tau)\,d\tau$	$F_1(s).F_2(s)$	convolution
8. $df(t)/dt$	$sF(s)-f(0)$	

1.11(b) *Poles and zeros*

In certain applications, such as the study of stability in feedback systems (chapter 3), the interest is in the form of the transfer function itself rather than the response to particular inputs. It is clear from the form of Eq. (1.11.9) that since a polynomial of order n has n roots, we can write:

$$Z_T(s) = \text{constant} \cdot \frac{(s-z_1)(s-z_2)\ldots(s-z_m)}{(s-p_1)(s-p_2)\ldots(s-p_n)} \quad (1.11.15)$$

The roots, z, of the numerator are called the *zeros* of the transfer function, since $Z_T(s)=0$ when $s=z_1, z_2$, etc. The roots p of the denominator are called the *poles*, and for values of $s=p_1, p_2$, etc., $Z_T(s)$ becomes infinite. As noted above the cases in which we are interested have $n>m$, and then Eq. (1.11.15) can be written as a sum of partial fractions:

$$Z_T(s) = \frac{K_1}{(s-p_1)} + \frac{K_2}{(s-p_2)} + \cdots + \frac{K_n}{(s-p_n)} \quad (1.11.16)$$

The response of such a system to a $\delta(t)$ impulse stimulus is easily found as each term in Eq. (1.11.16) has the simple inverse transform:

$$\mathcal{L}^{-1}\frac{K_n}{(s-p_n)} = K_n \exp(p_n t) \quad (1.11.17)$$

so that the response is the sum of n exponentials. The roots or poles p may be real or complex. For the former we get a simple monotonic response, while for the latter we get an oscillatory response as shown by Eq. (1.11.13). It is usual to plot the poles (shown by a small cross $\times$) and zeros (small circle $\circ$), in the complex s plane, once the roots are known, as in Eq. (1.11.15). Conversely, if we have a pole–zero diagram, the transfer function can be written down immediately except for any multiplicative constant. Note that complex roots always occur in conjugate pairs, but the complementary root in the lower half of the complex plane does not give any extra information and so is often omitted.

Figure 1.11.5 is a plot of a number of poles on the s plane with the corresponding free responses [h1].

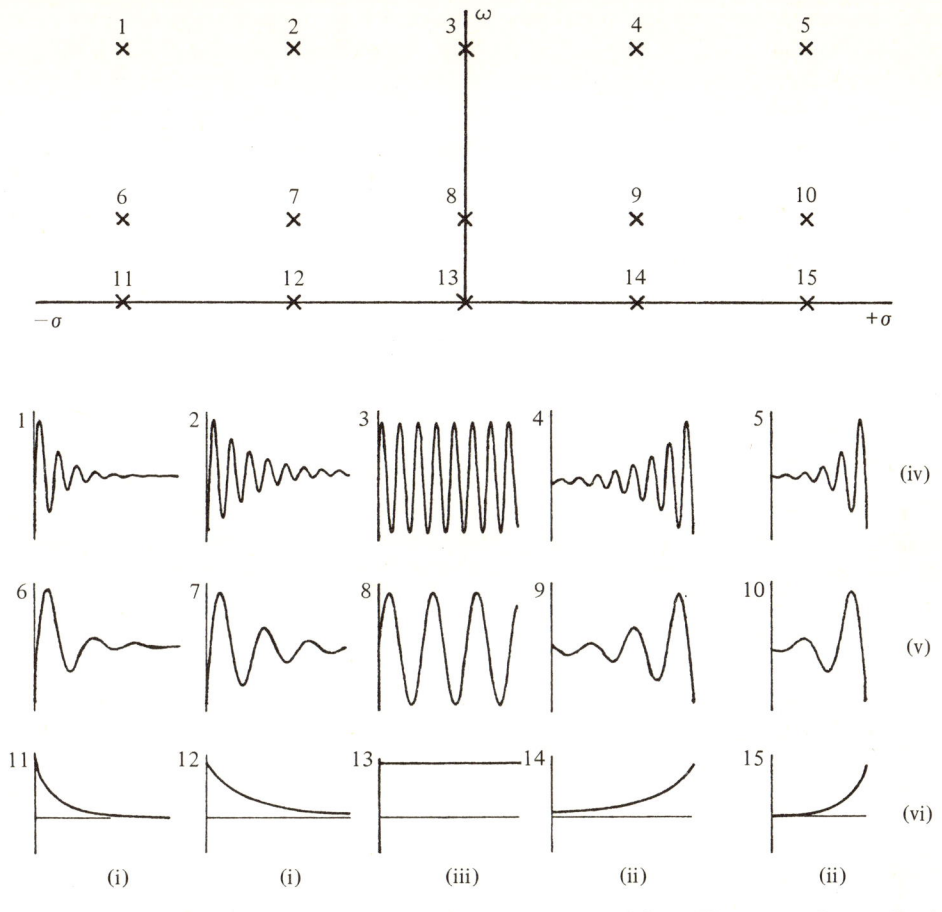

Fig. 1.11.5 Impulse response for various pole positions (Adapted from Thomason: *Linear Feedback Analysis*, **Pergamon Press, 1955, with permission**)

The responses may be summarized as follows:

(i) Negative σ gives decaying response.
(ii) Positive σ gives growing response.
(iii) Zero σ gives constant response, but see (vii).
(iv) Large ω gives high frequency.
(v) Small ω gives low frequency.
(vi) Zero ω gives an aperiodic response.
(vii) Multiple coincident poles on ω axis give growing response (responses will be similar to (ii)).

If a pole and a zero coincide then these two cancel one another, e.g., in Eq. (1.11.15) if $z_1 = p_1$ the two terms are equal and cancel.

In Sec. 1.3 the relationships between gain variation and phase shift were discussed.

These relationships hold for a large category of networks called by Bode *minimum phase shift* [c1, h1, n1]. A definition of this class is that they do not have poles or zeros in the right-hand half of the s plane. In practice, we need only consider the zeros since a pole in the right half-plane (RHP) indicates an unstable system. If there is a zero in this region then there is a complex frequency s with positive σ where the gain is zero. Active or passive systems with a RHP zero have at least two paths between input and output, so that at a particular frequency cancellation of the signals may occur [h1]. Examples of such circuits are shown in Fig. 1.11.6.

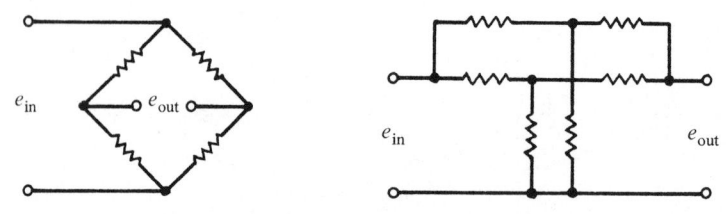

Fig. 1.11.6 Non-minimum phase networks

The null response of such networks is of great use (see, e.g., Secs. 4.4(f) and 5.1). However, these networks may introduce undesirably high phase shifts at high frequencies without the more usual attenuation. This could have serious effects in feedback systems so that special care is required in these situations.

1.11(c) *Application of Laplace transforms*

To give some idea of the use of Laplace transforms we will consider some examples and derive some useful results in the process. First, the damping of an inductor (e.g., a relay) so that it will appear non-oscillatory to the controlling switch (Fig. 1.11.7) [b1].

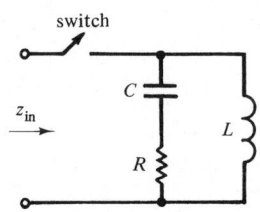

Fig. 1.11.7 Damping network for an inductor

This is often necessary to eliminate arcing at the switch contacts or breakdown of a transistor used in place of the switch. A standard technique is to connect a CR circuit across the coil as shown. We do not consider a transfer function here: in any case it is not obvious how we could have one. However, we only need to consider the impedance of the circuit and see what is required to make the free response non-oscillatory.

$$Z_{in}(s) = \frac{(R+1/sC)sL}{(R+1/sC)+sL}$$

$$= \frac{s^2 RLC + sL}{s^2 LC + sRC + 1} \qquad (1.11.18)$$

Thus, there are two zeros:

$$s_{z1} = 0 \qquad s_{z2} = \frac{-1}{RC} \qquad (1.11.19)$$

and two poles:

$$s_p = \frac{-RC \pm (R^2C^2 - 4LC)^{1/2}}{2LC} \qquad (1.11.20)$$

If $4LC > R^2C^2$ the poles are imaginary and the pole–zero diagram is as shown in Fig. 1.11.8.

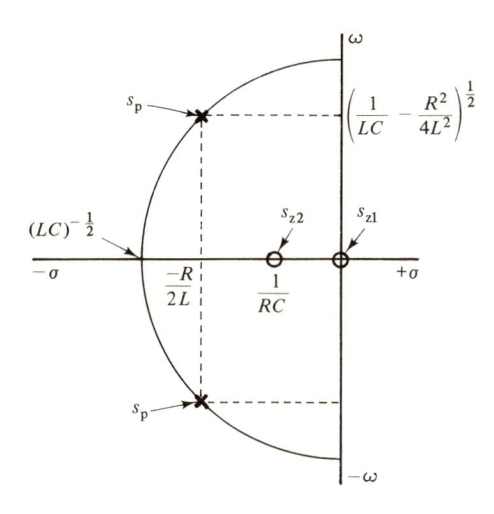

Fig. 1.11.8 Pole–zero diagram for damped inductor

Comparing the position of the poles with those shown in Fig. 1.11.5, we see that there will be a decaying oscillatory response. To get a monotonic damped response we must move the poles until they lie (together) on the σ axis, i.e., put $R^2C^2 = 4LC$ or:

$$R = 2(L/C)^{1/2} \quad \text{and} \quad s_p = \frac{-R}{2L} \qquad (1.11.21)$$

The response will then decay exponentially with time constant $\tau = 2L/R$. If we give the inductor some resistance, say R_1, then for no oscillation:

$$R + R_1 = 2(L/C)^{1/2} \qquad (1.11.22)$$

This is, in effect, the same result as before, as it should be, since after the switch opens the circuit is identical. (It is worth noting that if $R = R_1$ then $Z_{in} = R$, i.e., it is resistive at all frequencies.)

As a second example, we consider a network known as the Wien bridge which is commonly used in low-frequency oscillators (Sec. 5.1). As two arms of the bridge are purely resistive we will consider only the transfer function of the half-bridge as shown in Fig. 1.11.9 [b1, o1].

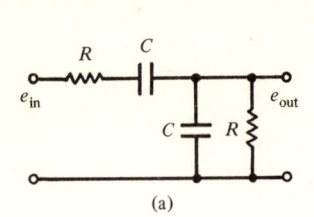

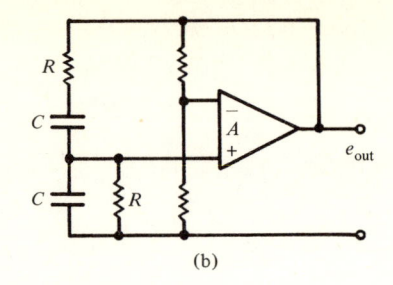

Fig. 1.11.9 Wien bridge

We have here a potential divider, so, adding R and C in parallel and in series:

$$Z_{\text{par}} = \frac{R}{1+sCR} \qquad Z_{\text{ser}} = \frac{1+sCR}{sC} \qquad (1.11.23)$$

the transfer function is readily found to be:

$$Z_T(s) = \frac{E_{\text{out}}(s)}{E_{\text{in}}(s)} = \frac{Z_{\text{par}}}{Z_{\text{par}}+Z_{\text{ser}}} = \frac{sCR}{s^2C^2R^2+3sCR+1} \qquad (1.11.24)$$

The poles are given by:

$$s_p = \frac{-3RC \pm (9R^2C^2 - 4R^2C^2)^{1/2}}{2R^2C^2}$$

$$= \frac{-3 \pm \sqrt{5}}{2RC} \qquad (1.11.25)$$

As the poles are real and negative we get exponentially decreasing time functions, e.g., points 11 or 12 in Fig. 1.11.5. If an amplifier of gain A is introduced, as in Fig. 1.11.9(b) such that:

$$Z_T(s) \cdot A = 1 \qquad (1.11.26)$$

the network losses will just be made up by the amplifier. The value of A required to satisfy Eq. (1.11.26) will depend on the frequency s. From Eq. (1.11.24), this gives:

$$AsCR = s^2C^2R^2 + 3sCR + 1$$

or
$$s^2C^2R^2 + sCR(3-A) + 1 = 0 \qquad (1.11.27)$$

If we make $A = +3$ (and have no phase shift in the amplifier) then:

$$s^2C^2R^2 = -1 \quad \text{or} \quad s = \frac{\pm j}{RC} \qquad (1.11.28)$$

The poles are now on the $j\omega$ axis, i.e., $\sigma = 0$, so there is no growth or decay of the oscillations (Fig. 1.11.5 point 3 or 8, say). The frequency of oscillation is thus:

$$f = \frac{\omega}{2\pi} = \frac{1}{2\pi RC} \qquad (1.11.29)$$

This example demonstrates the use of active elements to change the position of poles. The path, or locus, of the poles as a function of A is shown in Fig. 1.11.10.

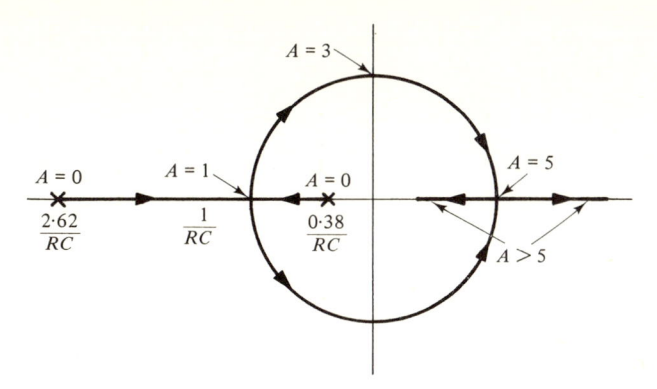

Fig. 1.11.10 Locus of poles of Wien bridge as a function of gain

If $A > 3$ the oscillations will grow until limited by the capabilities of the amplifier itself. If $A > 5$ the oscillations will be of the aperiodic flip-flop type (chapter 5). The use of these root-loci is considered further in Sec. 3.2.

References section 1.1: Ohm's law and all that

a1   Faulkner E A: Principles of Linear Circuits; Chapman and Hall 1966.
b1   Millman J, Taub H: Pulse, Digital, and Switching Waveforms; McGraw-Hill 1965.
c1   Faulkner E A: Introduction to the Theory of Linear Systems; Chapman and Hall 1969.
d1   Marconi Instruments: Impedance Measurements with a Q Meter; Marconi Instruments Handbook 1965.
e1   Golding J F: The Q–Bandwidth Relationship; Design Electronics July 1970, 80.
f1   Marconi Instruments: Reactance, Resistance and Q; Electron 25 Oct. 1973, 53.
g1   Marconi Instruments: C and L to Resonance; Electron 22 Nov. 1973, 47.
h1   Wilson A: Some Aspects of the Theory of Nonlinear Networks; Proc IEEE 61, 1092–1113, 1973.
i1   Terman F E: Radio Engineers' Handbook; McGraw-Hill 1950.
j1   Gibson W M: Basic Electricity; Penguin Books 1969.
k1   Scott R E: Elements of Linear Circuits; Addison Wesley 1966.
l1   Carter G W, Richardson A: Techniques of Circuit Analysis; Cambridge University Press 1972.
m1   Cutler P: Electronic Circuit Analysis, Volume 1 Passive Networks; McGraw-Hill 1967.
n1   Simons K: The dB-Anything; Proc IEEE 61, 495–496, 1973.
o1   Page C: Logarithmic Quantities and Units; Proc IEEE 61, 1516–1518, 1973.
p1   Ghausi M S: Electronic Circuits. Devices, Models, Functions, Analysis, and Design; Van Nostrand Reinhold 1971.
q1   'Cathode Ray': Ohm's Law. Do We Know What it Really Means?; Wireless World Aug. 1953, 383–386.

References section 1.2: Network theorems

a1   Marconi Instruments: Potential Dividers—Source Resistance and Ratio; Electron 3 Jan. 1974, 41–42.
b1   Golding J F: Attenuator Pads; Electron 7 Nov. 1974, 53, 55.
c1   Faulkner E A: Principles of Linear Circuits; Chapman and Hall 1966.
d1   Millman J, Taub H: Pulse, Digital, and Switching Waveforms; McGraw-Hill 1965.
e1   Cutler P: Electronic Circuit Analysis, Volume 1 Passive Networks; McGraw-Hill 1967.

References section 1.3: Phase and frequency response

a1 Hewlett-Packard: Low Frequency Gain Phase Measurements; Hewlett-Packard Application Note 157.
b1 D'Azzo J, Houpis C: Feedback Control Systems Analysis and Synthesis; McGraw-Hill 2nd. Edn. 1966.
c1 Bode H W: Network Analysis and Feedback Amplifier Design; Van Nostrand 1945.
d1 D'Azzo J, Houpis C: Linear Control System Analysis and Design: Conventional and Modern; McGraw-Hill 1975.
e1 Cutler P: Electronic Circuit Analysis, Volume 1 Passive Networks; McGraw-Hill 1967.

References section 1.4: Time constants, bandwidth and pulse response

a1 Murray J K: Oscilloscope Accessories; Marconi Instrumentation 10, No. 1, Apr. 1965, 2–7.
b1 Hall M W G: Probes with Sinewaves; Marconi Instruments Measuretest No.6, 6.
c1 Tektronix: P6008 Probe Instruction Manual; Tektronix 1963.
d1 Bunze V: Matching Oscilloscope and Probe for Better Measurement; Electronics 46, 1 Mar. 1973, 88–93.
e1 Bunze V: Probing in Perspective; Hewlett-Packard Application Note 152, 1972.
f1 Winningstad C N: Nanosecond Pulse Measurements; Tektronix Application Note.
g1 Marconi Instruments: Pulse-Risetime Calculations Nomograph; Electron 8 Nov. 1973, 75–76.
h1 Golding J F: Squarewave Testing of AC Coupled Amplifiers Nomograph; Electron 5 Dec. 1974, 61, and 16 Jan. 1975, 35.
i1 Skilling J K: Pulse and Frequency Response; General Radio Experimenter Nov.–Dec. 1968, 3–10.
j1 Delaney C F G: Electronics for the Physicist; Penguin Books 1969.
k1 Millman J, Taub H: Pulse, Digital, and Switching Waveforms; McGraw-Hill 1965.
l1 Goodyear C C: Signals and Information; Butterworths 1971.
m1 Betts J A: Signal Processing, Modulation and Noise; English Universities Press 1970.

References section 1.5: Impedance matching

a1 Tansal S, Sobol H: Wide-Band Pulse Transformers for Matching Low Impedance Loads; Rev. Sci. Instrum. 34, 1075–1081, 1963.
b1 Bosshard R, Zajde C, Zyngier H: Nanosecond Bifilar Wound Transformers; Rev. Sci. Instrum. 38, 942–945, 1967.
c1 Oxner E: Junction FETs in Active Double-Balanced Mixers; Siliconix Application Note AN48/A26, June 1973.
d1 Botos B: Nanosecond Pulse Handling Techniques in IC Connections; Design Electronics Nov. 1967, 42–49, 55.
e1 Kasinski T A: Simplifying Cable Impedance and Attenuation Measurements; Electronic Eng. 43, Dec. 1971, 46–47.
f1 Amsel G, Bosshard R, Rausch R, Zajde C: Time Domain Compensation of Cable Induced Distortions Using Passive Filters for the Transmission of Fast Pulses; Rev. Sci. Instrum. 42, 1237–1246, 1971.
g1 Marshall M: Be Kind to Your Pulse Generator!; Electronic Design 4 Jan. 1975, 84–88.
h1 Millman J, Taub H: Pulse, Digital, and Switching Waveforms, Chapter 3 Pulse Transformers and Delay Lines; McGraw-Hill 1965.
i1 Cutler P: Electronic Circuit Analysis, Volume 1 Passive Networks; McGraw-Hill 1967.
j1 Snelling E C: Soft Ferrites. Properties and Applications; Iliffe Books 1969.
k1 Davidson E E, Lane R D: Diodes Damp Line Reflections Without Overloading Logic; Electronics 19 Feb. 1976, 123–127.
l1 Nagle J J: Use Wideband Transformers in RF Systems; Electronic Design 2 Feb. 1976, 64–70.

m1 van der Poel J M: Improve Inductor Design Accuracy by Analyzing Flux Density and Winding-Form Effects on the Ferrite Pot Core; Electronic Design 2 Feb. 1976, 58–62.
n1 Hewlett-Packard: Cable Testing with Time Domain Reflectometry; Hewlett-Packard Application Note 67, Oct. 1965.

References section 1.6: Feedback
a1 Gray P E, Searle C L: Electronic Principles, Physics, Models, and Circuits; Wiley 1969.
b1 Tustin A: Feedback; Scientific American 187, No.3, Sep. 1952, 48–55.
c1 D'Azzo J, Houpis C: Feedback Control Systems Analysis and Synthesis; McGraw-Hill 2nd Edn. 1966.
d1 Millman J, Taub H: Pulse, Digital, and Switching Waveforms; McGraw-Hill 1965.

References section 1.7: Grounding, loops and guards
a1 McCullough W: Guarded Measurements with a Floating Voltmeter; Hewlett-Packard J 16, Aug. 1965, 5.
b1 Walter C, MacJuneau H, Thompson L: A New High Speed Multifunction DVM; Hewlett-Packard J 22, Jan. 1971, 2–13.
c1 Hewlett-Packard: Floating Measurements and Guarding; Hewlett-Packard Application Note 123, 1970.
d1 Demrow R: Evolution from Operational Amplifier to Data Amplifier; Analog Devices Application Note 1968.
e1 Andersen R A: A New Digital Voltmeter Having High Rejection of Hum and Noise; Hewlett-Packard J 13, Feb. 1962, 1–4.
f1 Jenkins D H: A Guarded Amplifier for Increasing Digital Voltmeter Sensitivity; Hewlett-Packard J 14, May–June 1963, 6–8.
g1 Hewlett-Packard: Model 456A AC Current Probe; Hewlett-Packard Operating Manual.
h1 Gumbrecht A J: Principles of Interference Rejection; Solartron/Schlumberger DVM Monograph No.3, 1972.
i1 Pearce J R: Digital Voltmeters and Interference; Solartron/Schlumberger DVM Monograph No.2, 1972.
j1 Forge C O: A New Clip-On Oscilloscope/Voltmeter Probe for 25Hz–20MHz Current Measurements; Hewlett-Packard J 11, July–Aug. 1960, 1–6.
k1 Hewlett-Packard; Precise DC Measurements; Hewlett-Packard Application Note 70, Oct. 1969.
l1 Pearce J R: Measurement of Small DC Signals in the Presence of Interference; Research Jan. 1969, 19–27.
m1 Grinney R: Patient Safety in Biomedical Engineering; Electron 11 Apr. 1974, 29.
n1 Craven W F: Protecting Hospitalized Patients from Electrical Hazards; Hewlett-Packard J 21, Mar. 1970, 11–17.
o1 Cowdell R B: Charts Simplify Prediction of Noise from Periodic Pulses; Electronics 41, 2 Sep. 1968, 62–69.
p1 Brower R: Taking Noise Out of Weak Signals; Electronics 41, 8 July, 1968, 80–90.
q1 Rostek P M: Avoid Wiring-Inductance Problems; Electronic Design 6 Dec. 1974, 62–65.
r1 Clark J: Electromagnetic Interference Shielding; Electron 9 May 1974, 80, 85, 87, 89.
s1 Brookshier W K: Noise Signal Pickup in Coaxial Cables; Nuc. Instr. Meth. 70, 1–10, 1969.
t1 Greame J: Improve Analog Data Transmission with Two-Wire Transmitters; Electronic Design 4 Jan. 1975, 94–101.
u1 Field J C G: Magnetic Screening; Electronic Eng. 42, Feb. 1970, 60–63.
v1 Huff D W, Johnson D E, Wade J M: High Sensitivity X–Y Recorder Has Few Input Restrictions; Hewlett-Packard J 26, Feb. 1975, 2–9.
w1 Soderquist D: Keep Your Op-Amp Circuits Quiet; Electronic Design 27 Sep. 1975, 88–91, 93.
x1 Morrison R: Grounding and Shielding Techniques in Instrumentation; Wiley 1967.

y1 Taylor J R, Sunda J A, Schaffner H: Thyristor RFI Suppression and Mains-Borne Voltage Transient Filters; Waycom Technical Publication Feb. 1974.
z1 Harrop Interference Suppression; Electron 11 Jan. 1973, 13–14.
A1 Tektronix: DC to 50 MHz Current Probe; Tektronix Data Sheet 1970.

References section 1.8: Noise

a1 Smith L, Sheingold D H: Noise and Operational Amplifier Circuits; Analog Dialogue 3, No.1, Mar. 1969, 1, 5–16.
b1 Faulkner E A: The Design of Low-Noise Audio-Frequency Amplifiers; Radio Electronic Engr. 36, 17–30, 1968.
c1 Jolley W P: Low Noise Electronics; English Universities Press 1967.
d1 Robinson F N H: Noise in Electrical Circuits; Oxford University Press 1962.
e1 Kittel C: Elementary Statistical Physics; Wiley 1967.
f1 Bell D A: Electrical Noise; Van Nostrand 1960.
g1 van der Ziel A: Noise; Chapman and Hall 1955.
h1 Robinson F N H: Noise in Transistors; Wireless World 339–340, July 1970.
i1 Rheinfelder W A: Design of Low-Noise Transistor Input Circuits; Iliffe 1964.
j1 Bennett W R: Electrical Noise; McGraw-Hill 1960.
k1 Betts J A: Signal Processing, Modulation and Noise; English Universities Press 1970.
l1 Reif F: Fundamentals of Statistical and Thermal Physics; McGraw-Hill 1965.
m1 Doyle N: A Low-Noise Tape Preamplifier; Fairchild Application Note APP-180, Sep. 1969.
n1 Buckingham M J, Faulkner E A: The Principles of Pulse Signal Recovery from Gravitational Antennas; Radio Electronic Engr. 42, 163–171, 1972.
o1 Institute of Physics: Thermal Noise and the Detection of Gravity Waves; J Phys. E Sci. Instrum. 6, 417–422, 1973.
p1 Motchenbacher C D, Fitchen F C: Low-Noise Electronic Design; Wiley 1973.
q1 Connor F R: Noise; Edward Arnold 1973.
r1 Broderick P: Noise Measurements with Electronic Voltmeters; Marconi Instrumentation 10, 18–22, Aug. 1965.
s1 Hill H D W, Richards R E: Limits of Measurement in Magnetic Resonance; J Phys. E Sci. Instrum. 1, 977–983, 1968.
t1 Feher G: Sensitivity in Microwave Paramagnetic Resonance Absorption Techniques; Bell Sys. Tech. J 36, 449–484, 1957.
u1 Bruncke W C, van der Ziel A: Thermal Noise in Junction Gate Field-Effect Transistors; IEEE Trans ED-13, 323–329, 1966.
v1 Jordan A G, Jordan N A: Theory of Noise in Metal Oxide Semiconductor Devices; IEEE Trans ED-12, 148–156, 1965.
w1 Shoji M: Analysis of High-Frequency Thermal Noise in Enhancement Mode MOS Field-Effect Transistors; IEEE Trans ED-13, 520–524, 1966.
x1 Fry P W: Low-Frequency Noise Measurements on the P-Channel MOST; Electronic Eng. 38, 650–653, 1966.
y1 Trinogga L A: JFET Noise Figure Measurement; Electronic Eng. 46, Apr. 1974, 69, 71, 73, 74.
z1 Baxendall P J: Noise in Transistor Circuits 1.Mainly on Fundamental Noise Concepts; Wireless World 74, 388–392, 1968.
A1 Baxendall P J: Noise in Transistor Circuits; Wireless World 74, 454–459, 1968.
B1 Watson F B: Find the Quietest JFETs by Testing Them with Some Simple Circuits; Electronic Design 8 Nov. 1974, 98–102.
C1 Usher M J: Noise and Bandwidth; J Phys. E Sci. Instrum. 7, 957–961, 1974.
D1 Choma J: A Model for the Computer-Aided Noise Analysis of Broad-Banded Bipolar Circuits; IEEE J SC-9, 429–435, 1974.
E1 Champney D C: Fourier Transforms and Their Physical Applications; Academic Press 1973.
F1 Faulkner E A, Harding D W: Some Measurements on Low-Noise Transistors for Audio-Frequency Applications; Radio Electronic Engnr. 36, 31–33, 1968.

G1 Nielsen E G: Behaviour of Noise Figure in Junction Transistors; Proc IRE 45, 957–963, 1957.
H1 van der Ziel A: Noise in Junction Transistors; Proc IRE 46, 1019–1038, 1958.
I1 RCA: Premium Type CA6741T Operational Amplifier; RCA Data Sheet 1972.
J1 Robe T J: Measurement of Burst ("Popcorn") Noise in Linear Integrated Circuits; RCA Application Note ICAN-6732.
K1 Faulkner E A: Principles of Linear Circuits; Chapman and Hall 1966.
L1 Faulkner E A: The Principles of Impedance Optimization and Noise Matching; J. Phys. E Sci. Instrum. 8, 533–540, 1975.

References section 1.9: Basic diode and transistor characteristics

a1 Delaney C F G: Electronics for the Physicist; Penguin Books 1969.
b1 Paterson W L: Multiplication and Logarithmic Conversion by Operational Amplifier-Transistor Circuits; Rev. Sci. Instrum. 34, 1311–1316, 1963.
c1 Gibbons J F, Horn H S: A Circuit with Logarithmic Transfer Response over 9 Decades; IEEE Trans CT-11, 378–384, 1964.
d1 Ebers J J, Moll J L: Large Signal Behaviour of Junction Transistors; Proc IRE 42, 1761–1772, 1954.
e1 Moll J L: Large Signal Transient Behaviour of Junction Transistors; Proc IRE 42, 1773–1784, 1954.
f1 Faulkner E A: A New Tool for the Circuit Designer; Design Electronics Jan. 1970, 30–33.
g1 Texas Instruments: Second Breakdown and Power Transistor Area of Operation; Texas Instruments Application Note 167.
h1 Hewlett-Packard Associates: The Hot Carrier Diode. Theory, Design and Application; Hewlett-Packard Associates Application Note 907.
i1 RCA: RF Power Transistor Manual; RCA Technical Series RFM-430, 1971.
j1 RCA: High-Speed, High-Voltage, High-Current Power Transistors; RCA Technical Series PM-80, 1970.
k1 Syms B R: Simple Transistor Equivalent Circuit; Electronic Components 30 June 1972, 636–640.
l1 Gronner A D: Transistor Circuit Analysis; Simon and Schuster, Revised Edn. 1970.
m1 Dean K J: Transistors, Theory and Practice; McGraw-Hill 1964.
n1 RCA: Silicon Power Circuits Manual; RCA Technical Series SP-51, 1969.
o1 Faulkner E A: The Bipolar Transistor as a Voltage-Operated Device; Radio Electronic Engnr. 37, 303–304, 1969.
p1 Philbrick/Nexus: Applications Manual for Operational Amplifiers; Philbrick/Nexus Research 1968.
q1 Whitfield G R: Frequency Response Measurements on Silicon Planar Transistors; Radio Electronic Engnr. 36, 335–340, 1968.
r1 Ferranti: The Use of Transistors in Avalanche Mode; Ferranti Application Report 1973.
s1 Hart B L: The Transistor Charge Model: A Tutorial Development; Electronic Components 29 Oct. 1971, 1113–1118.
t1 Salmon K: High-Voltage Switching Transistors; Texas Instruments Application Report B131, Oct. 1972.
u1 Gates T W, Ballard M F: Safe Operating Area for Power Transistors; Mullard Tech. Comm. 13, 42–65, 1974.
v1 Motorola: The Reliable Routes to Power; Motorola Chart 1973.
w1 Henebry W M: Avalanche Transistor Circuits; Rev. Sci. Instrum. 32, 1198–1203, 1961.
x1 Coleby P: Thermal Resistance of Semiconductor Devices Under Steady-State Conditions; Mullard Tech. Comm. 7, 127–140, 1963.
y1 Lomas R A, Walker A V: High Power Planar Transistors; Electron 18 July 1974, 24, 26.
z1 Fox R W: Six Ways to Control Transients; Electronic Design 24 May 1974, 52–57.
A1 Texas Instruments: Transistor Catalogue; Texas Instruments 1973.
B1 Getreu I: Modeling the Bipolar Transistor; Electronics 19 Sep. 1974, 114–120, 31 Oct. 71–75, 14 Nov. 137–143.
C1 Locher R E: On Switching Inductive Loads with Power Transistors; General Electric Application Note 200.56, 1970.

D1 Locher R E: The Characterization of Power Transistors to Avoid Forward Bias Second Breakdown; General Electric Application Note 200.52, 1969.

E1 Zettler R A, Cowley A M: Hybrid Hot Carrier Diodes; Hewlett-Packard J 20, Feb. 1969, 13–20.

F1 Watson W T, Morris R J: Silicon Power Transistors; Electron 13 Mar. 1975, 31, 33.

G1 Walker A V: Schottky Barrier Diodes for Small Signal Applications; New Electronics 18 Mar. 1975, 32–34.

H1 Semtech: Miniature Fast Recovery High Voltage Rectifiers SFES20K–50K; Semtech Data Sheet 1975.

I1 Sescosem: Power Transistor Handbook: Electrical Characteristics of Transistors, Recommendations for the Selection of Power Transistors, Power Transistor Technologies and Applications, Operating Mode of Power Transistors; Sescosem (Thomson-CSF) 1975.

J1 Siliconix: Low Leakage Pico Amp Diodes PAD1/500; Siliconix Data Sheet.

K1 Aharoni H: Bi-Polar Junction Transistor Characteristics in the Avalanche Mode in Common Emitter Configuration; Microelectronics 6, June 1975, 22–29.

L1 Jarl R B: Radiation Hardness Capability of RCA Silicon Power Transistors; RCA Application Note AN-6320, 1974.

M1 Morant M J: Introduction to Semiconductor Devices; Harrap 2nd Edn. 1970.

N1 Millman J, Taub H: Pulse, Digital, and Switching Waveforms; McGraw-Hill 1965.

O1 Faulkner E A, Dawnay J C G: Characteristics of Silicon Transistors; Electronics Lett. 1, 224–225, 1965.

P1 Gates T W: Safe Operating Area for Power Transistors; Mullard Technical Publication TP1374, 1973.

Q1 Turner C: Selection of Second-Breakdown-Resistant Transistors; RCA Application Note ST-3419 (EEE 15, 1967).

R1 Greenburg R: Determining Maximum Reliable Load Lines for Power Transistors; Motorola Application Note AN137, 1964.

S1 Faulkner E A: The Design of Low-Noise Audio-Frequency Amplifiers; Radio Electronic Engnr. 36, 17–30, 1968.

T1 Roehr W D: Avoiding Second Breakdown; Motorola Application Note AN-415, 1968.

U1 Murphy R H: Power Semiconductors; Electron 23 Nov. 1972, 31, 33, 35.

V1 Turner C R: Interpretation of Voltage Ratings for Transistors; RCA Application Note SMA-2, 1961.

W1 Schiff P: Second Breakdown in Transistors Under Conditions of Cutoff; RCA Application Note SMA-30, 1964.

X1 Grinich V H: Voltage Ratings for Double Diffused Silicon Switching Transistors; SGS-Fairchild Application Note APP-4.

Y1 Beneteau P J, Riva G: Transistor Operation at Maximum Voltage; SGS-Fairchild Application Note AR-54, 1963.

Z1 Soares R, Tuley J H, Hounam L: Planar Power Switching Transistors; Mullard Technical Publication TP1178, 1970.

a2 Sah C T: Effect of Surface Recombination and Channel on P-N Junction and Transistor Characteristics; IRE Trans ED-9, 94–108, 1962.

b2 Motorola: High Voltage Silicon Hot-Carrier Detector and Switching Diodes MBD501/701; Motorola Data Sheet Apr. 1970.

c2 Hewlett-Packard: Hybrid Hot-Carrier Diodes 5082-2810/2811; Hewlett-Packard Data Sheet.

d2 Shiner B C: Improving the Efficiency of Low Voltage, High Current Rectification; Motorola Application Note AN517, 1970.

e2 Motorola: Lead Mounted Hot Carrier Power Rectifier MBD5300; Motorola Data Sheet Nov. 1970.

f2 RCA: Solid-State Power Circuits Designer's Handbook; RCA Technical Series SP-52, 1971.

g2 Moore D W: Analyzing the Principles of Schottky Diodes; Electronic Equip. News Dec. 1973, 61–64.

h2 Millman J, Halkias C C: Electronic Devices and Circuits; McGraw-Hill 1967.

i2   Gray P E, Searle C L: Electronic Principles, Physics, Models, and Circuits; Wiley 1969.
j2   Lomas R A, Walker A V: High Power Planar Transistors; Electron 18 July, 1974, 24, 26.
k2   RCA: Application Guide, RCA Silicon Power Transistors; RCA Application Guide ICE-215, 1960.
l2   Kirk W J, Carter L S, Waddell M L: Eliminate Static Damage to Circuits by Tracing its Causes and Reducing the Voltage Levels; Electronic Design 29 Mar. 1976, 80–85.

References section 1.10: Some IC arrangements

a1   Wittlinger H A: Applications of the CA3080 and CA3080A High Performance Operational Transconductance Amplifiers; RCA Application Note ICAN-6668.
b1   Widlar R J: Some Circuit Design Techniques for Linear Integrated Circuits; IEEE Trans CT-12, 586–589, 1965.
c1   Schlotzhauer K G, Hanson J V: An Improved Multioutput Current-Controlled Source; Proc IEEE 61, 1154–1155, 1973.
d1   Hart B L, Barker R W J: A Low Current Voltage Reference Source; Electronic Components 23 Apr. 1974, 17, 19, 21.
e1   Bredenkamp G: A Precision Current Multiplier/Divider; Proc IEEE 60, 1440–1441, 1972.
f1   Camenzind H R: Circuit Design for Integrated Electronics; Addison Wesley 1968.
g1   Hunter L P (Ed): Handbook of Semiconductor Electronics; McGraw-Hill 3rd Edn. 1970.
h1   RCA: Linear Integrated Circuits; RCA Technical Series IC-42, 1970.
i1   Fitchen F C: Electronic Integrated Circuits and Systems; Van Nostrand Reinhold 1970.
j1   Bladowski R: Linear Monolithic Integrated Circuits; Orbit Oct. 1969, 20–27, Nov. 1969, 7–16, Jan. 1970, 7–16.
k1   Gronner A D: Transistor Circuit Analysis; Simon and Schuster Revised Edn. 1970.
l1   Widlar R J: IC Op Amp Beats FET's on Input Current; National Semiconductor Application Note AN-29, Dec. 1969.

References section 1.11: Laplace transforms

a1   D'Azzo J J, Houpis C H: Feedback Control System Analysis and Synthesis; McGraw-Hill 1960.
b1   Holbrook J G: Laplace Transforms for Electronic Engineers; Pergamon Press 1966.
c1   Bode H W: Network Analysis and Feedback Amplifier Design; Van Nostrand 1945.
d1   Roberts G E, Kaufman H: Table of Laplace Transforms; W B Saunders 1966.
e1   Savant C J: Fundamentals of the Laplace Transformation, with Tables by Levy E C; McGraw-Hill 1962.
f1   Spiegel M R: Theory and Problems of Laplace Transforms; McGraw-Hill 1965.
g1   Abramowitz M, Stegun I A: Handbook of Mathematical Functions with Formulas, Graphs, and Mathematical Tables; National Bureau of Standards Applied Mathematics Series 55, Nov. 1970.
h1   Thomason J G: Linear Feedback Theory; Pergamon Press 1955.
i1   Jaeger J C: An Introduction to the Laplace Transformation; Chapman and Hall 2nd Edn. 1969.
j1   Kirby J E D, Towill D R, Baker K J: Transfer Function Measurement Using Analog Modeling Techniques; IEEE Trans IM-22, 52–61, 1973.
k1   Nixon F E: Handbook of Laplace Transformation; Prentice-Hall 2nd Edn. 1965.
l1   McCollum P A, Brown B F: Laplace Tables and Theorems; Holt, Rinehart, Winston 1965.
m1 Truxal J G: Control Engineers' Handbook; McGraw-Hill 1958.
n1   Faulkner E A: Introduction to the Theory of Linear Systems; Chapman and Hall 1969.
o1   Strauss L: Wave Generation and Shaping; McGraw-Hill 2nd Edn. 1970.
p1   Scott R E: Elements of Linear Circuits; Addison Wesley 1966.
q1   Carter G W, Richardson A: Techniques of Circuit Analysis; Cambridge University Press 1972.
r1   D'Azzo J J, Houpis C H: Linear Control System Analysis and Design: Conventional and Modern; McGraw-Hill 1975.

2 Operational amplifiers

2.1 Introduction

The term *operational amplifier* referred originally to a class of amplifier that could be used in various feedback configurations to perform a number of mathematical operations such as addition, integration, and differentiation. A number of such amplifiers, together with other functional units, can be used to construct analogue computers for the solution of differential equations [e1]. Although operational amplifiers were originally developed to perform these mathematical operations, their versatility has made them useful in a host of other applications [b1, m1, d1, g1, h1, z1, y1, k1, u1, v1, w1, x1].

Operational amplifiers are used, together with external (usually passive) components, in such a way that the performance of the complete unit is primarily a function of the external components. Since these are usually of greater temporal and environmental stability, the resulting unit will show this improvement. Also, a single amplifier type may be used to construct many different functional building blocks with consequent economic advantage.

The original operational amplifiers were, of course, vacuum tube units requiring high voltages ($+300$ V) and filament supplies (6.3 V); they dissipated considerable power (30 W quiescent) and occupied a large volume (1000 cm^3). The advent of transistors led to a dramatic decrease in all the above quantities (50 mW, 4 cm^3), and to significant improvement in performance and reliability at lower price. These factors made it possible to utilize the units as components in the construction of many systems other than analogue computers to which they had previously been restricted. The subsequent development and mass production of integrated circuit (IC) operational amplifiers further decreased the size (0.2 cm^3) but more dramatically the price, which is now equivalent in many cases to that of a single good transistor! The performance of IC types is, in general, slightly below that of discrete types, but the development of many new techniques is rapidly closing the gap.

The size of IC units for normal use is governed by ease of handling and the need to make connections to the unit, rather than the size of the IC itself (4 mm^2). There are two common forms of package: the hermetically sealed metal can with a circular array of wire leads, and the dual-in-line (DIP or DIL) with two parallel rows of pins (Fig. 2.1.1).

As far as we are concerned here the metal can has the advantage of somewhat higher allowed power dissipation, while the DIP is usually cheaper, having a moulded plastic body. Hermetic ceramic DIP's are also available. As a personal preference the DIP is used and referred to throughout this book unless some device is not available

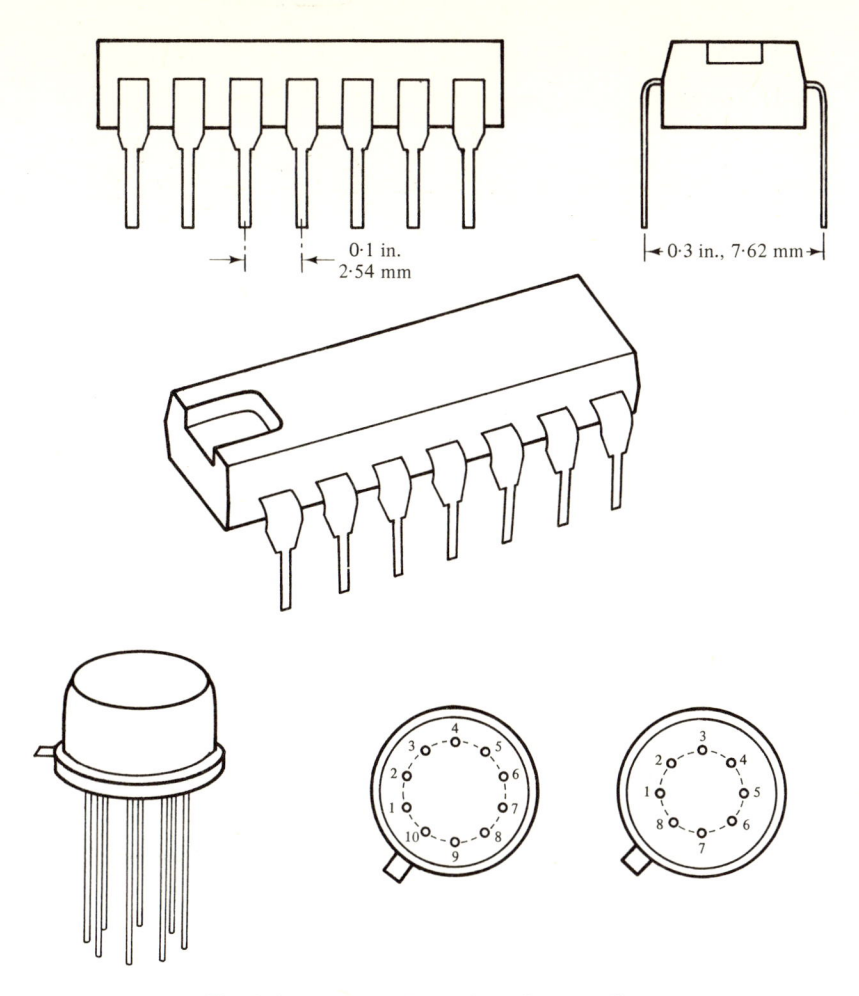

Fig. 2.1.1 Integrated circuit package outlines

in this form. Thus, any pin numbers given in specific circuit diagrams will relate to the DIP numbering system illustrated in Fig. 2.1.2.

The common sizes have 8, 14, or 16 pins spaced 0·1 inch (2·54 mm) apart, with 0·3 inches (7·62 mm) between rows. The component packing density that is achieved can be illustrated by an 8 pin DIP containing two operational amplifiers made up from a total of 34 transistors, 22 resistors, 10 diodes, and two capacitors. Small sockets for all sizes of DIP and metal can, are available and are a very great convenience in circuit development.

Small size, low price, well-defined parameters, and great versatility has led to an enormous increase in the use of IC operational amplifiers. The ways of making them perform the basic operations are discussed in the following sections of this chapter, and their use in many other ways in later chapters. The development of IC technology now makes it possible to produce many other functional sub-units of increasingly complex form such as multipliers, modulators, voltage regulators, voltage-controlled oscillators, and frequency selective switches. Many of these devices are discussed later.

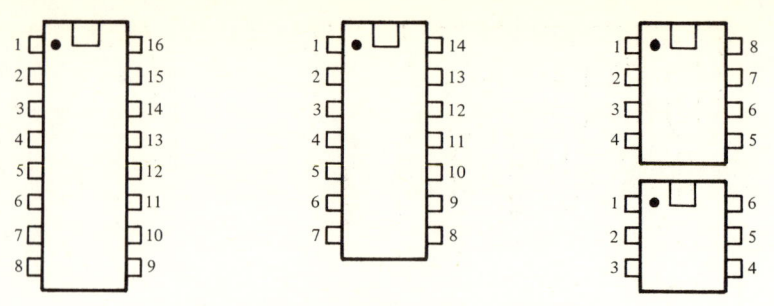

Fig. 2.1.2 Integrated circuit pin numbers

2.2 The ideal amplifier and the virtual ground

To demonstrate the basic points of operational amplifiers we will first consider the ideal amplifier. This will have the following characteristics:

  (i) infinite open-loop gain
 (ii) infinite bandwidth
(iii) infinite input impedance
 (iv) zero offset
  (v) zero output impedance
 (vi) zero drift
(vii) zero noise

This would appear to be a formidable list of constraints, but we will see later that the situation is not as critical as would appear at first sight. If it was, operational amplifiers would not be used as widely as they are. The general arrangement is shown in Fig. 2.2.1.

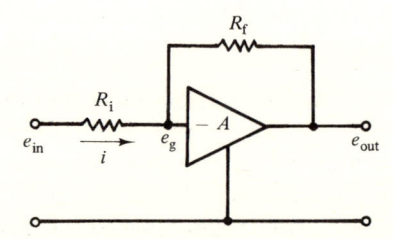

Fig. 2.2.1 Operational amplifier circuit

The amplifier is represented by the triangle and has the properties listed above, with the further proviso that it inverts the signal, i.e., the input and output signals are 180° out of phase (positive going inputs produce negative going outputs or vice versa). The input voltage, e_{in}, is applied through an input resistor, R_i, and negative feedback from amplifier output to input via resistor R_f. As will be seen later we need not confine ourselves to resistors, but for the moment consideration will be restricted to these [i1, k1, l1, m1, p1, f1, g1, s1, t1, refs. Sec. 2.1].

Application of e_{in} will cause a current i to flow in R_i:

$$i = \frac{e_{in} - e_g}{R_i} \qquad (2.2.1)$$

Since the input impedance of the amplifier is infinite, this current must flow through R_f to the output:

$$i = \frac{e_g - e_{out}}{R_f} \qquad (2.2.2)$$

The actual input to the amplifier, e_g, is related to the output e_{out} by:

$$e_{out} = -A e_g \qquad (2.2.3)$$

where A is the gain of the amplifier. For any finite value of e_{out} we must have $e_g = 0$, since A is assumed infinite. Thus, from Eqs. (2.2.1) and (2.2.2) we obtain:

$$\frac{e_{in}}{R_i} = \frac{-e_{out}}{R_f}$$

$$G_\infty = \frac{e_{out}}{e_{in}} = \frac{-R_f}{R_i} \qquad (2.2.4)$$

This, or some generalization of it, is the fundamental relation for operational amplifiers. G_∞ is called the closed-loop gain (in contrast to A, the open-loop gain), and in our ideal situation does not depend on variations in the amplifier characteristics. The negative sign indicates the phase inversion.

The vital concept arising out of this idealization is that of the virtual ground. We saw that $e_g = 0$, i.e., the input terminal of the amplifier is maintained at ground potential by the feedback action. It is called a *virtual* ground since, although it is effectively *connected* to ground, no actual current flows through this *connection*. The use of this concept of the virtual ground makes the analysis and understanding of many circuits very much simpler.

In deriving Eq. (2.2.4), A was considered to be infinite. In practice, although it may be high, it is not infinite and indeed at high frequencies falls off rapidly. It is necessary, therefore, to derive an expression for G for finite A. From Eqs. (2.2.1), (2.2.2), and (2.2.3):

$$G_A = \frac{e_{out}}{e_{in}} = \frac{-R_f}{R_i}\left(1 + \frac{R_f + R_i}{A R_i}\right)^{-1} = \frac{-R_f}{R_i}\left(\frac{A\beta}{1 + A\beta}\right) = \frac{-R_f}{R_i}\left(1 - \frac{1}{(1 + A\beta)}\right) \qquad (2.2.5)$$

where the feedback fraction $\beta = R_i/(R_i + R_f)$. Thus, the quantity that determines the approach to the ideal is $A\beta$, which is called the loop-gain, L. This is the gain around the loop when opened at any point and taking into account all gains and attenuations. If $L = A\beta \gg 1$ then $G_A = -R_f/R_i$ as before. When the closed-loop gain G is not too small, i.e., $R_f \gg R_i$, $G \doteq -1/\beta$ so that:

$$\text{Loop-gain } L = A\beta \doteq A/G = \frac{\text{open-loop gain}}{\text{closed-loop gain}}$$

$$= A(\text{dB}) - G(\text{dB}) \qquad (2.2.6)$$

The relationship between A, G, L, and β is shown in Fig. (2.2.2).

The ratio of the actual gain G_A, Eq. (2.2.5), to the ideal G_∞, Eq. (2.2.4), is called the error factor F_ε:

$$F_\varepsilon = \frac{G_A}{G_\infty} = \frac{A\beta}{1 + A\beta} = 1 - \frac{1}{(1 + A\beta)} \qquad (2.2.7)$$

The error ε is defined as:

$$\varepsilon = 1 - F_\varepsilon = \frac{G_\infty - G_A}{G_\infty} = \frac{1}{1 + A\beta} \doteq 1 - \frac{1}{A\beta} \quad \text{(for } A\beta \gg 1\text{)} \quad (2.2.8)$$

and the percentage error P_ε is given by:

$$\frac{P_\varepsilon}{100} = \frac{G_\infty - G_A}{G_A} = \frac{1}{A\beta} = \frac{\varepsilon}{F_\varepsilon} \quad (2.2.9)$$

For example with $A = 10^3$, $R_i/R_f = 0.1$ ($\beta = 1/11$), we find $G_\infty = 10$ from Eq. (2.2.4) and $G_A = 9.9$ from Eq. (2.2.5), an error of 1·1 per cent; Eq. (2.2.9) gives $P_\varepsilon = 100/91 = 1.1$ per cent. These values are only valid at d.c. or low frequencies, where there is no phase shift in A or β. As seen in Fig. 2.2.2, the gain A is a function of frequency which

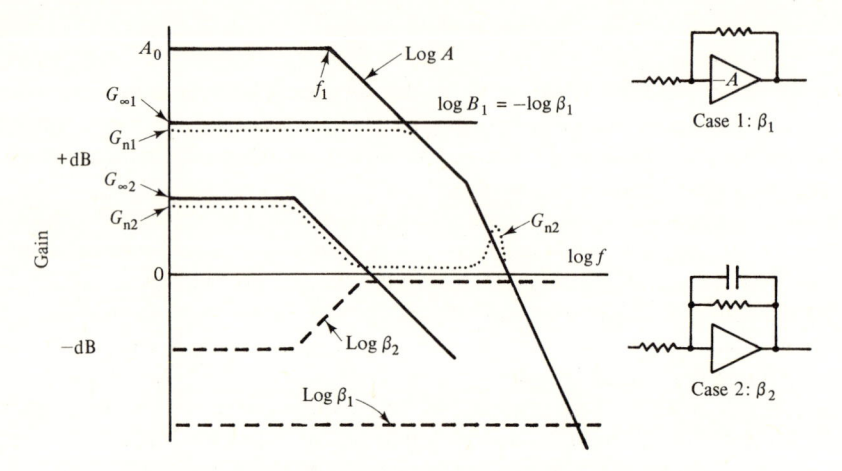

Fig. 2.2.2 Relationship of operational amplifier parameters

introduces consequent phase shifts (Sec. 1.3 and chapter 3). This can have a significant effect on the errors. For example, the error ε will apparently be doubled when A is halved, which for the response shown in Fig. 2.2.2 would occur at a frequency $1.8 f_1$. In fact, for the example above with $A\beta = 100$ and resistive feedback, the error is only doubled at about $14 f_1$ if the phase shift is taken into account. Thus, accurate results will be obtained to much higher frequencies than would at first appear [b1, j1]. The effects of phase shift are most simply determined from graphical results showing error factor against normalized frequency for given loop gain [a1]. For non-resistive feedback elements the phase shift of the β circuit must also be allowed for. In practice, the actual d.c. error is seldom important since R_f/R_i can be adjusted to compensate.

The closed-loop gain stability, however, is of great importance in most situations. Differentiating Eq. (2.2.5) with $R_f/R_i \doteq 1/\beta$ (most easily done by taking logarithms first $(d(\ln x) = dx/x)$:

$$\ln G = \ln A - \ln(1 + A\beta)$$

$$\frac{dG}{G} = \frac{dA}{A} - \frac{\beta dA}{(1 + A\beta)} = \frac{1}{(1 + A\beta)} \cdot \frac{dA}{A} \doteq \frac{1}{A\beta} \cdot \frac{dA}{A} \quad (2.2.10)$$

Thus, any variation dA in open-loop gain A is reduced by the feedback factor $(1+A\beta)$, or effectively the loop-gain L, in its effect on the closed-loop gain. This is one of the most important benefits of negative feedback. For example, with $A=10^4$, $\beta=0.01$, and $dA/A=20$ per cent variation in open-loop gain, the variation in closed-loop gain $dG/G=0.2$ per cent.

Noise internally generated in the amplifier may be referred to the amplifier input; Sec. 2.9 (s), (u). It is, in effect, just an a.c. offset. The gain for this noise voltage, v_{NA}, is found from the equations (e_d is the actual amplifier input; see Sec. 2.5):

$$e_d = e_{out}\beta + v_{NA}, \qquad e_{out} = -Ae_d, \qquad \beta = R_i/(R_i+R_f)$$

$$G_n = \frac{e_{out}}{v_{NA}} = \frac{A}{(1+A\beta)} = \frac{1}{\beta}\frac{1}{(1+1/A\beta)} \doteq \frac{1}{\beta} \quad \text{(for } A\beta \gg 1\text{)} \qquad (2.2.11)$$

G_n is called the noise gain and is equal to the gain for the non-inverting amplifier, Eq. (2.5.5). Equation (2.2.11) may also be derived by considering v_{NA} as a voltage between (+) and ground in Fig. 2.5.3. Since β is always ≤ 1 for passive elements, the noise gain will be at least unity, despite signal gains of less than unity, or even for narrow signal bandwidths [g1]. At high frequencies, where phase shifts occur in A,

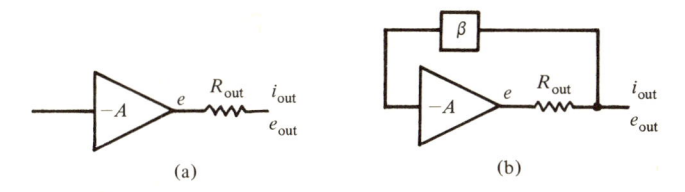

Fig. 2.2.3 Output impedance of operational amplifier

or in β, G_n may be considerably greater than unity even if the signal gain G_A rolls off at much lower frequencies (Fig. 2.2.2). This differentiation between signal and noise gains is important when considering frequency stability (chapter 3), and in considering offsets in any feedback configuration; Sec. 2.9 (u), (v) [h1, i1]. The equations for noise gain are derived on the assumption that the input voltage signal generator (of zero impedance) is connected, and the outer end of R_i is thereby grounded. If the generator is absent then R_i is effectively infinite and $\beta=1$, $G_n=1$ independent of R_f.

In some treatments the feedback equations are derived using a definition of β differing slightly from that used above [c1, d1, e1, f1]. In these an amount $\beta'e_{out}$ is fed back and added to the input e_{in}, so that if e_g is the input to the amplifier proper:

$$e_{in} + \beta'e_{out} = e_g = -e_{out}/A$$

$$G' = \frac{e_{out}}{e_{in}} = \frac{-A}{(1+A\beta')} = \frac{-1}{\beta'} \cdot \frac{A\beta'}{(1+A\beta')} \qquad (2.2.12)$$

Comparing this with Eq. (2.2.5) gives:

$$\beta' = \frac{(A+1)}{A} \cdot \frac{R_f}{R_i}, \qquad \beta' = \frac{(A+1)}{A} \cdot \frac{(R_i+R_f)}{R_f} \beta \qquad (2.2.13)$$

The output impedance of the system is also changed by feedback. If the amplifier is equivalent to an ideal voltage generator and series resistance R_{out} (Fig. 2.2.3), then

with no feedback:
$$e_{out} = e + i_{out} R_{out}$$
so that the output impedance is:
$$\frac{\partial e_{out}}{\partial i_{out}} = R_{out} \qquad (2.2.14)$$

With feedback:
$$e_{out} = e + i_{out} R_{out}, \quad e = -A\beta e_{out}$$
so
$$e_{out} = \frac{i_{out} R_{out}}{1 + A\beta}$$

The output impedance is now:
$$\frac{\partial e_{out}}{\partial i_{out}} = \frac{R_{out}}{1 + A\beta} \qquad (2.2.15)$$

i.e., the output impedance is reduced by the feedback factor.

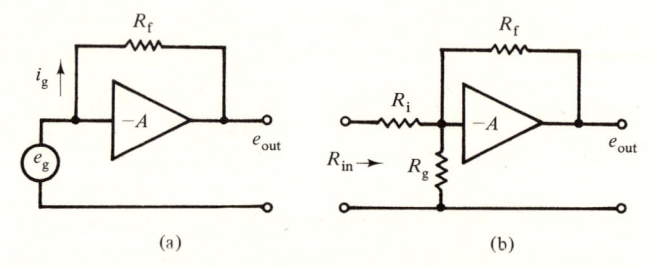

Fig. 2.2.4 Impedance of virtual ground

Distortion and phase shift in the A circuit are also reduced by the feedback factor, and although noise is also reduced the signal-to-noise ratio will not be improved; see Sec. 1.8 and [q1; s1, p. 98].

In considering multiple inputs (Sec. 2.5), we will need to know just how good the virtual ground is, i.e., the effective resistance R_g between this and ground. Consider a voltage source, e_g, between virtual ground and ground (Fig. 2.2.4).

We have:
$$i_g = \frac{e_g - e_{out}}{R_f}, \quad e_{out} = -A e_g$$
so
$$R_g = \frac{e_g}{i_g} = \frac{R_f}{1 + A} \doteq \frac{R_f}{A} \qquad (2.2.16)$$

The actual input impedance R_{in} of the operational amplifier configuration in Fig. 2.2.4(b), can easily be seen to be just R_i, since the amplifier end of R_i is a virtual ground (ignoring R_g). This means that it is difficult to obtain high input impedances in this configuration if high values of G are also required, as this results in undesirably high values of R_f. This can be overcome by using a modified feedback arrangement [r1, h1] or by employing a non-inverting configuration (Sec. 2.5).

So far we have discussed a rather idealized amplifier and used resistive feedback elements. Of the ideal characteristics listed at the beginning of this section, it is deviation from (ii), infinite bandwidth, that has the most significant effects. The problems arising from the limited bandwidth of real amplifiers are considered briefly in Sec. 2.4 and more fully in chapter 3.

There is nothing in what has been said so far that limits us to the use of purely resistive elements. The effects of replacing the resistive feedback elements by reactive components are discussed in Secs. 2.6, 2.7, and 2.8. If we had written our original equations in terms of general impedances Z instead of resistances R, Eq. (2.2.4) would become:

$$G = \frac{e_{out}}{e_{in}} = \frac{-Z_f}{Z_i} \qquad (2.2.17)$$

or in terms of transforms, Sec. 1.11:

$$\frac{E_{out}(s)}{E_{in}(s)} = \frac{-Z_f(s)}{Z_i(s)} = -Z_T(s) \qquad (2.2.18)$$

2.3 Classes of operational amplifier

Practical operational amplifiers (op-amps) may be divided into three classes and five types on the basis of differences in both structure and performance. These are shown in Table 2.3.1, which includes approximate ranges for a number of important parameters. Although more detailed consideration of the various parameters follows later in Sec. 2.9, the significance of many of them should be clear. The aim of this section, together with Sec. 2.4, is to give some reality to the ubiquitous little triangles that litter the pages of this book. The first class consisting of three types, discrete differential, FET input, and integrated circuit, are essentially the same in terms of mode of operation and circuit, and only differ in physical realization. They will,

Table 2.3.1 Comparison of amplifier types

	Discrete differential	Integrated differential	FET differential	Chopper stabilized	Varactor bridge	Units
Open-loop gain	10^4–10^6	10^2–10^6	10^4–10^6	10^6–10^9	10^4–10^6	
GB product	0.4–100	0.1–100	0.4–100	1–100	0.1–1	MHz
Slew rate	0.1–10^3	0.1–100	0.1–250	0.1–250		V/µs
Input offset V	0.1–1	0.5–10	0.5–5	10^{-2}–10^{-1}		mV
Input bias	1–500	1–10^3	10^{-3}–10^{-1}	10^{-2}–0.2	10^{-5}–10^{-3}	nA
Input offset I		0.05–10^2	10^{-3}			nA
Input drift	5–100	5–100	5–100	1–10	10^2/month	µV/day
Input noise narrow B	1–15	1–15	3–30	4–50	1–2	µV p-p
Input noise wide B	1–20	1–20	2–30	2–10^3	10	µV r.m.s.
Input V max diff.	5–15	1–15	5–15	1–15	±25	V
Input V max CM	5–20	1–15	5–15	1–15	±300	V
Input R diff.	10^5–10^7	10^4–10^8	10^{10}–10^{12}	10^5–10^6	10^{11}–10^{12}	ohm
Input R CM	10^7–10^9	10^7–10^9	10^{10}–10^{12}		10^{13}	ohm
CMRR	50–120	60–100	50–120		160	dB
Output I	1–10^3	1–20	1–10^2	1–10^2	20	mA
Output R	30–5000	50–5000	50–5000	10–5000	30–5000	ohm
Input drift	0.1–5	0.1–5	doubles/10°C	0.5–5	10^{-6}–10^{-4}	nA/°C
Input drift	5–100	1–50	2–100	0.1–10	10–60	µV/°C

therefore, be discussed together. The second and third classes, chopper-stabilized and parametric, operate on rather different principles from the former and are discussed separately.

2.3(a) *General differential*

The three types in this class basically differ only in physical realization, i.e., discrete components or monolithic integrated circuit, with either system using an FET input stage to achieve high input resistance and low offset current. It is necessary to mention here the so-called hybrid circuits, which use thin film resistor networks and interconnections together with discrete micro components, and are thus essentially miniaturized discrete systems. A more appositely named hybrid is the type combining discrete and monolithic integrated with thin film networks (OED: hybrid, Latin *hybrida*, offspring of tame sow and wild boar!).

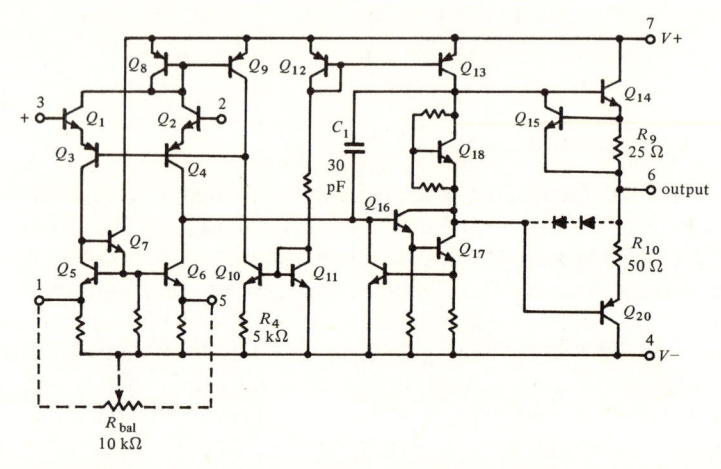

Fig. 2.3.1 Circuit of type 741 IC amplifier (Courtesy Fairchild Semiconductor)

To illustrate the operation of this class, and because we are primarily interested in IC's, the popular type 741 monolithic amplifier will be discussed. The circuit is shown in Fig. 2.3.1.

A number of integrated circuit techniques have already been discussed in Sec. 1.10, and reference will be made to these. The inputs are applied to a differential amplifier Q_{1-4}, each side consisting of a high gain (≈ 100) common collector *NPN* ($Q_{1,2}$) and a low gain (≈ 4) common base *PNP* ($Q_{3,4}$). The collector currents of $Q_{3,4}$ are set by the constant-current differential to single-end converter $Q_{5,6,7}$ (see Sec. 1.10), whose high impedance gives a high input stage gain of several thousand. This circuit arrangement has a number of important properties:

(i) Since the lateral *PNP* transistors $Q_{3,4}$ have large emitter–base breakdown voltages, large differential input voltages are allowed.
(ii) The follower configuration and high gain of $Q_{1,2}$ give low input bias currents without the disadvantage of any Miller capacity, since the output voltage variations appear at the collectors of $Q_{3,4}$. The circuit, therefore, has high input resistance and impedance.

(iii) A large common-mode input range from about the collector voltage of $Q_{1,2}$ ($\doteq V_+ - Q_8 V_{be}$) to the collector voltage of $Q_{3,5}$ ($\doteq V_- + 1\cdot 4$ volts).

(iv) Absence of latch-up; since the input stages are non-inverting, they can only limit rather than saturate and reverse the sense, so no latch-up can occur.

The bases of $Q_{3,4}$ are fed from two constant current sources Q_9 and Q_{10}. Q_{10} is biased by the diode-connected Q_{11} and R_4 to supply 27·5 µA, while Q_9 is biased by Q_8 to supply 20 µA. The difference, 7·5 µA, is the base current of $Q_{3,4}$, i.e., 3·75 µA each. With a current gain of 4 the collector currents of $Q_{3,4}$ are, therefore, 15 µA. $Q_{1,2}$ have a current gain of ≈ 100 so that the input currents are about 100 nA. The various currents are shown in Fig. 2.3.2.

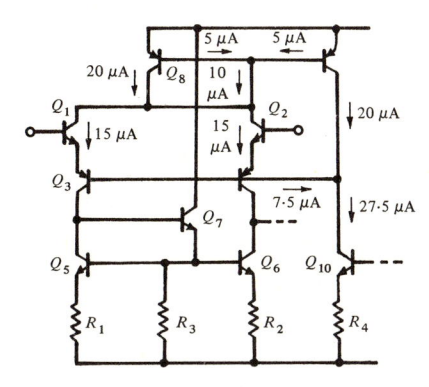

Fig. 2.3.2 Input circuit of type 741 amplifier (Courtesy Fairchild Semiconductor)

The output from Q_6 feeds the compound stage $Q_{16,17}$ which has high input impedance so as not to load Q_6, but is capable of supplying the necessary drive currents to the output stages $Q_{14,20}$. The gain of $Q_{16,17}$ is high, as a result of the constant current load Q_{13} (biased by Q_{12}), and the necessary bias difference between the bases of Q_{14} and Q_{20} is provided by the *zener* Q_{18} (Sec. 1.10). The complementary output stage $Q_{14,20}$ can give large swings so that maximum output voltages approach the supply voltages, and large output currents at low impedance.

Protection against short circuits of the output to ground or either supply line is provided by Q_{15} and Q_{22}. If the current through R_9 exceeds a certain value, Q_{15} is turned on and, by bypassing base current from Q_{14}, limits the possible output current. In the other direction current is limited by R_{10}, and drive to Q_{20} (i.e., when Q_{17} collector is low) is limited by the maximum current through R_{11} before Q_{22} is turned on to bypass base drive current from Q_{16}. On some manufacturers devices extra protective diodes (shown dotted) are included.

To give absolute stability irrespective of load or feedback, the amplifier is internally compensated by means of the 30 pF integrated capacitor, which gives a frequency response roll-off of a constant 6 dB/octave until unity gain is reached at about 1 MHz. Input offset balancing can be achieved by unbalancing the resistors R_1 and R_2 which varies the collector currents of $Q_{5,6}$, so balancing the offset. This is achieved with a 10 kΩ potentiometer, R_{bal}, as shown in Fig. 2.3.1.

2.3(b) Chopper-stabilized amplifier

Differential amplifiers have d.c. and low frequency drifts of the order of 1 to 10 μV/°C, as well as similar variations relative to time and supply voltage variation. Any attempt to measure microvolt signals, therefore, presents considerable difficulties. If the signals are of zero or very low frequency the chopper amplifier is the answer (Fig. 2.3.3). The idea is to chop the signal by means of a switch, so producing a square wave which can be amplified by an a.c. coupled amplifier. The output of the amplifier is demodulated by S_2 and smoothed by the $R_3 C_3$ filter to give the output signal. Since the amplifier is a.c. coupled the inherent internal d.c. drifts are not passed to the output.

The switching frequency f is usually in the range 50 to 1000 Hz, but the bandwidth of the system will be very much less than f, since the smoothing time constant, $R_3 C_3$,

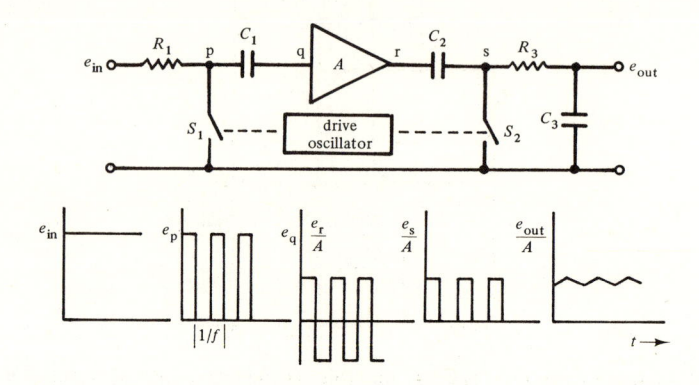

Fig. 2.3.3 Chopper amplifier

must be very much longer than $1/f$ to give satisfactory ripple reduction. Mechanical switches were originally used, but these can only be operated at low frequencies, are large, and most importantly have limited life. Now FET switches are used which are small, can be driven at very high frequencies if required, and have unlimited life. High chopping frequencies, however, lead to problems of capacitive feedthrough of the switch drive into the amplifier input.

With care and especially elimination of thermal voltages (even between one batch of copper and another) voltages as low as 10^{-9} volts can be successfully amplified [b1].

Because of the very restricted bandwidth of say a few Hz, the chopper amplifier is not of much use for general application as an operational amplifier. However, it forms the basis of the chopper stabilized amplifier, which combines the advantages of the chopper and differential amplifiers [a1]. This consists of a chopper amplifier and a differential amplifier, both of which could be of the type shown in Fig. 2.3.1, connected as shown in Fig. 2.3.4.

The d.c. and very low frequency components of e_{in} are chopped by the modulator M, amplified by A_1, demodulated by D, smoothed by $R_3 C_3$, and amplified by A_2. The net gain for these components is $A_1 A_2$. Higher frequency components of e_{in} pass directly to A_2 via $C_4 R_4$ so that the gain for these is only A_2. The response of the various sections is shown in Fig. 2.3.5.

The operation of the circuit can be considered in two ways. As described above, the chopper amplifier can amplify d.c. signals and contribute only a very small drift. The drifts at the input of A_2 due to A_2 must now be compared with A_1 times the input signal e_{in}, rather than with just e_{in}, and so are A_1 times less significant. This view

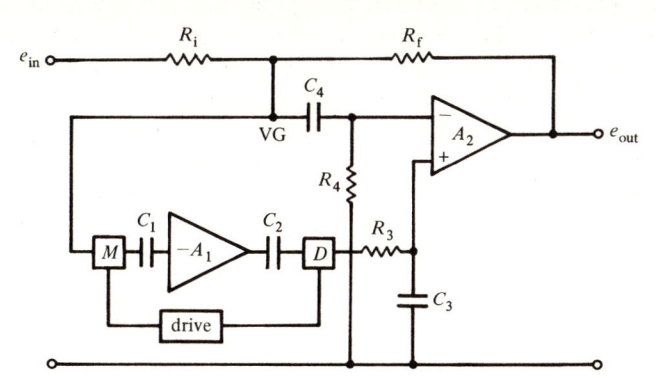

Fig. 2.3.4 Chopper-stabilized amplifier

holds without the necessity of the feedback components R_i and R_f. If the feedback is connected, then an alternative description, that gives the system its name, is more appropriate. Drifts at the input of A_2 will be amplified and fed back to VG. This signal will be amplified and inverted by A_1 and fed to A_2 in a sense to counteract the original drift. Thus, the chopper amplifier stabilizes the d.c. operating point of A_2, and hence the name [a1].

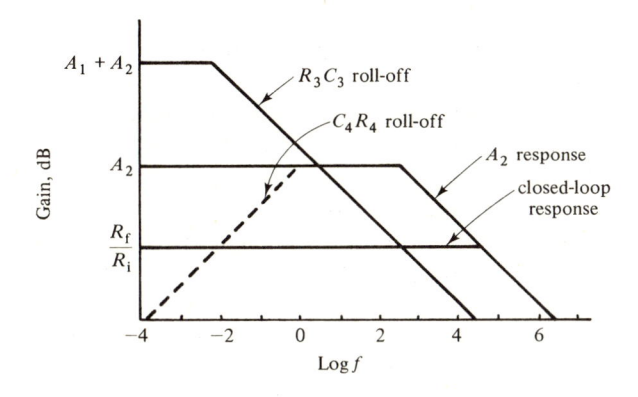

Fig. 2.3.5 Frequency response of chopper-stabilized amplifier

When the feedback loop is closed the gain will just be $-R_f/R_i$, and the response will be as shown in Fig. 2.3.5. The large variations of gain with frequency are removed, and a flat response up to the high frequency roll-off of A_2 is obtained. Consideration should be given to the relative values of the two time constants, R_3C_3 and R_4C_4, to avoid extreme variations of phase in the region where the A_1+A_2 and A_2 response curves merge, as instability could result (see chapter 3) [p1, m1].

2.3(c) *Parametric amplifier*

As the name may suggest, these amplifiers operate on the basis of a periodic variation of some parameter of the circuit. Although this parameter could be resistive or reactive, usually the latter is implied since the losses of the former preclude a power gain. The basic principles of parametric amplification have been known for a considerable time, but it needed the development of junction diodes, whose capacity varied with reverse bias, to make parametric amplifiers a practical proposition. Although ordinary diodes behave in this way, special diodes called varactors are made for the purpose. The great attraction of these amplifiers was the low noise possibilities, and the initial development was for the microwave region where the noise problem is most serious. Later it was realized that the technique could profitably be applied to the d.c. and low frequency region where the so-called $1/f$ noise becomes important.

In the parlance of parametric amplifiers the type we will discuss is designated an *up-converter reactance amplifier*, but it is probably more helpful to call it a *varactor-bridge amplifier*. An outline of the circuit is shown in Fig. 2.3.6. A high frequency

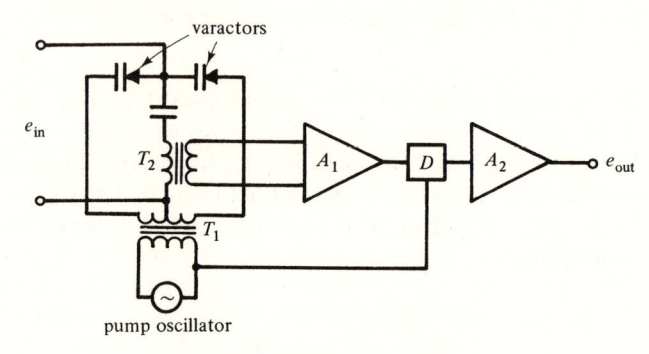

Fig. 2.3.6 Parametric amplifier

pump oscillator (say 10 MHz) excites a bridge consisting of a centre tapped transformer, T_1, and two varactor diodes. The signal applied to the varactors is a few tens of millivolts peak-to-peak. If no external signal is applied and the two varactors are matched, then there will be no signal across T_2. When a signal is applied this will bias the varactors in opposite directions, thus unbalancing the bridge and giving a suppressed-carrier modulated signal across T_2. This is amplified by A_1 and demodulated by a synchronous phase-sensitive demodulator, to recover the form of the original signal with its correct polarity. A standard amplifier A_2 follows to increase the overall gain and provide the required output capabilities.

For a particular model (Analog Devices 301 [d1]) the power gain of the bridge is 43 dB (20 000), while the use of a 10 MHz pumping frequency gives a unity-gain bandwidth of 1 MHz and allows the use of miniature ferrite coupling transformers. The isolation obtained with the latter provided common-mode rejection ratios of 160 dB (10^8) and common-mode voltage capability of 300 volts, with an input resistance of 10^{13} ohm.

In most types of amplifier the noise is associated with resistance or electronic processes having resistive parameters. The parametric amplifier depends on capacitance, which does not contribute noise to the circuit giving it its main advantage. Of course the varactors are not perfect capacitors and do have resistive components (as do the transformer arms), so some noise is generated.

The mechanism by which energy is transferred to the signal to amplify it, is of interest. If a capacitor C has charge Q then the voltage across it is given by $V = Q/C$. If C is decreased, for example by pulling the plates apart, then V will be increased because Q is effectively constant. However, work must be done against the forces between the charges on the plates and this mechanical work is transformed into the amplified voltage. The energy stored in a capacitor is given by $\frac{1}{2}CV^2$. If the capacity is halved V is doubled ($V = Q/C$) and, therefore, the energy is doubled. In the parametric amplifier the pump produces the change of capacity, but as it is a voltage signal it gets mixed up with the signal itself and the non-linearity of the C versus V relationship produce sum and difference frequencies in the output, which carry the information about the original signal. The signal has been up-converted to the new frequency region.

As varactor bridge amplifiers are considerably more expensive than IC types they are not of general use, but they do have important advantages over other types, particularly when high impedance sources are involved (say $>10^8$ ohm), or possibly for very long time constant integrators or sample-hold applications (Sec. 6.5) [c1, d1, e1, g1, h1, l1, S1, T1].

2.4 Frequency response and stability

It has so far been assumed that the operational amplifiers have infinite bandwidth. The fact that they do not has important effects not only on their general performance, but more vitally on their stability against oscillation when feedback is applied. Although this topic, and the means of achieving stability, will be considered in detail in chapter 3, it is necessary here to outline the problem and the possible consequences.

The frequency response of a typical IC amplifier is shown in Fig. 2.4.1. Above frequency f_1 the gain falls off at an increasing rate until unity gain is reached at a frequency of several MHz. The corresponding phase shift reaches 45° at f_1 and increases rapidly, reaching 180° at a few MHz. The variation in phase, and fall-off in gain, with frequency are of great importance for stability. If the open-loop gain is greater than unity at the frequency f_{180} at which the phase shift reaches 180°,

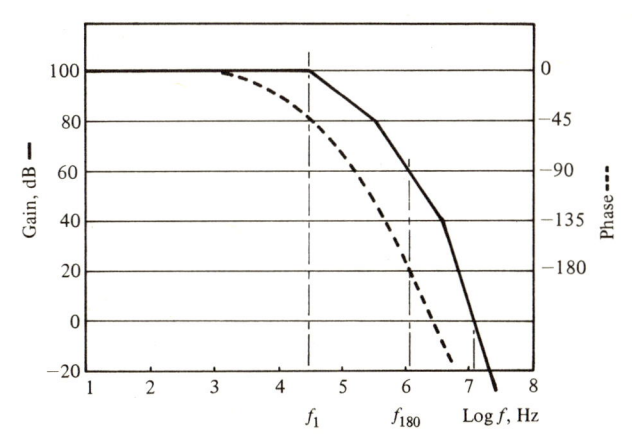

Fig. 2.4.1 Frequency and phase response of typical IC amplifier

then there is the possibility, depending on the feedback circuit, that the system will be unstable and oscillate. As can be seen from Eq. (2.2.11) this is the extreme case for $\beta = 1$. More generally, if the loop-gain $A(\omega)\beta$ is equal to (or greater than) unity at f_{180}, then the closed-loop gain becomes infinite as $A(\omega)\beta$ is now negative. Any small disturbance, for example the appropriate frequency component of the ever present noise, will be amplified and fed back in the correct phase to build up and sustain oscillations. These statements have assumed that β was independent of frequency. If this is not so, then the effective f_{180} will not be that of $A(\omega)$ alone, but will also depend on the frequency response of β.

Operational amplifiers, therefore, have several points in the circuit accessible for the connection of RC networks designed to modify the amplifier response in order to maintain stability with the particular feedback circuit. The determination of the correct networks is often the most difficult part of the overall design. Some IC's have built-in frequency compensation, which makes them much easier to use, but this involves the sacrifice of a considerable amount of available bandwidth, as can be seen by comparing Fig. 2.4.2 with Fig. 2.4.1.

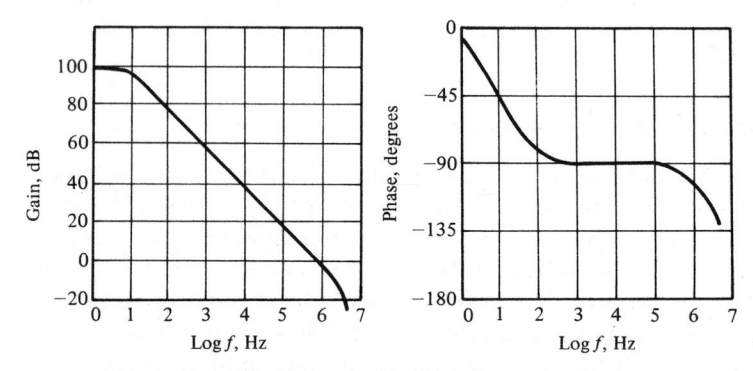

Fig. 2.4.2 Response of frequency compensated op-amp

Because of the possible variation in components or devices it is obviously unwise to operate too close to critical feedback conditions. In any case, as will be seen later (Sec. 3.7), operation even near the critical conditions leads to substantial peaking in the frequency response with consequential undesirable transient response. In general, margins of about 6 dB in gain and 30° to 45° in phase are allowed, for safety. Note that the lower the closed-loop gain G (the higher the loop gain L) the more critical the feedback, as a greater part of the output is being fed back. The voltage follower, with $G = 1$, provides the most difficult situation.

2.5 Inverting, summing, non-inverting, and differential amplifiers

The basic configuration we have considered so far is inherently an inverting amplifier, otherwise we would not have been able to apply negative feedback. Within the limits of the amplifier, the output will be a constant times the input, but with the phase shifted by 180°:

$$e_{\text{out}} = \frac{-R_f}{R_i} e_{\text{in}}, \quad \text{or} \quad G = \frac{e_{\text{out}}}{e_{\text{in}}} = \frac{-R_f}{R_i} \tag{2.5.1}$$

The existence of the virtual ground makes it possible to apply several inputs simultaneously without interaction, the output being the sum of the inputs multiplied by appropriate constants; see Fig. 2.5.1.

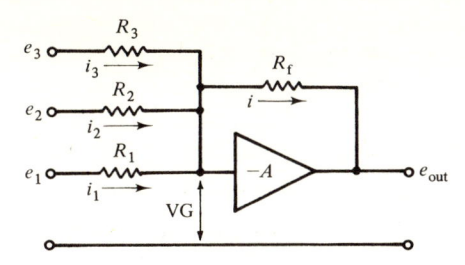

Fig. 2.5.1 Summing operational amplifier

Because of the virtual ground the currents i_1, i_2, i_3 will flow through the respective input resistors uninfluenced by each other, i.e.:

$$i_1 = \frac{e_1}{R_1}, \quad i_2 = \frac{e_2}{R_2}, \quad i_3 = \frac{e_3}{R_3}, \quad \text{etc.}$$

and
$$i = i_1 + i_2 + i_3 + \cdots \tag{2.5.2}$$

Each input will be amplified quite independently:

$$e_{\text{out 1}} = \frac{-R_f}{R_1} e_1, \quad e_{\text{out 2}} = \frac{-R_f}{R_2} e_2, \quad \text{etc.}$$

or
$$e_{\text{out}} = -R_f \left[\frac{e_1}{R_1} + \frac{e_2}{R_2} + \frac{e_3}{R_3} + \cdots \right] \tag{2.5.3}$$

i.e., the output is the sum of the inputs scaled by the appropriate factors R_f/R_i, etc., which could be made the same if desired. There will always be some interaction in practice, the degree of interaction depending on the value of the effective virtual ground resistance; see Eq. (2.2.16).

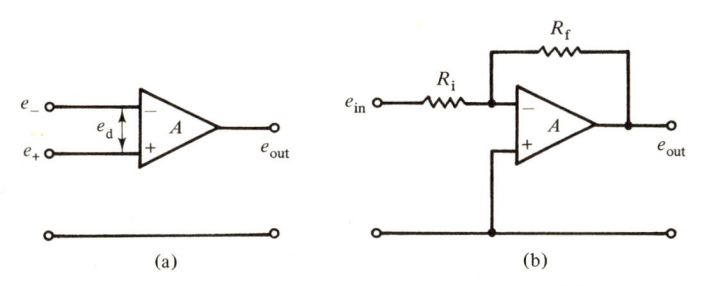

Fig. 2.5.2 Differential input operational amplifier

As explained in Sec. 2.3, IC operational amplifiers are almost always produced with two inputs, one inverting (labelled $(-)$) and one non-inverting (labelled $(+)$), the output being proportional to the difference between the two inputs (Fig. 2.5.2).

$$e_{\text{out}} = A(e_+ - e_-) = A e_d \tag{2.5.4}$$

The situation we have considered so far would be realized as shown in Fig. 2.5.2(b), the non-inverting input merely being grounded so that $e_+ = 0$. A non-inverting amplifier may be realized by grounding the usual input and using the (+) input instead (Fig. 2.5.3).

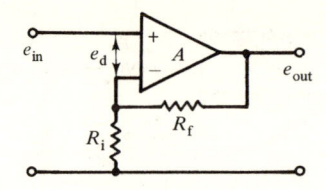

Fig. 2.5.3 Non-inverting operational amplifier

The gain G is *not*, however, given by Eq. (2.5.1) with the sign changed. This circuit may be analysed directly, but we can now use the short cuts we have developed. Since the gain A is very high, the input voltage $e_d = 0$, i.e., the fed back voltage = the input voltage, or:

$$e_{out} \frac{R_i}{R_i + R_f} = e_{in}, \quad G = \frac{e_{out}}{e_{in}} = \frac{R_i + R_f}{R_i} = 1 + \frac{R_f}{R_i} = \frac{1}{\beta} \quad (2.5.5)$$

The difference of unity from the equivalent expression for the inverting amplifier, Eq. (2.5.1), will not be significant for high values of G. There are, however, important differences regarding the input impedance and the voltage level of the inputs.

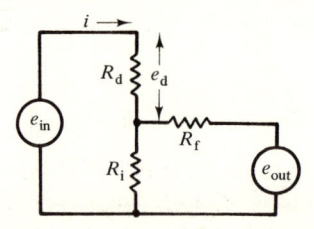

Fig. 2.5.4 Input impedance of non-inverting circuit

Figure 2.5.4 shows a circuit equivalent to Fig. 2.5.3. If there were no feedback, i.e., $R_i = 0$, then the input resistance will just be the differential input resistance R_d (the effective resistance between the inputs, see Sec. 2.9(k)). With feedback we can see that less current i will flow for the same e_{in}, because of the opposing feedback voltage across R_i, so that the effective input resistance is increased: for complete feedback ($R_i = \infty$) the input resistance becomes infinite, in theory. In practice, it does not go that far, as a result of common-mode resistances between (+) and (−) and ground, but it can become very large indeed. For example, for IC type µA741, $R_d = 2$ MΩ, and for $G = 10$ we find $R_{in} = 400$ MΩ! From Eqs. (2.5.4) and (2.5.5), and since $i = e_d/R_d$:

$$R_{in} = \frac{e_{in}}{i} = \frac{e_{in}}{e_d} R_d = \frac{e_{in}}{e_{out}} A R_d = A\beta R_d \quad (2.5.6)$$

This is a slight approximation in that Eq. (2.5.5) assumes $R_d = \infty$. The actual expression is $(1 + A\beta)R_d$ [p1, p. 86]. For the example above this would predict $R_{in} \approx 10^4$ MΩ, showing the effect of the common-mode resistances.

For any input voltage, e_{in}, both input terminals (+) and (−) will be at this voltage rather than at zero, as for the inverting configuration. There are practical limits placed on this voltage, and common-mode effects to be considered; see Sec. 2.9(b).

By using an attenuator on the (+) input that is the inverse of that on the (−) input, a more symmetrical circuit is obtained (Fig. 2.5.5), which has $G = R_f/R_i$ (just multiply

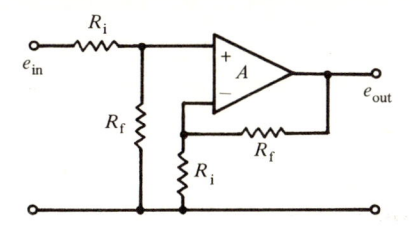

Fig. 2.5.5 Offset balanced non-inverting circuit

e_{in} by $R_f/(R_f + R_i)$ in Eq. (2.5.5)). This arrangement has the advantage of balancing the offset voltages due to bias currents from the inputs; see Sec. 2.9 (q), (t).

Using the arrangement shown in Fig. 2.5.6, i.e., also feeding a signal into the (−) input of Fig. 2.5.5, we get:

$$e_{out} = \frac{R_f}{R_i} \cdot (e_+ - e_-) \qquad (2.5.7)$$

The rejection of common-mode signals requires careful matching of the resistors and, hence, also depends on source impedances [q1, p. 202], Sec. (4.2).

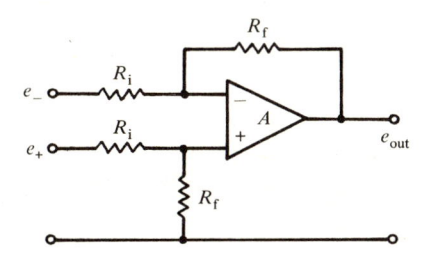

Fig. 2.5.6 Subtractor or difference circuit

The circuit of Fig. 2.5.6 may be combined with Fig. 2.5.1 to give an adder/subtractor (Fig. 2.5.7).

The general case with unrelated resistors would give a rather unwieldly expression, so we will consider the case shown in Fig. 2.5.7 (a). For the (−) input:

$$\frac{e_4 - e_-}{KR_2} + \frac{e_3 - e_-}{KR_1} = \frac{e_- - e_{out}}{KR_f}$$

or

$$e_- \cdot \left[\frac{1}{R_f} + \frac{1}{R_1} + \frac{1}{R_2}\right] = \frac{e_4}{R_2} + \frac{e_3}{R_1} + \frac{e_{out}}{R_f}$$

For the (+) input:

$$\frac{e_2 - e_+}{R_2} + \frac{e_1 - e_+}{R_1} = \frac{e_+}{R_f}$$

or
$$e_+ \cdot \left[\frac{1}{R_f} + \frac{1}{R_1} + \frac{1}{R_2}\right] = \frac{e_1}{R_1} + \frac{e_2}{R_2}$$

and since $e_+ - e_- = e_d = 0$, or $e_+ = e_-$:

$$e_{out} = R_f \cdot \left[\frac{e_1}{R_1} + \frac{e_2}{R_2} - \frac{e_3}{R_1} - \frac{e_4}{R_2}\right] \qquad (2.5.8)$$

The above configuration requires that there be an equal number of $(+)$ and $(-)$ inputs: this can always be done, the unused inputs being grounded, so that $e_n = 0$.

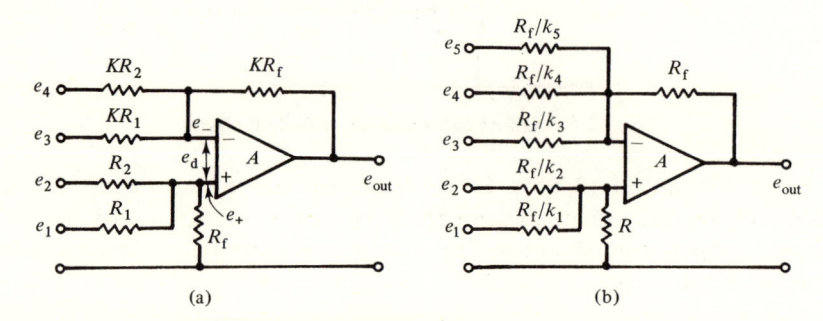

Fig. 2.5.7 Adder/subtractor circuits

An alternative arrangement is shown in Fig. 2.5.7(b), having an unequal number of inputs. Analysing the circuit in a similar way we find:

$$e_{out} = k_1 e_1 + k_2 e_2 - k_3 e_3 - k_4 e_4 - k_5 e_5 \qquad (2.5.9)$$

provided
$$k_1 + k_2 = k_3 + k_4 + k_5$$

Equivalent equations hold for any number of inputs on each side.

If the signal source has a very high output resistance it becomes a current source rather than a voltage source (see Sec. 1.2). The signal is then a variation in current, and we may wish to convert this to a voltage signal. Since the source resistance is very large, R_i may be discarded, giving Fig. 2.5.8.

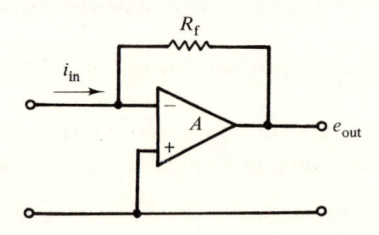

Fig. 2.5.8 Current-to-voltage converter

Since we have a virtual ground, i_{in} flows through R_f to give:

$$e_{out} = -i_{in} R_f \qquad (2.5.10)$$

This gives a direct conversion of current to voltage without in any way disturbing the current flow, as would be the case if a resistance, R_g, were simply connected between current source and ground. As for voltages, any number of currents may be summed without interaction.

The emitter follower is a familiar device for transforming from a high to a low impedance. The voltage follower performs the same service, with the advantage of higher input impedance and a gain that is closer to unity. The circuit is shown in Fig. 2.5.9.

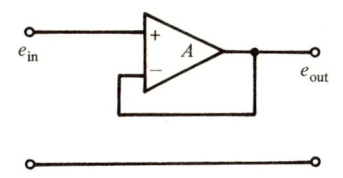

Fig. 2.5.9 Voltage follower

Since $R_i = \infty$, we have from Eq. (2.5.5):

$$e_{out} = e_{in} \tag{2.5.11}$$

The input impedance will be increased to AR_d, as can be seen from Eq. (2.5.6) since $G = 1$. (This technique is commonly known as *boot-strapping*, from the story by the well-known Baron Munchausen, of a soldier who extricated himself from quicksand by pulling on his own bootstraps!) For fast or large or particular polarity signals, many ordinary operational amplifiers are not very suitable for use as voltage followers. As we have maximum negative feedback, which is the most difficult case in which to obtain dynamic stability (see chapter 3), heavy frequency compensation must be applied, which reduces performance considerably. Special voltage follower IC's are made for the more demanding applications [c1, d1].

There are several general points that should be mentioned here. Any particular amplifier will be able to supply a maximum output current, set possibly by power dissipation, limiting, etc. The output current flows both in the feedback path and the load, so there is a minimum value for both load and/or feedback impedance.

Operational circuits will operate on the voltage appearing at the input terminal. If the signal source has other than zero output impedance, this must be added to Z_i to determine the overall response.

2.6 Operational integrator

In Sec. 2.2, it was pointed out that there was no limitation on the feedback elements, reactive or complex impedances also being allowed. Here we examine the case where the previously used feedback resistance R_f is replaced by a capacitor C_f (Fig. 2.6.1) [l1, m1, n1, c1, q1].

Using Eqs. (2.2.17) and (1.11.7) we get:

$$G = \frac{E_{out}(s)}{E_{in}(s)} = \frac{-Z_f(s)}{Z_i(s)} = \frac{-1}{R_i C_f s} \tag{2.6.1}$$

or transforming back into the time domain using Eqs. (1.11.7) and (1.11.6):

$$e_{out} = \frac{-1}{R_i C_f} \int_0^t e_{in}\, dt = \frac{-1}{C_f} \int_0^t i\, dt \tag{2.6.2}$$

where we have assumed no initial charge on the capacitor at time $t=0$: this would just mean an additive constant if present. The characteristic time of the integrator $T = R_i C_f$. This is the time required for the output to change by an amount equal to the average value of the input. If Δt is the time required then the average input is:

$$\langle e_{in} \rangle = \frac{\int_0^t e_{in}\, dt}{\Delta t}, \quad \text{so} \quad \Delta e_{out} = \frac{\langle -e_{in} \rangle \Delta t}{R_i C_f} \tag{2.6.3}$$

and, since Δt is the time for Δe_{out} to equal $\langle -e_{in} \rangle$, then $\Delta t = R_i C_f$.

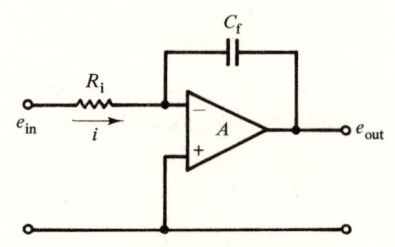

Fig. 2.6.1 Operational integrator

It is instructive to derive Eq. (2.6.2) by the direct method as used to derive Eq. (2.2.4), for example. Since we have a virtual ground, $i = e_{in}/R_i$, and, if Q is the charge on the capacitor, $e_{out} = Q/C_f$. The current i flows to charge C_f so:

$$Q = -\int_0^t i\, dt$$

and
$$e_{out} = \frac{-1}{R_i C_f} \int_0^t e_{in}\, dt \tag{2.6.4}$$

This emphasizes the point that currents flow *through* capacitors as explained in Sec. 1.4.

If we do not, *a priori*, assume a virtual ground and allow for finite differential input resistance R_d, then:

$$\frac{E_{in} - E_g}{R_i} = (E_g - E_{out})Cs + \frac{E_g}{R_d}, \quad \text{and} \quad E_{out} = -AE_g$$

or
$$\frac{E_{out}}{E_{in}} = \frac{-A}{1 + (1+A)R_i C_f s + R_i/R_d}$$

$$= \frac{-1}{R_i C_f s}\left[\frac{1}{AR_p C_f s} + \frac{1}{A} + 1\right]^{-1} \tag{2.6.5}$$

where $R_p = R_f R_d/(R_f + R_d)$. For A large, this reduces to the previous simple form, but Eq. (2.6.5) allows us to determine the errors involved in any particular situation.

The integrator may be combined with the summing amplifier, Fig. 2.5.1, to give a summing integrator, Fig. 2.6.2, which has the response:

$$E_{out} = \frac{-1}{C_f s}\left[\frac{E_1}{R_1} + \frac{E_2}{R_2} + \frac{E_3}{R_3} + \cdots\right] \tag{2.6.6}$$

A difference integrator is also possible, capacitors replacing both R_f's in Fig. 2.5.6.

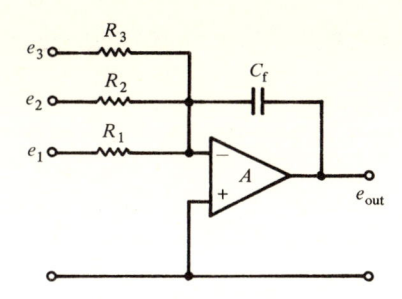

Fig. 2.6.2 Summing integrator

There is a serious difficulty in using integrators. Unless we have a perfectly drift-free amplifier, the offsets will cause the output, in time, to drift to one of its bounds set by the output capabilities of the amplifier. Thus, some means of resetting the output to the required initial condition must be provided, e.g., a switch or relay. If the input signal does not have frequency components below a certain frequency, the circuit of Fig. 2.6.3 may be used.

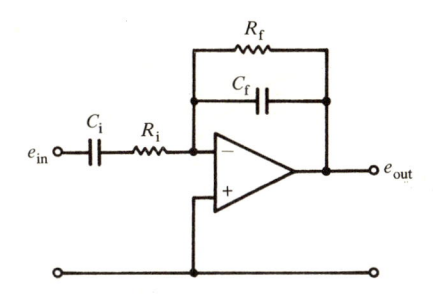

Fig. 2.6.3 High frequency (a.c.) integrator

This arrangement eliminates the drift to a bound, and eliminates offsets due to d.c. drifts associated with the input signal. At high frequencies C_i and R_f can be neglected, giving the required integrator. At low frequencies R_i and C_f may be ignored, which gives a differentiator, as will be discussed in Sec. 2.7. In the central region all elements will be more or less influential; the overall response is that of a bandpass amplifier (Fig. 2.6.4).

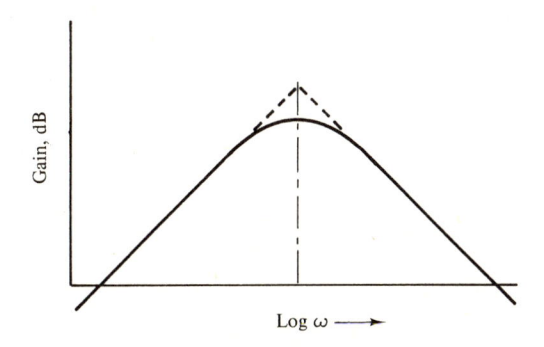

Fig. 2.6.4 Frequency response of a.c. integrator

The actual transfer function is easily found by writing down the input and feedback impedances:

$$Z_T(s) = \frac{-1}{R_i C_f s}\left[\frac{\tau s}{1+\tau s}\right], \quad \text{for} \quad R_i C_i = R_f C_f = \tau \qquad (2.6.7)$$

The input capacitor C_i will block any d.c. components of the input signal. If this is not a problem C_i may be omitted, giving a transfer function:

$$Z_T(s) = \frac{-R_f}{R_i}\left[\frac{1}{1+R_f C_f s}\right]$$

$$\doteq \frac{-1}{R_i C_f s} \quad \text{for} \quad s \gg 1/R_f C_f \qquad (2.6.8)$$

with a response shown in Fig. 2.6.5.

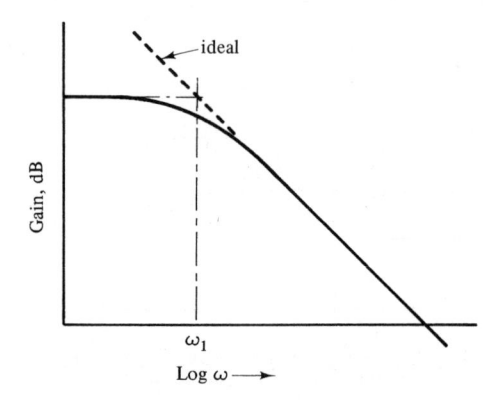

Fig. 2.6.5 Frequency response of Eq. (2.6.8)

The output will now not drift to a bound but settle at a value:

$$e_{out} = \frac{-R_f}{R_i} \cdot (\text{Sum of offset voltages of amplifier}) \qquad (2.6.9)$$

This should be kept small enough so as not to limit the dynamic range of the output [c1].

The difference between the ideal and the actual response is about 0·5 per cent for a frequency 10 times the corner frequency [m1]. This applies to Fig. 2.6.4 also.

We have so far assumed a perfect amplifier with infinite gain and bandwidth. Finite gain and bandwidth impose limitations on the accuracy of integration. Consider an amplifier with finite bandwidth, $1/T$, cutting off at 6 dB/octave, as shown in Fig. 2.6.6.

If the zero frequency gain is A_0, then the response can be expressed as:

$$A(s) = \frac{A_0}{1+Ts} \qquad (2.6.10)$$

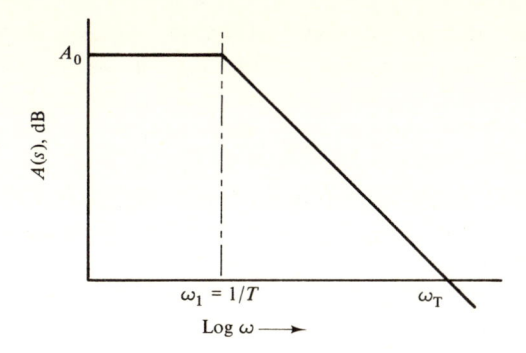

Fig. 2.6.6 Amplifier frequency response with 6dB/octave cut-off

From Eqs. (2.6.5) and (2.6.10) we get:

$$\frac{E_{out}(s)}{E_{in}(s)} = \frac{-1}{R_iC_fs}\left[1+\frac{1}{A_0}+\frac{1}{A_0R_pC_fs}+\frac{Ts}{A_0}+\frac{T}{A_0R_pC_fs}\right]^{-1}$$

$$= \frac{-1}{R_iC_fs}\left[1+\frac{s}{\omega_T}+\frac{1}{A_0R_pC_fs}\right]^{-1} \quad (2.6.11)$$

for $A_0 \gg 1$ and T/R_pC_f, and putting $\omega_T = A_0/T$. The effect of this finite bandwidth ($=1/T$) may be seen by examining the form of Eq. (2.6.11) at high frequencies. For $s \gg 1/A_0R_pC_f$:

$$\frac{E_{out}(s)}{E_{in}(s)} = \frac{-1}{R_iC_fs}\left[1+\frac{s}{\omega_T}\right]^{-1} = \frac{-\omega_T}{R_iC_fs}\cdot\frac{1}{(s+\omega_T)} \quad (2.6.12)$$

If $e_{in}(t) = -u(t)$, the unit step function, then since the transform of $u(t)$ is $1/s$ we have:

$$E_{out}(s) = \frac{\omega_T}{R_iC_fs^2}\cdot\frac{1}{(s+\omega_T)}$$

or

$$e_{out}(t) = \frac{1}{R_iC_f\omega_T}(e^{-\omega_T t}+\omega_T t - 1) \quad (2.6.13)$$

using standard transforms (e.g., [o1], transform 15). This response is shown in Fig. 2.6.7.

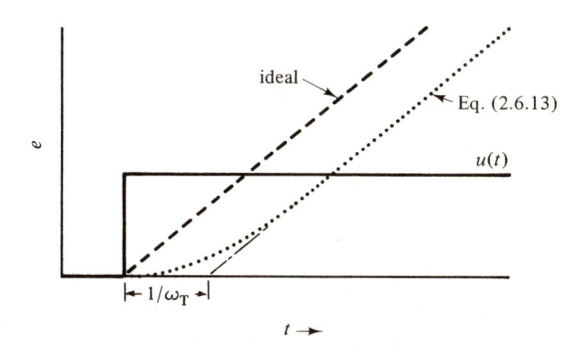

Fig. 2.6.7 Effect of finite amplifier bandwidth on integrator response

For small t we get the curved response due to the term $(e^{-\omega_T t}-1)$, but after a time of the order of $1/\omega_T$, the exponential decays and we are left with:

$$e_{out}(t) = \frac{1}{R_i C_f} \cdot (t - 1/\omega_T) \qquad (2.6.14)$$

which runs parallel to the ideal response (shown dotted) but shifted in time by an amount $1/\omega_T$, i.e., the output lags by an amount dependent on the unity-gain bandwidth ω_T, but not on R_i or C_f.

The effect of finite gain may be seen by considering the low frequency region where $s \ll \omega_T$. Then Eq. (2.6.11) becomes:

$$\frac{E_{out}(s)}{E_{in}(s)} = \frac{-1}{R_i C_f s}\left[1+\frac{1}{A_0 R_p C_f s}\right]^{-1} = \frac{-A_0 R_p}{R_i(1+A_0 R_p C_f s)} \qquad (2.6.15)$$

If this is compared with Eq. (2.6.9) it will be seen that the response is identical to an amplifier with infinite gain and input impedance, but with a resistor $R_f = A_0 R_p$ in parallel with C_f (Fig. 2.6.8) [m1, p. 46].

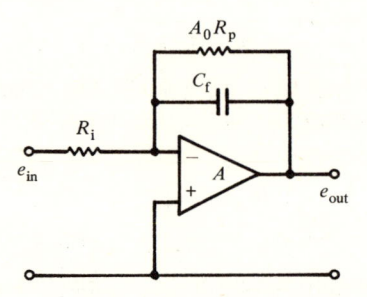

Fig. 2.6.8 Equivalent circuit of integrator with finite gain amplifier

If we apply a unit step function as above then the response is:

$$E_{out}(s) = \frac{A_0 R_p}{R_i s(1+A_0 R_p C_f s)} = \frac{A_0 R_p}{R_i R_p A_0 C_f} \cdot \frac{1}{s(s+1/A_0 R_p C_f)}$$

or in the time domain:

$$e_{out}(t) = \frac{A_0 R_p}{R_i}[1-\exp(t/A_0 R_p C_f)] \qquad (2.6.16)$$

$$= \frac{A_0 R_p}{R_i}\left[1-1+\frac{t}{A_0 R_p C_f}-\frac{t^2}{2 A_0^2 R_p^2 C_f^2}+\cdots\right]$$

$$\doteq \frac{t}{R_i C_f} - \frac{t^2}{2 R_i C_f A_0 R_p C_f} \qquad (2.6.17)$$

The first term is just the ideal response, while the second shows that the error increases as the square of the time. After a time long compared with $A_0 R_p C_f$, the exponential term becomes negligible in Eq. (2.6.16) and e_{out} tends to $A_0 R_p / R_i$ (Fig. 2.6.9).

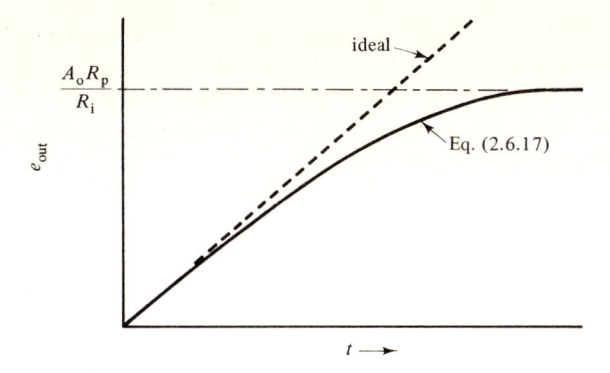

Fig. 2.6.9 Effect of finite grain on integrator response

Addition of a resistor in series with the feedback capacitor produces the augmenting integrator (Fig. 2.6.10).

This circuit gives an output containing a proportional term together with an integral term, and finds use in closed-loop servo systems (Sec. 4.5).

$$\frac{E_{out}(s)}{E_{in}(s)} = \frac{-R_f}{R_i}\left[1 + \frac{1}{R_f C_f s}\right] \qquad (2.6.18)$$

Offset and *drift* are discussed in detail in Sec. 2.9, but the results for integrators are included here for convenience. The effects of bias current and voltage offset can

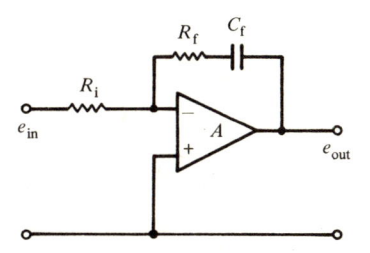

Fig. 2.6.10 Augmenting integrator

be derived easily from the results obtained for amplifiers, Eq. (2.9.7). For bias current the equivalent input generator is just as before [s1, c1, d1, f1]:

$$e_{ib} = i_b R_i \qquad (2.6.19)$$

For the offset voltages, as essentially d.c. conditions apply, the impedance of $C_f \gg R_i$ so that the equivalent input generator is:

$$e_{eo} = e_{os} \qquad (2.6.20)$$

The equivalent circuit, therefore, is as shown in Fig. 2.6.11.

For integrators, the output drift rate is of interest rather than the output offset. This can be obtained by differentiating Eq. (2.6.4) and using Eqs. (2.6.19) and (2.6.20):

$$\frac{de_{out}}{dt} = \frac{e_{os}}{R_i C_f} + \frac{i_b}{C_f} \qquad (2.6.21)$$

For a given characteristic time $R_i C_f$, the drift rate will be minimized with minimum R_i and maximum C_f. Source impedance sets the minimum R, and the maximum C is controlled by size and leakage. For differential amplifiers, the effect of bias current can be reduced by connecting a resistor $R_c = R_i$ between (+) and ground. The offset current then replaces the bias current [d1].

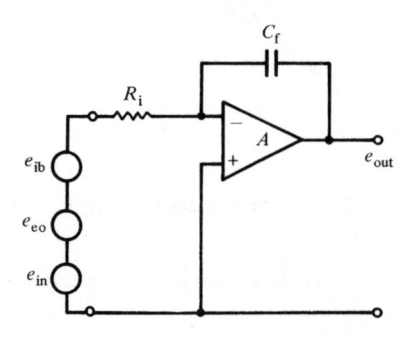

Fig. 2.6.11 Offset and drift in operational integrator

2.7 Operational differentiator

For the integrator, the transfer function $Z_T(s)$ is proportional to $1/s$, Eq. (2.6.1). If this is inverted we would get s, i.e., differentiation. This is simply achieved by interchanging R and C in Fig. 2.6.1, as shown in Fig. 2.7.1.

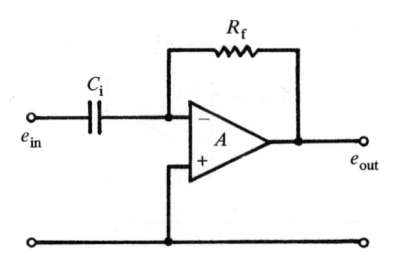

Fig. 2.7.1 Operational differentiator

The circuit can be analysed as before, from considerations of i and the virtual ground, but we will just write down the transfer function by inspection [j1, h1, k1]:

$$\frac{E_{out}(s)}{E_{in}(s)} = Z_T(s) = \frac{-Z_f(s)}{Z_i(s)} = -R_f C_i s \qquad (2.7.1)$$

or in the time domain:

$$e_{out} = -R_f C_i \cdot \frac{de_{in}}{dt} \qquad (2.7.2)$$

As before, summing and difference differentiators may be realized.

When we examine the frequency response of the differentiator (Fig. 2.7.2) it is seen that the gain increases linearly with frequency (at least until the inherent amplifier response becomes effective), which has two important consequences. Firstly, an increasing amount of high frequency noise will be amplified to the detriment of the signal. This is usually avoided by connection of a small resistor, R_i, in series with C_i, so that for frequencies above some value the circuit behaves as a proportional amplifier with gain $-R_f/R_i$. Secondly, there is considerable danger of dynamic instability (see chapter 3), this being reduced by R_i and even further by the addition of C_f in parallel with R_f. The situation and response will then be similar to that shown in Figs. 2.6.3 and 2.6.4 (note $R_iC_i = R_fC_f$ there). If the corner frequency ω_2 is ten times the maximum frequency it is wished to differentiate, there will only be 1 per cent magnitude and 11 per cent phase error [k1, II.21].

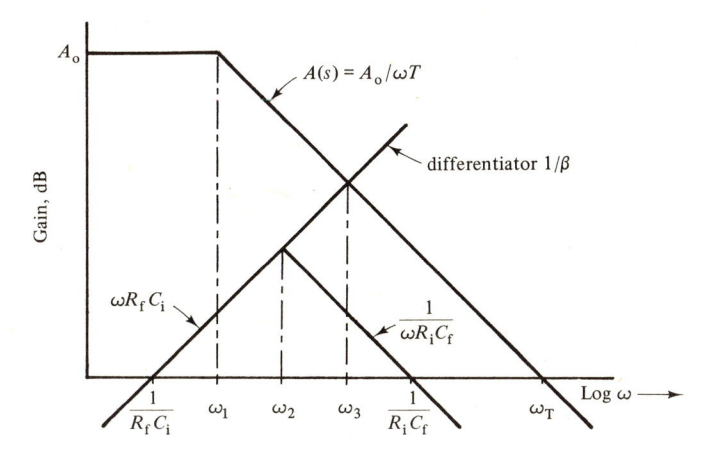

Fig. 2.7.2 Frequency response of differentiator (Courtesy Electronic Engineering)

For the simple differentiator, Fig. 2.7.1, the input impedance will just be $1/C_is$, since the amplifier input is a virtual ground. Thus, to drive the differentiator, a low impedance source is required that can supply large currents at high frequencies. The use of R_i limits this current, and any source impedance can be lumped together with R_i.

The differentiator time constant, R_fC_i, should be chosen so that the maximum rate of change of input signal will produce full scale output, or possibly a little less to allow for errors or the unexpected. If occasional larger inputs can occur, and instant response immediately following is required, a limiting circuit should be connected across R_f, e.g., a zener diode. This will limit the output and prevent excess charging of C_i [k1].

For very long time constants it is desirable not to use capacitors of greater than about 10 µF because of leakage and size, and for exceptional cases a resistive-tee feedback network may be used. With this technique it is possible to achieve a time constant as long as two weeks! [k1, III.56].

Because of the less desirable characteristics of differentiators relative to integrators, the latter have usually been used where possible, e.g., in analogue computers, for the solution of differential equations. However, differentiators can often be of use, so we will consider the response characteristics. This will be done in some detail as it is seldom considered elsewhere. The difference from the treatment above is the inclusion of the actual amplifier response, Eq. (2.6.10), in the transfer function.

Using Eq. (2.2.5), the transfer function for the basic differentiator is [j1, h1]:

$$\frac{E_{out}(s)}{E_{in}(s)} = -R_f C_i s \left[1 + \left(\frac{1+Ts}{A_0}\right)(1+R_f C_i s) \right]^{-1}$$

$$= -s\omega_T \left[s^2 + s\left(\frac{1}{T} + \frac{1}{R_f C_i}\right) + \frac{\omega_T}{R_f C_i} \right]^{-1} \quad (1/A_0 = 0, \quad \omega_T = A_0/T)$$

$$= -s\omega_T \left[\left(s + \left[\frac{1}{2T} + \frac{1}{2R_f C_i}\right]\right)^2 + \left(\frac{\omega_T}{R_f C_i} - \left[\frac{1}{2T} + \frac{1}{2R_f C_i}\right]^2\right) \right]^{-1}$$

(2.7.3)

To simplify this, the last squared term can be dropped since for typical values:

$$\frac{\omega_T}{R_f C_i} \gg \left[\frac{1}{2T} + \frac{1}{2R_f C_i}\right]^2 \tag{2.7.4}$$

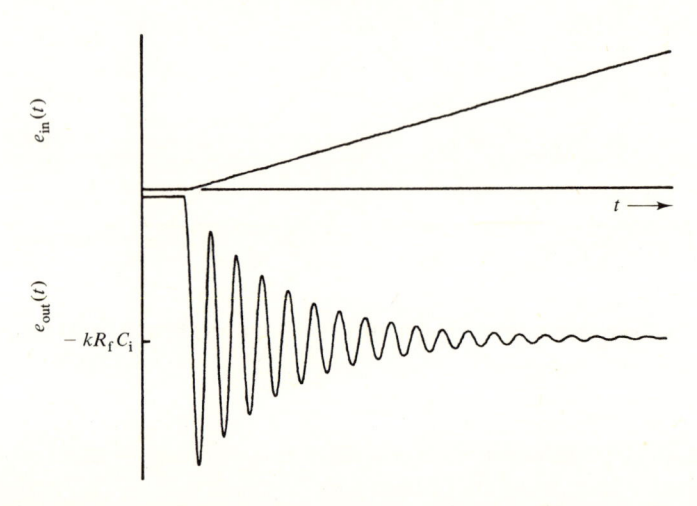

Fig. 2.7.3 Response of differentiator to input ramp (Courtesy Electronic Engineering)

For differentiation, the basic input of interest is a linear ramp:

$$e_{in}(t) = kt, \qquad E_{in}(s) = k/s^2 \tag{2.7.5}$$

for which the output of an ideal differentiator is a constant, proportional to k. Equation (2.7.3) then becomes:

$$E_{out}(s) = \frac{-k\omega_T}{s} \left[\left(s + \left[\frac{1}{2T} + \frac{1}{2R_f C_i}\right]\right)^2 + \frac{\omega_T}{R_f C_i} \right]^{-1} \tag{2.7.6}$$

Using standard transforms [l1, no. 31] and Eq. (2.7.4), this may be transformed to give:

$$e_{out}(t) = -kR_f C_i \left[1 - \exp\left(-\left[\frac{1}{2T} + \frac{1}{2R_f C_i}\right]t\right) \cdot \cos\left(\frac{\omega_T}{R_f C_i}\right)^{1/2} t \right] \tag{2.7.7}$$

which is shown in Fig. 2.7.3. The response is far from ideal.

The *gain* of the system is $-R_f C_i$ giving an eventual output, after the transient oscillation, of $-kR_f C_i$. The oscillation has a frequency ω and decay time τ_0:

$$\omega = \left(\frac{\omega_T}{R_f C_i}\right)^{1/2} = (\omega_T \omega_4)^{1/2} = \omega_3, \qquad \tau_0 = \left[\frac{1}{2T} + \frac{1}{2R_f C_i}\right]^{-1} \qquad (2.7.8)$$

where ω_3 is the frequency at the intersection of the differentiator characteristic $\omega R_f C_i$ and the amplifier response $A_0/\omega T$. This indicates the origin of these oscillations. As a result of the large phase shift, approaching 180°, in the region of ω_3, the system is on the verge of instability. The two characteristics do not intersect normal to one another but as shown in Fig. 2.7.4. These are actual measured responses using a type 741 amplifier; see Sec. 2.3(a).

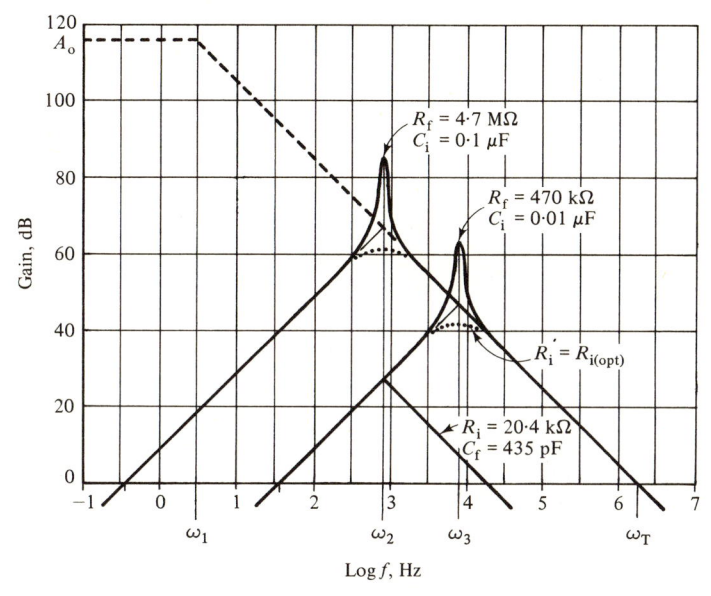

Fig. 2.7.4 Frequency response of practical operational differentiator (Courtesy Electronic Engineering)

As mentioned above the answer to this is the inclusion of R_i, as shown in Fig. 2.7.6(a). The transfer function is then:

$$\frac{E_{out}(s)}{E_{in}(s)} = \frac{-R_f C_i s}{1 + R_i C_i s}\left[1 + \left(\frac{1+Ts}{A_0}\right)\left(1 + \frac{R_f R_i s}{1 + R_i C_i s}\right)\right]^{-1}$$

$$\doteq -s\omega_T \left[s^2 + \frac{\omega_T R_i s}{R_f} + \frac{\omega_T}{R_f C_i}\right]^{-1} \qquad (2.7.9)$$

This second order response will be critically damped when the poles are equal; Sec. 1.11(a):

$$\left(\frac{\omega_T R_i}{R_f}\right)^2 = \frac{4\omega_T}{R_f C_i}, \quad \text{or} \quad R_{i(opt)} = \left(\frac{4R_f}{\omega_T C_i}\right)^{1/2} = \left(\frac{4TR_f}{A_0 C_i}\right)^{1/2} = \frac{2R_f}{A_3} \qquad (2.7.10)$$

and the response for this case is:

$$e_{out}(t) = -kR_fC_i[1-(1+\omega_3 t)\exp(-\omega_3 t)], \quad \omega_3 = \left(\frac{\omega_T}{R_fC_i}\right)^{1/2} \quad (2.7.11)$$

If $R_i < R_{i(opt)}$ the response is similar to Eq. (2.7.7), with the same oscillation frequency ω_3, but a decay time:

$$\tau_R = \frac{2R_f}{\omega_T R_i}, \quad \text{for} \quad \tau_R \ll \tau_0 \quad (2.7.12)$$

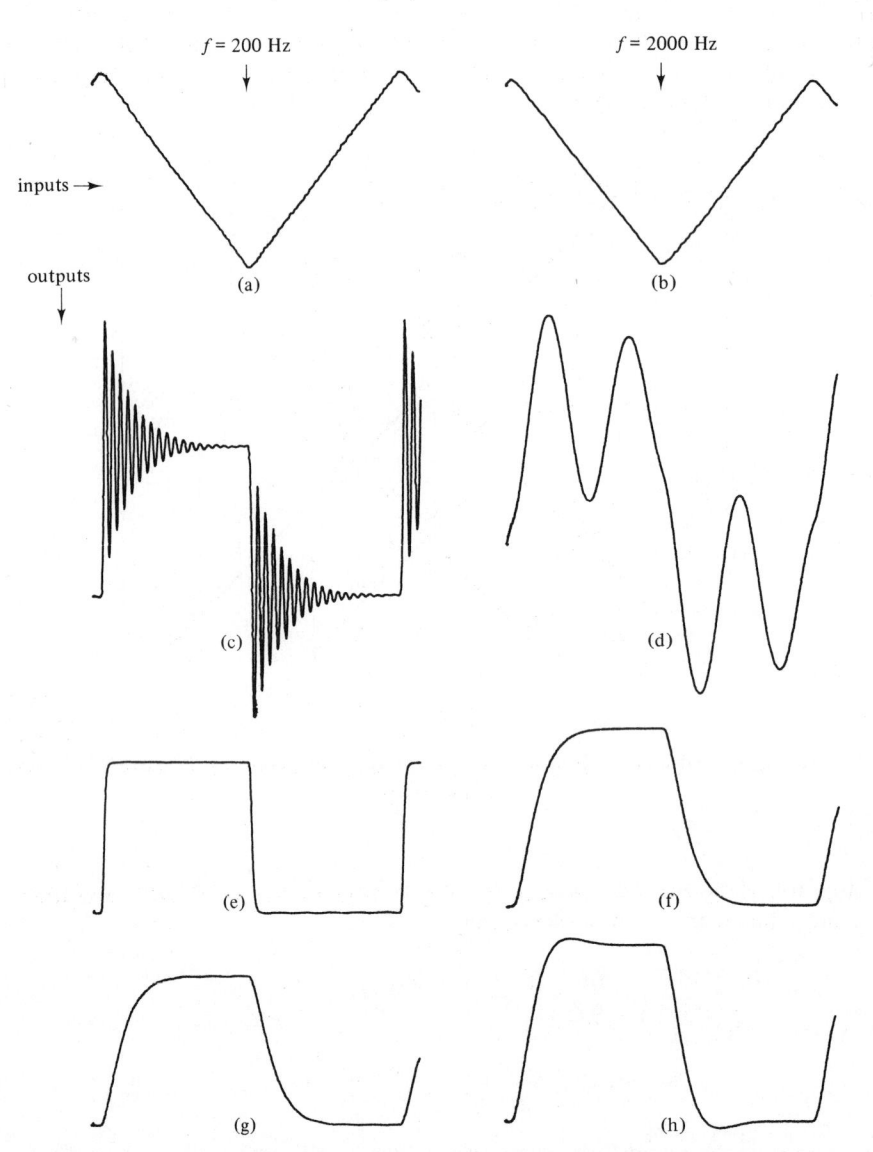

Fig. 2.7.5 Measured responses of a differentiator to a ramp input. (a), (b) inputs, (c), (d) $R_i = 151\ \Omega < R_{i(opt)}$, (e), (f) $R_i = 4070\ \Omega = R_{i(opt)}$, (g) $R_i = 20.4$ kΩ, $C_f = 435$ pF ($f_2 = 780$ Hz), (h) $R_i = 3030\ \Omega < R_{i(opt)}$ giving shorter risetime with small overshoot. Amplifier gain $A_0 = 6 \times 10^5$, transition frequency $f_T = 1.8$ MHz ($\omega_T = 11.3 \times 10^6$ s^{-1}), corner frequency $f_1 = 3$ Hz ($\omega_1 = 18.8$ s^{-1}), $R_f = 470$ kΩ, $C_i = 0.01$ μF. (Courtesy Electronic Engineering)

If a higher input impedance is required this can be achieved by increasing R_f and decreasing C_i, keeping $R_f C_i$ constant, since from Eq. (2.7.10) $R_{i(opt)}$ is increased proportionally.

The above conclusions have been tested experimentally, with the results shown in Fig. 2.7.5.

Addition of C_f in parallel with R_f gives the frequency response shown in Fig. 2.7.4 and the transfer function:

$$\frac{E_{out}(s)}{E_{in}(s)} = \frac{-R_f C_i s}{(1+R_i C_i s)(1+R_f C_f s)} \quad (2.7.13)$$

where the amplifier bandwidth is taken as effectively infinite if $\omega_2 \ll \omega_3$. Using the usual simplifying condition $R_i C_i = R_f C_f$ the response to the ramp input, Eq. (2.7.5), is identical to Eq. (2.7.11) except that ω_3 is replaced by $\omega_2 = 1/R_i C_i = 1/R_f C_f$. Since $\omega_2 < \omega_3$ the risetime will be degraded relative to Eq. (2.7.11).

A differentiating circuit that does not include an actual differentiator has been devised [a1]. Consider the damped differentiator shown in Fig. 2.7.6(a).

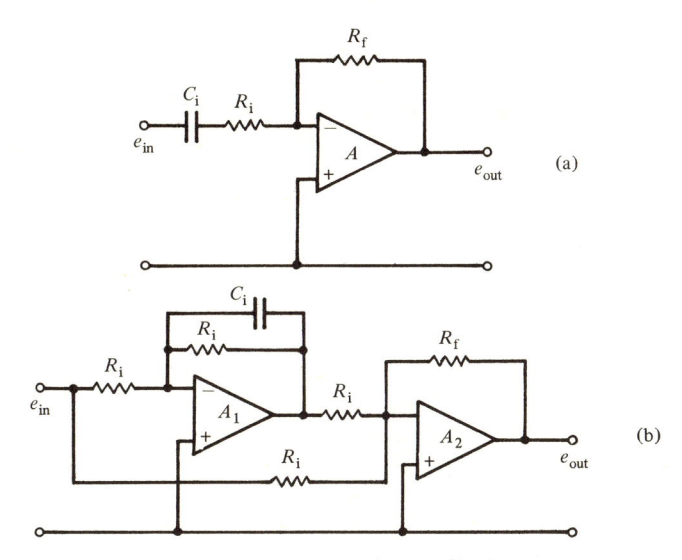

Fig. 2.7.6 (a) Damped differentiator circuit, (b) alternative realization

The transfer function is readily found to be:

$$\frac{E_{out}(s)}{E_{in}(s)} = \frac{-R_f C_i s}{1+R_i C_i s} = \frac{R_f}{R_i}\left[\frac{1}{(1+R_i C_i s)} - 1\right] \quad (2.7.14)$$

The form of this function suggests that it may be realized as the difference of two parts, the first a simple lag or leaky integrator (Fig. 2.6.8) and the second an amplifier. This is shown in Fig. 2.7.6(b). The transfer function of the first stage is $-1/(1+R_i C_i s)$ which is then multiplied by that of the second, $-R_f/R_i$, to give the first term in Eq. (2.7.14). The second term $-R_f/R_i$ is given by the bypass direct to the second stage. It is claimed that this circuit results in improved performance with lower noise since it uses a smoothing *integrator*.

Although this is an interesting example of the manipulation of a transfer function, there are several pitfalls. Even ignoring the direct omission of the amplifier response, there are several points not considered. The zero response at d.c. is obtained by the mutual cancellation of the two signals fed to A_2. If the resistors are not closely proportioned, distorted output results. Secondly, to adjust the damping, four resistors must be changed. Thirdly, the factor 2 improvement in noise may be accounted for by the smaller bandwidth of two amplifiers in series.

2.8 Charge amplifier

So far we have considered resistive and both orientations of R, C feedback elements. The next step is to make both elements capacitive (Fig. 2.8.1).

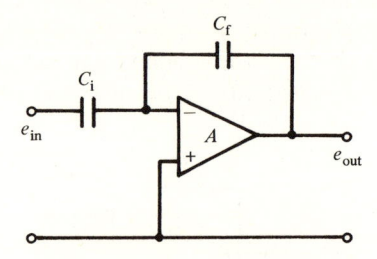

Fig. 2.8.1 Charge amplifier

The transfer function can easily be written down by inspection:

$$\frac{E_{out}}{E_{in}} = \frac{-C_i}{C_f} \qquad (2.8.1)$$

This is, in effect, the same relation as was obtained for resistive elements, Eq. (2.2.4), with gains independent of frequency (apparently down to zero frequency) and no phase shift (all within the A bandwidth, of course). The question arises, why use capacitive rather than resistive elements? This has been considered by Holbrook [d1] who makes the following points:

(i) Noise generated in an input resistor, which will be amplified by the open-loop gain A, is eliminated by using the purely reactive capacitor (but see [h1]).
(ii) Very large input impedances can be realized without requiring unreasonably high feedback resistors, which tend to be rather unstable. Stray capacity across R_f also seriously limits the bandwidth.

The use of the circuit of Fig. 2.8.1 thus appears to have several advantages, but our intuition should tell us that one of the apparent claims, operation down to zero frequency, cannot be true. This arises because of the approximations made in obtaining Eq. (2.8.1). The limiting factors are that the amplifier has neither infinite input impedance nor infinite gain. The transfer impedance in this case, Fig. 2.8.2, may be written down using Eq. (2.2.4), by putting $R_i \to 1/C_i s$ and $R_f \to 1/C_f s$:

$$\frac{E_{out}(s)}{E_{in}(s)} = \frac{-C_i}{C_f} \left[\frac{C_i}{AC_f} + \frac{1}{AR_d C_f s} + \frac{1}{A} + 1 \right]^{-1} \qquad (2.8.2)$$

Then, at low frequencies ($s \to 0$) and A reasonably large:

$$\frac{E_{out}(s)}{E_{in}(s)} \doteq \frac{-C_i}{C_f}\left[\frac{1}{AR_dC_fs}+1\right]^{-1} \qquad (2.8.3)$$

As we would expect, the gain goes to zero at zero frequency. The low frequency corner will occur when from Eq. (2.8.3):

$$1/AR_dC_fs = 1 \quad \text{or} \quad AR_dC_fs = 1 \qquad (2.8.4)$$

In the example given by Holbrook [d1, p. 155] we have $C_i = C_f = 10$ pF (i.e., unity closed-loop gain), $R_d = 22$ MΩ, $A = 60$ which would give a low frequency corner at 12 Hz and an input impedance at this frequency of 1600 MΩ! For common IC

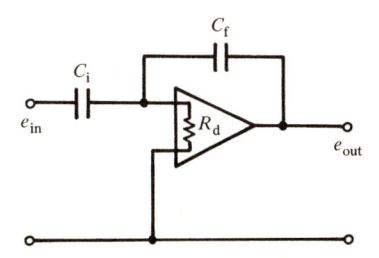

Fig. 2.8.2 Charge amplifier with finite input impedance

operational amplifiers, with $A = 10^5$ and $R_d = 1$ MΩ, the corresponding frequency would be 0·16 Hz.

The main interest in this type of amplifier has been in applications with certain types of electrical transducer that generate charge rather than voltage outputs. Examples of these are capacitor microphones, piezoelectric transducers, and semiconductor nuclear particle detectors. The latter consist of reverse biased *P–N* junctions, often of considerable junction width up to centimetres, in which nuclear particles or gamma rays produce electron–hole pairs which are separated by the junction potential gradient, so that a certain charge appears on the junction capacity C_D. The problem is that C_D is not fixed or stable, depending on the junction width and hence the applied voltage. Thus, we cannot take the voltage produced as a measure of the energy of the incident radiation; we need a system for recovering the charge independently of the capacity. The amplifier we have been discussing above will perform this function, and hence it is called a charge amplifier. The operation may be considered in two ways.

In Fig. 2.8.3 we have a current generator i with the capacity C_D in parallel, together representing the detector. On the assumption of a virtual ground, there will be no

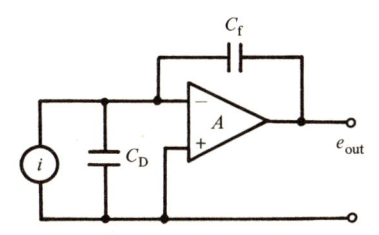

Fig. 2.8.3 Charge amplifier with current source

voltage across C_D and hence no current flowing through it, so we have a simple current input integrator:

$$i = -C_f \cdot \frac{de_{out}}{dt}, \quad \text{or} \quad e_{out} = \frac{-1}{C_f} \int i \, dt = \frac{-Q}{C_f} \tag{2.8.5}$$

where, for the short current pulse due to the passage of the incident particle, the charge Q is equal to the integrated current.

An alternative view, Fig. 2.8.4, looking more like the earlier arrangement Fig. 2.8.1, shows the Thévenin equivalent circuit of the detector (see Sec. 1.2).

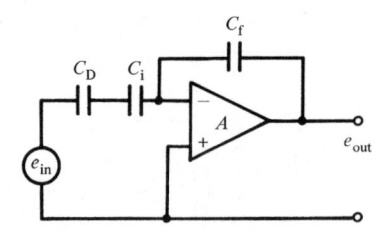

Fig. 2.8.4 Charge amplifier with voltage source

If $C_i \gg C_D$ (C_i may be required to isolate the amplifier from the detector bias voltage), then the series combination of C_i and C_D is effectively equal to C_D. From Eq. (2.8.1) the output is:

$$e_{out} = \frac{-C_D}{C_f} e_{in} = \frac{-C_D}{C_f} \frac{i}{C_D s} = \frac{-1}{C_f} \int i \, dt = \frac{-Q}{C_f} \tag{2.8.6}$$

as before. The output is thus proportional to the total charge Q and independent of the detector capacity C_D, or for that matter of any capacity of the connecting cables, etc., in parallel with C_D. Thus, long cables will not degrade the performance. The gain of the system can simply be set by choice of C_f. In practice, some resistance is connected across C_f to allow the charge Q to decay between pulses [a1, b1, c1, e1, f1, g1].

2.9 IC amplifier characteristics

As mentioned before amplifiers are near perfect but always have limitations of one sort or another. This section is concerned with identifying and defining the more important of these limitations and, where possible, suggesting some methods of alleviating the effects. Examination of the data sheet for any fully specified integrated microcircuit, reveals the tremendous amount and range of information presented. For example, for the popular 741 operational amplifier the data sheet gives numerical limits for 39 different characteristics and 25 graphs containing a total of 32 curves. A knowledge of the definition, meaning, and origin of the various characteristics is necessary before this information can be useful in practice.

First, we group together a number of parameters for which *absolute maximum* values are quoted. The term absolute maximum does *not* mean a maximum value at which the system may be designed to operate. It does mean that these values *must not* be exceeded under *any* circumstances, otherwise the IC circuit function may be impaired. Of course, there is a spread of limiting values for some particular parameter if measurements are made on a number of units, but that well-known and universal law will almost guarantee that your unit only just meets the specification! These maxima, therefore, must never be exceeded and, in general, systems should be designed to work well within these values.

The two main limitations concern voltage and temperature. Exceeding limits for the former results in instant and catastrophic damage, but for the latter a rather longer time scale is involved which often allows rectification of the fault before damage occurs. For moderate excess the effects may be a progressive degradation of performance rather than catastrophic failure [B1, z1, x1, r1, n1, g1, f1, G1].

2.9(a) *Supply voltage*

The absolute maximum voltages that may be applied to the IC without causing damage. The positive and negative values are commonly the same, but in some cases are different. It is important that the wrong polarity is not applied as this will almost certainly destroy the IC; see Sec. 2.9(x).

2.9(b) *Common-mode input voltage*

The absolute maximum input voltage that may be applied between ground and the two inputs moving effectively together, without causing damage. This rating is in some cases dependent on the actual supply voltages.

2.9(c) *Differential input voltage*

The absolute maximum voltage that may be applied between inputs without causing damage. Early IC's generally have values of ± 5 volt, whereas more recent types allow values up to the supply voltages.

2.9(d) *Internal power dissipation*

The absolute maximum internal power that may be dissipated at a specified ambient temperature without causing damage. This rating is derated linearly at a given rate for temperatures above that specified, until zero dissipation is reached at the maximum temperature. The dissipation will depend on supply voltages and output load.

2.9(e) *Output short circuit duration*

The absolute maximum time for which the output may be shorted to ground, or either supply line, without causing damage. This condition can result in excessive currents and hence excessive internal power dissipation. In breadboard situations a suitable resistance can be connected in series with the IC output to protect against accidents. More recent types of IC have built-in protection circuits that limit the short-circuit current so that the output may be shorted indefinitely [A1].

2.9(f) *Temperature*

There are several temperature limits, storage, operating, and lead soldering, that must be observed. For most IC's the storage temperature limits are $-65°C$ to $+150°C$, and the lead soldering temperature 300°C for a specified time. The operating ambient temperature is usually specified in two ranges: 0°C to 70°C for general use, and −55°C to 125°C for special use (at substantially increased cost). For most laboratory uses the 0°C to 70°C range is quite satisfactory. These two ranges specify the temperature limits within which certain parameters are guaranteed to lie within stated limits, rather than limiting operating temperatures, which are given by the storage temperature range.

2.9(g) *Open-loop voltage gain $A(s)$, A_0*

This is defined as the ratio of the change in output voltage to the change in input voltage causing it. Reference is made to changes in voltage to exclude any offset voltages. As gain decreases with increase in frequency, A_0 is defined at zero frequency.

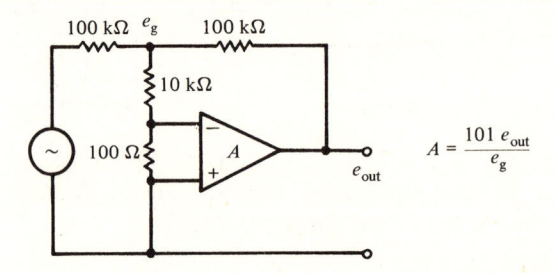

Fig. 2.9.1 Measurement of open-loop gain A_0 of amplifier

The variation of $A(s)$ is usually shown graphically, and commonly varies from about 10^5 or 10^6 at zero frequency to unity at a frequency of a few MHz. The gain also has a small dependence on supply voltage and, because of finite output impedance, the gain has a dependence on load resistance, so that the supply voltage and load resistance under which the gain was measured, are always specified. The gain is often specified in dB, e.g., $10^5 = 100$ dB. Owing to the high gains involved direct measurement of A_0 and $A(s)$ presents difficulties. To overcome these, the circuit shown in Fig. 2.9.1 may be used. Note that e_g must be measured by means of a high impedance meter [h1].

2.9(h) *Output voltage swing*

The maximum peak output swing, referred to zero, that can be obtained without clipping. This is a function of output load (maximum output current), frequency (maximum slewing rate, see Sec. 2.9(p)) and supply voltage.

2.9(i) *Common-mode rejection ratio (CMRR)*

Common-mode refers to equal voltages of the same sense applied to both inputs simultaneously, or a single voltage applied to the two inputs tied together. For a true differential amplifier there will be no change in output if there is no difference between the inputs. For practical amplifiers there will always be some change, and the CMRR is a specification of the ratio of the applied d.c. common-mode voltage

V_{cm} to the effective change in differential input voltage:

$$\text{CMRR} = \frac{V_{cm}}{e_{out(cm)}/A_0} = \frac{V_{cm}A_0}{e_{out(cm)}} \qquad (2.9.1)$$

This ratio is generally in the range of 10^4 to 10^5 (80 to 100 dB), but will decrease for large V_{cm}, and with increase in frequency [d1, e1, k1, l1, y1].

2.9(j) *Latch-up*

This is a condition that can occur if large positive (for *NPN* input transistors) signals or transients are applied to the inputs. In this situation, the input transistor will saturate and the collector will move in the same sense as the base, rather than in the opposite sense in the normal mode of operation. The amplifier will then no longer be inverting, so that the feedback is now positive. The circuit will act like a bistable circuit and latch-up in that state, if it is possible for the feedback to maintain the input transistor in saturation when the input signal is removed. The voltage follower is particularly prone to this condition, since the output is fed directly back to the input (Sec. 2.5). Inclusion of a feedback resistor can prevent this by limiting the feedback current, and has little effect on the normal operation because of the high input impedance R_d. More recent operational amplifiers are designed so that latch-up cannot occur.

2.9(k) *Input resistance R_d (capacity C_d)*

The resistance (capacity) looking into either input terminal with the other grounded. The input resistance may be measured using the circuit shown in Fig. 2.9.2. e_g and e_d must be measured by a high impedance meter [h1].

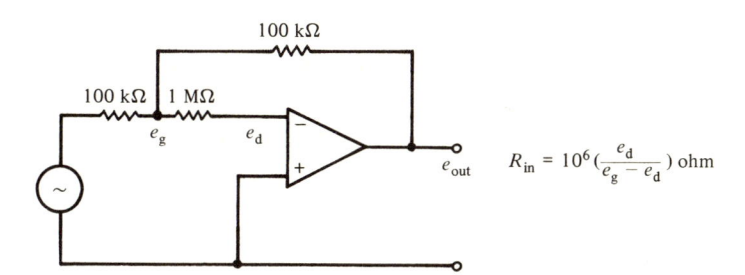

Fig. 2.9.2 Measurement of input resistance R_d of amplifier

Common-mode input impedance, R_{cm}, is the impedance between each input and ground or power supply common, i.e., the common supply line of the two power supplies, generally used for operational amplifiers, which may or may not be connected to system ground.

Note that it is a function of both temperature and common-mode voltage.

2.9(l) *Output resistance*

The resistance seen looking back into the output terminal with the output at zero. The range is usually from tens to hundreds of ohms.

2.9(m) *Supply voltage rejection ratio*

The ratio of the change in input voltage to the change in supply voltage producing it. A change in one of the supply voltages will produce a certain change in output voltage. Knowing the amplifier gain, this change can be referred to the input. Equal changes in both supplies will produce less effect than the same change in only one. The ratio is commonly of the order of 100 μV/V, but will vary with frequency.

2.9(n) *Bandwidth*

This is the standard 3 dB down bandwidth (Sec. 1.4) measured for small signals, so that there is no overloading in the amplifier. The value will usually be modest for open-loop conditions, but increases with increasing loop-gain, until the small-signal unity-gain frequency, f_T, is reached.

2.9(o) *Unity-gain small-signal frequency*

This is the frequency, f_T, at which the small-signal open-loop gain becomes unity (0 dB) (Fig. 2.4.2). For 6 dB/octave roll-off amplifiers, f_T is also numerically equal to the gain-bandwidth product, i.e., for a gain of 10, say, the bandwidth will be $f_T/10$. This is not true for amplifiers with different roll-offs.

2.9(p) *Large-signal bandwidth and slewing rate*

An amplifier will not respond to large signal changes as fast as the small-signal bandwidth would indicate. Circuit limitations impose a maximum rate at which internal and external capacities can be charged. This limitation is expressed as a maximum slewing rate, i.e., the maximum rate at which the output voltage can change in response to a step input. Since the feedback cannot instantly match the input signal, the 'virtual ground' is temporarily shifted from ground potential, so that amplifier overload occurs. The clipped signal is integrated by compensation capacitors, giving a voltage changing at a fixed rate.

The maximum slewing rate can be related to the maximum frequency and amplitude of sine wave output that can be delivered without distortion. For a sine wave:

$$E = E_0 \sin 2\pi ft, \qquad \frac{dE}{dt} = 2\pi f E_0 \cos 2\pi ft \qquad (2.9.2)$$

The rate of change dE/dt is a maximum when the cosine term is a maximum, i.e., $=1$, and equating this rate to the maximum slewing rate S gives:

$$(fE_0)_{max} = S/2\pi \qquad (2.9.3)$$

Thus, for a given peak amplitude there is a maximum frequency. This does not hold at low frequencies because of maximum output voltage swing, nor at high frequencies as a result of the roll-off in open-loop frequency response.

Transient response is closely related to bandwidth. For 6 dB/octave roll-offs the simple relation (Sec. 1.4):

$$\text{risetime (10 to 90 per cent)} = 0{\cdot}35/\text{bandwidth} \qquad (2.9.4)$$

holds, but this is not the optimum roll-off for best transient response. The detailed shape of the frequency response, together with the corresponding phase shifts, affects not only the rise time but overshoot and settling time. The frequency response appropriate to the signal amplitude must of course be used. For example, Fig. 2.9.3 shows the response to be expected for a fast square pulse input [c1, s1, t1, u1].

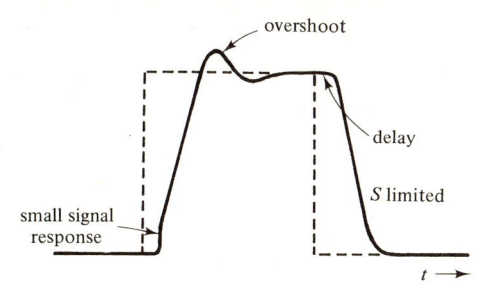

Fig. 2.9.3 Pulse response of amplifier

2.9(q) *Bias current*, i_b

Since the gain of the input transistors is not infinite some current must flow in the input (base) lead to support the collector current. These currents, flowing through any impedances connected to the input terminals, give voltages that are amplified to produce an output offset voltage. The bias current is defined as the current required, at the input, to zero the output, under specified conditions, and assuming infinite source impedance.

2.9(r) *Offset voltage*, e_{os}

If the inputs are shorted or grounded it is found that there still exists an output offset. This is, for example, due to lack of symmetry in the input stage leading to differences in V_{be} characteristics. The offset voltage is defined as the voltage required, at the input, to zero the amplifier output assuming zero source impedance.

2.9(s) *Equivalent offset circuit for single-ended amplifier*

In order to determine the effects of bias current and offset voltage, it is convenient to derive an equivalent circuit. For a single-ended amplifier this is shown in Fig. 2.9.4.

The amplifier, A, now has infinite input resistance and zero offset, but finite gain and bandwidth. The offsets are represented by the voltage and current generators, e_{os} and i_b. The amplitude of these generators are dependent not only on manufacturing tolerances, etc., which give some fixed values I_b, E_{os} for given conditions, but also on

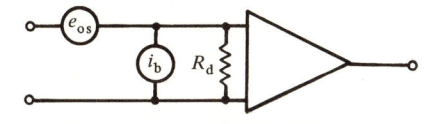

Fig. 2.9.4 Bias current and offset voltage of IC amplifier

external factors such as temperature, power supply variation, and time. Thus, any offset can be written in the general form:

$$x = X + \frac{\partial x}{\partial T} dT + \frac{\partial x}{\partial V_+} dV_+ + \frac{\partial x}{\partial V_-} dV_- + \frac{\partial x}{\partial t} dt \qquad (2.9.5)$$

The rates of change $\partial x/\partial$ will not be constants over a large range of variation, so that some average value is quoted. In comparing various treatments of the effects of offsets, the equivalent circuit model being used should be checked, as different models may be used. [b1, D1, E1, m1, o1, p1, q1, w1. These references also apply to Secs. 2.9(t), (u), (v).]

2.9(t) *Input offset current, i_{os}*

In differential IC amplifiers the two bias currents i_{b+}, i_{b-}, are well matched and, if the effective impedances seen from the inputs are equal, the output offsets will largely cancel. It is, thus, the difference in the two bias currents—the input offset current i_{os}—that is often of more interest. This difference is measured with the amplifier output at zero volts.

It is necessary here to insert a word of warning. Manufacturers of discrete component amplifiers have described what we have defined as bias current as offset current, and what is here called offset current as difference offset current. This is most unfortunate and can cause great confusion so, once again, check carefully before making any comparisons.

2.9(u) *Equivalent input generator circuit for offsets*

In using the measured values of the offsets it is most convenient to refer these to the actual input where the external signal is applied. Consider the example of the standard inverting operational amplifier (Fig. 2.9.5).

We wish to determine the magnitudes of the equivalent input voltage generators, e_{ib} and e_{eo}, that give the same e_{out} as the offset generators shown in Fig. 2.9.4. The effect of these relative to the actual applied signal, e_{in}, can then readily be seen. Since we have a virtual ground the two generators can be considered separately. The bias current, i_b, is defined for infinite source impedance ($R_i = \infty$) and so flows only in R_f. The output voltage due to this is simply:

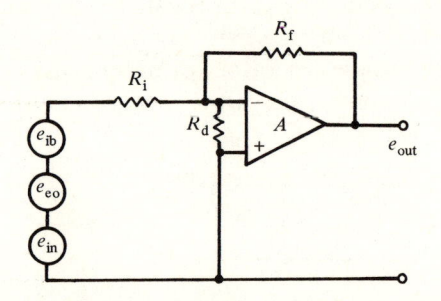

$$e_{out}(i_b) = i_b R_f \qquad (2.9.6)$$

Fig. 2.9.5 Equivalent input generators for offsets

remembering the properties of the virtual ground. The value of e_{ib} required in Fig. 2.9.5 to give the same output as in Eq. (2.9.6) is:

$$e_{ib}(R_f/R_i) = i_b R_f, \quad \text{or} \quad e_{ib} = i_b R_i \qquad (2.9.7)$$

Since e_{os} is inside the feedback loop, the output voltage due to this is given by (see Eq. (2.2.11)):

$$e_{out}(e_0) = e_{os}(R_i + R_f)/R_i \qquad (2.9.8)$$

The value of e_{eo} that gives the same output is:

$$e_{eo} R_f/R_i = e_{os}(R_i + R_f)/R_i$$

or
$$e_{eo} = e_{os}(R_i + R_f)/R_f \qquad (2.9.9)$$

Note that since the offsets can be of either sign this is not specified in the data sheet, and the sign of the gain has been ignored above.

The results indicate that the offsets are independent of R_d, as we should expect since i_b and e_{os} are measured with R_d included. This is not quite correct, since we have used the approximate operational gain formula rather than Eq. (2.2.5). However, since this will affect the signal equally, this is of little consequence. The equivalent input offset generators do depend on the configuration being considered, i.e., the single-ended inverting amplifier here. In this case, the relative size of the voltage and current offset depends on R_i, and high input impedance ($=R_i$) can only be obtained at the expense of increased offset. e_{eo} varies from e_{os} for high gain ($R_f \gg R_i$) to $2e_{os}$ for unity gain ($R_f = R_i$).

2.9(v) *Differential amplifier offset equivalent circuit*

The balanced differential input arrangement of most IC operational amplifiers allows a significant reduction in output offset. To see how this may be achieved, consider the equivalent offset circuit Fig. 2.9.6.

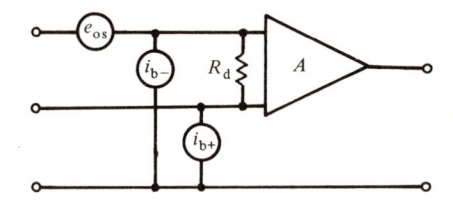

Fig. 2.9.6 Differential amplifier offset equivalent circuit

If the offsets are referred to the input, we have the input equivalent offset circuits, Fig. 2.9.7.

For e_{os} and i_{b-} the results are the same as before, i.e., Eqs. (2.9.9) and (2.9.7); while for i_{b+} the output is:

$$e_{out+} = i_{b+} R_c (R_i + R_f)/R_i$$

so that
$$e_{ib+} R_f/R_i = i_{b+} R_c (R_i + R_f)/R_i$$

or
$$e_{ib+} = i_{b+} R_c (R_i + R_f)/R_f \qquad (2.9.10)$$

Since i_{b+} and i_{b-} both flow in the same sense (i.e., into or out of the amplifier) and are amplified in the opposite sense, then if R_c is chosen to be equal to R_i and R_f in parallel:

$$R_c = R_i R_f/(R_i + R_f) \qquad (2.9.11)$$

the nett input current-offset generator is:

$$e_{io} = e_{ib-} - e_{ib+} = R_i(i_{b-} - i_{b+}) = R_i i_{os} \qquad (2.9.12)$$

The offset now depends on the offset current rather than the bias current, which may be 3 to 5 times greater. In practice, it is usual to bypass R_c with a capacitor, to reduce unwanted pickup into the non-inverting input (+).

The technique used above for referring offsets to the input can be applied to other configurations, e.g., non-inverting amplifier, integrator, etc. (see, for example, Sec. 2.6).

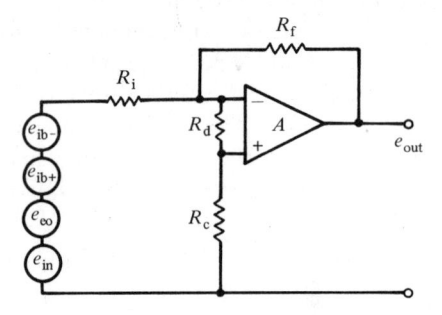

Fig. 2.9.7 Equivalent input generators for differential circuit

2.9(w) *Offset balancing*

If it is desired that offsets be reduced to zero, the technique to be used to balance these out depends on the circuit configuration and impedances. Some IC's provide specific circuit points, other than the inputs, for balancing purposes, but these are intended to cope with limited and mainly voltage offsets. If there is a large current offset, for example due to a high input resistance, then the large imbalance in the input stage circuit due to the external balance potentiometer can degrade the temperature drift performance.

For an inverting amplifier with low source resistance ($R_i \leqslant 10$ kΩ say) the arrangement of Fig. 2.9.8 can be used for offset current or voltage.

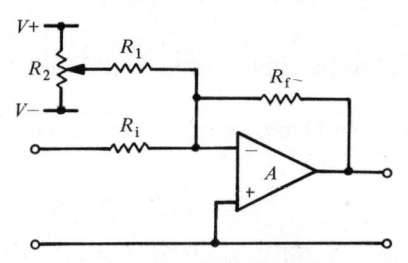

Fig. 2.9.8 Offset balancing circuit for inverting circuit with low source resistance (Reproduced by courtesy National Semiconductor)

If $R_i \gg 10$ kΩ, the value of R_1 exceeds normally available resistances and it is easier to balance using the (+) input.

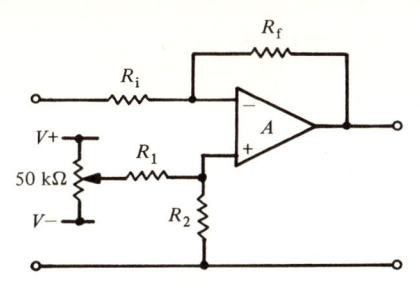

Fig. 2.9.9 Offset balancing circuit for inverting circuit with high source resistance (Reproduced by courtesy National Semiconductor)

For the non-inverting amplifier it is often necessary to maintain the high input resistance, so that the balancing must be done via the (−) input only, Fig. 2.9.10.

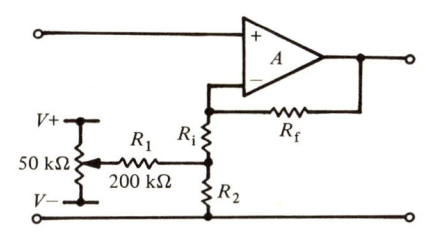

Fig. 2.9.10 Offset balancing circuit for non-inverting amplifier (Reproduced by courtesy National Semiconductor)

This can be adapted for the voltage follower, Fig. 2.9.11.

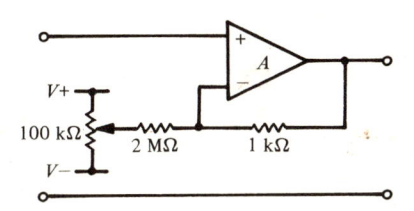

Fig. 2.9.11 Offset balancing circuit for voltage follower (Reproduced by courtesy National Semiconductor)

Differential amplifiers usually require a good CMRR, and this can be reduced by an unsuitable balance circuit. The arrangement shown in Fig. 2.9.12 has a negligible effect on this ratio.

R_3 is of such a value that the variation of the effective value of R_2 (i.e., R_2 in parallel with R_3 and the potentiometer output resistance) due to moving the potentiometer tap, does not significantly reduce the CMRR below the value set by the amplifier itself [a1, F1].

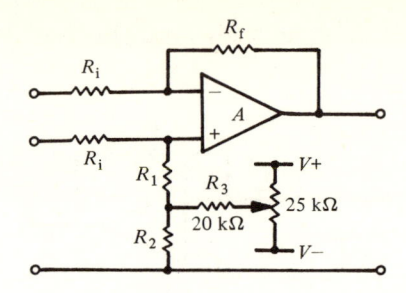

Fig. 2.9.12 Offset balancing circuit for differential amplifier (Reproduced by courtesy National Semiconductor)

2.9(x) *Protection circuits*

It is always wise to give some thought to the desirability of protection circuits for the IC. For example, in breadboard situations application of incorrect supply polarities can occur with disastrous effects. To obviate this, the supplies may be connected to the IC through a diode which will protect the unit if the polarities are reversed. Note that the diodes will drop the supply voltages by about 0·6 volt. When IC's are being used in circuits where high voltages are present then, as a result of a fault in some component, these may appear at unexpected places and destroy the IC. External inputs and outputs are also potential sources of disaster. As a result of ignorance,

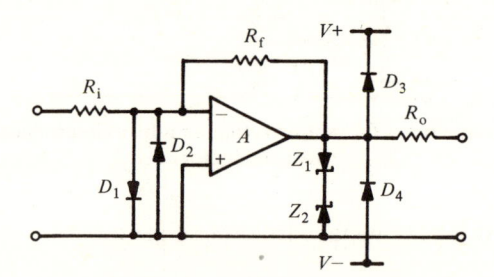

Fig. 2.9.13 Amplifier protection

accident, or breakdown, excessive voltages can be applied. It cannot be too strongly emphasized that the voltage breakdown is an effectively instantaneous phenomenon and there is no time in which to correct the fault: in a few nanoseconds it's all over bar the shouting! Protection measures can often be provided with no effect or minimal effect on the circuit operation.

For example, for an operational amplifier, the virtual ground will always be within a few millivolts of ground potential. If two diodes are connected from this point to ground (Fig. 2.9.13) then, since they do not sensibly conduct until the potential reaches several hundred millivolts, they will have little effect on the circuit except under fault conditions, when excessive input voltage will be dropped across R_i. The diodes, however, will add a small capacity at the virtual ground.

Output protection is not so simple, as there is normally no convenient resistor, so one must be added. However, since low output impedance is usually required, the additional resistor will degrade performance, and so must be chosen to be no larger than really necessary. Two arrangements are illustrated in Fig. 2.9.13. The zener diode voltages are chosen to be a little larger than the required output voltage swing. Alternatively, the diodes $D_{3,4}$ will limit the output swing to the supply voltages, $\pm V$ [v1, A1, H1].

References section 2.1: Operational amplifiers introduction

a1 Holbrook J G: Laplace Transforms for Electronic Engineers 2nd Ed.; Pergamon 1966.
b1 RCA: Linear Integrated Circuits; RCA Technical Series IC-42, 1970.
c1 Demrow R: Evolution for Operational Amplifier to Data Amplifier; Analog Devices 1968.
d1 Smith J I: Modern Operational Circuit Design; Wiley-Interscience 1971.
e1 Korn G A, Korn T M: Electronic Analog and Hybrid Computers; McGraw-Hill 1964.
f1 Beneteau P J, Pullen K A: Operational Amplifiers, Chapter 19 of Shea R F (Ed) Amplifier Handbook; McGraw-Hill 1966.
g1 Martin A G, Stephenson F W: Linear Microelectronic Systems; Macmillan 1973.
h1 Millman J, Halkias C C: Integrated Electronics: Analog and Digital Circuits and Systems; McGraw-Hill 1972.
i1 RCA: Application Notes, Linear Integrated Circuits and MOS Devices; RCA Solid State Databook Series SSD-202, 1972.
j1 Solomon J E: The Monolithic Op Amp: A Tutorial Study; IEEE J SC-9, 314–332, 1974.
k1 Roberge J K: Operational Amplifiers. Theory and Practice; Wiley 1975.
l1 Grebene A B: Analog Integrated Circuit Design; Van Nostrand Reinhold 1972.
m1 Philbrick/Nexus: Applications Manual for Operational Amplifiers; Philbrick/Nexus Research 1968.
n1 Bhola S: Transitron Operational Amplifiers and Their Applications; Transitron Application Report MD/AP4–68.
o1 Gray J O, Jackson M J: Monolithic Amplifiers as Operational Elements; Electronic Eng. 41, May 1969, 34–38.
p1 Bhola S K: Monolithic Operational Amplifier as a Computing Element; Transitron Application Report MD/AP-2-68.
q1 SGS-Fairchild: µA702 Circuit Design Ideas; SGS-Fairchild Application Report AR 140, Sep. 1965.
r1 Widlar R J: Optimum Utilization of Linear Microcircuits; SGS-Fairchild Application Report AR 150, May 1966.
s1 English M: Some Applications of the µA741 Operational Amplifier; Fairchild Application Report.
t1 Huehne K: A Definitive Look at Operational Amplifiers; Electronic Equipment News June 1972, 59–62.
u1 National Semiconductor: Linear Applications; National Semiconductor Handbook Feb. 1972.
v1 Hoenig S A, Payne F L: How to Build and Use Electronic Devices Without Frustration, Panic, Mountains of Money, or an Engineering Degree; Little, Brown & Co. 1973.
w1 SGS-Fairchild: The Application of Linear Microcircuits; SGS-Fairchild Handbook Aug. 1967.
x1 Clayton G B: Operational Amplifiers; Butterworths 1971.
y1 Graeme J G: Applications of Operational Amplifiers: Third Generation Techniques; McGraw-Hill 1973.
z1 Tobey G E, Graeme J G, Huelsman L P: Operational Amplifiers Design and Applications; McGraw-Hill 1971.

References section 2.2: The ideal amplifier and the virtual ground

a1 Mathews P J D: Allow for Phase Shift in Feedback Error Calculations; Electronic Eng. 43, 75, 1971.
b1 Marzetta L A: Misuse of Exact Gain Formula; Analog Dialogue 2, No.1, 6, 1968.
c1 Edwin G, Roddam T: Principles of Feedback Design; Iliffe Books 1964.

d1 Thomason J G: Linear Feedback Analysis; Pergamon 1955.
e1 DeRoy B E: Automatic Control Theory; Wiley 1966.
f1 RCA: Linear Integrated Circuits; RCA Technical Series IC-41, 1967.
g1 Smith L, Sheingold D H: Noise and Operational Amplifier Circuits; Analog Dialogue 3, No.1, March 1969, 1, 5–16.
h1 Smith J I: Modern Operational Circuit Design; Wiley-Interscience 1971.
i1 Stata R: Operational Amplifiers. Part I—Principles of Operation, Part II—Inverting, Non-Inverting and Differential Configurations, Part IV—Offset and Drift in Operational Amplifiers; Analog Devices 1965.
j1 D'Alton L B: Phase Shift in Feedback Error Calculations; Electronic Eng. 43, 68, 1971.
k1 Pridham G J: Analysis of Feedback Amplifiers; Electronic Eng. 39, 436–439, 1967.
l1 David E: Applied Principles—Operational Amplifiers; Electronic Eng. 43, Jan. 1971, 48–51.
m1 Mullard: An Introduction to Operational Amplifiers; Mullard Application Note TP1060, Feb. 1969.
n1 Osborne R J: Comprehensive Analysis of Operational Amplifiers; Electron 25 Jan. 1973, 33, 35, 36.
o1 Union Carbide: Operational Amplifier Static Gain Errors Analysis and Nomographs; Union Carbide Application Note AN-7, Dec. 1966.
p1 Weden C V: Review of Operational Amplifier Principles; Fairchild Application Bulletin Dec. 1968.
q1 Faulkner E A: The Design of Low-Noise Audio Frequency Amplifiers; Radio Electronic Engnr. 36, 17–30, 1968.
r1 Philbrick/Nexus: Applications Manual for Operational Amplifiers; Philbrick/Nexus Research 1968.
s1 Faulkner E A: Principles of Linear Circuits; Chapman and Hall 1966.
t1 RCA: Integrated-Circuit Operational Amplifiers; RCA Application Note ICAN-5290.
u1 Keller J P: Linear IC's: Part 3 Differential Amplifiers at Work; Electronics 18 Sep. 1967, 96–105.
v1 Leeds M B: Linear IC's: Part 4 Inside the Operational Amplifier; Electronics 16 Oct. 1967, 86–91.

References section 2.3: Classes of operational amplifier

a1 Goldberg E A: Stabilization of Wideband Amplifiers for Zero and Gain; RCA Review 11, 296–300, 1950.
b1 Hoell P C: Low-Level DC Amplifier with Whole-Loop Feedback; Rev. Sci. Instrum. 29, 1120–1124, 1958.
c1 Conti M, Cini C: Low Noise Parametric Preamplifier for Electroencephalography; SGS-Fairchild Application Report AR160.
d1 Smith L R: A Parametric Operational Amplifier; Analog Dialogue 1, No.2, June 1967, 6–7.
e1 Analog Devices: New Varactor Bridge Op-Amps Models 302, 303; Analog Dialogue 1, No.3, Sep. 1967, 9–14.
f1 Conti M: The Amplification of DC Signals (Italian); Alta Frequenze 36, 284–300, 1967.
g1 Conti M, Malosti D, Novelli P: Parametric DC Amplifier (Italian); Alta Frequenze 35, 965–977, 1966.
h1 Radeka V, Chase R L: A Parametric Radiation Detector Preamplifier; IEEE Trans NS-13, 477–494, 1966.
i1 Blackwell L A, Kotzebue K L: Semiconductor-Diode Parametric Amplifiers; Prentice Hall 1961.
j1 Stevens K W H: Parametric Amplification; J Sci. Instrum. 37, 1–5, 1960.
k1 Mumford W W: Some Notes on the History of Parametric Transducers; Proc IRE 48, 848–853, 1960.
l1 Decroly J C, Laurent L, Lienhard J C, Marechal G, Vorobeitchik J: Parametric Amplifiers; Macmillan/Philips Technical Library 1973.

m1 Jones D: A Monolithic Chopper Stabilized Amplifier HA-2900: New Electronics 13 Nov. 1973, 55, 56, 61, 63, 65.

n1 Union Carbide: IC Operational Amplifiers UC4741; Union Carbide Data Sheet 1969.

o1 Sherwin J: Use the LM158/LM258/LM358 Dual, Single Supply Op Amp; National Semiconductor Application Note AN-116, May 1974.

p1 Zicko P: Designing with Chopper Stabilised Operational Amplifiers; Design Electronics Sep. 1970, 66, 68, 70, 73, 74, 131.

q1 Renschler E: The MC1539 Operational Amplifier and its Applications; Motorola Application Note AN-439, 1968.

r1 Huehne K: The MC1556 Operational Amplifier and its Applications; Motorola Application Note AN-522, 1970.

s1 Ehrsam B, Wolf K: The MC1535 Monolithic Dual Operational Amplifier; Motorola Application Note AN-411, 1968.

t1 Wisseman L L: A High Voltage Monolithic Operational Amplifier (MC1433); Motorola Application Note AN-248, 1967.

u1 Robertson S T: Designing-In Integrated Differential Amplifiers; Motorola Application Note AN-164, 1966.

v1 RCA: Integrated Circuit Operational Amplifiers; RCA Application Note ICAN-5290.

w1 Witten S: Designing Junction FET Input Op Amps; Siliconix Application Note AN74-3, 1974.

x1 Solomon J E: The Monolithic Op Amp: A Tutorial Study; IEEE J SC-9, 314–332, 1974.

y1 Apfel R J, Gray P R: A Fast Settling Monolithic Operational Amplifier Using Doublet Compression Techniques; IEEE J SC-9, 332–340, 1974.

z1 Wooley B A, Wong S Y J, Pederson D O: A Computer-Aided Evaluation of the 741 Amplifier; IEEE J SC-6, 357–366, 1971.

A1 Gray P R, Meyer R G: Recent Advances in Monolithic Operational Amplifier Design; IEEE Trans CAS-21, 317–327, 1974.

B1 Haynes G: Higher Performance IC's New Electronics 18 Feb. 1975, 61, 62, 64.

C1 Henderson R S: Linear MSI; New Electronics 18 Feb. 1975, 55.

D1 Maidique M A: A High Precision Monolithic Super-Beta Operational Amplifier; IEEE J SC-7, 480–487, 1972.

E1 Pouliot F: Simplify Amplifier Selection by Analyzing the Environment; Electronic Design 2 Aug. 1973, 72–77.

F1 Avery L R: Multiple Technology Extends Role of Op Amps (RCA 3130); Electronic Eng. 47, Sep. 1975, 45–47.

G1 Widlar R J: IC Op Amps Close the Gap on Discretes; National Semiconductor Application Note TP-9, Dec. 1968.

H1 Murari B, Bondini A: L148—Operational Amplifier; SGS Technical Bulletin No.110, Mar. 1971.

I1 Beneteau P J, Blaser L, Lane R Q: Transistor Operational Amplifiers; Fairchild Technical Publication TP-20, 1961.

J1 Huehne K: A Definite Look at Operational Amplifiers; Electronic Equipment News June 1972, 59–62.

K1 Long D K: The μA749 Dual Operational Amplifier; Fairchild Application Brief APP-126/1, July 1970.

L1 Widlar R J: A Monolithic Operational Amplifier (702); SGS-Fairchild Applications Bulletin AR-129, Apr. 1964.

M1 Fullagar D: A New High Performance Monolithic Operational Amplifier (741); Fairchild Bulletin.

N1 Bhola S: The Outstanding Features of Fully Compensated Operational Amplifiers; Transitron Applications Report No. MD/AP-17/69, June 1969.

O1 Bladowski R: Linear Monolithic Integrated Circuits; Orbit Oct. 1969, 20–22, 24, 25, 27, Nov. 1969, 7–9, 13–16, Jan. 1970, 7–10, 13–16.

P1 Datel Systems: Monolithic, Differential Input, Chopper Stabilized Operational Amplifier AM-490-2; Datel Systems Data Sheet 1975.

Q1 Keller J P: Linear IC's: Part 3 Differential Amplifiers at Work; Electronics 18 Sep. 1967, 96–105.

R1 Widlar R J: Design Techniques for Monolithic Operational Amplifiers; National Semiconductor Application Note TP-12, Aug. 1969.
S1 Analog Devices: Models 310/311 Ultra Low Bias Current Varactor Bridge Operational Amplifiers; Analog Devices Data Sheet and Application Notes 1969.
T1 Analog Devices: Models 301/302/303 Ultra Low Bias Current Varactor Bridge Operational Amplifiers; Analog Devices Data Sheet and Application Notes 1969.

References section 2.5: Inverting, summing, non-inverting, and differential amplifiers

a1 Kostanty R G: Doubling Op Amp Summing Power; Electronics 45, Feb. 14 1972, 73–75.
b1 Pease R: 1000V Ubity Gain Follower. R(in) = 10(14) Ohm; Electronic Eng. 43, Mar. 1971, 78.
c1 National Semiconductor: A Fast Integrated Voltage Follower with Low Input Current (LM302); National Semiconductor Application Note AN-5, May 1968.
d1 National Semiconductor: The LM110—An Improved IC Voltage Follower; National Semiconductor Linear Brief LB11 Mar. 1970.
e1 Pouliot F: Amplifiers in Instrumentation; Electron 23 May 1974, 30, 32, 36, 39 and 1 Aug., 30.
f1 Miller B: For Tough Measurements, Try IA's (Instrumentation Amplifiers); Electronic Design 2 Aug. 1974, 84–87.
g1 Dobkin R C: True RMS Detector; National Semiconductor Linear Brief LB-25, June 1973.
h1 Analog Devices: Low-Cost RMS Measuring Circuit; Analog Dialogue 8, No.1, 13, 1974.
i1 Graeme J: Getting Inside a Peak Detector to Make it Do the Job; Electronics 14 Nov. 1974, 145–149.
j1 Fidler J K: The Generalised Analogue Summer; Electronic Eng. 45, Nov. 1973, 15–16.
k1 Pease R A: Op Amps and Feedbank Capacitance; Electronic Eng. 44, Feb. 1972, 44, 54, 56.
l1 Bortolotti G, Gottardi S: Linear Rectification of Analogue Signals; Electronic Eng. 44, Feb. 1972, 46–47.
m1 Graeme J: Improve Analog Data Transmission with Two-Wire Transmitters; Electronic Design 4 Jan. 1975, 94–101.
n1 Graeme J: Op Amps Form Self-Buffered Rectifier; Electronics 43, 12 Oct. 1970, 98.
o1 Dobkin R C: Op Amp Circuit Collection; National Semiconductor Application Note AN-31, Feb. 1970.
p1 RCA: Linear Integrated Circuits; RCA Technical Series IC-42, 1970.
q1 Tobey G E, Graeme J G: Huelsman L P: Operational Amplifiers Design and Applications; McGraw-Hill 1971.
r1 RCA: Linear Integrated Circuits; RCA Technical Series IC-41, 1967.

References section 2.6: Operational integrator

a1 Jenkin L R: Signal Integrators of Wide Bandwidth; J Phys. E Sci. Instrum. 3, 148–150, 1970.
b1 Deboo G J: A Novel Integrator Results by Grounding its Capacitor; Electronic Design 7 June 1967, 90.
c1 Stata R: Operational Integrators; Analog Dialogue 1 No.1, 6–11, Apr. 1967.
d1 Conant R: How to Select R and C for Minimum Integrator Drift; Analog Dialogue 2 No. 1, 10–11, Mar. 1968.
e1 Daniels R E: Stable Electronic Integrator Switch; Rev. Sci. Instrum. 33, 487–488, 1962.
f1 Dow P C: An Analysis of Certain Errors in Electronic Differential Analyzers. II Capacitor Dielectric Absorption; IRE Trans EC-7, 17–22, 1958.
g1 Giacoletto L J: Errors in Operational Integrators Due to Limited Amplifier Response; Int. J Electronics 24, 269–273, 1968.
h1 Ljung E, Bergland S: Versatile Integrator-Multiplier; Electronic Eng. 46, Aug. 1974, 38–40.
i1 Hardy W R, Yager R, Shewchun J: Inexpensive Current Integrator uses IC Modules; Nuc. Instrum. Meth. 77, 331–332, 1970.

j1 Chater W T: A Digitizing Electrometer System Using an Integrating Circuit Preamplifier; Rev. Sci. Instrum. 42, 129–134, 1971.
k1 Kerr L W, Wilson J W G, Gillen C H: A Wide-Band Electronic Integrator; J Sci. Instrum. 40, 477, 1963.
l1 Clayton G B: Operational Amplifiers; Butterworths 1971.
m1 Philbrick/Nexus: Applications Manual for Operational Amplifiers; Philbrick/Nexus Research 1968.
n1 Smith J I: Modern Operational Circuit Design; Wiley-Interscience 1971.
o1 Holbrook J G: Laplace Transforms for Electronic Engineers; Pergamon 2nd Edn. 1966.
p1 Conant R: Equivalent Circuits for Operational Amplifier Drift and Noise; Analog Dialogue 2 No.1, 8–9, Mar. 1968.
q1 Tobey G E, Graeme J G, Huelsman L P: Operational Amplifiers Design and Applications; McGraw-Hill 1971.
r1 Teledyne Philbrick: V–F's as Long-Term Integrators; Teledyne Philbrick Bulletin AN-9, Jan. 1974.
s1 Morrison J M: Op Amp Increases RC Time Constants; Electronic Eng. 44, June 1972, 62–63.

References section 2.7: Operational differentiator

a1 Diamantides N D: Improved Electronic Differentiator has Low Noise Factor; Electronics 27 July 1962, 46–47.
b1 Nordlund D R: High Accuracy Analog Differentiator; Rev. Sci. Instrum. 43, 1699–1700, 1972.
c1 Chapman R: Instrumentation for Analog Differentiator at Low Frequencies; Rev. Sci. Instrum. 40, 95–98, 1969.
d1 Kress K A, Lapeyre G J: Operational Amplifier Differentiator for Photoemission Studies: Origin and Control of Errors; Rev. Sci. Instrum. 40, 74–78, 1969.
e1 Fairchild B T, Krovetz L J: 10 Circuits for Differentiation on Analog Computers; Control Eng. 12, Feb. 1965, 65–68.
f1 Farrish D T: Differentiator Circuit Monitors Stability of Slowly Changing Signals; Electronic Design 11 Oct. 1974, 128.
g1 Graeme J: Bootstrapped RC Differentiator Performs Accurately Without Phase Inversion; Electronic Design 1 Mar. 1974, 60.
h1 Hamilton T D S: Operational Differentiators; Electronic Eng. 46, Oct. 1974, 53–55.
i1 Murata T: A Device for Differentiating Signals of Very Low Speed; J Phys. E Sci. Instrum. 8, 83–84, 1975.
j1 Hoft D: Applying the Analog Differentiator; Analog Dialogue 4, No.1, June 1970, 12–14.
k1 Philbrick/Nexus: Applications Manual for Operational Amplifiers; Philbrick/Nexus Research 1968.
l1 Holbrook J G: Laplace Transforms for Electronic Engineers; Pergamon 2nd Edn. 1966.

References section 2.8: Charge amplifier

a1 Tobey G E, Graeme J G, Huelsman L P: Operational Amplifiers Design and Applications; McGraw-Hill 1971.
b1 Delaney C F G: Electronics for the Physicist; Penguin Books 1969.
c1 Koch J K: A Charge-Sensitive Preamplifier for Nuclear Work; Hewlett-Packard J 19, Mar. 1968, 16–18.
d1 Holbrook J G: Laplace Transforms for Electronic Engineers; Pergamon 2nd Edn. 1966.
e1 Krycuk G, Walling J D: Miniature Charge Sensitive Preamp-Amplifier for use with Silicon Surface Barrier Detectors; IEEE Trans NS-20, 228–231, 1972.
f1 Mullard: Field-Effect Transistors in a Pre-Amplifier for Use with Solid State Radiation Detectors; Mullard Application Report TP-1106, 1969.
g1 Radeka V: Field-Effect Transistors for Charge Amplifiers; IEEE Trans NS-20, 182–189, 1972.
h1 Faulkner E A: The Principles of Impedance Optimization and Noise Matching; J Phys. E Sci. Instrum. 8, 533–540, 1975.

References section 2.9: IC amplifier characteristics

a1 Dobkin R C: Universal Balancing Techniques; National Semiconductor Linear Brief LB-9, 1969.

b1 Conant R: Equivalent Circuits for Operational Amplifier Drift and Noise; Analog Dialogue 2 No.1, 8–9, Mar. 1968.

c1 Van der Kooi M K: Predicting and Avoiding Slew-Rate Limiting; Electronic Eng. 45, Feb. 1973, 18–19.

d1 Miller W D: Sources of Common Mode Error in Op Amps; Control Eng. 18, Aug. 1971, 64–67.

e1 Smith D R: Boost Common-Mode Rejection in Differential Applications with a Special Transformer that Cancells Common-Mode Currents but Permits Differential Signals to Pass Unhampered; Electronic Design 27 Sep. 1973, 94–95.

f1 Stata R: A Guide to Applying and Measuring Operational Amplifier Specifications; Orbit Mar. 1968, 20–22, 24, 26–28.

g1 Blair K: Getting More Value Out of an Operational Amplifier Data Sheet; Motorola Application Note AN-273, 1966.

h1 Union Carbide Semiconductor: IC Operational Amplifiers UC4741; Union Carbide Data Sheet 1969.

i1 Jung W G: Improve Op-Amp Audio Circuits by Mating Op-Amp Dynamic Characteristics and Compensation to the Circuit Applications; Electronic Design 27 Sep. 1973, 68–73.

j1 Jaeger R C, Hellwarth G A: Dynamic Zero-Correction Method Suppresses Offset Error in Op Amps; Electronics 4 Dec. 1972, 109–110.

k1 Demrow R I: Narrowing the Margin of Error; Electronics 41, 15 Apr. 1968, 108–117.

l1 Demrow R I: Protecting Data from the Ground Up; Electronics 41, 29 Apr. 1968, 58–64.

m1 Harris S: How to Really Look at Low-Drift IC Op Amps; Electronics 9 Oct. 1972, 120–121.

n1 Stata R: Users Guide to Applying and Measuring Operational Amplifier Specifications; Analog Dialogue 1, Sep. 1967, 1–8.

o1 Harris S: Not by Drift Alone.... Chapter 2. The 741 Op Amp Family; Analog Dialogue 7, No.1, 11–12.

p1 Harris S: Not by Drift Alone; Analog Dialogue 6, No.2, 12.

q1 Dobkin R C: Low Drift Amplifiers; National Semiconductor Linear Brief LB-22, June 1973.

r1 Botos B: Breadboard Techniques for Low Frequency Integrated Circuit Feedback Amplifiers; Motorola Application Note AN-271, 1966.

s1 Fishman J: High Speed Op Amps Revisited—1 What Does 'High Speed' Mean to the User?; Analog Dialogue 8, No.1, 10–12, 1974.

t1 Apfel R J, Gray P R: A Fast Settling Monolithic Operational Amplifier Using Doublet Compression Techniques; IEEE J SC-9, 332–340, 1974.

u1 Kamath B Y, Meyer R G, Gray P R: Relationship Between Frequency Response and Settling Time of Operational Amplifiers; IEEE J SC-9, 347–352, 1974.

v1 Appleby T H: An Investigation of Integrated Circuit Destruction by Noise Pulses; Radio Electr. 43, 279–287, 1973.

w1 Dobkin R C: IC Preamp Challenges Choppers on Drift; National Semiconductor Application Note AN-79 Feb. 1973.

x1 Calkins R: Dynamic Tests for Op Amps Use Synchronous Demodulation; Electronics 41, 5 Aug. 1968, 118–123.

y1 Gans F: Common-Mode Rejection Ratio: What the Spec Sheet Doesn't Say; Electronics 42, 23 June 1969, 116–119.

z1 Microsystems International: Testing Operational Amplifiers Easily and Accurately; Microsystems International Application Note 1974.

A1 Graeme J: Protect Op Amps from Overload; Electron 16 Jan. 1975, 67, 69.

B1 National Semiconductor: An Applications Guide for Operational Amplifiers; National Semiconductor Application Note AN-20, Feb. 1969.

C1 Svetz P: The $\alpha\beta\gamma$s of Bioelectric Measurements; Electronic Design 2 Aug. 1975, 68–72.

D1 Stata R: Operational Amplifiers, Part IV Offset and Drift in Operational Amplifiers; Analog Devices 1965.

E1 Tobey G E, Graeme J G, Huelsman L P: Operational Amplifiers Design and Applications; McGraw-Hill 1971.
F1 Widlar R J: Linear IC's: Part 6 Compensating for Drift; Electronics 5 Feb. 1968, 90–93.
G1 Harris E L: Linear IC's: Part 5 Foggy 'Specs' Blur Designs; Electronics 16 Oct. 1967, 91–94.
H1 Gifford J F, Markkula M: Linear IC's: Part 5 Ins and Outs of Op Amps; Electronics 27 Nov. 1967, 84–87.

3 Stability of feedback systems

3.1 Introduction

The problem of stability in feedback systems has been outlined in Sec. 2.4. There are two classic techniques for investigating the stability of a feedback system: the root-locus and the Nyquist diagram. The former is a purely mathematical approach requiring complete knowledge of the response functions of all the elements of the system, while the latter uses actual response measurements made on the open loop. The techniques are directly related, and both are designed to show whether there is a pole in the right half-plane (RHP) of the complex frequency diagram; see Sec. 1.11(b). If there is, the closed feedback system will be unstable.

Although these approaches are useful in providing insight into the stability problem, they are not convenient for the present purposes, either because the parameters are not known, or the required measurements are not easy to make. However, they will be considered for the benefit of the insight provided, and then the more commonly used Bode plot will be examined. From this some useful rules-of-thumb will be derived, that will serve in all but the most unusual circumstances.

Those interested in the mathematical justification of some of the results may consult Thomason [b1]. Other useful references are [e1, c1, h1, i1, f1, d1, k1, l1, a1].

In most cases, the basic frequency response will have to be modified to achieve stability and some simple techniques for doing this will be examined.

3.2 The root-locus

This technique is based on the calculation of the location of the poles from the total transfer function of the system. This operation has been demonstrated in Sec. 1.11(c), where it was also seen how the pole positions could be changed considerably depending on the gain of the system. The extension involved here is simply to plot the loci of the poles as a function of the loop-gain, L. This then allows one to see the possibilities and consequences of changing L, or indicates measures that may be taken to improve a marginal situation. A formal statement that a system will be stable if there are no poles in the RHP, although correct, does not imply that the system will have a satisfactory or desirable response. For example, a pole close to the $j\omega$ axis leads to a lightly damped oscillatory response which is seldom desirable (see Fig. 1.11.5). The difficulty of this technique, even if all the parameters of the system (time constants, gains, etc.) are known, lies in the extraction of roots of polynomials of order higher than the second. There are approximation techniques, and the accessibility of computers renders this problem trivial in principle, but in general applications this is far too ponderous and, in the context of this book, impractical.

One, two, and three pole systems, however, will be considered as these demonstrate the behaviour of poles and the effect on the frequency response and stability of the system. The closed-loop gain of the feedback system is, from Eq. (2.2.11), given by:

$$G(s) = \frac{A(s)}{1 - A(s)\beta(s)} = \frac{A(s)}{1 - L(s)} \quad (3.2.1)$$

where β may also be a function of s. This relation demonstrates how the poles are changed when the feedback connection is made. The poles of $A(s)$ are no longer effective: when $A(s) = \infty$, $L(s) = A(s)\beta(s) = \infty$, as $\beta(s) \neq 0$. The effective poles are those of $G(s)$ and are determined by the roots of:

$$1 - L(s) = 0 \quad (3.2.2)$$

Consider a single lag system with time constant T and $\beta(s) = \beta_0$. The gain will be given by:

$$A(s) = \frac{-A_0}{1 + sT}, \quad \text{i.e., pole at } s_a = -1/T \quad (3.2.3)$$

The equation for the pole of $G(s)$ is then, from Eqs. (3.2.3) and (3.2.2):

$$1 + sT + A_0\beta_0 = 0, \quad \text{or} \quad s_1 = -(A_0\beta_0 + 1)/T \quad (3.2.4)$$

Thus, as the gain A_0 increases, the pole s_1, which is always real, moves along the $-\sigma$ axis further into the left half-plane (LHP), i.e., the stability increases (Fig. 3.2.1).

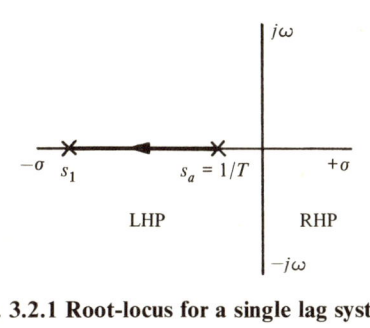

Fig. 3.2.1 Root-locus for a single lag system

For a two lag system with time constants T_1, T_2 ($T_1 > T_2$ say):

$$A(s) = \frac{-A_0}{(1 + sT_1)(1 + sT_2)}, \quad s_a = -1/T_1, \quad s_b = -1/T_2 \quad (3.2.5)$$

and assuming $\beta(s) = \beta_0$ as before, Eq. (3.2.2) becomes:

$$1 + s(T_1 + T_2) + s^2 T_1 T_2 + A_0\beta_0 = 0 \quad (3.2.6)$$

which has roots:

$$s_{1,2} = \frac{-(T_1 + T_2) \pm [(T_1 + T_2)^2 - 4(A_0\beta_0 + 1)T_1 T_2]^{1/2}}{2T_1 T_2} \quad (3.2.7)$$

As $A_0\beta_0$ increases, the roots move from their original positions, $s_{a,b}$, towards one another along the σ axis (Fig. 3.2.2).

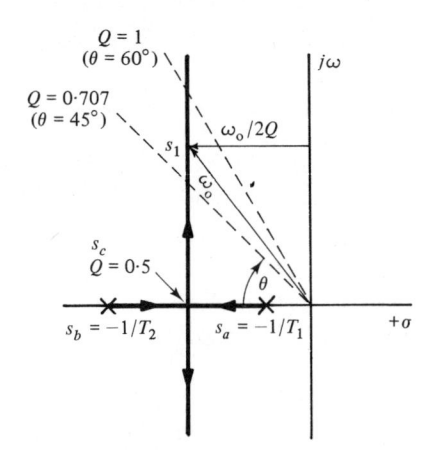

Fig. 3.2.2 Root-locus for a two lag system

The roots are equal when:

$$(T_1+T_2)^2 = 4(A_0\beta_0+1)T_1T_2 \qquad (3.2.8)$$

and

$$s_{1,2} = -(T_1+T_2)/2T_1T_2 = s_c \qquad (3.2.9)$$

For higher values of loop gain, the poles become complex and move away from the real axis along a locus parallel to the $j\omega$ axis. The poles, therefore, can never enter the RHP and the system is unconditionally stable. The system response when the poles are real is aperiodic, and equal roots, Eq. (3.2.9), corresponds to critical damping. When the poles become complex the response is damped oscillatory and the frequency response develops a hump (Fig. 3.2.3).

To characterize the hump, or resonance, it is convenient to write Eqs. (3.2.6) and (3.2.7) in terms of the Q of the circuit (Sec. 1.1):

$$1 + s/Q\omega_0 + (s/\omega_0)^2 = 0 \qquad (3.2.10)$$

where

$$Q^2 = \frac{(A_0\beta_0+1)T_1T_2}{(T_1+T_2)^2}, \qquad \omega_0^2 = (A_0\beta_0+1)/T_1T_2$$

and

$$s_{1,2} = \frac{-\omega_0}{2Q} \pm \left[\left(\frac{\omega_0}{2Q}\right)^2 - \omega_0^2\right]^{1/2} \qquad (3.2.11)$$

Fig. 3.2.3 Frequency response for a two lag system

The geometrical meaning of Q and ω_0 is shown in Fig. 3.2.2. The term *damping factor* (ζ) is also often used and is simply related to Q by $\zeta = 1/2Q$.

The lines of constant Q make a fixed angle θ with the σ axis: $\cos\theta = 1/2Q$. When the roots are equal, Eq. (3.2.9), $Q = 0.5$. A Q of 0.707 is often used as this gives increased bandwidth (3 dB point moves from 0.65 ω_0 to ω_0) with a negligible hump (0.002 dB rise) and a good risetime with a single overshoot of 4.3 per cent. A Q of 1 is usually acceptable where transient response is not a consideration, giving a bandwidth to 1.2 ω_0 and only 1.2 dB peaking (see Sec. 3.7). Transient response is considered further in Sec. 3.7.

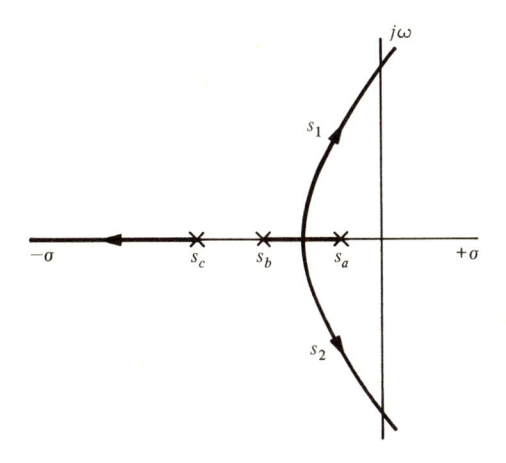

Fig. 3.2.4 Root-locus for a three lag system

If the feedback were positive rather than negative, the two poles would move along the σ axis in the opposite directions to those shown in Fig. 3.2.2. s_a would soon be in the RHP and the system would then lock over to one limit. Because of the non-linearity of any system in the limit, the gain will be reduced in this state. Depending on the circumstances, the system may remain in one state or flop backwards and forwards between two states, i.e., bistable or astable circuits (flop-flops). The poles remain on the σ axis, so the waveforms during transition are aperiodic.

It can be seen that the mathematics is already becoming complicated for second-order systems, so third-order systems will not be investigated in any detail. There are of course now three poles, two of which behave somewhat like the two second-order poles, and one that moves along the $-\sigma$ axis (Fig. 3.2.4).

When s_1 and s_2 cross the $j\omega$ axis, the system becomes unstable and oscillations will be maintained; the Q of the system is, in effect, infinite. All three-pole systems will become unstable if the loop gain is great enough. For example, for three equal time constants the critical value is $L = 8$ [a1].

Without a handy computer further progress on these lines is rather difficult, which leads to consideration of an alternative technique, the Nyquist diagram.

3.3 The Nyquist diagram

The Nyquist diagram is a plot of the loop-gain, L, as a function of frequency. Phase and amplitude are shown by plotting the locus, in polar coordinates, of the tip of a vector L drawn from the origin. A typical diagram may look like Fig. 3.3.1. This diagram represents a system with a.c. coupling so that the loop-gain falls to zero at zero frequency. For a d.c. coupled system that part of the locus between $\omega=0$ and $\omega=\omega_m$ would be missing. The sense of rotation of L is arbitrary: the convention used here is that lagging phase is measured in a clockwise direction from the reference phase of the input.

The measurements of amplitude and phase, relative to the input, are in principle easy to make for the open-loop system with gain $A(s)\beta(s)=L(s)$. In practice small amplitudes, and phase at high frequencies, present problems, and some care must be exercised as to where the loop is opened to ensure the system is not otherwise changed.

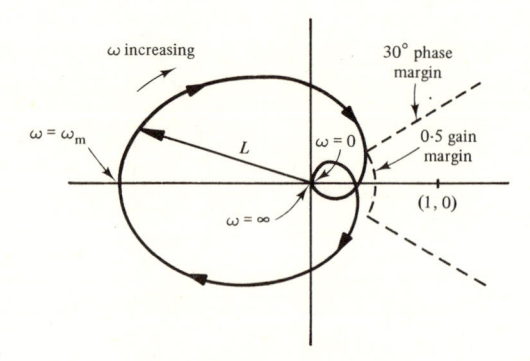

Fig. 3.3.1 Nyquist diagram

It was shown by Nyquist [f1] that if the locus of $L(s)$ encloses the point (1, 0), then when the loop is closed it will be unstable. This is called *Nyquist's criterion of stability*. It should be noted that the complex conjugate locus may need to be drawn, representing the *negative* frequencies, to check the enclosure of (1, 0). In many cases, as in Fig. 3.3.1, the two will be coincident [e1, d1, a1, b1, c1].

What is the basis of this test and is there any connection with previous discussions? The criterion is, in fact, just a generalized test of whether there are any poles in the RHP, exactly as before. It is based on a remarkable theorem which states that if a contour encompassing the entire (infinite) right half of the s-plane is drawn, then there will be a contour in a suitably related w-plane (i.e., $w=f(s)$) in which the sense and number of revolutions around the origin will indicate the difference between the numbers of poles and zeros in the RH s-plane. It would take us too much out of our way to prove here, so reference should be made to Thomason [b1, p. 133–143]. The trick is to find the suitable w-function.

The poles of $G(s)$ are given by the roots, or zeros, of Eq. (3.2.2). Thus, if:

$$w' = 1 - L(s) \tag{3.3.1}$$

then the w' contour will encircle the origin once for every zero of $1-L(s)$, i.e., every pole of $G(s)$, which is just what is wanted. This does not account for possible zeros of $G(s)$, but since $L(s)$ corresponds to a stable circuit it has no poles in the RHP and so $G(s)$ has no zeros there. It is convenient to shift the origin to give a contour:

$$w = 1 - w' = L(s) \tag{3.3.2}$$

in which case the encirclements are of the point (1, 0) rather than the origin.

The Nyquist criterion corresponds closely to the intuitive feeling that for stability the loop-gain shall be less than unity before the phase shift reaches 180°. It says somewhat more however. It is possible to realize a system in which the loop-gain is greater than unity with a phase shift of 180°, but whose contour still does not enclose the critical point (1, 0). Nyquist's criterion says that such a system will be stable and so contradicts our intuitive feeling. Such systems are said to be conditionally stable and are not of much practical use, as disturbances, e.g., switching on, gain drift, may well move it into the unstable condition where it may remain.

It should be pointed out here that in systems containing a.c. coupling, as illustrated by Fig. 3.3.1, there is a stability problem at low frequencies just as much as at high, since the low frequency part of the locus could equally well enclose (1, 0). The resulting low frequency oscillations, often distorted and intermittent as a result of overloading, are commonly referred to as *motorboating*. The reason will be obvious if your hi-fi system ever suffers from this, but many modern power audio amplifiers use d.c. feedback (Sec. 4.7) and so do not have this problem.

The Nyquist diagram is commonly used for low frequency systems, e.g., servo-mechanisms, where the measurement of phase is easier, but for the present purposes it does not prove very convenient. This leads to the third approach, the Bode Plot.

3.4 The Bode plot

This is essentially the Nyquist diagram drawn out as two separate parts, phase and amplitude. As explained previously (Sec. 1.3) it is very convenient to plot amplitude in dB and phase linearly against the log of the frequency. The great advantages of the Bode plot are that the phase response may be inferred from the slope of the gain plot, and that knowing the primary time constants of the system a good approximation of the gain (and hence phase) can be quickly sketched using simple straight line approximations. A typical approximate plot for a three pole system is shown in Fig. 3.4.1. Knowing the three time constants and gains involved, all that is required is to calculate $f_{1,2,3}$, draw the approximate *curves* for each, and add to get the resultant amplifier response. The phase shift diagram may be drawn in a similar way, although this is often unnecessary, the phase being inferred from the slope of the gain curve [b1].

The question now arises, how is stability determined from these diagrams. From Eq. (3.2.2), the critical condition occurs when the loop-gain $L(s) = 1$ and the phase shift is 180°:

$$L(s) = A(s)\beta(s) = 1, 180°$$

or $\quad \log(A(s)) - \log(B(s)) = 0 \quad$ and $\quad \phi_A - \phi_B = 180°$ \quad (3.4.1)

where $B \equiv 1/\beta$. The response of $\log(B(s))$, which is effectively the closed-loop gain (for high loop-gain), is drawn on the plot of $\log(A(s))$ to give the complete Bode plot. The loop-gain is then just the difference between the A and B curves. If, at the frequency at which the two curves intersect, the phase shift $\phi_A - \phi_B \geq 180°$, the system will be unstable. This is illustrated in Fig. 3.4.2 for several cases with different B's, i.e., simple amplifier, integrator, and differentiator.

Note the signs of the phase angles. The amplifier response lags, so the phase ϕ_A is negative. For the two amplifier responses shown, the phase shifts at intersection are $-81°$ and $-153°$. Thus, both are stable although A_2 is on the safety borderline. For the differentiator the feedback circuit looks like a lag from the amplifier output, so $\phi_{\beta D} \to -90°$ or $\phi_{BD} \to +90°$. The reverse holds for the integrator. Thus, the differentiator *increases* the lagging phase angle and so makes the system *less* stable, while the integrator improves stability.

Provided the closure point of A and B is not too near a break point, the stability of the system may be assessed by the difference between the slopes of the two curves. For example, for the differentiator shown, the B plot has a slope of $+20$ dB/decade ($\phi_{BD} = +90°$) and A a slope of -20 dB/decade ($\phi_A = -90°$), so that the difference

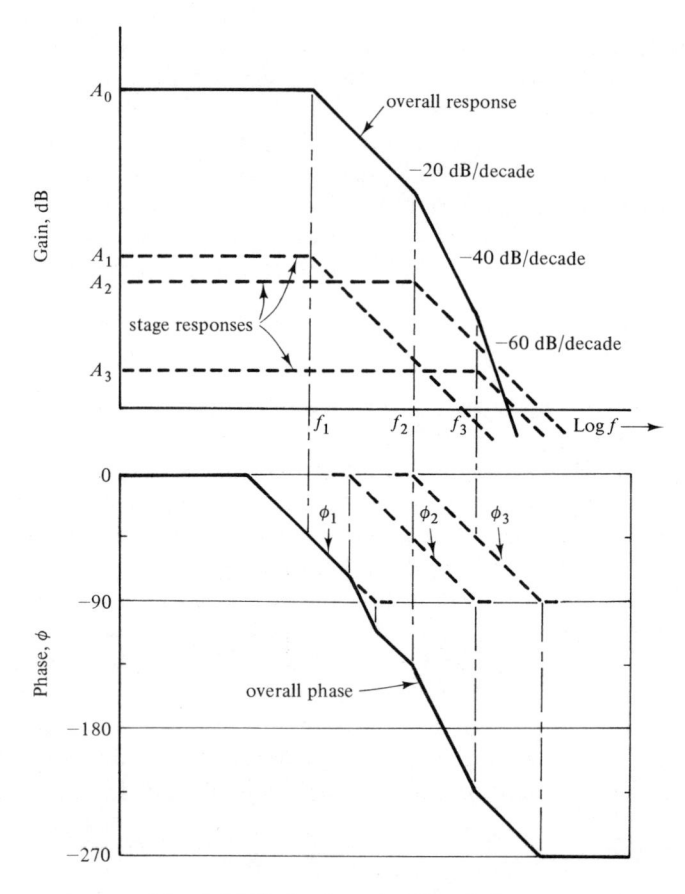

Fig. 3.4.1 Bode plots of gain and phase

$\phi_A - \phi_{BD} = -180°$ and the system is on the border of instability. As can be seen from the phase diagram, the proximity of ω_2 increases the phase to $-198°$ so the system is definitely unstable. For safety, and for reasons previously outlined, a phase margin of $> 30°$ is desirable, i.e., $\phi_A - \phi_B \leqslant -150°$, together with a gain margin of 0.5 (see Fig. 3.3.1). For the integrator shown $\phi_A - \phi_{BI} = -40 - (-20) = -20$ dB/decade → $-90°$ and the system is quite stable. (The maximum phase shift actually reached is $-126°$, in this case.) If the integrator B curve does not intersect the A curve above unity gain (i.e., $\omega_1 < \omega_T$) then it will be the intersection of the noise gain, Eq. (2.2.11), with the A curve that must be considered (see Fig. 2.2.2).

We have assumed that an input voltage generator (i.e., zero impedance) is connected at all times so that the feedback networks behave as intended. If the generator were not present then this would not be so, and we would effectively have complete feedback (unity gain) which is the most severe condition: for the response shown in Fig. 3.4.2 the system would certainly oscillate. This explains an apparently puzzling effect that may be met especially when testing a circuit.

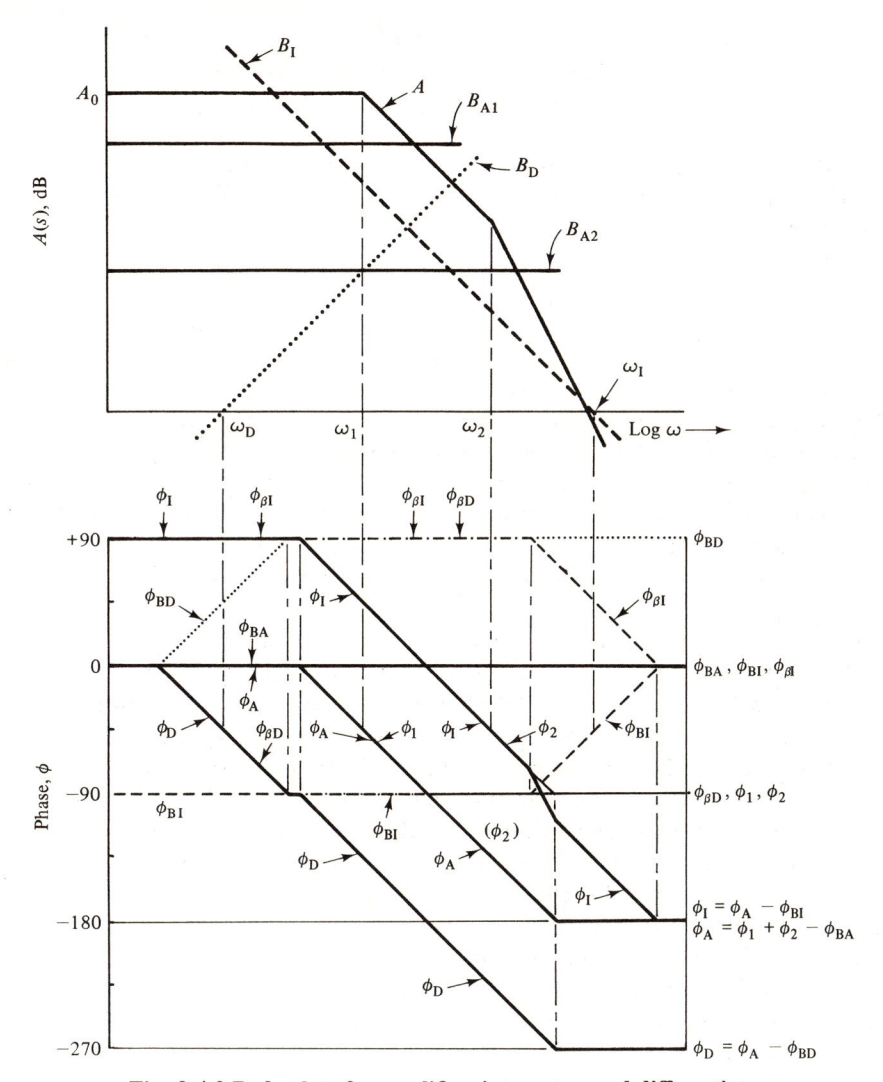

Fig. 3.4.2 Bode plots for amplifier, integrator, and differentiator

It is clear that although the *difference of slopes* approach gives a fair guide to stability, there can be significant errors in the actual phase value. If the phase curve can be drawn this may well be worthwhile, but this requires a reasonably good knowledge of the location of the poles.

It should be emphasized here that we have been plotting the *loop* phase-shifts and not the signal phase shifts—the latter will be quite different when the B circuit is frequency dependent. For the differentiator the signal phase shift ϕ_{SD} will be $+90°$ at low frequencies changing to $\phi_A \approx -90°$ in the region of frequency ω_{AD}. This must occur, since at high frequencies the differentiator capacitor C_i becomes negligible and we have, essentially, the open-loop amplifier response, ϕ_A. For the integrator, the phase shift ϕ_{SI} will be $-90°$ in the region where the loop-gain is significant, but at low and high frequencies the phase reverts to that of the amplifier—below ω_{1I} to $0°$, and above ω_{AI} to ϕ_A. This emphasizes that if the loop-gain is substantial the signal response is controlled by the feedback network, but when L goes to zero the amplifier itself takes over. There can be no response outside the open-loop response, except at higher frequencies where there may be positive feedback (see Fig. 2.2.2 and Sec. 2.7).

Now that a means of ascertaining the stability of a system is available, techniques for modifying the response of unstable or marginally stable systems can be investigated.

3.5 Phase compensation

Most feedback systems will require some form of phase compensation to ensure stability. The provision of this optimum compensation is often the most difficult and critical part of the overall design. Since, in the systems under consideration, there is a close connection between gain and phase, the control of the latter can only be achieved at the expense of variation in the former. This affects the loop-gain which is the prime parameter controlling the performance of the system. Compensation, therefore, should be applied with care, as overcompensation may incur penalties in other respects.

For IC operational amplifiers there are two main techniques for phase compensation; the series–RC shunt across a suitable collector load and Miller-effect multiplication of a feedback capacitor (Sec. 1.6). One of these techniques or both together are used, although in the so-called internally compensated amplifiers, e.g., the 741 discussed in Sec. 2.3, Miller compensation only is required. In the latter, the phase shift is usually limited to 90° until unity-gain frequency so that, for the usual feedback networks producing at most 90° of phase lag, the system will be stable unconditionally though the response may be far from ideal. This is achieved at the expense of considerable loss of open-loop bandwidth. If this is critical the more complicated RC shunt technique must be resorted to.

There are, of course, techniques involving modification of the feedback components as, for example, application of the integrator configuration. In general, modification of the response by compensation connected to the amplifier internally is preferable, and is the most widely used. The compensation is then isolated from the feedback components, and the point of application can be selected so that one of the existing poles is modified rather than introducing a completely new one.

3.5(a) *RC shunt compensation*

To illustrate the effect of this form of compensation, consider the response of the single stage differential amplifier typical of an IC amplifier (Fig. 3.5.1):

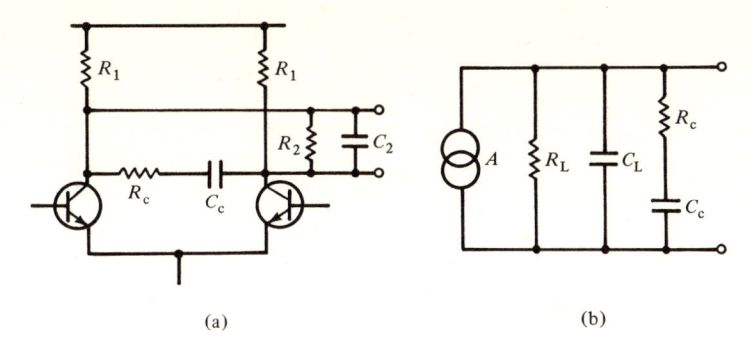

Fig. 3.5.1 (a) *RC* shunt compensation, (b) equivalent circuit

R_2, C_2 represent the input of the following stage, and R_c, C_c the shunt compensation. An equivalent circuit can be drawn (Fig. 3.5.1(b)) where R_L represents the effective load resistance (R_1, R_2, transistor output resistance) and C_L the effective load capacitance. With no compensation, there is a single pole at ω_1, and gain A_u:

$$\omega_1 = 1/R_L C_L, \qquad A_u = \frac{A R_L}{1 + R_L C_L s} \tag{3.5.1}$$

With the compensation, the parallel impedance is easily found to be:

$$Z = \frac{R_L(1 + R_c C_c s)}{1 + R_c C_c s + R_L C_L s + R_L C_c s + R_L C_L R_c C_c s^2} \tag{3.5.2}$$

This is a little cumbersome to work with, so the approximations $R_c \ll R_L$, $C_L \ll C_c$ are made, which are good for typical compensation networks. This also separates the various break points, so the effects are more clearly seen. The gain is then given by AZ:

$$A_c = \frac{A R_L(1 + R_c C_c s)}{1 + R_L C_c s + R_L C_L R_c C_c s^2} \tag{3.5.3}$$

The poles are found by equating the denominator to zero, and occur when:

$$s = \frac{-R_L C_c \pm (R_L C_c - 4 R_L C_L R_c C_c)^{1/2}}{2 R_L C_L R_c C_c}$$

$$= \frac{-1}{2 R_c C_L} \left[1 \pm \left(1 - \frac{4 R_c C_L}{R_L C_c}\right)^{1/2} \right] \tag{3.5.4}$$

$$\doteq \frac{-1}{2 R_c C_L} \left[1 \pm \left(1 - \frac{2 R_c C_L}{R_L C_c}\right) \right]$$

The last step follows from the earlier approximation in that $R_c C_L \ll R_L C_c$, and by the binomial expansion $(1-x)^{1/2} \doteq 1 - x/2$ for x small. The two poles are, therefore:

$$s_a = \frac{-1}{2 R_c C_L}\left(2 - \frac{2 R_c C_L}{R_L C_c}\right), \qquad s_b = \frac{-1}{2 R_c C_L} \cdot \frac{2 R_c C_L}{R_L C_c}$$

$$\doteq -1/R_c C_L \qquad\qquad\qquad\qquad = -1/R_L C_c \tag{3.5.5}$$

so that the corresponding break-point frequencies are:

$$\omega_a = 1/R_c C_L, \qquad \omega_b = 1/R_L C_c \qquad (3.5.6)$$

From Eq. (3.5.3) it is clear that there is also a zero at:

$$\omega_c = 1/R_c C_c \qquad (3.5.7)$$

Thus, the original pole at ω_1 is effectively moved down to ω_b, and a new pole appears at ω_a together with a zero at ω_c. The original and compensated responses are shown in Fig. 3.5.2. The gain in the region between ω_c and ω_a may be derived from

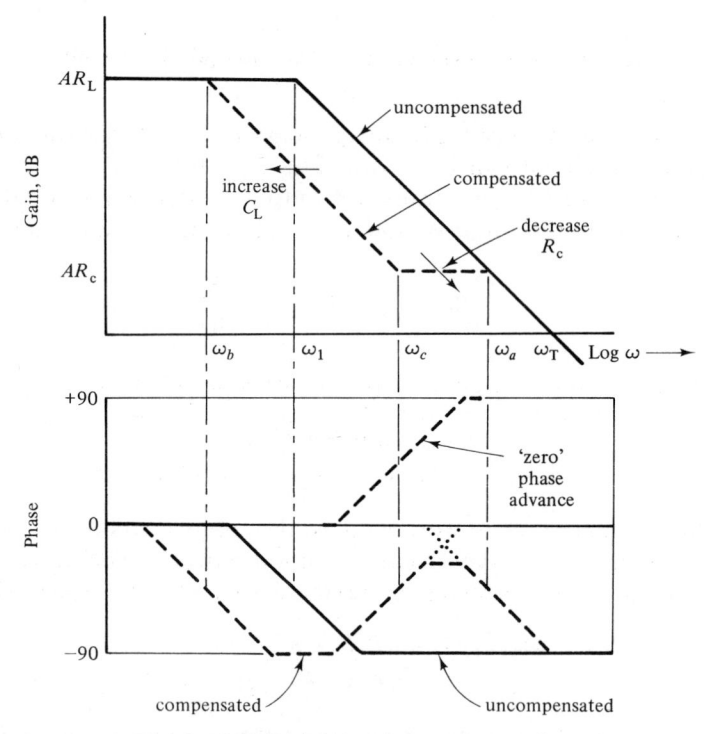

Fig. 3.5.2 Bode plot for shunt compensation

Eq. (3.5.3) by noting that on the basis of our assumption, the s^2 term $\ll s$ term in the denominator. Thus, in this region:

$$A_{c,a} = \frac{AR_L(1 + R_c C_c s)}{1 + R_L C_c s} \doteq AR_c \qquad (3.5.8)$$

A simpler method is to take the equation for the response between ω_b and ω_c, $-AR_L/R_L C_c s$, and find its value when $-s = \omega_c = 1/R_c C_c$. This gives AR_c as before. A similar approach gives the frequency of the intercept of $A_{c,a}$ with the uncompensated response:

$$AR_c = \frac{AR_L}{R_L C_L \omega} \quad \text{or} \quad \omega = 1/R_c C_L = \omega_a \qquad (3.5.9)$$

thus locating the pole at ω_a on the uncompensated response. This is to be expected since the compensated must eventually be limited by the uncompensated response.

The phase shift at high frequencies, especially around ω_T where excessive shift usually causes difficulty, has been reduced. In the above example there was little need for compensation, but where there are two or three poles in the uncompensated response the real effectiveness of the technique will be seen. This is due not only to the shifting of poles, but in particular to the possibility of pole–zero cancellation; i.e., the new zero introduced, Eq. (3.5.7), can be sited at the frequency of one of the

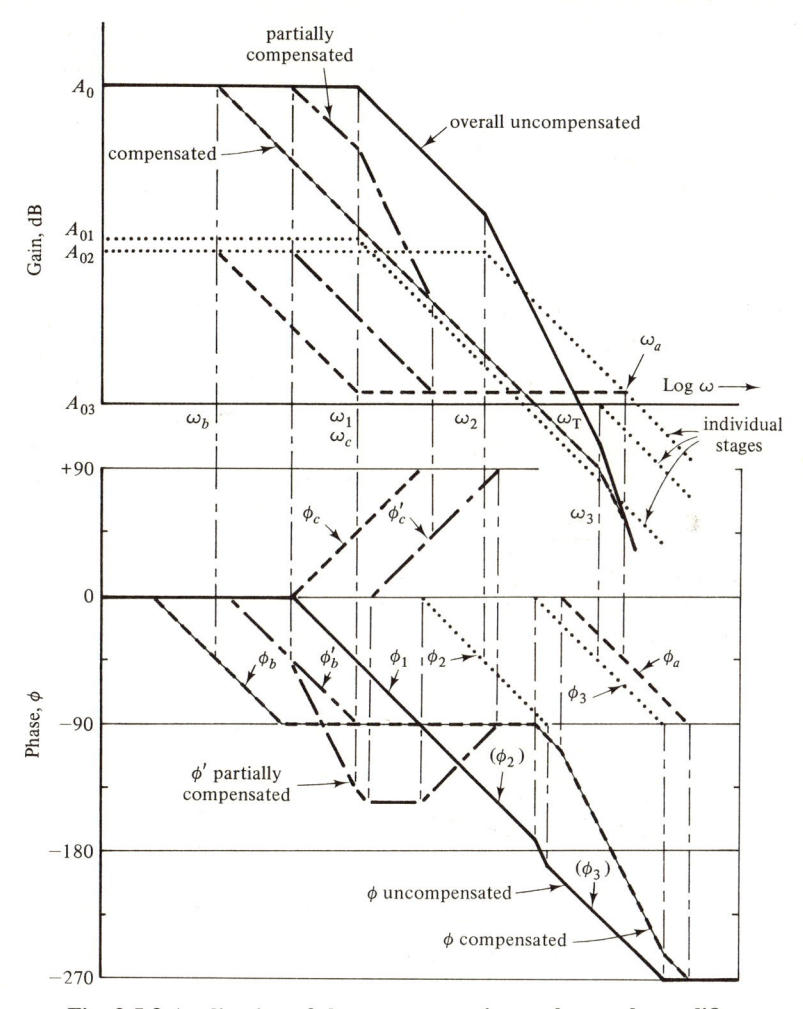

Fig. 3.5.3 Application of shunt compensation to three pole amplifier

poles arising from the stages of the amplifier so that these two (factors in the response function) cancel.

This cancellation technique is illustrated in Fig. 3.5.3 where a three pole uncompensated response (one pole above ω_T) is shown.

The value of C_c is chosen to shift ω_2 say to $\omega_b = 1/R_L C_c$; R_c is chosen to make $\omega_c = 1/R_c C_c$ coincide with and cancel the pole ω_1 and $\omega_a = 1/R_c C_L$ will be shifted above ω_T, depending on the compensation resistance R_c. The pole at ω_3 is unaffected by the compensation, but will give some phase shift below ω_T unless $\omega_3 \gtrsim 10\omega_T$. The phase margin at unity gain is 45° as shown, but is very conservative at lower frequencies, i.e., a long way from the critical value of 180°. If C_c is decreased somewhat, then ω'_b and ω'_c are increased, giving greater bandwidth and only partial cancellation of the pole at ω_1. This greater bandwidth is bought at the cost of decreased phase margin in the midfrequency region, but the unity-gain value can still be maintained at the same value as before. This reduced value of C_c also improves the slewing rate of the amplifier.

In general, the main difficulty with this technique is the lack of knowledge of R_L and C_L. These values are not quoted in the specification sheet, possibly because they tend to be somewhat variable. Application reports on particular devices [g1] often give more information, and data sheets commonly give tables of compensation values. The latter will be on the conservative side so as to cover the worst cases, so some latitude is usually possible. Direct measurement of R_L and C_L would be ideal, but considerable care is required particularly at high frequencies.

3.5(b) *Miller-effect capacity compensation*

As the name implies this technique uses capacitive feedback around part of the amplifier and utilizes Miller-effect multiplication (Sec. 1.6), so that only small actual values of capacity are required. This is attractive if the capacitor is to be integrated in the IC, as large values are difficult or expensive (in terms of chip area) to make. This technique of compensation is, in fact, the one used for the common types of internally compensated operational amplifier, e.g., type 741 described in Sec. 2.3, Fig. 2.3.1.

The attraction of this method is that it automatically ensures a response zero coincident with the pole of the stage to which it is applied, and is arranged in commercial units to give a constant 6 dB/octave slope until close to unity gain. To see how this compensation operates, consider a simplified equivalent circuit shown in Fig. 3.5.4.

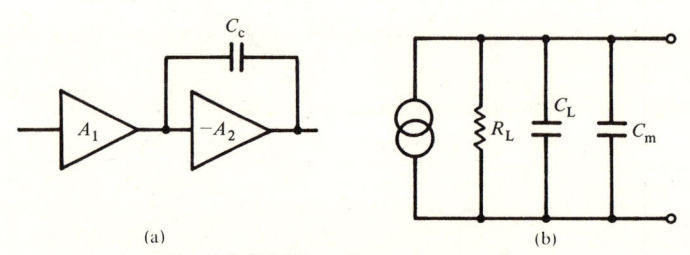

Fig. 3.5.4 Miller-effect compensation

The value of C_m depends on the gain of stage A_2 around which C_c is applied. Assuming A_2 has a single pole (at ω_2) response, then:

$$C_m = (1+A_2)C_c = \left(1+\frac{A_{02}}{1+s/\omega_2}\right)C_c \qquad (3.5.10)$$

By adding the three impedances in parallel, in Fig. 3.5.4(b), the gain of A_1 can be written:

$$A_1 = \frac{A_{01}}{1+R_L C_L s + R_L C_m s} \qquad (3.5.11)$$

Substituting for C_m from Eq. (3.5.10), and using the frequencies:

$$\omega_1 = 1/R_L C_L, \qquad \omega_3 = 1/R_L C_c A_{02}, \qquad \omega_4 = 1/R_L C_c \qquad (3.5.12)$$

gives:

$$A_1 = \frac{A_{01}(1+s/\omega_2)}{1+s/\omega_1+s/\omega_2+s/\omega_3+s/\omega_4+s^2/\omega_1\omega_2+s^2/\omega_2\omega_4} \qquad (3.5.13)$$

To simplify this expression the relative values of the ω's must be examined. Because of the A_{02} factor, ω_3 will be much less than the others so the only s term retained is s/ω_3. For s^2 the choice is less clear. For satisfactory response at high frequency a value $C_c \approx C_L$ is appropriate, so assume $\omega_1 \doteq \omega_4$. Small deviations will have small effect and, in practice, strays will also be important here. Equation (3.5.13) can then be written:

$$A_1 = \frac{A_{01}(1+s/\omega_2)}{1+s/\omega_3+2s^2/\omega_1\omega_2} \qquad (3.5.14)$$

There is, thus, a zero at $\omega_z = \omega_2$, as required to cancel the pole of A_2, and two poles at:

$$s = \frac{-\omega_1\omega_2}{4\omega_3} \pm \frac{\omega_1\omega_2}{4\omega_3}\left(1-\frac{8\omega_3^2}{\omega_1\omega_2}\right)^{1/2}$$

$$= \frac{-\omega_1\omega_2}{4\omega_3} \pm \frac{\omega_1\omega_2}{4\omega_3}\left(1-\frac{4\omega_3^2}{\omega_1\omega_2}\right)$$

$$s_a = -\omega_3, \qquad s_b = \frac{-\omega_1\omega_2}{2\omega_3}+\omega_3 \doteq \frac{-\omega_1\omega_2}{2\omega_3} = \frac{-\omega_2 A_{02}}{2} \qquad (3.5.15)$$

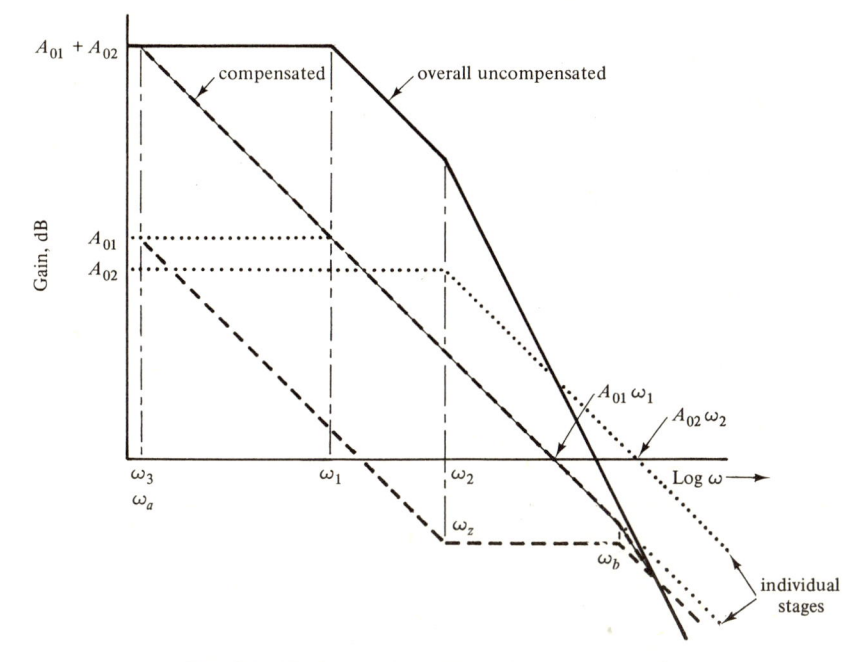

Fig. 3.5.5 Bode plot for Miller-effect compensation

The gain at the zero will be:

$$G_z = \frac{A_{01}\omega_3}{\omega_2}, \quad \text{cutting } A_1 \text{ at } \omega_2 A_{02} \qquad (3.5.16)$$

The individual and combined responses can now be drawn, as in Fig. 3.5.5.

The unity-gain frequency of the compensated combined response is easily seen to be $A_{01}\omega_1$. The validity of this treatment is shown by the responses for an actual amplifier [b1] illustrated in Fig. 3.5.6. (The compensation capacitor $C_c = 30$ pF.) For consideration of values of C_L see Tobey *et al.* [a1, p. 17], who find values varying from 1·5 to 150 pF depending on source impedance.)

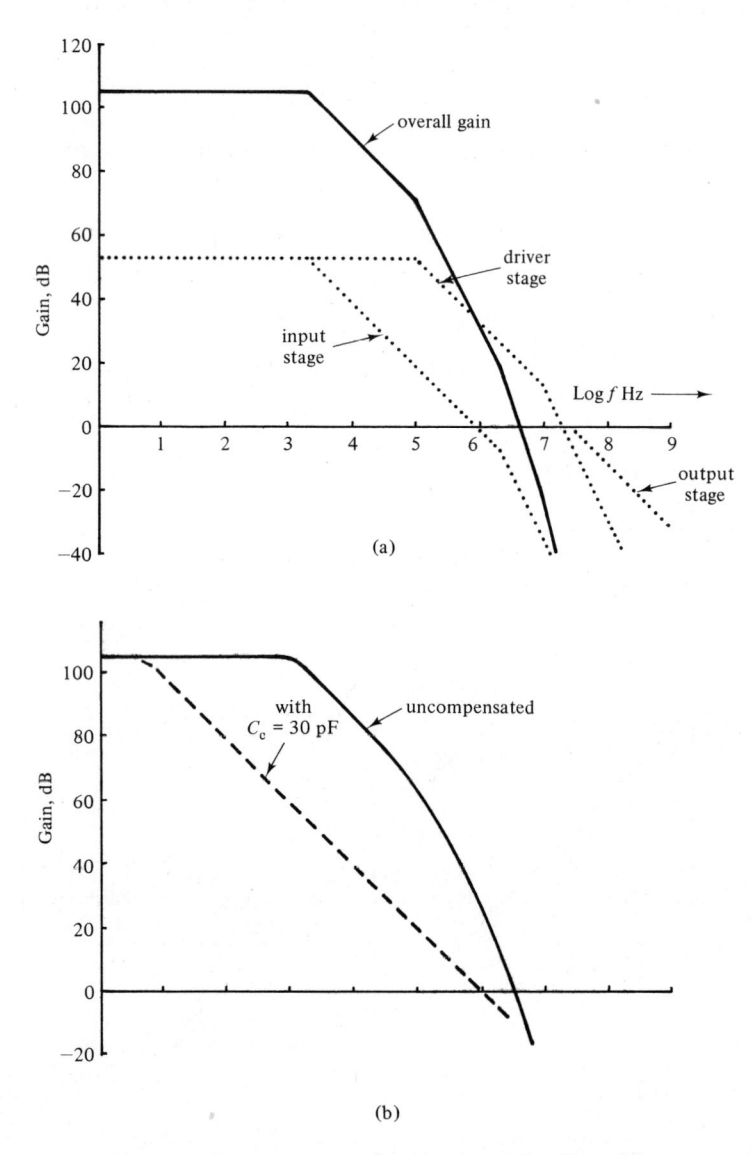

Fig. 3.5.6 **Frequency response for compensated amplifier**

3.5(c) *Feedforward compensation*

Operational amplifiers generally have high gain, high impedance, input stages, and often use lateral *PNP* transistors in this part of the circuit; see Sec. 1.10(d). All these factors adversely affect the frequency response. If this stage can be bypassed for high frequencies only, the lower gain wide bandwidth stages will be effective. The situation will then be similar to that discussed for the chopper-stabilized amplifier (Sec. 2.3(b)), except that there the intention is to improve the low-frequency (d.c.) performance. A capacitor, C_f, connected as shown in Fig. 3.5.7 feeds the high frequency signal forward around the input stage, in contrast to the more usual feedback.

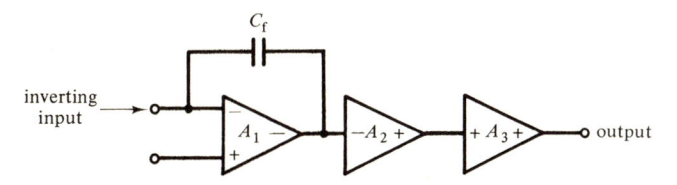

Fig. 3.5.7 Feedforward compensation

The feedforward capacitor must be connected between non-inverted signal points as shown: if C_f were connected otherwise overall positive feedback and, hence, instability would result when the external feedback loop is closed. As shown, however, there is positive feedback around the input stage, so care must be taken that this does not itself lead to local instability. Because of the lower gain now involved, and if C_f is not too large, this local positive feedback can be maintained below the critical level, i.e., $A\beta < 1$. A resistance in series with C_f, and the overall negative feedback when the main loop is closed, improve stability.

To illustrate the technique and its effects, consider the same stage responses as illustrated in Fig. 3.5.6 and redrawn in Fig. 3.5.8.

At low frequencies the signal will pass via A_1 rather than C_f and vice versa at high frequencies. In an intermediate region the two signals will be of near equal magnitude and, if the phases were opposite, the combined gain would be zero. This would lead to large phase shifts and hence instability, so some care is necessary here. At low frequencies the gain will be $A_1.A_2.A_3 (= A_1 + A_2 + A_3$ dB) while at high frequencies it will be only $A_2.A_3$ $(= A_2 + A_3$ dB). Provided no significant cancellation occurs as just described, the total overall response will pass smoothly from one to the other.

Table 3.5.1 Effect of compensation method on response of L141 amplifiers

Type:	L148		L148		L141 (741)	
Compensation:	Feedforward		Standard		Internal Miller	
G, dB	BW	SR	BW	SR	BW	SR
0	900	25	850	0·5	850	0·5
10	900	30	700	1·5	280	0·5
20	750	30	700	3	85	0·5
30	700	40	500	5	28	0·5
40	500	13	200	5	8·5	0·5

BW = bandwidth, kHz; SR = slewing rate, V/μs

It is evident from the figure, that increased bandwidth is available for all values of closed-loop gain. Partly as a consequence of this, but mostly because of the form of the compensation, there is a considerable improvement in slewing rate. The magnitude of the improvement possible is indicated by the figures in Table 3.5.1 [b1]. Included are values for the type 741 amplifier which is essentially the same, but is internally compensated using the Miller technique.

The full bandwidth shown in Fig. 3.5.8 is not obtained, because of the small amount of extra compensation required for stability. The greater slope of the gain curve and hence the greater phase shift means that this form of compensation is more susceptible to the effect of capacitive loads on the output. The effect can be

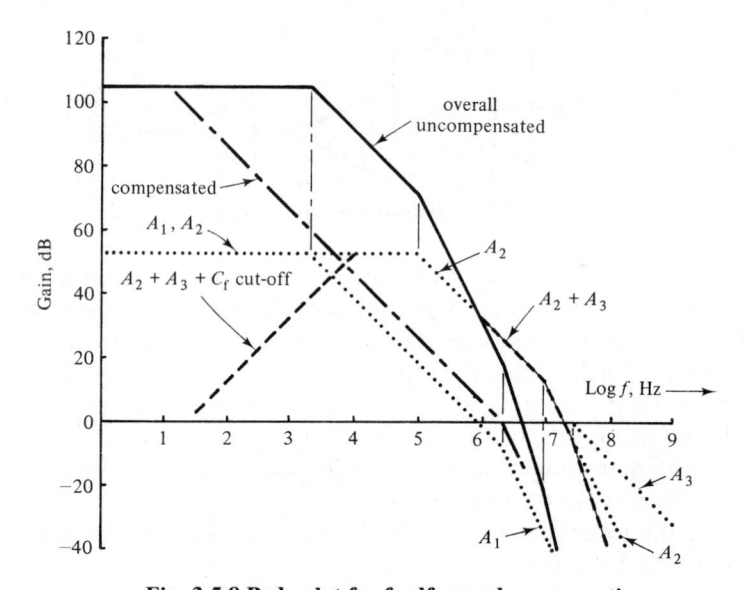

Fig. 3.5.8 Bode plot for feedforward compensation

eliminated by connecting a small resistor of a few hundred ohms between the amplifier output and the load. The feedback resistor should then be connected to the load to maintain the low output impedance (see Fig. 3.6.3).

Feedforward is not applicable to non-inverting amplifiers as the bypassing of the large phase shift stages would not exist for the overall feedback signal.

Feedforward compensation of particular amplifiers is discussed in [d1, c1, e1, l1].

3.6 12 dB/octave operational amplifiers

The emphasis so far has been on realizing a 6 dB/octave roll-off to ensure stability with various feedback configurations. Although this makes amplifiers easy to use, a price must be paid. The price is a considerable limitation in bandwidth with consequent limitation of loop-gain, and decrease in slewing rate. If a faster roll-off can be coped with, considerably improved performance in these respects is the result. Figure 3.6.1 compares the bandwidth and loop-gain of a 6 dB and 12 dB/octave amplifier for a given closed-loop gain and unity-gain frequency.

In this case:

$$\frac{\omega_{12}}{\omega_6} = \frac{\omega_{12c}}{\omega_{6c}} = A_0^{1/2} \qquad (3.6.1)$$

i.e., for a gain of 100 the bandwidth is 10 times greater. The advantages of 12 dB/octave amplifiers have been considered by Burwen [a1]. In addition to the increase in loop-gain at high frequencies, slewing rate, recovery from overloads, and broadband noise performance are improved.

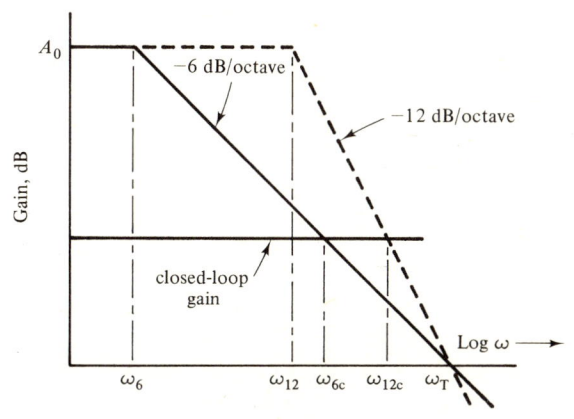

Fig. 3.6.1 12 dB/octave amplifier frequency response

From what has been said before, it is evident that considerable care is necessary if instability is to be avoided even with purely resistive feedback elements. For this case, stability may be achieved by shunting the feedback resistor, R_f, with a small capacitor, C_f, chosen so that the pole introduced at $\omega_2 = 1/R_f C_f$ occurs somewhat below (say 20 to 30 per cent below) the intercept frequency (Fig. 3.6.2).

The intercept is now no longer at a slope of 12 dB/octave at ω_3, but ≈ 6 dB/octave at ω_4. As discussed in Sec. 3.4 the system, therefore, will be stable. The optimum value for C_f is best obtained experimentally by feeding in a square wave and adjusting C_f for best transient response.

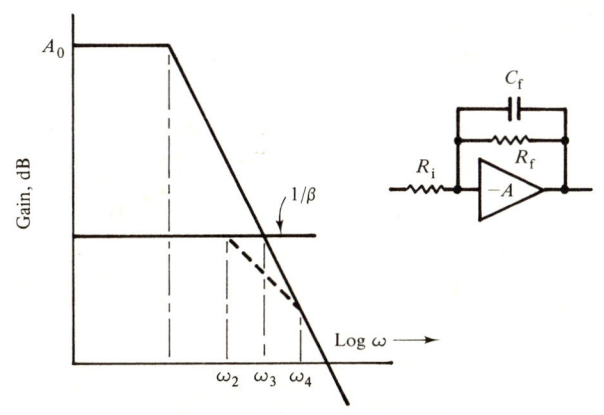

Fig. 3.6.2 12 dB/octave amplifier compensation

This stabilization technique is also applicable to the non-inverting configuration, but because of stray capacity between output and (+) input it may be necessary to connect a capacitor between (+) and ground, especially with high source impedance. This unfortunately reduces the input impedance (usually one of the main reasons for using this configuration) so it is desirable to introduce some shielding between input and output.

The stability of 12 dB/octave amplifiers is also more affected by load impedance than is a 6 dB/octave amplifier. Large capacitive loads may be isolated as before by a small resistance, R_o, so that the high frequency feedback via C_f is unaffected by the load (Fig. 3.6.3).

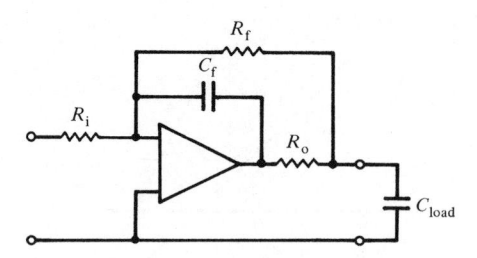

Fig. 3.6.3 Stabilization against capacitive loads

Large capacitive loads may arise, for example, when driving a long cable which may have a capacity of 60 to 100 pF/m. If the input is also connected via a cable, or in the case of a differentiator, then a small resistor is interposed between the capacity and the virtual ground.

3.7 Transient response

Not only is this important from the point of view of the response to fast step or pulse input signals, but also because examination of the response to such input provides a quick and easy indication of the frequency response. The instrumentation necessary to carry out such measurements is generally simpler than for sine waves, and there are other advantages such as independent control over signal level (pulse height) and average power (pulse repetition frequency) [b1]. Measurements may not be quite as accurate as with sine waves, but for the present purpose this difference is quite acceptable.

Some mention of transient response has already been made in Sec. 3.2 in considering the root-locus plot for a two pole system. Such systems lead to second order equations that are readily solved to give reasonably simple parametric results. In systems of interest here, even if these are more than two poles, there will usually be one or two dominant poles that control the response, the others having only minor effect. These factors indicate that restriction of discussion to two pole systems will still provide a generally useful guide to transient response.

The closed-loop gain for a two pole system is from Eqs. (3.2.1), (3.2.5), and (3.2.10):

$$G(s) = \frac{-A_0}{1 + \dfrac{s}{Q\omega_0} + \left(\dfrac{s}{\omega_0}\right)^2} \qquad (3.7.1)$$

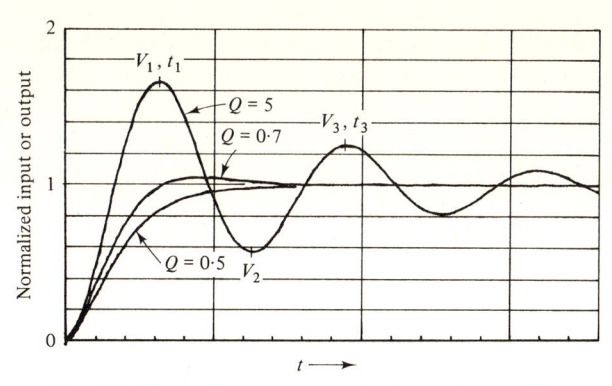

Fig. 3.7.1 Transient response of a two pole amplifier

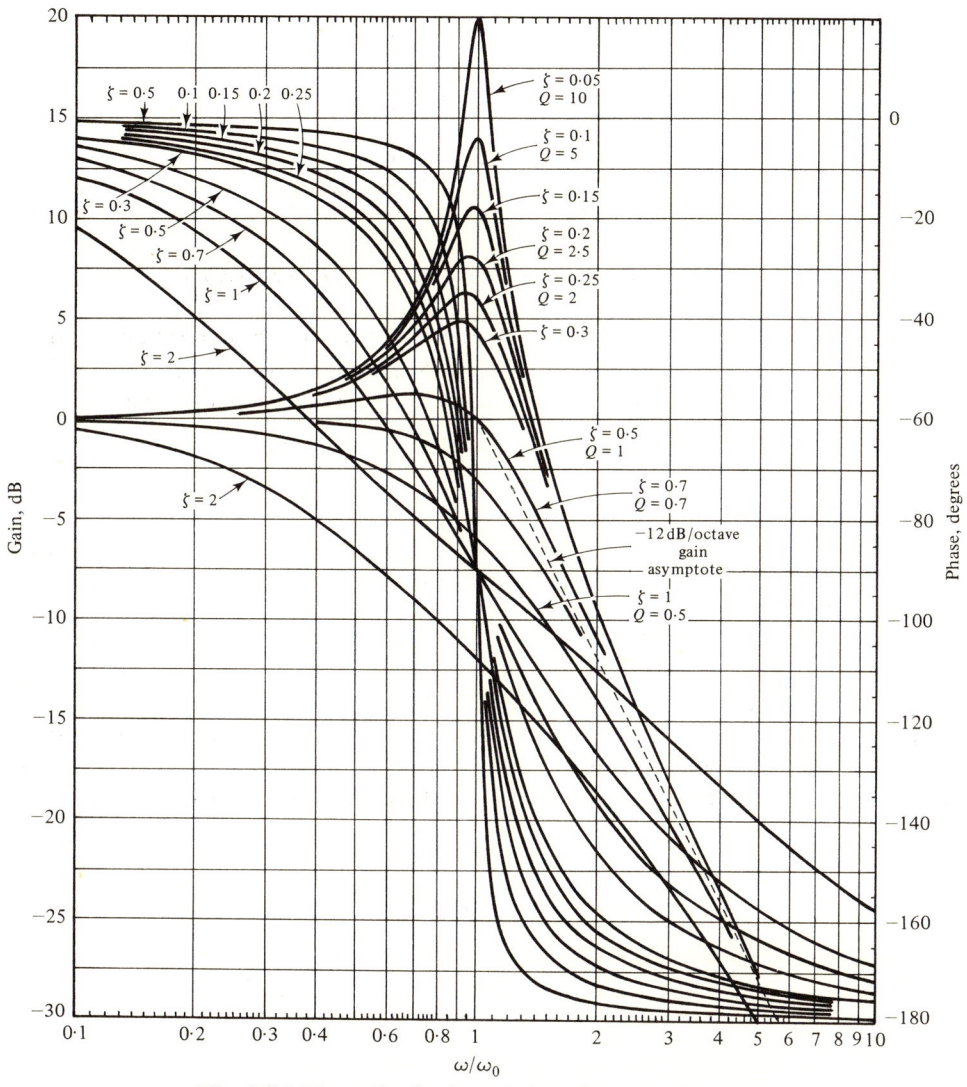

Fig. 3.7.2 Normalized gain and phase for two pole system

From Eq. (3.2.11) the response will be aperiodic for $Q \leq 0.5$, and overshoot or ring for values greater than this. This is shown in Fig. 3.7.1 for a unit step input.

Normalized curves of Eq. (3.7.1) can be drawn (Fig. 3.7.2) showing the magnitude and phase response as a function of normalized frequency ω/ω_0 [a1, c1, e1]. (Note that in reference [a1] the symbols correspond to those used here as: $\zeta = 1/2Q$, $\omega_n = \omega_0$, $\omega_0 = 1/T_1$, $\omega_1 = 1/T_2$.)

The amount of peaking as a function of Q is shown in Fig. 3.7.3.

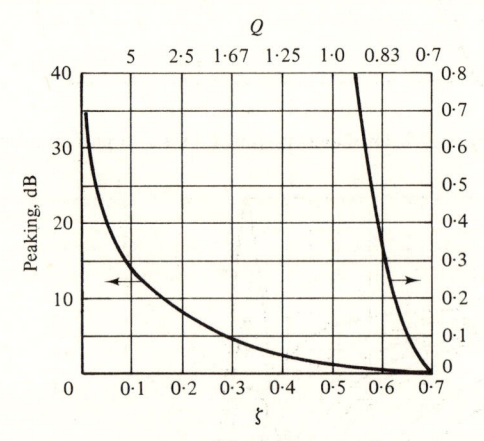

Fig. 3.7.3 Peaking as a function of Q for a two pole system; see Eq. (3.7.4)

The question is now, how can the actual response curves be determined from the transient response? This has been considered by Huehne [a1], who shows that if the amplitudes and time measurements indicated in Fig. 3.7.1 are made, then:

$$Q = \frac{[(\log X)^2 + 1.86]^{1/2}}{2 \log X}, \quad X = \frac{V_1 - V_3}{V_2} \quad (3.7.2)$$

$$\omega_0 = \frac{4\pi Q}{(t_3 - t_1)(4Q^2 - 1)^{1/2}} \quad (3.7.3)$$

$$\text{dB peaking} = 20 \log \left[\frac{2Q^2}{(4Q^2 - 1)^{1/2}} \right] \quad (3.7.4)$$

Thus, the high frequency response may be readily determined. If the system response does not extend to d.c. there will also be a low frequency cut-off. If this is due to a single CR coupling (Fig. 3.7.4), or if one of the couplings is dominant, then the low frequency cut-off, f_1, can again easily be determined by pulse testing [b1].

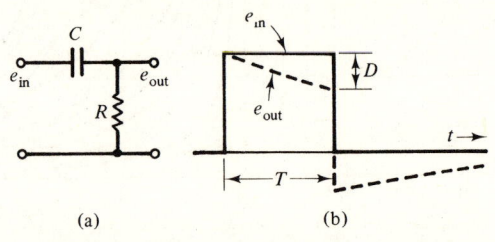

Fig. 3.7.4 (a) Equivalent amplifier time constant, (b) effect on square pulse

In this case a suitably long pulse duration is used and the amount of droop, D, in the output pulse height is measured. The amplitude will decay as $\exp(-t/RC)$ which, if t is not too long, can be approximated by $(1-t/RC)$. For $t=\tfrac{1}{3}RC$ the error is about 15 per cent. Thus, if the pulse period, T, is adjusted until $D \leqslant 30$ per cent, say, then:

$$D = \frac{100T}{RC}, \qquad f_1 = \frac{1}{2\pi RC} = \frac{0.16\, D}{100T} \qquad (3.7.5)$$

If more than one time constant is effective the response is not so simple [d1, p. 40], but sinusoidal measurements are relatively easy at low frequencies, and the response is obtained directly.

References section 3.1: Introduction

- a1 Kahn M: The Versatile Op Amp; Holt, Rinehart and Winston 1970.
- b1 Thomason J G: Linear Feedback Analysis; Pergamon 1955.
- c1 Faulkner E A: Introduction to the Theory of Linear Systems; Chapman and Hall 1969.
- d1 DeRoy B E: Automatic Control Theory; Wiley 1966.
- e1 Gray P E, Searle C L: Electronic Principles, Physics, Models and Circuits; Wiley 1969.
- f1 D'Azzo J, Houpis C: Feedback Control Systems Analysis and Synthesis; McGraw-Hill 1966.
- g1 Hewlett-Packard: Using the 675A/676A Network Analyzer as an Educational Tool; Hewlett-Packard Application Note 112–2.
- h1 Thaler G J, Brown R G: Analysis and Design of Feedback Control Systems; McGraw-Hill 1960.
- i1 James H M, Nichols N B, Phillips R S: Theory of Servomechanisms; McGraw-Hill 1947.
- j1 Roddam T: Root Hog or Die: Frequency in Two Dimensions; Wireless World 76, 281–284, June 1970.
- k1 Ghausi M S: Electronic Circuits. Devices, Models, Functions, Analysis, and Design; Van Nostrand Reinhold 1971.
- l1 Bode H W: Network Analysis and Feedback Amplifier Design; Van Nostrand 1945.
- m1 Clayton G B: Operational Amplifiers; Butterworths 1971.

Reference section 3.2: The root locus

- a1 Thomason J G: Linear Feedback Analysis; Pergamon 1955.

References section 3.3: The Nyquist diagram

- a1 Edwin G, Roddam T: Principles of Feedback Design; Iliffe 1964.
- b1 Thomason J G: Linear Feedback Analysis; Pergamon 1955.
- c1 Faulkner E A: Introduction to the Theory of Linear Systems; Chapman and Hall 1969.
- d1 Gray P E, Searle C L: Electronic Principles, Physics, Models and Circuits; Wiley 1969.
- e1 Millman J, Taub H: Pulse Digital and Switching Waveforms; McGraw-Hill 1965.
- f1 Nyquist H: Regeneration Theory; Bell Sys. Tech. J 11, 126–147, 1932.

References section 3.4: The Bode plot

- a1 Thibodeaux E: The HA-2530/2535 Wideband High Slew Inverting Amplifier; Harris Semiconductor Application Note 516, Feb. 1974.
- b1 Bode H W: Network Analysis and Feedback Amplifier Design; Van Nostrand 1945.
- c1 Albrecht W G: Stability from Bode Diagrams; Electronic Products, June 1963, 40–42.

References section 3.5: Phase compensation

a1 Tobey G E, Graeme J G, Huelsman L P: Operational Amplifiers: Design and Applications; McGraw-Hill 1971.
b1 Murari B, Bondini A: L148 Operational Amplifier; SGS Technical Bulletin 110, Mar. 1971.
c1 Bladowski R, Murari B, Riva G M: A DC-Broadband Amplifier Using Feedforward; SGS Technical Note 374, Apr. 1966.
d1 Dobkin R C: LM118 Op Amp Slews 70V/µs; National Semiconductor Linear Brief 17, Sep. 1971.
e1 Dobkin R C: Feedforward Compensation Speeds Op Amp; National Semiconductor Linear Brief 2, 1969.
f1 Kesner D: A Simple Technique for Extending Op Amp Power Bandwidth; Motorola Application Note AN-459, 1969.
g1 Slomkowski J, Mann R: SN72709 Frequency Compensation; Texas Instruments Application Report B59, 1968.
h1 RCA: Linear Integrated Circuits; RCA Technical Series IC-41, 1967, 91–108.
i1 Wojslaw C F: Prevent Op-Amp Output Instability; Electronic Design 16 Aug. 1974, 98–100.
j1 Widlar R J: Monolithic Op Amp with Simplified Frequency Compensation; EEE 15, 58–63, July 1967.
k1 Barker R W J: Compensation Techniques for Operational Amplifiers; Electronic Components 23 July 1971, 813–814.
l1 Dobkin R C: Speed Up the LM108 with Feedforward Compensation; National Semiconductor Linear Brief LB-14, 1970.
m1 Dobkin R C: Fast Compensation Extends Power Bandwidth; National Semiconductor Linear Brief LB-4, 1969.
n1 Gazin J F: Manuel d'Applications CIL. Tome 3: Filtres Actifs a Amplificateurs Operationnels; Sescosem (Thomson-CSF) 1974.
o1 Murari B, Bondini A: L115 Wide Band Operational Amplifier; SGS Product Profile 101, Feb. 1971.
p1 Ott W: Combine Two Op Amps to Avoid the Speed Accuracy Compromise; Electron 27 Feb. 1974, 42.
q1 Pease R A: Op Amps and Feedback Capacitance; Electronic Eng. 44, Feb. 1972, 54, 56.

Reference section 3.6: 12dB/octave operational amplifiers

a1 Burwen R S: Advantages of 12dB/octave Operational Amplifier and their Application; Analog Devices Application Note.

References section 3.7: Transient response

a1 Huehne K: Using Transient Response to Determine Operational Amplifier Stability; Motorola Application Note AN-460, 1969.
b1 Skilling J K: Pulse and Frequency Response; General Radio Experimenter Nov.–Dec. 1968, 3–10.
c1 D'Azzo J, Houpis C: Feedback Control Systems Analysis and Synthesis; McGraw-Hill 1966.
d1 Millman J, Taub H: Pulse Digital and Switching Waveforms; McGraw-Hill 1965.
e1 James H M, Nichols N B, Phillips R S: Theory of Servomechanisms; McGraw-Hill 1947.
f1 Apfel R J, Gray P R: A Fast Settling Monolithic Operational Amplifier Using Doublet Compression Techniques; IEEE J SC-9, 332–340, 1974.
g1 Kamath B Y, Meyer R G, Gray P R: Relationship Between Frequency Response and Settling Time of Operational Amplifiers; IEEE J SC-9, 347–352, 1974.
h1 Thibodeaux E: Predict Wideband Amplifier Response with a Simple Graphical Procedure; Electronic Design 6 Dec. 1974, 68–71.

4 Amplifiers

4.1 Low-noise amplifiers

Basic noise considerations are discussed in Sec. 1.8. We consider here the noise characteristics of bipolar and FET devices, and the effect of these on practical low-noise circuit design. The treatment outlined here follows Faulkner [m1].

4.1(a) Bipolar transistors

The noisy bipolar transistor can be represented by one of the standard equivalent circuits (Sec. 1.9(b)) with extra noise generators added [m1, n1, o1, p1, q1, l1] (Fig. 4.1.1).

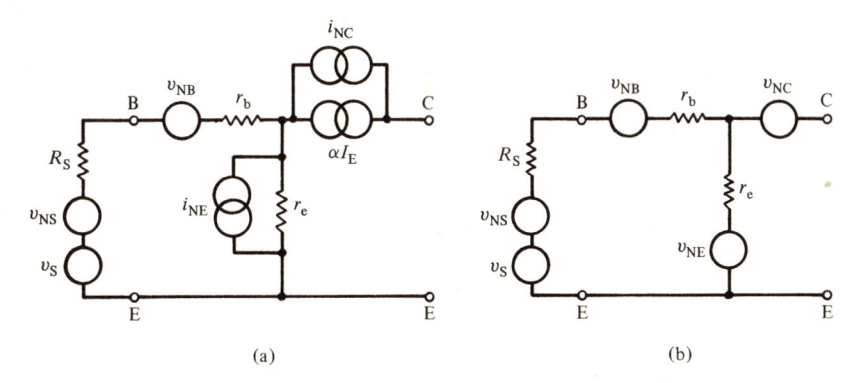

Fig. 4.1.1 (a) Equivalent circuit for noisy bipolar amplifier, (b) Thévenin equivalent circuit

The values of the noise generators are given by:

$$\langle v_{NB}^2 \rangle = 4kTr_b \, \Delta f$$
$$\langle i_{NE}^2 \rangle = 2qI_E \, \Delta f \qquad (4.1.1)$$
$$\langle i_{NC}^2 \rangle = 2qI_C \, \Delta f / \beta$$

$\langle i_{NC}^2 \rangle$ increases at high frequencies as a result of fall off of β, and will be 3 dB up at $\omega = \omega_T / (\beta_0)^{1/2}$. It also increases at low frequencies because of $1/f$ noise, see Sec. 1.8(c), the corner frequency being ω_F. $\langle i_{NC}^2 \rangle$ can then be written for the low frequency region:

$$\langle i_{NC}^2 \rangle = 2qI_C \, \Delta f (1 + \omega_F / \omega) / \beta_0 \qquad (4.1.2)$$

To find the noise figure, Fig. 4.1.1(a) can be transformed to the Thévenin equivalent, Fig. 4.1.1(b), where the collector noise generator is transferred to the base circuit. The noise voltage generators are given by:

$$\langle v_{NC}^2 \rangle = \frac{\langle i_{NC}^2 \rangle}{g_m^2} = \frac{2kT\Delta f(1+\omega_F/\omega)}{g_m \beta_0} \quad \left(g_m = \frac{qI_C}{kT}\right)$$

$$\langle v_{NE}^2 \rangle = \langle i_{NE}^2 \rangle r_e^2 = 2kT\Delta f r_e \quad \left(r_e = \frac{kT}{qI_E}\right) \quad (4.1.3)$$

$$\langle v_{NS}^2 \rangle = 4kT\Delta f R_S$$

The noise figure, Eq. (1.8.5), is then [with $R^2 \equiv (R_S + r_b + r_e)^2$]:

$$F = \frac{\langle v_S^2 \rangle R^2}{\langle v_S^2 \rangle \langle v_{NS}^2 \rangle r_e^2} \left[\frac{\langle v_{NS}^2 \rangle r_e^2}{R^2} + \frac{\langle v_{NB}^2 \rangle r_e^2}{R^2} + \frac{\langle v_{NE}^2 \rangle r_e^2}{R^2} + \langle v_{NC}^2 \rangle \right]$$

$$= 1 + \frac{r_b}{R_S} + \frac{r_e}{2R_S} + \frac{(R_S + r_b + r_e)^2(1+\omega_F/\omega)}{2r_e R_S \beta_0} \quad (4.1.4)$$

To get this into the standard form, Eq. (1.8.7), let:

$$\beta_0' = \beta_0/(1+\omega_F/\omega) \gg 1; \quad R_S \gg r_e, r_b \quad (4.1.5)$$

then:

$$F = 1 + \frac{(r_b + r_e/2)}{R_S} + \frac{R_S}{2\beta_0' r_e} \quad (4.1.6)$$

From Eqs. (1.8.7), (1.8.8), (1.8.9), therefore, we have:

$$R_{NV} = r_b + r_e/2; \quad R_{NI} = 2\beta_0' r_e \quad (4.1.7)$$

$$R_{S(opt)} = (R_{NV} R_{NI})^{1/2} = [(r_b + r_e/2)(2\beta_0' r_e)]^{1/2} \doteq r_e(\beta_0')^{1/2} \quad (4.1.8)$$

$$F_{min} = 1 + 2\left(\frac{R_{NV}}{R_{NI}}\right)^{1/2} = 1 + 2\left[\frac{(r_b + r_e/2)}{2\beta_0' r_e}\right]^{1/2}$$

$$\doteq 1 + \frac{1}{(\beta_0')^{1/2}} \quad (\text{for } r_b \ll r_e, \omega > \omega_F) \quad (4.1.9)$$

Thus, for low noise performance a high value of β is of the first importance, allowing that the various conditions, Eq. (4.1.5) and $r_e \gg r_b$, are met. At low or high frequencies there will be further requirements, i.e., low ω_F and high ω_T [11].

The low frequency input resistance of the transistor in common emitter configuration is (Sec. 1.9):

$$R_i = r_b + h_{feo} r_e \doteq \beta_0 r_e = (\beta_0)^{1/2} R_{S(opt)} \quad (4.1.10)$$

This shows that for low noise operation the input resistance $R_i \gg R_{S(opt)}$, i.e., the transistor is operating as a voltage amplifier; see Sec. 1.9(b). It should be noted that there is very little difference in noise performance between the three transistor configurations, common base, emitter, or collector [p1, q1] at least at low and medium frequencies. The variation of F with frequency at higher frequencies is shown schematically in Fig. 4.1.2. The apparent advantage of the common collector circuit at higher frequencies is usually of little use, since the power gain will be less than unity and there will be substantial noise contribution from the following stage [q1].

Measurements on a number of low-noise transistors with particular regard to the $1/f$ noise corner frequency, ω_F, are reported in [11]. Note there that the results are given in terms of $\omega_L = \omega_F/\beta_0$, where ω_L is the frequency below which low noise performance has effectively ceased.

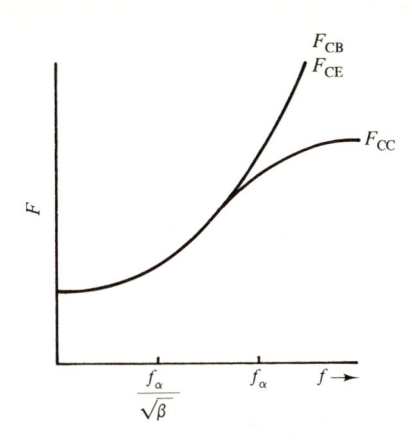

Fig. 4.1.2 Variation of noise figure of a transistor with frequency

4.1(b) *Field effect transistors*

Insulated gate devices (IGFETS or MOSFETS) have much higher noise figures than junction types (JFETS) so we will only consider the latter [r1, f2, d2, G1, H1, K1, U1, t2].

The noise sources in the JFET are:

(i) thermal noise in the channel equivalent to a drain current generator [n1]:

$$\langle i_{ND}^2 \rangle = \tfrac{2}{3} 4kT \Delta f\, g_m$$

or $\qquad \langle v_{ND}^2 \rangle = \dfrac{8kT \Delta f}{3 g_m}$ in the gate circuit (4.1.11)

(ii) shot noise due to reverse gate leakage current I_G:

$$\langle i_{NG}^2 \rangle = 2q I_G \Delta f \qquad (4.1.12)$$

which is of importance at low frequencies particularly:

(iii) fluctuations in the channel under the gate:

$$\langle i_{NC}^2 \rangle = \frac{\omega^2 C^2}{4 g_m} \cdot 4kT \Delta f \qquad (4.1.13)$$

where C is the input capacitance. At high frequencies $i_{NC} \gg i_{NG}$ owing to the ω^2 term. The equivalent circuit is then as shown in Fig. 4.1.3.

These noise generators can be transformed to equivalent series (R_{NV}) and parallel (R_{NI}) noise resistances. At low frequencies i_{NC} may be neglected, giving:

$$R_{NV} = 2/3\, g_m \text{ ohm} \quad (g_m \text{ in A/V})$$
$$R_{NI} = 2kT/qI_G = 0.052/I_G \text{ ohm} \quad (I_G \text{ in ampere})$$ (4.1.14)

In JFET's flicker noise affects R_{NV}, from Eq. (4.1.11), rather than R_{NI} in the bipolar case, see Eq. (4.1.7), so that for frequencies below ω_F, R_{NV} should be multiplied by $(1+\omega_F/\omega)$ to give an approximate representation of the noise in this region.

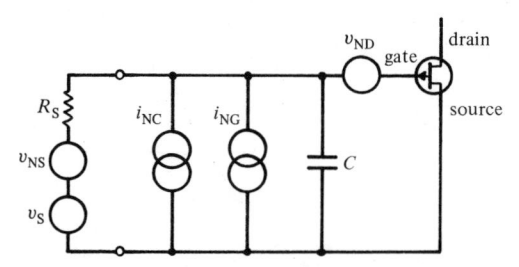

Fig. 4.1.3 Equivalent circuit for noisy JFET

Knowing R_{NV} and R_{NI}, Eq. (4.1.14), we find as before:

$$F = 1 + \frac{2}{3R_S g_m} + \frac{qI_G R_S}{2kT}$$

$$F_{min} = 1 + \left(\frac{4qI_G}{3kTg_m}\right)^{1/2} = 1 + 7\cdot 2\left(\frac{I_G}{g_m}\right)^{1/2} \quad (4.1.15)$$

$$R_{S(opt)} = \left(\frac{4kT}{3g_m qI_G}\right)^{1/2} = \frac{0\cdot 185}{(g_m I_G)^{1/2}} \text{ ohm} \quad (4.1.16)$$

For example, with $I_G = 10^{-10}$ A, and $g_m = 5\cdot 10^{-3}$ A/V:

$$R_{NV} = 132 \ \Omega \qquad F_{min} = 1\cdot 001 = 0\cdot 004 \text{ dB}$$
$$R_{NI} = 515 \text{ M}\Omega \qquad R_{S(opt)} = 260 \text{ k}\Omega$$

It is evident that the JFET can be an excellent low-noise amplifier and is inherently better than the bipolar transistor. However, this advantage is at present only obtained for high source resistances, $R_{S(opt)}$, which are less commonly encountered in low noise systems. With these high resistances, the effects of source and device capacity must be considered. It seems likely that improvements in the fabrication of JFET's will enable them to be used for much lower values of R_S.

For capacitive sources the JFET is a good choice, and it may also be suitable when matching over a wide range of source impedances. Note that paralleled devices can be used to match to lower source impedance; Sec. 4.1(c) [u1, b2, m2, X1, s1].

4.1(c) *Practical low noise circuit design*

Practical design will generally make use of discrete devices rather than IC's, to enable optimum conditions to be obtained. Some consideration of IC devices will be given in Sec. 4.1(d). The approach used in the following discussion again is taken from [m1].

If R_S is known, then the correct operating condition is set by choice of I_C for a bipolar transistor. Since the flicker-noise corner frequency falls as I_C is decreased, a minimum value of I_C should be used if this frequency region is of interest. However, this assumes that β_0 is independent of I_C, whereas it also decreases. Thus, for a desired noise figure, F_1, the condition fixing I_C is obtained by equating the last two terms of Eq. (4.1.6); see Eq. (1.8.8):

$$r_b + r_e/2 = R_s(F_1 - 1)/2 \qquad (4.1.17)$$

where
$$r_e = \frac{kT}{qI_E} = \frac{kT}{qI_C} = \frac{26}{I_C} \quad (I_C \text{ is in milliampere})$$

In practice, a noise figure of 1 dB ($\times 1\cdot 26$) is hardly distinguishable from the ideal of 0 dB ($\times 1$). However, if matching over a wide range of R_S is required, a value of $F_{min} \ll 1$ dB should be aimed at, to ensure low noise operation over the range of R_S. As a practical measure we may take $F \lesssim 3$ dB ($\times 2$) as the criterion of a low noise amplifier.

Assuming a good (100 ohm) or typical (200 ohm) value for r_b, r_e is calculated and hence I_C. If $r_e \gg r_b$, then the value of r_b has little effect. This implies that $I_C \lesssim 250$ μA. If $r_b \gtrsim r_e$, or r_e is negative, an alternative approach must be used. One means is to connect n^2 transistors in parallel, which leads to a combined amplifier with R_{NV} and R_{NI} both reduced by n^2. F_{min}, Eq. (1.8.9), is unchanged but $R_{S(opt)}$ is reduced by n^2 [s1, m1]. A second approach is the use of a transformer of ratio n. A good transformer will not contribute significant noise, but will transform the source resistance R_S to $n^2 R_S = R_{S(opt)}$ for the amplifier. Consideration should be given to the high frequency response, which will be affected by the transformer winding capacity and by the materials and mode of construction.

Once the input stage has been designed, the second stage must be examined to ensure that it does not increase the noise figure significantly. Consider the situation when $R_S = 0$, in which case the first stage generates minimum noise so that any contribution from stage two will be of the greatest significance. With $R_S = 0$, the contribution of R_{NI1} will be zero, and that of R_{NV1}, $\langle v_{NV1}^2 \rangle = 2kT \Delta f r_{e1}$ for $r_{b1} \ll r_{e1}$. This gives an output noise current from the first stage of $2kT \Delta f/r_{e1}$. Since we usually require a good voltage gain, and a good noise figure is obtained when the transistor is operated as a voltage amplifier, a large value of collector load resistance, R_{C1}, will be used (this includes the shunting effect of the second stage input resistance). In this situation, it is R_{NI2} that is of importance rather than R_{NV2}. Thus, a first condition to be satisfied is that the first stage output noise current be much greater than that due to R_{NI2}:

$$2kT \Delta f/r_{e1} \gg 2kT \Delta f/\beta'_{02} r_{e2}$$

or
$$\beta'_{02} r_{e2} \gg r_{e1} \qquad (4.1.18)$$

In an extreme situation β'_{02} may approach unity so that, to be quite sure, we should make:

$$r_{e2} = r_{e1} \qquad (4.1.19)$$

i.e., the two d.c. collector currents equal. This is a conservative condition and may be relaxed towards Eq. (4.1.18) in many cases. To ensure that R_{NV2} is insignificant, as assumed, we must have the voltage noise across R_{C1} much greater than this:

$$2kT \Delta f R_{C1}^2/r_{e1} \gg 2kT \Delta f r_{e2}$$

or
$$R_{C1}^2 \gg r_{e1} r_{e2} \qquad (4.1.20)$$

which condition is easily satisfied. Here we are considering only common base or emitter circuits. Common collector (emitter follower) circuits are generally not suitable for low noise operation.

For JFET's the conditions are straightforward. The reverse gate current, I_G, should be small. The transfer conductance, g_m, must be as large as possible, which means that the drain current, I_D, should be as high as possible. Remember, however, that substantial power dissipation will raise the temperature and, hence, increase noise and gate leakage current. Values of R_{NV} of a few hundred ohms at frequencies

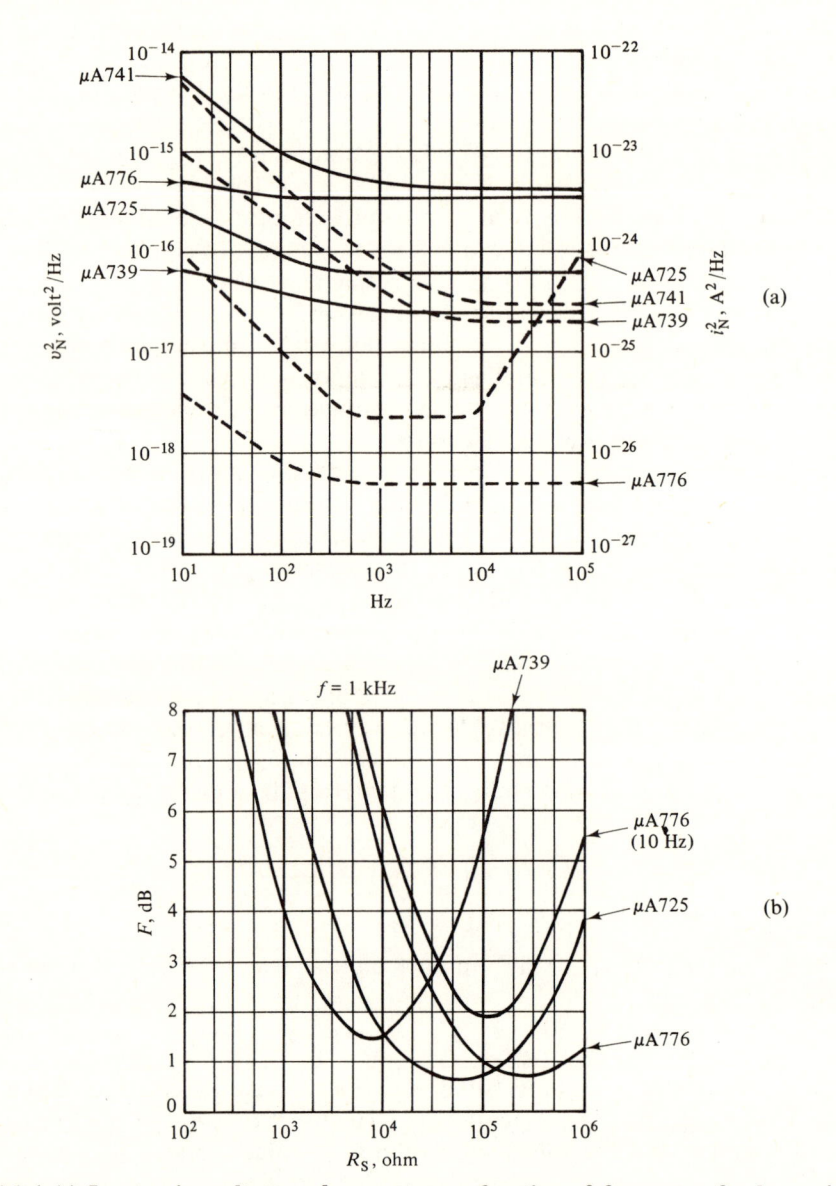

Fig. 4.1.4 (a) Input noise voltage and current as a function of frequency, for low noise IC amplifiers, (b) noise figure as a function of source resistance for low noise IC amplifiers ($f = 1$ kHz) (Courtesy Fairchild Semiconductor)

much greater than ω_F are possible, increasing to about 5 kΩ at 10 Hz. Even lower values have been reported [t1]. As for the bipolar transistor, paralleling and the use of transformers are applicable for achieving a match. A particular use of transformers is described in [j1].

The determination of the noise factor as described above does not necessarily give a complete picture of the noise performance of an amplifier. If the noise resistances, R_{NV}, R_{NI}, are independent of frequency then extending the bandwidth will increase source and amplifier noise equally, so that the noise factor is unchanged. However, in practice R_{NV} and R_{NI} are not independent of frequency, particularly in the low frequency $1/f$ region (see, for example, Fig. 4.1.4). Thus, the noise figure for wide-band operation depends on the actual frequencies, and the contributions of the different spectral regions must be added up in the appropriate manner. A discussion of this is given in [k1]. Although this refers in particular to operational amplifiers the discussion is quite general.

4.1(d) *Low noise IC amplifiers*

Integrated circuits are generally at a disadvantage in very low noise applications, since they cannot be matched to an arbitrary source resistance as the operating conditions of the input stage are fixed. There are a number of IC's specially made for low noise operation, e.g., μA739 (TBA231), MC1303, and μA725 [z1, b1, D1, h1]. These have noise spectra as shown in Fig. 4.1.4. On the basis of our 3 dB criterion, the μA739 is suitable for R_S values from about 1 to 50 kΩ, while the μA725 covers 10 kΩ to 1 MΩ. For the MC1303 the noise performance is given by graphs of output noise voltage against source resistance for various bandwidths.

The μA776 amplifier, see Sec. 4.8(a), is attractive in the context of low noise operation, since the operating conditions of the input stage can be controlled over quite a wide range to give optimum noise performance for differing R_S. For the

Table 4.1.1 Noise parameters of some IC amplifiers

	$f=1$ kHz				$f=10$ kHz			
	R_{NV}	R_{NI}	F_{min}	$R_{S\,(opt)}$	R_{NV}	R_{NI}	F_{min}	$R_{S\,(opt)}$
μA741	31·3	22·9	5·2	27	375	0·3	18·4	11
μA739 / TBA231	1·6	40	1·4	8	6·3	1·6	5	3·2
μA725	4·4	700	0·65	55	15·6	16	4·8	16
LM301 / LM307	15·6	229	1·8	60	31	16	5·8	22
μA776 (a)	22	3200	0·7	265	31	400	1·9	112
(b)	220	8900	1·2	1400	250	2670	2·1	820
(c)	3130	2×10^4	1·8	8000	—	—	—	—
8007	313	730	3·7	480	5600	133	11·5	860
MC1303	1 μV input for 10 Hz–10 kHz, 2 μV for 10 Hz–100 kHz, with $R_S=1$							
CA3048	3 μV input for 10 Hz–50 kHz, 2 dB at 1 kHz, 10 dB at 10 Hz, with $R_S=10$							
LM381	0·5 μV for 10 Hz–10 kHz with $R_S=0·6$							

Notes: All resistances, R, in kΩ, F in dB.
For μA776, I_{bias} for (a) = 15 μA, (b) = 1·5 μA, (c) = 0·1 μA

allowable variation of I_{bias}, the optimum source resistor varies from 100 kΩ to 10 MΩ for frequencies above about 100 Hz. This variation is shown graphically in the data sheet, so the appropriate bias current may be readily chosen. For low values of I_{bias}, the effect of the reduced transition frequency should be considered [11].

The performances of a number of low noise IC's are compared in Table 4.1.1. This shows calculated values of the parameters at two frequencies using the published noise spectra. The flicker noise corner frequency is generally in the region of a few hundred Hz to 1 kHz. Thus, as mentioned before, the effect of wide-band operation on the noise depends on the actual frequency limits, since the spectrum is not white [k1]. Figures for the μA741 are included as an indication of the difference between this *standard* IC and the low noise types.

Even if an IC amplifier is not suitable for the input stage it may be convenient to use one for the following stages. An example of this, using a 2N4019 dual low noise input transistor and a 741 IC amplifier is described in [a1].

4.2 Differential and instrumentation amplifiers

The simple operational difference amplifier is discussed in Sec. 2.5. Here we are concerned with special forms such as the differential in, differential out (DIDO [b1]) configuration and the non-operational instrumentation or data amplifier.

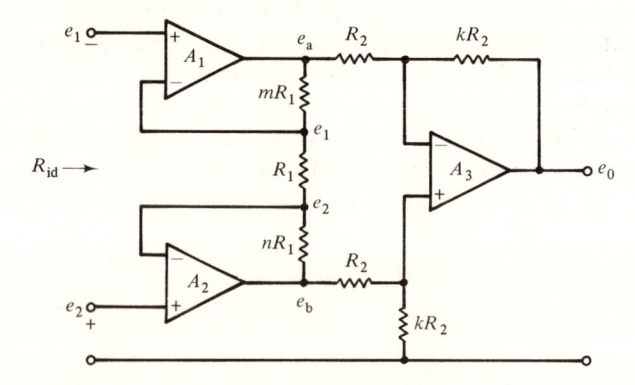

Fig. 4.2.1 Differential input, differential output instrumentation amplifier with converter to single-ended output

In many situations the basic operational differential amplifier suffers from several drawbacks [a1, A1, p1]. To reduce source loading errors a high input impedance is required. This requires high value input resistances, which result in unreasonably high feedback resistances if any gain is required, and in excessive bias current offsets. The prime reason for using differential amplifiers is to eliminate common-mode effects, and for this the values of the various resistors relative to each other must be carefully controlled. If the gain is to be varied two resistors must be changed, and the ratios of the values of the resistors must be kept constant to a high degree of accuracy. An arrangement that overcomes these difficulties is shown in Fig. 4.2.1. Two voltage followers provide high input impedance, and the cross-coupling substantially reduces common-mode effects.

Assuming ideal amplifiers (Sec. 2.2, $\Delta e \to 0$):

$$\frac{e_b - e_2}{nR_1} = \frac{e_2 - e_1}{R_1} = \frac{e_1 - e_a}{mR_1}$$

so $\qquad e_a = (1+n)e_2 - ne_1, \qquad e_b = -me_2 + (1+m)e_1$

and $\qquad G_d = \dfrac{e_a - e_b}{e_1 - e_2} = 1 + m + n \qquad (4.2.1)$

which gives the differential gain. The common-mode gain can be found by letting $e_1 = e_2 = e_{cm}$, then:

$$e_a = e_b = e_{cm}, \qquad G_{cm} = 1 \qquad (4.2.2)$$

so the common-mode gain is unity compared with a differential gain of $(1+m+n)$, and this does not depend on resistor values [a1, A1, b1]. Since $e_a = e_b$ the differential output CMRR is infinite in this treatment. In practice, the finite gains of the amplifiers and their common mode errors reduce this. To obtain a single-ended output, amplifier A_3 is added to give a final gain:

$$G_s = \frac{e_o}{e_1 - e_2} = k(1 + m + n) \qquad (4.2.3)$$

The attenuation of this stage for common-mode signals is dependent on resistor matching of the R_2's. However, even a modest rejection performance by this stage is multiplied by that of the input stage, i.e., $(1+m+n)$ which can give very good performance indeed.

To find the input resistance of the amplifier we must include the differential input resistance, R_d, and finite gain, A_0, of amplifiers A_1 and A_2 [b1]. The system differential input resistance is then found to be:

$$R_{id} = 2R_d \left[1 + \frac{A}{1 + m + n} \right] \qquad (4.2.4)$$

which can be very large. For example, with $R_d = 500$ kΩ, $A_0 = 10^5$, and $m = n = 100$, we find $G_d = 200$, $G_{cm} = 1$, and $R_{id} = 500$ MΩ. In practice, the resistances between each amplifier input $(+)$ and $(-)$ and ground may limit the value of R_{id} (Sec. 2.5) [a1, p. 4]. High input resistance is of importance not only to reduce source loading, but also to reduce the effect of source imbalance (Sec. 1.7) [a1]. Dual operational amplifiers make the DIDO configuration quite convenient, and triple or quad amplifiers give a compact realization with single-ended output. However, it is only necessary that A_1 and A_2 are matched and track; A_3 may be selected for good common-mode rejection [k1, E1, F1].

A discussion of instrumentation amplifiers is given by Smith [A1, p. 122].

The considerable demand for amplifiers with excellent CMRR, high input resistance, and variable gain has led to the development of an IC instrumentation amplifier which fulfils these requirements without the use of operational feedback. The AD520 has a common-mode rejection ratio of 80 to 100 dB depending on gain, which is variable from 1 to 1000, and differential and common-mode input resistances of 10^9 ohm. The simplified circuit is shown in Fig. 4.2.2. The actual circuit contains 39 transistors which would make it a fairly complex system in discrete terms [d1, c1, f1, s1, y1].

For normal operation the sense terminal is connected to e_{out} as shown, and the reference terminal to some preset voltage e_{ref}. The four current source transistors $Q_{11}, Q_{13}, Q_{36}, Q_{37}$ are closely matched and supply equal currents for equal input voltages, so that:

$$i_{13} = i_{37}, \quad i_{11} = i_{36} \qquad (4.2.5)$$

Consider a signal applied between the input terminals such that $(+)$ goes more positive. As a consequence, i_3 increases and i_2 decreases. These changes are amplified

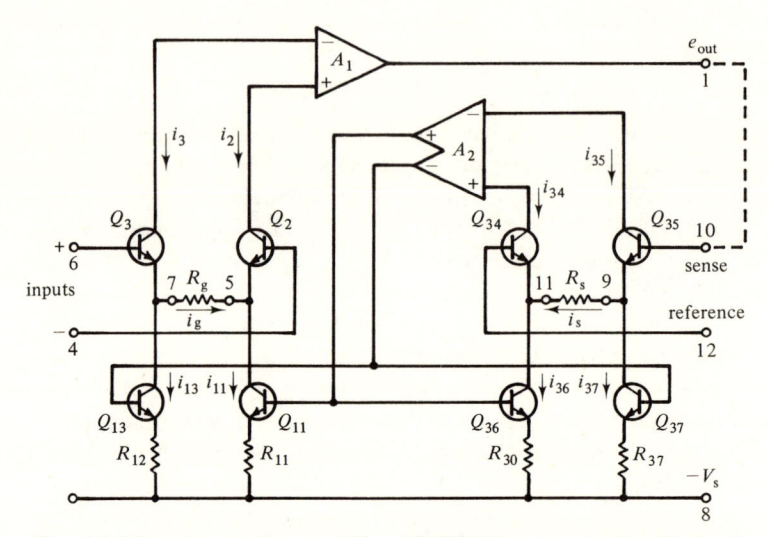

Fig. 4.2.2 Instrumentation amplifier AD520 (Courtesy Analog Devices)

via A_1, Q_{34}, Q_{35}, and A_2 to increase i_{11}, i_{36} and decrease i_{13}, i_{37}. This feedback acts to reduce the differential input to A_1 and A_2 to zero, i.e.:

$$i_2 = i_3, \quad i_{34} = i_{35} \qquad (4.2.6)$$

or $\quad i_{11} - i_g = i_{13} + i_g \quad$ and $\quad i_{36} - i_s = i_{37} + i_s$

Thus, using Eqs. (4.2.5) and (4.2.6) we find:

$$i_g = i_s \qquad (4.2.7)$$

Now, since:

$$e_{in} = e_+ - e_- = i_g R_g \quad \text{and} \quad e_{out} - e_{ref} = i_s R_s$$

then, from Eq. (4.2.7):

$$\frac{e_+ - e_-}{R_g} = \frac{e_{out} - e_{ref}}{R_s}$$

or

$$e_{out} = e_{ref} + \frac{R_s}{R_g}(e_+ - e_-) \qquad (4.2.8)$$

The scale resistance, R_s, is set by the values of the current generators to be in the region of 100 kΩ. The gain resistance, R_g, is selected to give the desired gain which may be varied between 1 and 1000. Interchanging the roles of R_g and R_s leads to rather high resistance values ($R_s = 100$ MΩ for $G = 1000$). The reference voltage, e_{ref}, may be varied independently to give any desired output offset voltage ($< \pm 10$ volt). The high input resistance of the sense (and reference) terminal ($> 10^7$ ohm) allows the feedback to be derived from points other than the output terminal (e_{out}).

If the sense terminal is not connected directly to e_{out}, then Eq. (4.2.8) must be replaced by:

$$e_{sns} = e_{ref} + \frac{R_s}{R_g}(e_+ - e_-) \quad (4.2.9)$$

but e_{sns} must still be related to e_{out} in some way. Two applications are illustrated in Fig. 4.2.3. Figure 4.2.3(a) shows the inclusion of a power booster, with the sense terminal connected to the booster output to maintain overall accuracy. Figure 4.2.3(b) shows the connection for a current drive to either a floating (R_{LF}) or a grounded (R_{LG}) load.

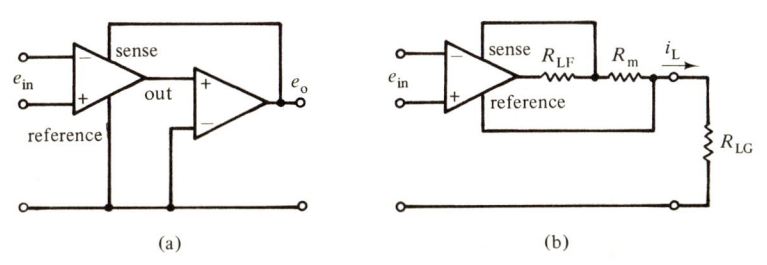

Fig. 4.2.3 Applications of the AD520 (Courtesy Analog Devices)

4.3 Logarithmic amplifiers

Logarithmic circuits are used for signal compression, e.g., the generation of dB responses, curve generation and linearization, and, together with multipliers, the extraction of roots and raising to powers. They can be used for multiplication and division (addition and subtraction of logarithms) but these applications are now also served by the specialized multiplier IC's (Sec. 6.2).

The logarithmic characteristic of a P–N junction has been considered in Sec. 1.9(a). The voltage across the junction is proportional to the logarithm of the current through it. Thus, the signal must be in the form of a current, and the most convenient way of doing this is by operational techniques (Fig. 4.3.1).

As mentioned in Sec. 1.9(a), diode connected transistors (shorted base to collector) are more closely logarithmic junctions than simple diodes, but it has been found that the transdiode connection has a significantly greater range of operation [a1, c1, d1,

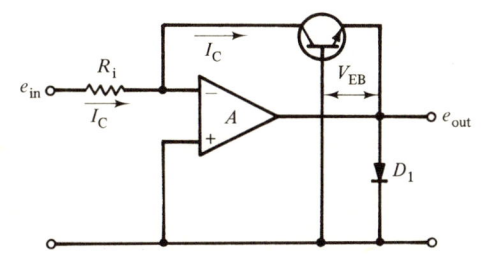

Fig. 4.3.1 Logarithmic amplifier using transdiode

t1, K1]. In the latter, the collector is not shorted to the base but the collector–base voltage is maintained equal to zero. The properties of the virtual ground are well suited to this form of operation. Since the virtual ground remains at zero volts, $V_{CB}=0$ and:

$$e_{out} = V_{EB} = V_J \ln(I_C/I_S) = V_J \ln(e_{in}/R_i I_S) \qquad (4.3.1)$$
$$= 60 \text{ mV/decade } e_{in}, \text{ at } 27°C$$

Note that the circuit can be used only for unipolar signals (positive for the *NPN* transistor shown). For the opposite polarity a *PNP* transistor must be used, or in the case of a simple diode, this must be reversed. If the incorrect polarity input is applied, the transdiode emitter–base will be reverse biased and may exceed the breakdown voltage (commonly about 5 to 7 volts). To protect against this, a clamping diode D_1 should be included. As shown in Fig. 4.3.1 this would short-circuit the amplifier output which should, therefore, be able to withstand this condition or be protected against it. An output resistor will limit the maximum current, and may be necessary in any case for reasons of stability (see below).

If a wide dynamic range is required, operation down to very low currents is necessary. This means that the amplifier must have high input impedance and low bias or offset currents [a1, K1]. The transdiode circuit will operate over a range of about 9 decades ($10^{-11} < I_C < 10^{-2}$ ampere) while the diode circuit operates over about 6 or 7 decades ($10^{-9} < I_C < 10^{-2}$ ampere). One advantage of the diode is that several may be connected in series to give an increased logarithmic constant V_J [b1].

The logarithmic constant, V_J, is temperature sensitive, as is I_S. V_J has a coefficient of $+0.3$ per cent/°C, while I_S doubles approximately every 10°C. The variation of I_S can be compensated most conveniently by using logarithmic ratio circuits with matched transistors, the second input simply being an appropriate constant [d1, h1, f1, K1]. Variation of V_J is usually compensated by a thermistor [G1] controlling the gain of a following amplifier. An arrangement using a silicon resistor [H1] is given in [b1]. In practice, the use of commercial logarithmic device pairs and temperature compensation elements is well worth while [m1, n1, o1, M1].

A further important consideration is the frequency stability of the system [a1, K1, d1]. The feedback impedance is a function of signal level, which considerably complicates the situation. For the simple diode element, stability may be achieved by using a 6 dB/octave roll-off amplifier, or by addition of C_f and R_E as shown in Fig. 4.3.2. The value of R_E lies in the range from zero to about $\frac{1}{2}R_1$ [d1], and is dependent on load resistance, R_L, and the maximum amplifier output current and voltage. The value of C_f ranges from zero to about 100 pF.

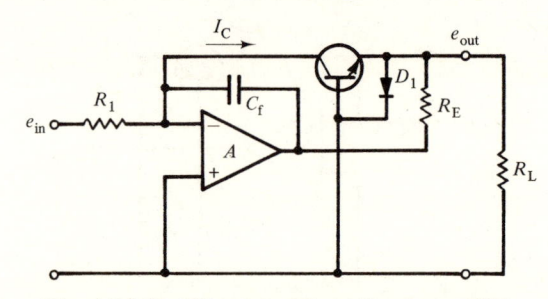

Fig. 4.3.2 Stabilization of logarithmic amplifier

The situation with the transdiode is rather more complex, since it provides a variable amount of extra gain inside the feedback loop. The question of stability is considered in some detail in [a1, d1, K1, t1] where it is shown that the same arrangement as for the diode may be used with $R_E = \frac{1}{3}R_1$ to $\frac{1}{2}R_1$, and $C_f = 10$ to 100 pF.

The bandwidth, or more significantly the slewing rate, is signal dependent. Stability must be considered at the highest collector current, I_C, where the bandwidth will be greatest and the feedback maximum ($r_e \propto 1/I_C$). The usable bandwidth, on the other hand, is that at the lowest current [K1]. Means of improving the slewing speed by using a split amplifier are discussed in [a1].

An antilogarithmic ($\ln^{-1}$) or exponential amplifier is obtained if the input resistor and logarithmic element are interchanged (Fig. 4.3.3).

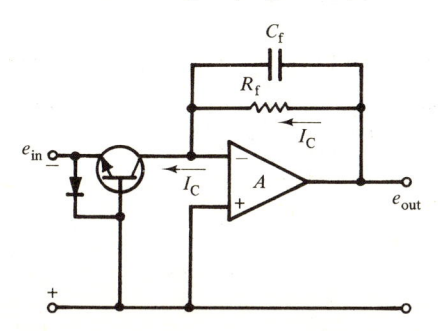

Fig. 4.3.3 Antilogarithmic (exponential) amplifier using transdiode

Because of the virtual ground the base–collector voltage is again zero, as required. The input voltage, $e_{in} = V_{EB}$, causes an exponentially related current, I_C, to flow, which is converted to an output voltage:

$$e_{out} = R_f I_C = R_f \exp(e_{in}/V_J) \quad (4.3.2)$$

As before, temperature compensation is obtained by using matched transistors and thermistors [f1, d1, h1, K1, t1]. Circuits for the extraction of powers or roots are discussed in [h1, K1, g1].

Circuits so far discussed can only accept unipolar signals. To process a.c. signals, a different approach is necessary. Though this makes use of the exponential relationship between I_C and V_{EB}, it does not do so in a direct manner [q1, L1]. For a differential amplifier stage, e.g., Q_1, Q_2 in Fig. 4.3.4(a), with a constant current I_E tail (Q_{11}), the relationships between I_C and V_{EB} are given by:

$$I_{C1} = I_S \exp\frac{V_{EB1}}{V_J}, \quad I_{C2} = I_S \exp\frac{V_{EB2}}{V_J}, \quad I_E = I_{C1} + I_{C2} \quad (4.3.3)$$

where unity has been neglected relative to the exponential in Eq. (1.9.1), and the I_S of matched transistors are equal. If E is the input voltage between the two bases, then:

$$E = V_{EB1} - V_{EB2}, \quad \frac{I_{C1}}{I_{C2}} = \exp\left(\frac{E}{V_J}\right)$$

or

$$\frac{I_{C1} - I_{C2}}{I_{C1} + I_{C2}} = \frac{I_{C1} - I_{C2}}{I_E} = \frac{\exp(E/V_J) - 1}{\exp(E/V_J) + 1} \quad (4.3.4)$$

and

$$\frac{I_{C1}}{I_E} = \frac{\exp(E/V_J)}{1 + \exp(E/V_J)}, \quad \frac{I_{C2}}{I_E} = \frac{1}{1 + \exp(E/V_J)}$$

A plot of these functions is shown in Fig. 4.3.5(a), where it is seen that there is an accurate logarithmic region covering an input range of 13 to 75 mV (15 dB). If a number of these stages, offset by the appropriate amounts, can be combined, then an extended range is obtained, Fig. 4.3.5(b). This is conveniently realized in IC form as in the type SN76502 [l1, q1] which contains two identical circuits, one of these being shown in Fig. 4.3.4.

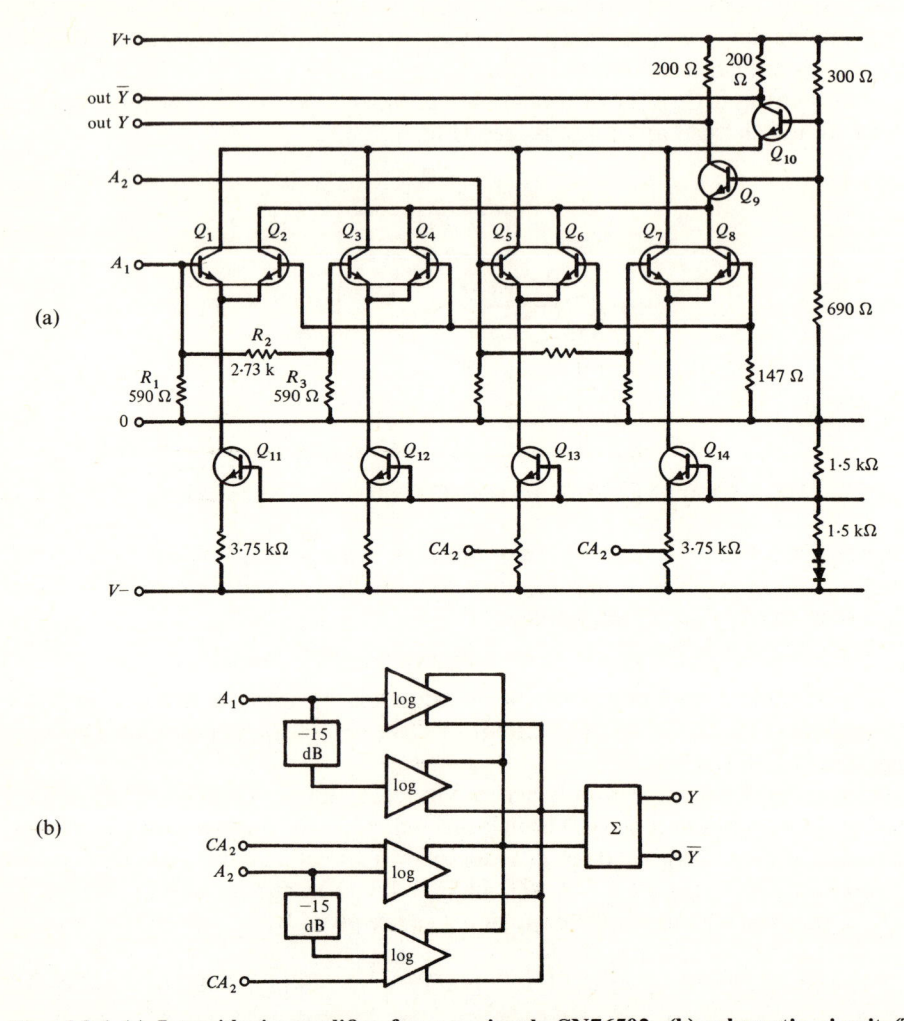

Fig. 4.3.4 (a) Logarithmic amplifier for a.c. signals SN76502, (b) schematic circuit (Texas Instruments, with permission)

Four differential stages are connected in two pairs Q_{1-4} and Q_{5-8}. The input signal (A_1 or A_2) is fed directly to one stage, e.g., $Q_{1,2}$, and via an attenuation network R_{1-3} of -15 dB, to the second stage $Q_{3,4}$. This gives a logarithmic range of 30 dB. The output currents of all four stages are summed by Q_9 and Q_{10}, to give a differential output Y, $\overline{Y}$. The gains of the two stages $Q_{5,6}$ and $Q_{7,8}$ can be compensated, for matching purposes, by small changes of voltage at C_{A2} and $C_{A2'}$. Q_{11-14} act as constant current sources.

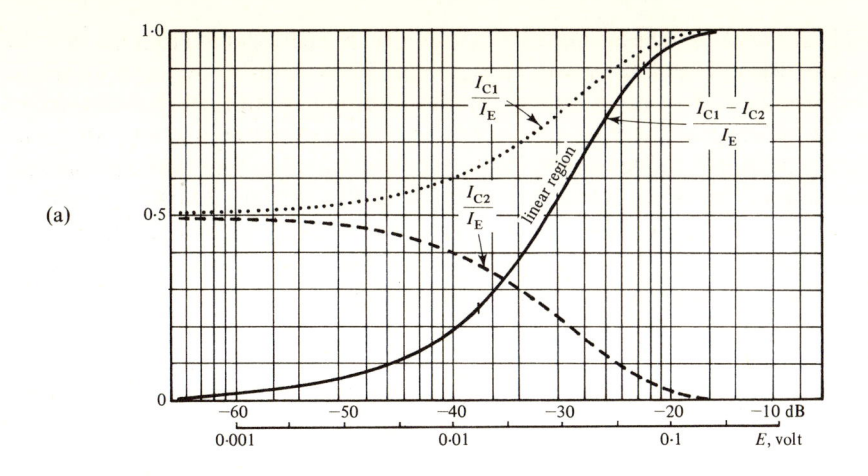

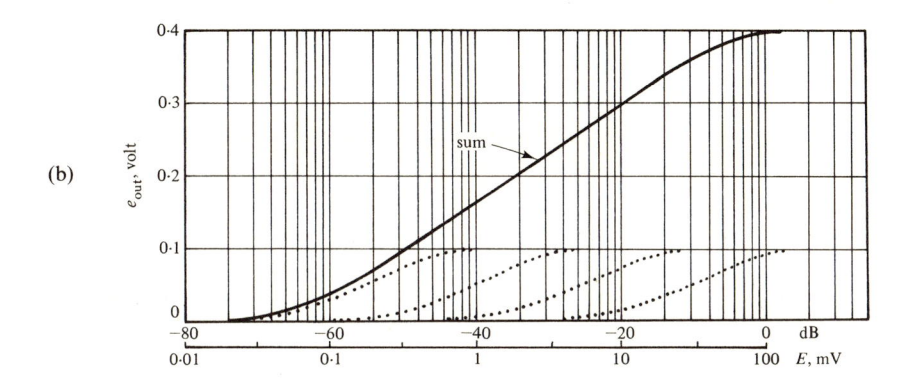

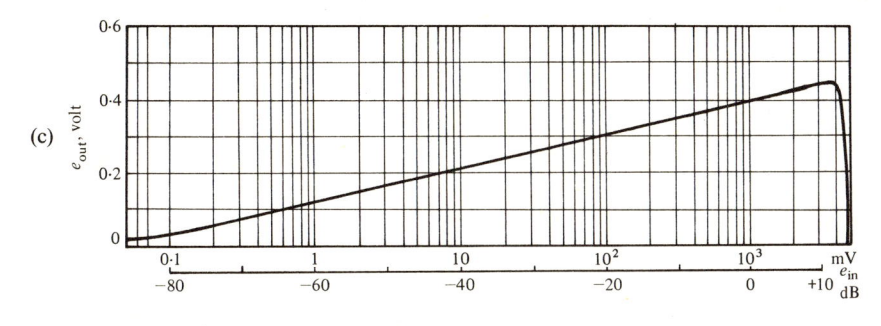

Fig. 4.3.5 Response of SN76502 amplifier (Texas Instruments, with permission)

Each stage starts to limit at about ± 0.5 volt, but if the input exceeds ± 3.5 volt saturation occurs, resulting in severe distortion. Thus, external limiting must be provided to avoid this.

To obtain a wider range of operation, several pairs may be paralleled as shown in Fig. 4.3.6.

157

The smallest signals will be amplified by G_1 and G_2 (60 dB) and fed to input B_2. As the signal increases, B_1 becomes effective and amplifier A_4 (run at low supply voltage ± 4 volt) saturates, and so provides the external limiting. With further increase, A_3 saturates and the input is direct to A_1. Finally, A_1 limits (but does not saturate up to ± 3.5 volt input) and A_2 takes over. The input impedance is 500 ohm, so that the attenuation due to the 15 kΩ resistor feeding A_2 is $500/15\,500 = 30$ dB as required. Though the theoretical range is $4 \times 30 = 120$ dB, in practice a range of 80 dB or more with a logarithmic linearity of ± 0.5 dB is realized. Amplifier A_5 takes the difference of the output signals as required by Eq. (4.3.4), and produces a single-ended signal.

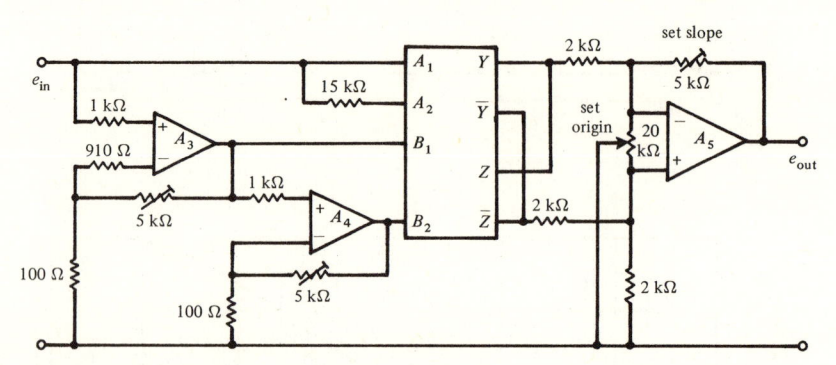

Fig. 4.3.6 Logarithmic amplifier with > 80 dB input range (Texas Instruments, with permission)

The bandwidth of the SN76502 is 40 MHz, but the bandwidth of the circuit of Fig. 4.3.6 will be set by the amplifiers A_{3-5}. For low frequency operation (say < 10 kHz) a standard operational amplifier may be used for A_{3-5}, e.g., µA741. For high frequency use a wide-band device is necessary, a differential input video amplifier such as the µA733 being a good choice. The data sheet [11] shows how this should be done.

The two controls on A_5 allow the setting of the origin, i.e., output for effectively zero input, and the slope of the output response. The gains of A_3 and A_4 are adjusted to achieve a smooth response.

4.4 Active filters

4.4(a) *Introduction*

To describe, adequately, all aspects of filters would need several books [b1, t1]. For most experimental uses a few standard filters will be sufficient, and here we will consider only active filters and not passive types. There are, however, many *active* realizations of the standard filter responses, so we have chosen those that are commonly used and readily realized. In simple systems, only one active element is used, but these have limitations such as low Q (≈ 10) and sensitivity to component values. If several active elements can be included these limitations can be overcome to give circuits with low sensitivity and high Q ($\approx 10^4$!).

Before considering particular types some general comments may be useful in relating to the general literature. The detailed shape of the filter characteristic can be varied to suit the particular application. For a given class of filter, say low-pass, many different forms can be realized which are referred to by the names of the persons who developed them (e.g., Butterworth, Chebychev, Darlington, etc.). These use differing relationships for the position of the poles and zeros, and between gain and phase [o2]. For example, the simplest type, the Butterworth, has a maximally-flat frequency response with a fairly rounded corner. The Chebychev has a sharper corner and greater attenuation above this, but at the expense of some ripple in the in-band response (this may be quite small, e.g., <1 dB). These factors affect not only selectivity but transient response as well [J1, r2]. For our present purposes reference will generally be made to Butterworth response: if improved performance is required other sources should be consulted [M1, K1, t1, o2, b1].

The general transfer functions for the various classes of filter, together with their pole–zero configurations, are shown in Table 4.4.1.

Much of the literature on active filters is concerned with the question of sensitivity, i.e., the variation of filter performance with small changes of component value or

Table 4.4.1 Transfer functions and pole–zero configurations for active filters

Transfer function	Pole – zero configuration	Frequency response
Low-pass $$G_{1p} = \frac{H}{s^2 + as + b}$$		
Band-pass $$G_{bp} = \frac{Hs}{s^2 + as + b}$$		
High-pass $$G_{hp} = \frac{Hs^2}{s^2 + as + b}$$		
Band-stop $$G_{bs} = \frac{H(s^2 + c)}{s^2 + as + b}$$		

amplifier gain. In some configurations the response is dependent on the difference of two terms, and a small change in one of them can produce a large change in the difference, resulting in a sensitive system. Since insensitive configurations generally can be found, this should not be a problem. In this connection it may be noted that, in the case of a narrow band (high Q) filter, the stability of the centre frequency will usually be of greater importance than the realization of a particularly high Q Variation due to actual component tolerance is seldom a problem, since an experimental system can usually be trimmed to obtain the desired response.

Choice between the various general classes for filter depends on the application and requirements. A comparison is given by Olsen [K1] and is summarized in Table 4.4.2.

Table 4.4.2 Comparison of active filter types

	Single feedback	Multiple feedback	Voltage control, voltage source	State variable
Realizable Q	high	low	low (lp, hp) high (hp)	high
Ease of tuning	difficult	moderate	good	good
Component value spread	moderate	large	low	moderate
Achievable gain	high	low	moderate	high
Stability/sensitivity	good	good	poor	good

The general advantage of the multiple amplifier class, particularly for experimental applications, is increased by the availability of triple and quad amplifier IC's. Filter modules are available from several sources [p1, s2].

The simple RC circuit is often referred to as an integrating filter, and is very commonly used as a low-pass filter. The frequency response is not, however, the same as that of a true integrator [j1]. Unawareness of this has led to at least one controversy [i2].

4.4(b) *Infinite gain, single feedback loop, active filters*

These circuits derive directly from the general operational amplifier configuration discussed in chapter 2. Appropriate networks are chosen for Z_i and Z_f, to give the desired response.

To obtain complex poles, which are required to give sharp cut-off in the filter, networks capable of producing complex zeros are required. Two networks capable of this are the bridged-tee and the twin-tee (or parallel-tee). The former is shown in the low-pass filter in Fig. 4.4.1(a), while the latter will be discussed further in Sec. 4.4(f).

To find the transfer function we must determine the impedances of the input and feedback networks. In this case, it will be easier to operate with admittances Y so that the transfer function is of the form:

$$G(s) = \frac{E_o}{E_i} = \frac{-Y_i}{Y_f} = \frac{N_i/D_i}{N_f/D_f} \qquad (4.4.1)$$

Since the input and feedback impedances are passive RC networks, the poles will be on the negative real axis. If the poles of these two networks are made equal (i.e., $D_i = D_f$) then they will not affect the poles of $G(s)$. The poles of $G(s)$ will then be fixed by the zeros of N_f, and the zeros of $G(s)$ will be fixed by the zeros of N_i. Since a passive RC network can have its admittance zeros anywhere in the complex plane, we can realize any pole–zero configuration we require for $G(s)$.

To find expressions for Y_i and Y_f requires a little algebra and use of the properties of the virtual ground (Sec. 2.2), i.e., the admittances are for a *short-circuited* output. Using conductances, $G_{i,f}$, we find for Y_i:

$$Y_i = \frac{I}{E_i} = \frac{G_{i1}G_{i2}/C_i}{[s+(G_{i1}+G_{i2})/C_i]} = \frac{G_i^2/C_i}{(s+2G_i/C_i)} \tag{4.4.2}$$

(for $G_{i1} = G_{i2}$ as here).

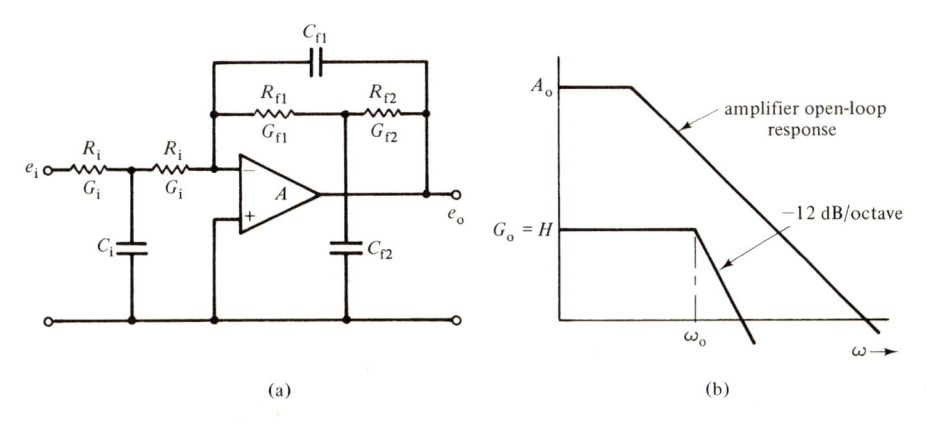

Fig. 4.4.1 (a) Low-pass infinite gain single feedback filter, (b) frequency response

To find Y_f is a bit more laborious but gives, eventually:

$$Y_f = \frac{I}{E_o} = \frac{C_{f1}[s^2+(s(G_{f1}+G_{f2})/C_{f2})+(G_{f1}G_{f2}/C_{f1}C_{f2})]}{[s+(G_{f1}+G_{f2})/C_{f2}]} \tag{4.4.3}$$

The condition that $D_i = D_f$ in Eq. (4.4.1) gives, using Eqs. (4.4.2) and (4.4.3):

$$s + \frac{2G_i}{C_i} = s + \frac{(G_{f1}+G_{f2})}{C_{f2}} \quad \text{or} \quad 2G_iC_{f2} = C_i(G_{f1}+G_{f2}) \tag{4.4.4}$$

The transfer function now has the form:

$$G(s) = \frac{-Y_i}{Y_f} = \frac{G_i^2}{C_iC_{f1}}\left[s^2 + \frac{s(G_{f1}+G_{f2})}{C_{f2}} + \frac{G_{f1}G_{f2}}{C_{f1}C_{f2}}\right]^{-1} \tag{4.4.5}$$

The standard low-pass transfer function can be written, from Table 4.4.1, and Eq. (3.7.1):

$$G_{1p}(s) = \frac{-H\omega_0^2}{s^2+s\omega_0/Q+\omega_0^2} \tag{4.4.6}$$

where H is the in-band (d.c.) gain, and ω_0 the break frequency; Fig. 4.4.1(b). Comparing Eqs. (4.4.5) and (4.4.6) gives:

$$H\omega_0^2 = \frac{G_i^2}{C_iC_{f1}}, \quad \frac{\omega_0}{Q} = \frac{G_{f1}+G_{f2}}{C_{f2}}, \quad \omega_0^2 = \frac{G_{f1}G_{f2}}{C_{f1}C_{f2}}$$

so that
$$H = \frac{R_{f1}+R_{f2}}{2R_i} \quad \text{using Eq. (4.4.4) for } C_i \qquad (4.4.7)$$

as it should, by inspection of Fig. 4.4.1(a).

The poles of $G_{1p}(s)$ now depend on the choice of Q. There is a limited choice for this, since too high a value gives a peaky frequency response and too low a value gives a very rounded corner (see Fig. 3.7.2). This limits the range to:

$$\tfrac{1}{2} \leqslant Q \leqslant 2 \qquad (4.4.8)$$

There are many ways of choosing a set of values for the components, depending on the initial choice of one value. We will choose C_{f1} as shown, where k is a scale constant. $k = 10^{-5}$ leads to suitable values in most cases [g1]. From Eq. (4.4.7):

$$C_{f1} = \frac{k}{\omega_0}, \qquad Q = \frac{G_{f1}G_{f2}}{k(G_{f1}+G_{f2})}$$

or
$$R_{f1}+R_{f2} = \frac{1}{kQ} \equiv \frac{a}{k} \qquad (4.4.9)$$

A further choice of $G_{f1} = (2\cdot 5 - a)k \equiv bk$, leads to values of $G_{f2} = \infty$ (i.e., $R_{f2}=0$) for the extremes of Q, Eq. (4.4.8). Then the complete set of values is given by:

$$R_{f1} = \frac{1}{bk}, \qquad R_{f2} = \left(a-\frac{1}{b}\right)\frac{1}{k}, \qquad R_i = \frac{a}{2kH}$$

$$C_{f1} = \frac{k}{\omega_0}, \qquad C_{f2} = \frac{kb^2}{\omega_0(ab-1)}, \qquad C_i = \frac{4Hk}{a^2\omega_0} \qquad (4.4.10)$$

$$Q = \frac{1}{a}, \qquad b = (2\cdot 5 - a), \qquad \omega_0 = 2\pi f_0$$

Thus, for a given ω_0 and H one chooses a value of k and of Q, say $1/\sqrt{2}$ (the Butterworth or maximally flat response, $a=\sqrt{2}$, $b=1\cdot 086$, $b^2/(ab-1)=2\cdot 201$) and calculates the various values. It would be convenient if at least C_{f1} is made a standard value.

This circuit has been worked through in some detail to show the technique. In similar fashion the high-pass circuit of Fig. 4.4.2(a) may be analysed.

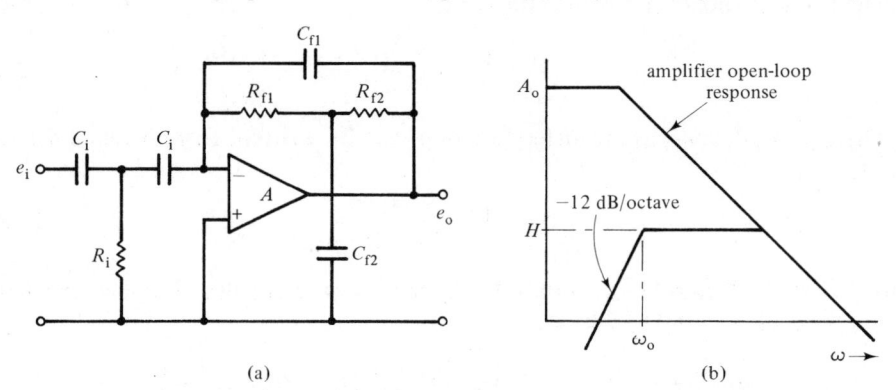

Fig. 4.4.2 (a) High-pass infinite gain single feedback filter, (b) frequency response

The transfer function will be of the form (Table 4.4.1):

$$G_{hp}(s) = \frac{-Hs^2}{s^2 + a\omega_0 s + \omega_0^2} \qquad (4.4.11)$$

and with a, b, ω_0 having the same meaning as for the low-pass circuit [g1]:

$$R_{f1} = \frac{1}{bk}, \qquad R_{f2} = \left(a - \frac{1}{b}\right)\frac{1}{k}, \qquad R_i = \frac{1}{4aHk}$$

$$C_{f1} = \frac{k}{\omega_0}, \qquad C_{f2} = \frac{kb^2}{\omega_0(ab-1)}, \qquad C_i = \frac{2Hk}{\omega_0} \qquad (4.4.12)$$

Advantages of these circuits are:

(i) pole locations are a function of passive elements only
(ii) low output impedance
(iii) a summing input is available due to virtual ground.

While the disadvantages are:

(i) large number of elements required
(ii) difficult to tune or trim due to interactions.

The band-pass amplifier uses a twin-tee network which is discussed separately in Sec. 4.4(f).

4.4(c) *Infinite-gain multiple-loop feedback active filters*

A modification of the configuration discussed in Sec. 4.4(b) is the use of additional feedback paths. This has the advantage of a smaller number of passive elements but the virtual ground can no longer be used as a summing point. Consideration will be limited to two feedback paths, a general circuit in terms of admittances Y being shown in Fig. 4.4.3.

The transfer function is found from the equations

$$I_1 = (E_i - E_1)Y_1, \qquad I_2 = E_1 Y_2, \qquad I_3 = E_1 Y_3 = I_5 = -E_o Y_5,$$

$$I_4 = (E_1 - E_o)Y_4, \qquad I_1 = I_2 + I_3 + I_4$$

which give:

$$G(s) = \frac{E_o}{E_i} = \frac{-Y_1 Y_3}{Y_5(Y_1 + Y_2 + Y_3 + Y_4) + Y_3 Y_4} \qquad (4.4.13)$$

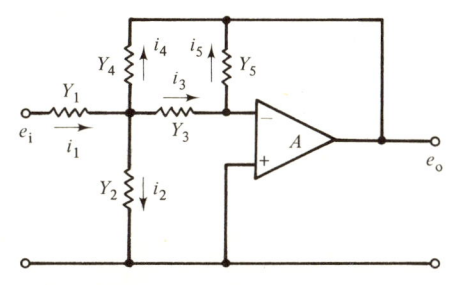

Fig. 4.4.3 Infinite gain multiple-loop feedback filter

Equating this transfer function to the desired generalized form given in Table 4.4.1, leads to equations that do not have unique solutions. Some choice must be made on relationships between some of the components. Choices and design formulae suggested by [g1] are given in Table 4.4.3.

Table 4.4.3 Parameters for infinite gain multiple-loop feedback active filters

Type	Choose	Y_1	Y_2	Y_3	Y_4	Y_5
Low-pass	$C_5 = \dfrac{k}{\omega_0}$	$R_1 = \dfrac{a}{2Hk}$	$C_2 = \dfrac{4(H+1)C_5}{a^2}$	$R_3 = \dfrac{a}{2(H+1)k}$	$R_4 = HR_1$	C_5
Band-pass	$C_3 = \dfrac{k}{\omega_0}$	$R_1 = \dfrac{1}{Hk}$	$R = \dfrac{1}{(2Q-H)k}$	C_3	$C_4 = C_3$	$R_5 = \dfrac{2Q}{k}$
High-pass	$C_1 = \dfrac{k}{\omega_0}$	C_1	$R_2 = \dfrac{a}{k(2+1/H)}$	$C_3 = C_1$	$C_4 = \dfrac{C_1}{H}$	$R_5 = \dfrac{H(2+1/H)}{ak}$

Note: For high- and low-pass $a = 2^{1/2}$ for Butterworth response, and inband gain $= H$. For band-pass, peak gain $= HQ$, and $Q \leqslant 20$.

A procedure for designing band-pass filters is given in [c1] with a number of examples using the type 741 amplifier. A computer program for carrying out the design and plotting the response of low and band-pass filters is described in [K1].

The cut-off or band-pass frequencies may be varied by making one of the elements variable. This can be done electrically by using a photoresistor or FET as a voltage-controlled resistor [g2]. An interesting application to a band-pass amplifier is illustrated in [c2]. A phase-sensitive detector (PSD) compares the phases of the input, e_i, and output, e_o, signals, the output controlling R_2 (Fig. 4.4.4) optoelectronically. The system acts to keep e_i and e_o in antiphase (allowing for the overall signal inversion) which occurs only when the filter centre frequency is the same as the input frequency. Thus, the system is self-tuning.

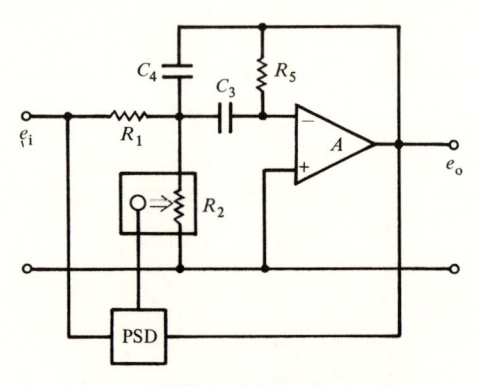

Fig. 4.4.4 Self-tuning band-pass filter

4.4(d) *Low-gain controlled source active filters*

These filters use a simple amplifier of finite gain (often unity) and a single feedback loop. The amplifier is called a controlled source [z1, p. 6] in that the value of the output voltage or current is dependent on the value of another voltage or current.

This sounds no different from the amplifiers considered in chapter 2, but it is the nomenclature used in the literature. These active filter circuits were first described by Sallen and Key [A1; b1; a1 part (6)] and so are commonly referred to by their names. We will consider here only voltage-controlled voltage sources (VCVS) as these are generally used. Such a source may be a simple emitter follower, if unity gain is required in the circuit, or an operational amplifier fed back to give the required stable gain K. A circuit for a low-pass filter is shown in Fig. 4.4.5.

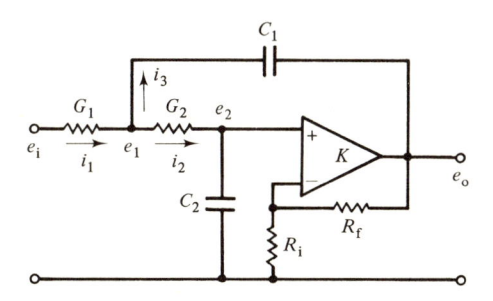

Fig. 4.4.5 Low-pass controlled source filter

For an operational amplifier the two resistors R_f, R_i will set the gain K. Writing the usual network equations:

$$I_1 = I_2 + I_3, \quad E_i - E_1 = I_1/G_1, \quad E_1 - E_2 = I_2/G_2$$

$$E_2 = I_2/sC_2, \quad E_1 - E_o = I_3/sC_1, \quad E_o = +KE_2$$

the transfer function is found to be:

$$G_{1p}(s) = \frac{E_o}{E_i} = \frac{KG_1G_2}{s^2C_1C_2 + s(C_2G_1 + C_2G_2 + C_1G_2 - KG_1C_2) + G_1G_2} \quad (4.4.14)$$

This must be equated to the standard transfer function (Table 4.4.1) to find which components control the various parameters such as gain, band flatness, and cut-off frequency. There are more variables than required so that some may be chosen as convenient. Sallen and Key [A1, b1] give tables of design formulae depending on initial choice, and a recipe given in [g1]; see also Table 4.4.4. The damping factor depends on the difference of terms in the coefficient of s in the denominator of Eq. (4.4.14) so it is important that K be stable. This also makes the circuit unsuitable for high Q realizations (say $Q \gtrsim 10$). However, Q can be varied by means of K without affecting ω_0. This will be most useful in the band-pass case.

The high-pass filter is realized by interchanging C and G in Fig. 4.4.5 to give a transfer function:

$$G_{hp}(s) = \frac{E_o}{E_i} = \frac{Ks^2C_1C_2}{s^2C_1C_2 + s(C_2G_1 + C_2G_2 + C_1G_2 - KC_2G_1) + G_1G_2} \quad (4.4.15)$$

Table 4.4.4 Parameters for low gain controlled-source active filters

Type	Choose	R	R_2	R_3	C_2	K	
Low-pass (Fig. 4.4.5)	$C_1 = \dfrac{k}{\omega_0}$	$\dfrac{2}{ak}$	$\dfrac{a}{2mk}$	—	mC_1	$G(0)$	$a = 2^{1/2}$ for Butterworth $m = \dfrac{a^2}{4} + (K-1)$ $\omega_0 = \left[\dfrac{G_1 G_2}{C_1 C_2}\right]^{1/2}$
Band-pass (Fig. 4.4.6)	$C_1 = \dfrac{k}{\omega_0}$	$\dfrac{2}{k}$	$\dfrac{2}{3k}$	$\dfrac{4}{k}$	$\dfrac{C_1}{2}$	$\dfrac{1}{3}\left(6\cdot5 - \dfrac{1}{Q}\right)$	$G(\omega_0) = KQ, \quad Q \leqslant 10$ $Q = 1/(6\cdot5 - 3K)$ $\omega_0 = \left[\dfrac{G_3(G_1 + G_2)}{C_1 C_2}\right]^{1/2}$
High-pass (Fig. 4.4.5 with $C \leftrightarrow G$)	$C_1 = \dfrac{k}{\omega_0}$	$\dfrac{m}{4k}$	$\dfrac{4}{mk}$	—	C_1	$G(0)$	$a = 2^{1/2}$ for Butterworth $m = a + [a^2 + 8(K-1)]^{1/2}$ $\omega_0 = \left[\dfrac{G_1 G_2}{C_1 C_2}\right]^{1/2}$

A band-pass characteristic results from the circuit of Fig. 4.4.6, with a transfer function:

$$G_{\text{bp}}(s) = \frac{E_o}{E_i}$$

$$= \frac{KsC_1 G_1}{s^2 C_1 C_2 + s(C_1 G_3 + C_2 G_1 + C_2 G_2 + C_1 G_1 + C_1 G_2 - KC_1 G_2) + G_3(G_1 + G_2)} \quad (4.4.16)$$

Though the Q may be varied by means of K, the gain will also vary.

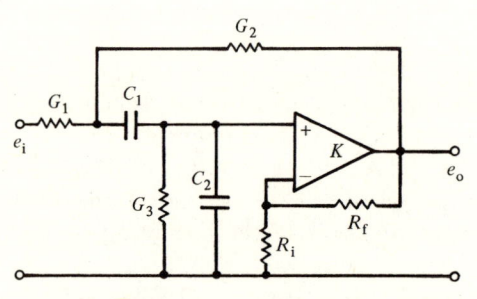

Fig. 4.4.6 Band-pass controlled source filter

4.4(e) *Multiple amplifier active filters*

These circuits use more than one amplifier which gives the advantages of low sensitivity, high Q, and independently adjustable frequency, gain, and Q. Standard operational amplifier circuits are combined to synthesize any biquadratic transfer function:

$$G = \frac{E_o}{E_i} = \frac{m(s^2 + s\omega_z Q_{z0} + \omega_z^2)}{(s^2 + s\omega_p Q_{p0} + \omega_p^2)} \qquad (4.4.17)$$

The so-called *state variable* [E1] configuration is shown in Fig. 4.4.7.

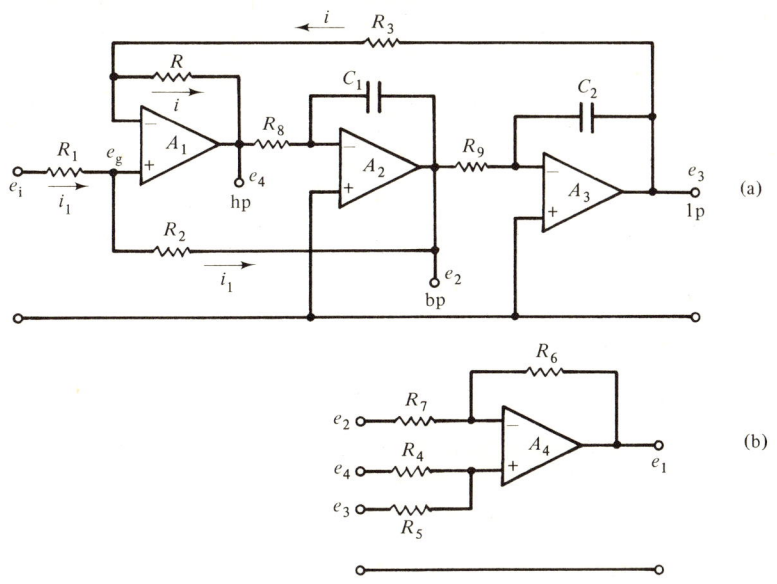

Fig. 4.4.7 (a) State variable active filter, (b) combining amplifier

The circuit may be analysed by using the ideal operational amplifier conditions (chapter 2), remembering that the inputs to A_1 are at the same potential e_g (Sec. 2.5). Thus:

$$I_1 = \frac{E_i - E_g}{R_1} = \frac{E_g - E_2}{R_2}, \qquad \frac{E_3}{E_2} = \frac{-1}{R_9 C_2 s}$$

$$I = \frac{E_3 - E_g}{R_3} = \frac{E_g - E_1}{R}, \qquad \frac{E_2}{E_1} = \frac{-1}{R_8 C_1 s} \qquad (4.4.18)$$

Eliminating the appropriate voltages gives the low-pass, band-pass and high-pass transfer functions:

$$G_{1p} = \frac{E_3}{E_i} = \frac{R_2(R+R_3)}{R_3(R_1+R_2)} \left[\frac{1}{s^2 R_8 C_1 R_9 C_2 + s R_9 C_2 \cdot \frac{R_1(R+R_3)}{R_3(R_1+R_2)} + \frac{R}{R_3}} \right] \qquad (4.4.19)$$

$$G_{bp} = \frac{E_2}{E_i} = \frac{-R_2(R+R_3)}{R_3(R_1+R_2)} \left[\frac{s R_9 C_2}{s^2 R_8 C_1 R_9 C_2 + s R_9 C_2 \cdot \frac{R_1(R+R_3)}{R_3(R_1+R_2)} + \frac{R}{R_3}} \right] \qquad (4.4.20)$$

$$G_{hp} = \frac{E_1}{E_i} = \frac{R_2(R+R_3)}{R_3(R_1+R_2)} \left[\frac{s^2 R_8 R_9 C_1 C_2}{s^2 R_8 C_1 R_9 C_2 + s R_9 C_2 \cdot \frac{R_1(R+R_3)}{R_3(R_1+R_2)} + \frac{R}{R_3}} \right] \qquad (4.4.21)$$

Including the combining amplifier, A_4 (Fig. 4.4.7(b)), gives the general transfer function:

$$G_{gp} = \frac{E_4}{E_i} = \frac{R_2(R+R_3)R_5(R_6+R_7)}{R_3(R_1+R_2)R_7(R_4+R_5)} \left[\frac{s^2 R_8 C_1 R_9 C_2 + s R_9 C_2 \cdot \frac{R_6(R_4+R_5)}{R_5(R_6+R_7)} + \frac{R_4}{R_5}}{s^2 R_8 C_1 R_9 C_2 + s R_9 C_2 \cdot \frac{R_1(R+R_3)}{R_3(R_1+R_2)} + \frac{R}{R_3}} \right]$$

(4.4.22)

Thus, any general biquadratic function (4.4.17) may be realized from Eq. (4.4.22). It is convenient to make (since some choice is arbitrary):

$$R_1 = R_3 = R = 1 \text{ unit}, \qquad R_8 C_1 = R_9 C_2 = \tau \qquad (4.4.23)$$

For a high Q pole-pair, the resonant frequency and Q are given by:

$$R_8 C_1 R_9 C_2 s^2 + R/R_3 = 0 \quad \text{or} \quad \omega_0 = \frac{1}{\tau} \quad \text{from Eq. (4.4.23)}$$

$$\frac{\omega_0}{Q} = \frac{R_1(R+R_3)R_9 C_2}{R_3(R_1+R_2)R_8 C_1 R_9 C_2} \quad \text{or} \quad Q = \frac{R_1+R_2}{R+R_3} = \frac{1+R_2}{2} \qquad (4.4.24)$$

where R_2 is in units as defined in Eq. (4.4.23). Thus, ω_0 and Q can be chosen or varied independently. Since a high Q does not depend on a difference of terms, the sensitivity may be expected to be low. It is in fact less than unity.

It should be noted that the response of the amplifiers has been neglected so the analysis holds only for that region where this can be justified (say $f_0 \leqslant 10$ kHz for single-pole amplifiers). This point is of greater importance here than in single amplifier circuits, because of cumulative effect with three or four amplifiers. At low frequencies, Q's of the order of 1000 may be realized [E1].

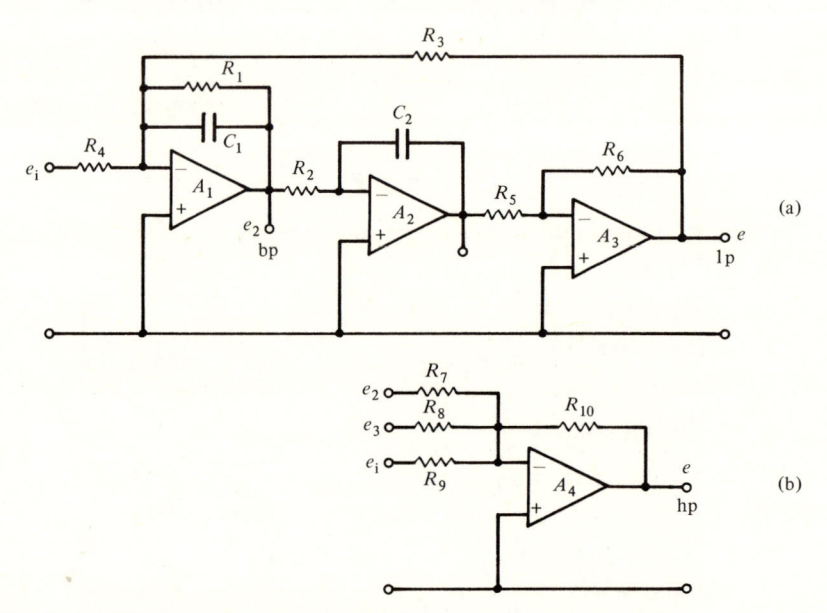

Fig. 4.4.8 (a) Biquad active filter, (b) combining amplifier

This circuit is available in hybrid form, requiring only those external components needed to set ω_0, Q, and gain [C1, y2].

A modification of the state variable filter, the biquad, is shown in Fig. 4.4.8 [F1, G1, p2].

This circuit is also referred to as analogue computer simulation [e1, f1], a ring-of-three [d1, D1], or a two integrator loop [a1 parts 7, 8]. The basic circuit gives low and band-pass response. If a high-pass, all-pass, or notch response is required a fourth stage, A_4, must be added [F1, G1, I1]. A Q value of several hundred may be realized up to frequencies of several hundred kHz. The range is again a function of the amplifier frequency responses, and as better amplifiers become available the upper limit will be raised. Only a minimum of amplifier compensation is needed, since the integrator topology itself serves this purpose. The stability may be even further improved by addition of some leading phase, by connection of a small capacitor across R_2 or R_3. A value of only a few picofarads should be sufficient [F1].

Design formulae are given in Table 4.4.5 [G1, I1] and practical considerations are discussed in [F1, e2].

Table 4.4.5 Parameters for state variable/biquad active filters

Type	R	R_2	R_3	R_4	Q	ω_0	G in band	
Low-pass	$\dfrac{Q}{\omega_0 C_1}$	$\dfrac{1}{\omega_0 C_2}$	$\dfrac{1}{\omega_0 C_1}$	$\dfrac{\omega_0}{HC_1}$	$\dfrac{R_1}{R_3}$	$\dfrac{1}{R_3 C_1}$	$\dfrac{R_3}{R_4}$	For H see Table 4.4.1
Band-pass	$\dfrac{Q}{\omega_0 C_1}$	$\dfrac{1}{\omega_0 C_2}$	$\dfrac{1}{\omega_0 C_1}$	$\dfrac{1}{HC_1}$	$\dfrac{R_1}{R_3}$	$\dfrac{1}{R_3 C_1}$	$\dfrac{H}{2\omega_0}$	$H = \dfrac{1}{R_4 C_1}$
High-pass	$\dfrac{Q}{\omega_0 C_1}$	$\dfrac{1}{\omega_0 C_2}$	$\dfrac{1}{\omega_0 C_1}$	$\dfrac{Q}{HC_1 \omega_0}$	$\dfrac{R_1}{R_3}$	$\dfrac{1}{R_3 C_1}$	$\dfrac{R_{10}}{R_9}$	$R_7 = R_{10}$, $R_8 = R_{10}/Q$, $R_9 = R_{10}/H$

Note for all types $R_5 = R_6$, $R_2 C_2 = R_3 C_1$

Mattera [B1] recommends the biquad circuit for low or band-pass, and the state variable for high-pass. If the component values of the biquad become so high that stability (temperature and temporal) is a problem, then the state variable is preferable, since its performance parameters depend on component ratios and it can use low value components. The availability of multiple amplifier IC's makes these circuits easy and economical to realize, e.g., types LM3900, MC3401P, L144 [p2, R3, S3, J3, P3, Q3].

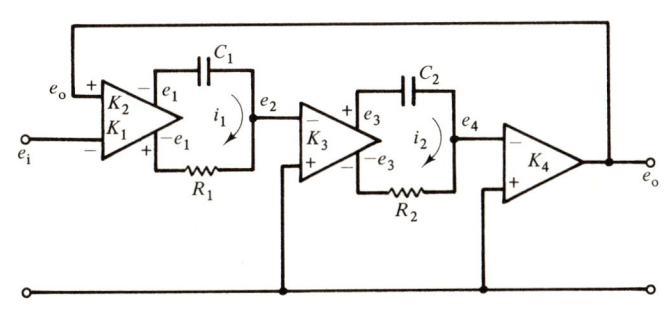

Fig. 4.4.9 High frequency active filter using DIDO amplifiers

The state-variable and biquad both have limitations on high frequency performance. A means of achieving high Q at high frequency has been described by [H1, z1]. This makes use of DIDO type video amplifiers, Sec. 4.8(c), which are also available in IC form [T3, U3, V3]. Q values of 5000 were readily obtained. The circuit is shown in Fig. 4.4.9.

The transfer function is found from the equations:

$$E_1 = K_1 E_i - K_2 E_o; \qquad 2E_1 = I_1(R_1 + 1/sC_1) = I_1 R_1 \left(\frac{sT_1 + 1}{sT_1}\right)$$

$$E_2 = I_1 R_1 - E_1 \quad \text{or} \quad I_1 = \frac{E_2 + E_1}{R_1}$$

$$E_3 = -K_3 E_2; \qquad 2E_3 = I_2(R_2 + 1/sC_2) = I_2 R_2 \left(\frac{sT_2 + 1}{sT_2}\right)$$

$$E_4 = I_2 R_2 - E_3 \quad \text{or} \quad I_2 = \frac{E_4 + E_3}{R_2}$$

$$E_o = -K_4 E_4; \qquad T \equiv RC$$

$$G = \frac{E_o}{E_i} = \frac{K_1 K_2 K_3 (1 - sT_1)(1 - sT_2)}{s^2 T_1 T_2 (1 + K_2 K_3 K_4) + s(T_1 + T_2)(1 - K_2 K_3 K_4) + (1 + K_2 K_3 K_4)} \quad (4.4.25)$$

Usually $T_1 = T_2 = T$ for high Q, giving:

$$\omega_0 = \frac{1}{T}, \qquad Q = \frac{1 + K_2 K_3 K_4}{2(1 - K_2 K_3 K_4)} \quad (4.4.26)$$

Though Q depends on the difference of two terms, the sensitivity is not necessarily great, being of the same order as the previous filter circuits [H1]. The gain values are chosen to be:

$$K_2 = 1 - \frac{1}{Q}, \qquad K_3 = K_4 = 1, \qquad K_1 = \frac{1}{Q} \quad (4.4.27)$$

Since $|K_2 K_3 K_4| < 1$ the system is absolutely stable regardless of inherent amplifier phase shift.

4.4(f) *Active filters using twin-tee networks*

The property of the twin-tee (or parallel-tee) network that makes it of interest for filters is the transmission zero at some finite frequency. Though it may be used in its basic passive form the interest here is in its use in active systems. It was first used in this way by Scott [O1]. General properties of the network itself are covered in [i1, P1] and application by [h1; a1, parts 10 and 11].

The basic network is shown in Fig. 4.4.10. The basic equations for the twin-tee are:

$$G(\omega) = \frac{1}{1 - j\left[\dfrac{\omega/\omega_0}{Q(\omega/\omega_0)^2 - 1}\right]}, \qquad \omega_0 RC = \sqrt{n} \quad (4.4.28)$$

and for a symmetrical response $G(0) = G(\infty)$:

$$R_i R_L = \frac{R^2}{(n+1)}, \quad G(0) = G(\infty) = \frac{2R}{2R + R_i + R_L} \quad (4.4.29)$$

The Q of the circuit is dependent on n and $G(0)$, and varies from about 0·25 to 0·5 [h1]. For example, for $n=1$:

$$Q = \frac{\left(\frac{R_i + R_L}{R}\right) + 2}{4\left[\left(\frac{R_i + R_L}{R}\right) + 1\right]} \quad (4.4.30)$$

Though useful, higher Q's are commonly required and are obtained by including the twin-tee in an active feedback system. Numerous configurations are discussed in

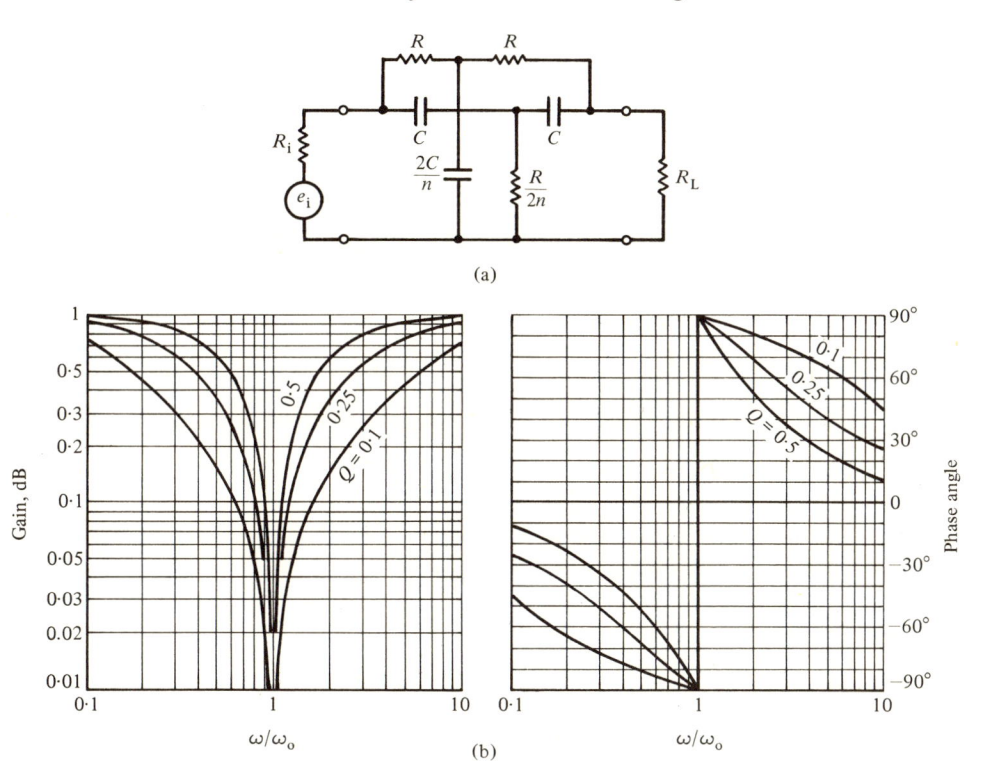

Fig. 4.4.10 (a) Twin-tee network, (b) gain and phase response curves

[a1, parts 10, 11], covering all the standard pass filters. We will consider here only the band reject (or notch) filter, and a universal second order arrangement.

A circuit for a high Q notch filter is shown in Fig. 4.4.11(a) [N1, o1, X1, Y1, b2, A1]. The two amplifiers act as unity gain voltage followers (Sec. 2.5). The feedback fraction m is set by R_3 and may range between 0 and 1. For the standard symmetrical twin-tee shown, the transfer function is found to be [N1]:

$$G(s) = \frac{E_o}{E_i} = \frac{1 + s^2 T^2}{s^2 T^2 + 4sT(1-m) + 1} \quad (T \equiv RC) \quad (4.4.31)$$

which has two zeros and two poles, Fig.4.4.11(b):

$$s_z = \pm \frac{j}{T}, \quad s_p = \frac{-2(1-m)}{T} \pm \frac{j}{T}[1-4(1-m)^2]^{1/2} \quad (4.4.32)$$

The zeros are fixed on the $j\omega$ axis, and the poles move around a semicircle of radius $1/T$ with centre at the origin. Increasing the value of m moves the poles towards the zeros, and they coincide when $m=1$. The transfer function then becomes unity—the Q is infinite and the notch disappears. In practice, the amplifiers will not be perfect and the twin-tee not exactly balanced, so this will not occur. The Q may be found as indicated in Fig. 3.2.2:

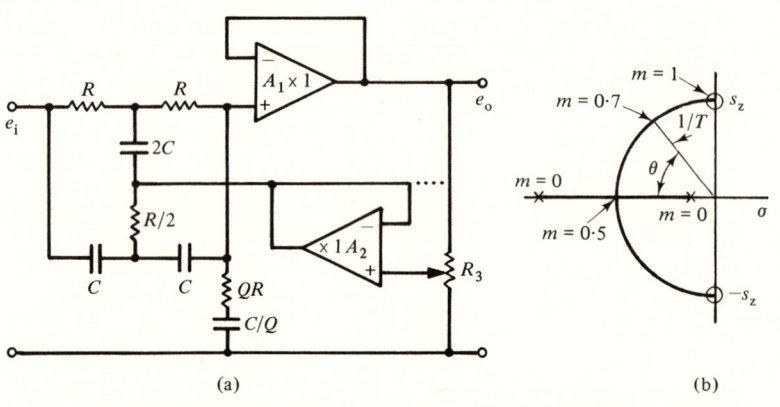

$$\cos\theta = 2(1-m) = \frac{1}{2Q} \quad \text{or} \quad Q = \frac{1}{4(1-m)} \quad (4.4.33)$$

Fig. 4.4.11 (a) High-Q notch filter, (b) root-locus as a function of feedback

e.g., a value of $m = 0.99$ gives a Q of 25. If the highest possible Q only is required, amplifier A_2 may be omitted and a direct feedback connection (shown dotted in Fig. 4.4.11(a)) used. Q values of about 50 may be achieved with these circuits [x1, o1]. An alternative notch filter is described by [11].

It has been shown by Lamden [Z1] that the null using a twin-tee does not fall exactly at the network value. As explained by Good [W1; a1 part 10, Fig. 9] this can be overcome fairly simply by adding an extra RC series network, shown in Fig. 4.4.11(a). This then allows the construction of a universal second order filter, shown in Fig. 4.4.12 [a1, parts 10 and 11].

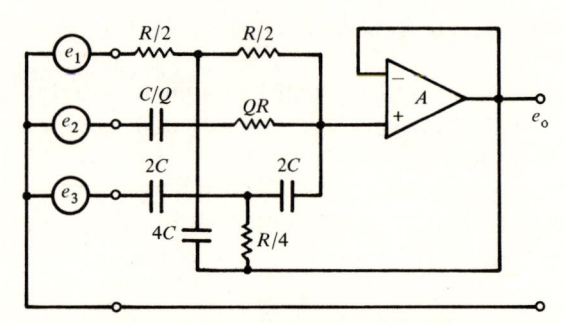

Fig. 4.4.12 Universal second order filter

The various forms of response are obtained by feeding the input to combinations of $e_{1,2,3}$, unused inputs being made zero by shorting out the particular generator. In some cases, an attenuated or inverted input is required ($a<1$ in Table 4.4.6) which can be obtained from a low impedance potential divider or, ideally, from another amplifier.

Table 4.4.6 Connections for universal second order active filter

	e_1	e_2	e_3
Band pass	0	e_{in}	0
Band stop	e_{in}	0	e_{in}
Low pass	e_{in}	0	ae_{in}
High pass	ae_{in}	0	e_{in}
All pass	e_{in}	$-e_{in}$	e_{in}

Note: $a < 1$

Response curves for most of these configurations are given by [N1].

An interesting application of the twin-tee is described in [f2]. This shows how a d.c. chopper amplifier may be combined with a high frequency amplifier to give a low-drift wide-band amplifier; see also Sec. 2.3(b).

It should be noted that to obtain the best performance from the twin-tee the components must be carefully matched. For the common configuration where components R, C and $R/2$, $2C$ are required, it is usually simpler to obtain four equal components of each type and connect two in parallel for the vertical leg. Further consideration is given in [a1, part 11] and some guidance on types and combination of resistor and capacitor in [h1].

4.5 Servo amplifiers and systems

4.5(a) *Servo systems*

Before considering the requirements and design of servo amplifiers, it is necessary to examine the basic types of servo with particular reference to their transient and steady-state responses. These will depend not only on the type of servo, but also on the form of the input signal or command. For a full treatment of servo and control systems, reference should be made to the many books on the subject [d1, e1, f1, g1, h1, i1, j1, n1, v1, P1, S1].

A basic servo may be represented as shown in Fig. 4.5.1.

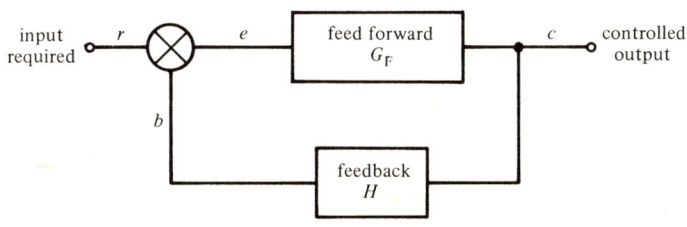

Fig. 4.5.1 Basic proportional-error servo

The required or set input is r and the controlled output c. The difference between r and the feedback, b, is the error, e, which is the input to the feedforward controller, G_F. From the basic relations:

$$B(s) = H(s)C(s);$$
$$E(s) = R(s) - B(s) = R(s) - H(s)C(s); \quad (4.5.1)$$
$$C(s) = G_F(s)E(s)$$

the overall, G_O, and error, G_E, transfer functions are easily determined:

$$G_O = \frac{C}{R} = \frac{G_F}{1+G_F H}; \quad G_E = \frac{E}{R} = \frac{1+G_F H - G_F}{1+G_F H}$$

so that,
$$G_O = \frac{G_F}{1+G_F} \quad G_E = \frac{1}{1+G_F} \quad (4.5.2)$$

where, for consideration of the basic properties of servos, and since it is common in practice, we put $H=1$. The forward transfer function, G_F, can be written in general terms; see Eq. (1.11.9):

$$G_F = \frac{K_N(q_m s^m + q_{m-1} s^{m-1} + \cdots + 1)}{s^N(p_n s^n + p_{n-1} s^{n-1} + \cdots + 1)} \quad (m \leq n) \quad (4.5.3)$$

The order of the exponent N of s in the denominator is used to designate the type of servo, i.e., as $N = 0, 1, 2 \ldots$ we have type 0, 1, 2. . . . While N may in principle be > 2, this results in problems with stability and is uncommon in practice. Type 0 servos are often called regulators, and are usually designed to maintain some controlled quantity constant, in spite of external disturbances [i1], e.g., a voltage regulator (Sec. 7.2). The type determines the steady-state errors, $e_{ss}(t)$, i.e., the errors after any transients have settled, or as $t \to \infty$. The magnitude of the error depends on the form of the input r. We will consider two standard forms here, the step $r = r_0 u(t)$ ($R = r_0/s$) and the ramp $r = r_1 t$ ($R = r_1/s^2$). Determination of steady-state conditions is most easily done by means of the final-value theorem, Sec. 1.11(a), which gives:

$$e_{ss}(t) = \lim_{t \to \infty} e(t) = \lim_{s \to 0} sE(s) = \lim_{s \to 0} sG_E(s) \cdot R(s) \quad (4.5.4)$$

Using Eqs. (4.5.2) and (4.5.3) in Eq. (4.5.4), results in:

Input step: $R = r_0/s$ Input ramp: $R = r_1/s^2$

$$e_{ss}(t) = \lim_{s \to 0} \frac{r_0}{(1+K_N/s^N)} \quad e_{ss}(t) = \lim_{s \to 0} \frac{r_1}{(1+K_N/s^N)} \cdot \frac{1}{s}$$

Type 0 ($N = 0$) $= \dfrac{r_0}{1+K}$ $= \infty$

Type 1 ($N = 1$) $= 0$ $= r_1/K_1$ (4.5.5)

Type 2 ($N = 2$) $= 0$ $= 0$

Thus, for a type 0 servo, there is always an offset between r and c ($e = r - c$, for $H = 1$), finite for a step change and tending to ∞ for a ramp input. To eliminate the step-input error a type 1 servo is required, which will however still have a finite ramp-input error. A type 2 servo will have both errors zero, but will have a finite error for a parabolic input $r = r_2 t^2$.

To examine the transient performance, consider a simple servo (Fig. 4.5.2) consisting of an amplifier A and motor M, controlling the position of a load with moment of inertia J, and subject to a viscous frictional force proportional to the velocity of the load.

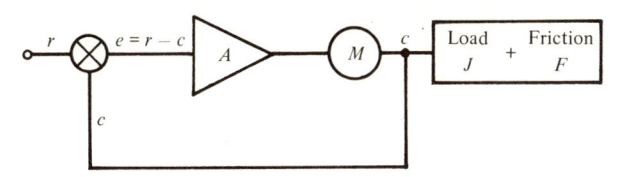

Fig. 4.5.2 Proportional-error position servo

The torque output of the controller (A and M) is proportional to the input signal e, so this is referred to as a proportional-error servo. The equation of motion of the system is:

torque = (moment of inertia × angular acceleration) + (frictional force)

or $\quad KE = Js^2 C + FsC \quad$ (4.5.6)

From this, and the relation $E = R - C$, the three transfer functions can be easily found:

$$G_F = \frac{C}{E} = \frac{K}{Js^2 + Fs} = \frac{K/F}{s(sJ/F + 1)} \quad \text{(Type 1 servo with } K_1 = K/F\text{)}$$

$$G_E = \frac{E}{R} = \frac{Js^2 + Fs}{Js^2 + Fs + K} \quad (4.5.7)$$

$$G_O = \frac{C}{R} = \frac{K}{Js^2 + Fs + K} = \frac{1}{s^2(J/K) + s(F/K) + 1}$$

The steady-state errors are found using G_E:

step (r_0/s) $\quad e_{ss}(t) = \lim_{s \to 0} s \cdot \frac{s(Js + F)}{Js^2 + Fs + K} \cdot \frac{r_0}{s} = 0$

ramp (r_1/s^2) $\quad e_{ss}(t) = \lim_{s \to 0} s \cdot \frac{s(Js + F)}{Js^2 + Fs + K} \cdot \frac{r_1}{s^2} = \frac{Fr_1}{K} = \frac{r_1}{K_1}$

(4.5.8)

which agree with the generalized values in Eq. (4.5.5) for a type 1 servo. It is also of interest here to examine the effect of an externally applied load torque l_T. This is added to the right-hand side of Eq. (4.5.6), and noting that, since r is not changing, $s^2 R = sR = 0$, we get:

$$G_{EL} = \frac{E}{L_T} = \frac{1}{Js^2 + Fs + K},$$

$$e_{ss}(t) = \lim_{s \to 0} s \cdot \frac{1}{Js^2 + Fs + K} \cdot \frac{l_T}{s} = \frac{l_T}{K}$$

(4.5.9)

For this second order system, as indicated by G_O, Eq. (4.5.7), the transient response will depend on the relative values of the constants, i.e., on whether the system is

175

under, critically, or overdamped (see Sec. 3.7). To make comparisons with other treatments the following relations may be used:

$$Q = (KJ)^{1/2}/F = 1/2\zeta \qquad \zeta^2 = F^2/4KJ$$
$$\omega_0^2 = K/J \qquad \omega_n = \omega_0(1-\zeta^2)^{1/2} \qquad (4.5.10)$$
$$\tau = 1/\zeta\omega_0 = 2J/F \qquad T = 2\zeta/\omega_0 = 1/Q\omega_0$$

In normal use, it is common to operate servos slightly underdamped to improve response times, so we will consider this condition here; the conclusions reached will be generally applicable and the other conditions may be readily examined if required [e.g., e1 chapter 4]. The underdamped condition requires $Q > 0.5$, or $F^2 > 4KJ$.

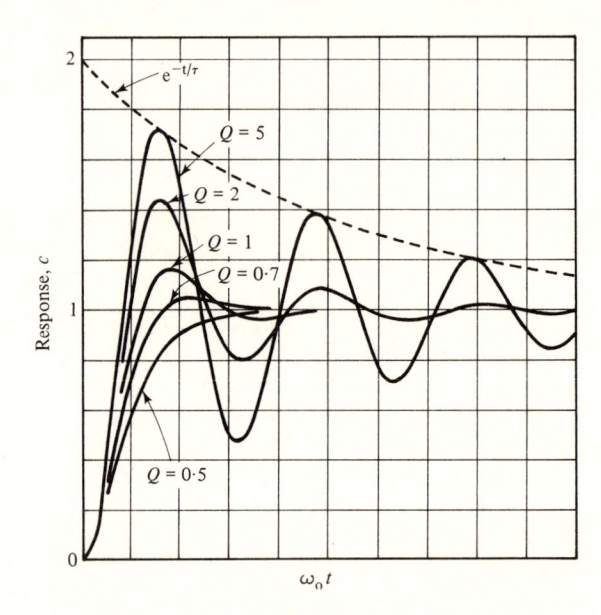

Fig. 4.5.3 Response of second-order servo to step input

The transient response is found using G_0 from Eq. (4.5.7) with the appropriate input r. For the step $r = r_0 u(t)$ the solution for underdamping is:

$$c = r_0 \left\{ 1 - \exp\left(\frac{-Ft}{2J}\right) \left[\cos\left(\frac{K}{J} - \frac{F^2}{4J^2}\right)^{1/2} t + \frac{F}{2J}\left(\frac{K}{J} - \frac{F^2}{4J^2}\right)^{-1/2} \sin\left(\frac{K}{J} - \frac{F^2}{4J^2}\right)^{1/2} t \right] \right\}$$
$$= r_0 \left\{ 1 - e^{-t/\tau} \left[\cos(\omega_n t) + \frac{1}{\tau \omega_n} \sin(\omega_n t) \right] \right\} \qquad (4.5.11)$$
$$= r_0 \left\{ 1 - \frac{\exp(-\zeta\omega_0 t)}{(1-\zeta^2)^{1/2}} \sin[\omega_0(1-\zeta^2)^{1/2} t + \cos^{-1}\zeta] \right\}$$

Thus, there will be damped oscillations of angular frequency ω_n decaying with time constant τ (Fig. 4.5.3).

For a ramp input $r = r_1 T$, the output is given by:

$$c = r_1 \left[\frac{(T-\tau)}{\tau \omega_n} e^{-t/\tau} \sin(\omega_n t) + T e^{-t/\tau} \cos(\omega_n t) + t - T \right]$$

$$= \frac{r_1}{\omega_0} \left\{ \frac{(2\zeta^2 - 1)}{(1-\zeta^2)^{1/2}} \exp(-\zeta \omega_0 t) \sin[(1-\zeta^2)^{1/2} \omega_0 t] + \right. \quad (4.5.12)$$

$$\left. + 2\zeta \exp(-\zeta \omega_0 t) \cos[(1-\zeta^2)^{1/2} \omega_0 t] + \omega_0 t - 2\zeta \right\}$$

The output oscillates for a time and then settles down with a fixed velocity lag $r_1 T = r_1 F/K$, as predicted by Eqs. (4.5.5) and (4.5.8) (Fig. 4.5.4).

To obtain faster settling for a step input, F must be increased so that τ is decreased, Eqs. (4.5.10) and (4.5.11), assuming J is fixed by the application. However, this leads to increased velocity lag, Eq. (4.5.12), unless the gain K can be increased to compensate, but this in turn leads to increased overshoot since the damping ratio ζ is decreased (Q increased, see Fig. 3.7.3) [e1, p. 105–109]. For a load torque, only increasing K will decrease the steady-state error, Eq. (4.5.9).

Thus, if good performance in all these aspects is required, it is necessary to consider some additional techniques. In practical systems there will be some static or coulomb friction and backlash which introduce further errors. What is required is an independent means of damping the transients so that the gain, K, may be increased to reduce the steady-state errors. This may be achieved by introducing the appropriate derivative of r, c, or e into the system [e1, p. 98–105]. First derivative output (sC) and error (sE) control will be considered here.

For derivative output control, the input to the controller is a linear function of E and sC giving the equation of motion:

$$KE = Js^2 C + FsC \pm K_3 sC$$

$$G_F = \frac{C}{E} = \frac{K}{Js^2 + s(F \pm K_3)}$$

$$G_E = \frac{E}{R} = \frac{Js^2 + s(F \pm K_3)}{Js^2 + s(F \pm K_3) + K} \quad (4.5.13)$$

$$G_O = \frac{C}{R} = \frac{K}{Js^2 + s(F \pm K_3) + K}$$

where the derivative feedback may be either positive (−ve sign) or negative (+ve sign). It is seen that F in Eq. (4.5.7) has been replaced by $(F \pm K_3)$, so K_3 simply acts as ±viscous friction. For negative feedback e_{ss} (ramp) is increased, τ is decreased, and vice versa for positive feedback. In both cases, e_{ss} (load torque) is unchanged. If K_3 is increased until $F - K_3 = 0$, there will be no damping and the system will oscillate.

In position servos, where velocity lag is not important, this type of control is commonly used, the derivative signal being obtained from a tachometer attached to the motor, or integral with it.

For derivative error control the input to the controller is a linear combination of

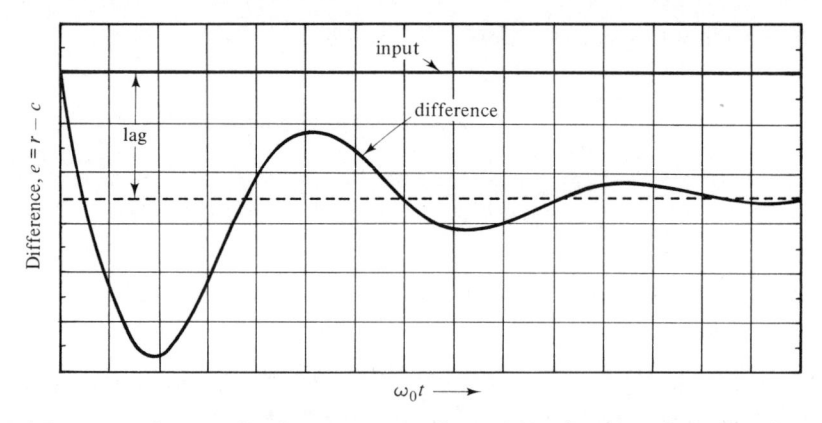

Fig. 4.5.4 Response of proportional-error servo to input ramp showing velocity lag (for $r_1 = \omega_0$, $\zeta = 0 \cdot 25$)

E and sE, giving the equation of motion:

$$KE + K_1 sE = Js^2 C + FsC$$

$$G_F = \frac{C}{E} = \frac{K + K_1 s}{Js^2 + Fs}$$

$$G_E = \frac{E}{R} = \frac{Js^2 + Fs}{Js^2 + s(F + K_1) + K} \quad (4.5.14)$$

$$G_O = \frac{C}{R} = \frac{K + K_1 s}{Js^2 + s(F + K_1) + K}$$

which give, in the usual way:

$$e_{ss} \text{ (ramp)} = \frac{Fr_1}{K}, \quad e_{ss} \text{ (load torque)} = \frac{l_T}{K} \quad (4.5.15)$$

There is no change in e_{ss} (ramp) or e_{ss} (load torque), but there is a decrease in damping time-constant τ_e and in the oscillation frequency ω_{ne}:

$$\tau_e = \frac{2J}{F + K_1}, \quad \omega_{ne} = \left[\frac{K}{J} - \left(\frac{F + K_1}{2J} \right)^2 \right]^{1/2} \quad (4.5.16)$$

Now F can be reduced to decrease e_{ss} (ramp), τ_e being controlled by increasing K_1. Both ramp and load errors will be reduced by increasing K, the consequent increase in overshoot and oscillation frequency, ω_{ne}, again being controlled by variation of K_1.

For a step input we have at $t = 0$, $sR = \infty$, $sC = 0$, so $sE = \infty$. This produces a much larger torque from the servo than for the simple error signal. Similarly, for the ramp $sR = r_1$, and so even at $t = 0$, when there is no velocity lag, a large output torque is produced even though there is, as yet, no error. Thus, the derivative-error control introduces *anticipation* into the system.

Steady-state errors can be reduced, but not eliminated, by increasing the gain K. There will, however, be problems of stability. The errors can be eliminated, in principle, by adding integral-error control (E/s), which is equivalent to having infinite gain at zero frequency, but with attenuation at higher frequencies to control the stability (see Sec. 2.6). The equation of motion is now:

$$KE + \frac{K_2 E}{s} = Js^2 C + FsC$$

$$G_F = \frac{C}{E} = \frac{Ks + K_2}{Js^3 + Fs^2}$$

$$G_E = \frac{E}{R} = \frac{Js^3 + Fs^2}{Js^3 + Fs^2 + Ks + K_2} \qquad (4.5.17)$$

$$G_O = \frac{C}{R} = \frac{Ks + K_2}{Js^3 + Fs^2 + Ks + K_2}$$

$$e_{ss} \text{ (ramp)} = \lim_{s \to 0} s \cdot G_E \cdot \frac{r_1}{s^2} = 0$$

$$e_{ss} \text{ (load torque)} = \lim_{s \to 0} s \cdot G_E \cdot \frac{l_T}{s} = 0$$

and the steady-state errors are now all zero. Though a general solution for a third-order equation is available [m1, p. 118–120; e1, p. 380–385] it is not easy to deduce general results. A root-locus diagram can be drawn which will illustrate the general effects (Fig. 4.5.5) [j1, p. 136; e1, p. 216; d1, p. 230–241].

The poles and zeros are found from G_F, and the locus from G_O as a function of $K = K/J$ (note that $K_2 \propto K$). The detailed shape will depend on the proximity of the zero to the two poles at the origin. If the zero is at the origin (i.e., $K_2 \to 0$, or no integral term) it will cancel one of the poles there, and we will be back to the basic second-order system (Fig. 3.2.2). As the integral term is increased, the zero moves to the left and the locus as a whole moves to the right. This makes the system response slower [j1, p. 133]. If the zero is at the pole $-F/J$, or to the left of it the system will be unstable. (This condition may also be arrived at using the Routh–Hurwitz conditions [n1, p. 82; e1, p. 202; j1, p. 78].)

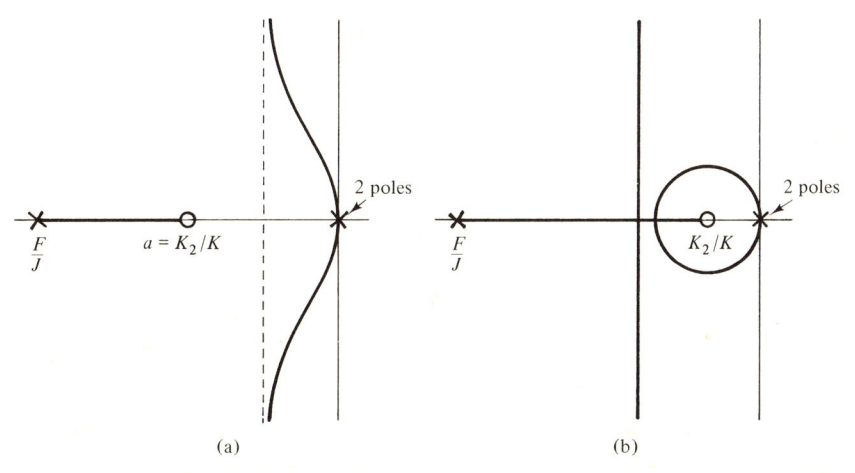

Fig. 4.5.5 Root-locus for proportional-plus-integral-error control for two locations of the zero

In practice, of course, we cannot achieve a perfect integrator (see Sec. 2.6), so there will still be some residual errors, but these can be made very small. The price paid is the increased time that must elapse before the steady-state is reached.

4.5(b) *Servo controller*

The servo controller serves two functions. It must accept the required input, r, and controlled output, c, and operate on these to produce the error, e, and the necessary proportional, derivative, and integral signals. Secondly, it must have a suitable output stage to drive the intended load. This will depend very much on the nature of the load and servo. Thus, we may have a motor to move a load in a position or velocity servo [p1, 11], a high voltage output for a piezoelectric ceramic spacer in a Fabry-Pérot étalon [w1, y1], or a current output for a *loudspeaker* type drive to obtain a linear velocity Mössbauer source [R1]. It is difficult, therefore, to describe a general purpose output stage, but typical power amplifiers are described in Sec. 4.7.

In many experimental servo systems it is convenient to have all three forms of control available. Such a system is often referred to as a three-term controller. We will examine here a simple operational arrangement [Q1, p. 100, III.77] (Fig. 4.5.6).

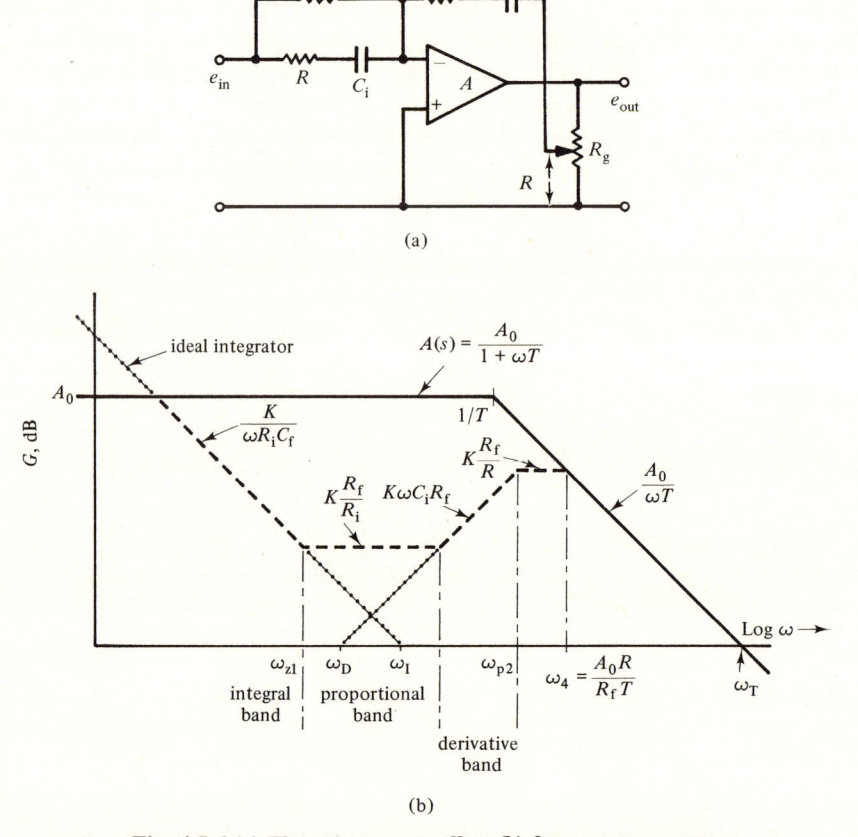

Fig. 4.5.6 (a) Three-term controller, (b) frequency response

$R \ll R_i$ is required for stability reasons and $R_f C_f \ll R_i C_i$. The gain control $R_g \ll R_f$ and $K = R_g/R$. The input and feedback impedances are:

$$Z_i = \frac{R_i(sRC_i+1)}{sRC_i+1+sR_iC_i}, \qquad Z_f = \frac{K(sR_fC_f+1)}{sC_f}$$

so

$$G = \frac{-Z_f}{Z_i} = \frac{-K(s^2 R_f R_i C_f C_i + sR_i C_i + 1)}{s(sRR_i C_f C_i + R_i C_f)} \qquad (4.5.18)$$

Thus, there are two poles:

$$\omega_{p1} = 0, \qquad \omega_{p2} = \frac{1}{RC_i} \qquad (4.5.19)$$

and two zeros:

$$\omega_{z1} = \frac{1}{R_i C_i}, \qquad \omega_{z2} = \frac{1}{R_f C_f} \qquad (4.5.20)$$

The integrating and differentiating time constants are

$$\tau_I = \frac{1}{\omega_I} = \frac{R_i C_f}{K}, \qquad \tau_D = \frac{1}{\omega_D} = KR_f C_i \qquad (4.5.21)$$

The resulting frequency response is shown in Fig. 4.5.6(b). Note that only one pole, ω_{p1}, appears at the origin, since we have assumed $A_0 = \infty$ in deriving Eq. (4.5.18). It cannot be shown, since it is at $-\infty$ on the logarithmic scale. The integral and derivative gains can be set independently by varying C_f and C_i. The proportional gain is varied by means of R_i or R_f, or more conveniently by R_g. However, in all cases this will also affect the integral and derivative gains, so that the proportional gain should be set first.

Note also that Eq. (4.5.18) is not G_F since we have not yet included the load characteristics, e.g., the terms depending on J and F in Eq. (4.5.6).

In practice, the controller can be optimized by adjusting the three *terms* successively. With no integral and derivative terms the proportional gain is increased to the maximum value that gives no overshoot of output. Then the integral gain is increased (τ_I decreased) to the value that just gives no overshoot of output on change of input r. Finally the derivative gain is increased (τ_D increased) to the maximum value without hunting (small oscillation about the control point).

A typical example of this type of controller is described in [k1], and response curves for controllers with various forms of feedback are shown in [g1, p. 117]. In many cases there will be extra poles in the system as a result of mechanical resonances, e.g., belt drives, shaft torsion, etc., and they could cause instability. Measures such as additional damping or the use of non-linear gain [l1] may be effective in overcoming this. References to a number of different servo applications are given in chapter 11.

4.6 High input impedance and electrometer amplifiers

4.6(a) *Introduction*

There are two aspects to consider: high input impedance and low input current. These are not necessarily distinct problems, but which one is more, and which is less, important depends on the signal source. For a high impedance voltage source, e.g., a capacitive or piezoelectric transducer or a pH meter, it is important for the amplifier to have a high input impedance so as not to load the source. With a current source, e.g., an ionization gauge, photocell, or photomultiplier, the measurement of very small currents is the aim, so that currents contributed by the measuring system must be minimized. Since currents of the order of 10^{-16} A or less can be measured it is evident that there will be many potential sources of interference.

There is no clear discrimination between a high input impedance and an electrometer amplifier, but an examination of commercial instruments would suggest that an electrometer would have at least 10^{12} Ω input resistance and less than 10^{-12} A bias current.

The techniques used are dependent on bandwidth requirements, since this will control the allowable magnitude of certain components, and the contributions of the various noise sources that set an ultimate limit to the resolution obtainable. There are also many practical difficulties in this field. For example, an insulation resistance of the circuit board of 10^{12} Ω between a supply voltage of 10 V and the amplifier input terminal, would result in a leakage current of 10 pA. Even if the board has a higher resistance, the presence of surface films such as photoresist, flux, or particularly water, can considerably reduce this. One effective technique for overcoming this problem is to surround the input terminal with a guard (Sec. 1.7) maintained at the same voltage as the input. No current will then flow between guard and input, and all currents from outside the guard will be bypassed.

The problem of low leakage dielectrics also affects the type of capacitor that can be used in some cases. Polystyrene types are probably the best and have a leakage resistance of 10^6 MΩμF. Some information on dielectrics is given in Table 4.6.1 [z1, y1]. If circuit time constants are long, then the effects of dielectric absorption or

Table 4.6.1 Insulation characteristics of dielectrics

	Volume resistance (Ω cm)	Resistance to water absorption	Minimal piezoelectric effects	Minimal triboelectric effects
Sapphire	10^{16}–10^{18}	G	G	F
PTFE	10^{17}–10^{18}	G	P	P
Polyethylene	10^{14}–10^{18}	F	G	F
Polystyrene	10^{12}–10^{18}	F	F	P
Ceramic	10^{12}–10^{14}	P	F	G
Nylon	10^{12}–10^{14}	P	F	P
Glass–epoxy	10^{10}–10^{17}	P	F	P
PVC	10^{10}–10^{15}	G	F	F

G = good, F = fair, P = poor.
Quartz: similar to sapphire but higher piezoelectric effect.
Glass: good resistance but poor water absorption. Glass and ceramics may be improved by coating with silicone resins but they should then not be handled.

Capacitor insulation resistance, MΩμF

PTFE	5–10×10^6
Polystyrene	$2·5$–10×10^6
Polycarbonate	$0·7$–4×10^6
Polypropylene	8×10^4
Mylar	2×10^5

soakage may be important [x1, D1, f1]. This is a slow polarization effect which can be detected after temporarily short-circuiting a charged capacitor. The voltage drops to zero, but after some time on open circuit a voltage reappears, as a result of dielectric absorption or relaxation.

High value resistors also present problems. Up to 10^8 Ω, stable metal film resistors may be used, while glass enclosed metal oxide types are available up to 10^{14} Ω [C1]. Carbon film types, similar to high value metal film resistors, generally used in the past have larger temperature and voltage coefficients and are temporally less stable. These high value resistors look like transmission lines when their stray distributed capacities are included in their equivalent circuits. This has undesirable effects on the signal and noise spectra, but can be partly compensated for by means of additional feedback paths [f1, v1]. Using tee networks for the feedback resistance avoids the use of such high value resistances, but at the cost of increased noise and drift [a2, p. 99].

4.6(b) *High input impedance amplifiers*

For measurement of voltage from a high impedance source without errors due to loading, an input impedance several orders of magnitude greater than the source impedance is required. Input bias current, i_b, must be small since this current flowing in the high impedance of the source could give large voltage errors. Input offset voltages, e_{os}, will be important for small input signals, and voltage and/or current noise will limit the resolution, depending on the source resistance [b2].

The amplifiers considered here are standard types using either super-beta or FET input stages, to give low bias currents and high input resistance, R_{in}. The main advantage of the super-beta type is that the input bias current, i_b, is almost independent of temperature [g1], whereas the junction FET gate currents double for every 10°C rise. However, at normal operating temperatures, say <50°C, the FET types have substantially lower i_b, and recent IC types have much improved matching of the input pair and hence low offset current varying little with temperature.

In both types of amplifier there are two input resistances to consider: differential, R_d, and common-mode, R_{cm} (Secs. 2.9(k) and 2.5). Specifications for FET's usually show R_{cm} about 3 to 10 times R_d, while for bipolar IC amplifiers the ratio is very much larger, say ≈ 100. Bootstrapping, therefore, can increase the value of R_{in}. For the voltage follower (Fig. 2.5.9) R_{in} is increased from R_d to R_{cm} (nearly) while the follower with gain (Fig. 2.5.3) will have an intermediate value, Eq. (2.5.6).

The high input resistance of super-beta types is achieved through input transistors of very high beta (≈ 1000 to 5000) running at low emitter current. This results in reduced slewing rate and large-signal bandwidth. In FET's the gate leakage current is not a function of channel current, so the bandwidth is much greater [l1, c1]. However, in some cases involving high resistances, and hence long time constants, high slewing rate is not of great importance.

Basic characteristics of a number of high input resistance amplifiers are given in Table 4.6.2.

4.6(c) *Electrometer ammeters*

We are concerned here with the measurement of very small currents, down to about 10^{-17} A. There are two basic techniques for measuring these currents: by means of a

Table 4.6.2 Characteristics of high input resistance devices

		JFET	MOSFET	Varactor	Electrometer tubes	Vibrating capacitor
Input resistance (Ω)	>	10^{12}	10^{14}	10^{12}	10^{14}	10^{16}
Input offset current (fA)	<	100	5	2	10	0·02
Noise current (0·1–10 Hz, fA)			2	10	5	0·02
R.M.S. noise current (at 1 Hz, fA/$\sqrt{Hz}$)		1	0·3	0·3	0·2	Johnson noise
Current stability (fA/day)			1	100	1	0·05
Current stability (fA/°C)		×2 per 10°C	1	×2 per 8°C	1	
Voltage drift (μV/day)		50	1–5000	20–100	4000	30
Voltage drift (μV/°C)		10–50	150	10–30	500	30
R.M.S. noise voltage (at 1 Hz, uV/$\sqrt{Hz}$)		0·5 (1/f)	3 (1/f)	1 (flat)	0·5 (1/f)	0·5 (flat)
Input capacity (pF)						
typical		5	10	30	5	10
minimum		2	0·5	30	5	2

Note: (1/f), (flat) refer to noise frequency spectrum.

galvanometer [u1], or by passing the current through an impedance and measuring the voltage across it [k1, b2, s1, r1, q1]. Galvanometers are usually inconvenient, slow, and do not reach the highest sensitivities, and will not be considered here. In the electrometer ammeter the current is passed through a high resistance and the resulting voltage either measured directly, Fig. 4.6.1(a), or in the operational configuration, Fig. 4.6.1(b). An alternative technique is to use a vibrating input capacitor [E1, H1, F1, V1, W1] (Fig. 4.6.4) and measure the rate at which charge accumulates. This method is the most sensitive of those at present used, and will be considered later.

For convenience, high speed, and low noise, the operational current-feedback configuration, Figs. 2.5.8 and 4.6.1(b), is most satisfactory. The virtual ground input provides minimal disturbance to the current generator, even for much less than ideal current sources. This, therefore, will be examined in more detail. Clearly, the amplifier must have very high input resistance and very low bias current, and we assume that the amplifier response has a rather larger bandwidth than is required, i.e., we will not specifically include its response in the transfer functions. For Fig. 4.6.1(a) the bandwidth is simply

$$\omega_a = \frac{1}{R_f C_p} \qquad (4.6.1)$$

where C_p includes the capacity of the amplifier, the current source, and any connecting cable. For example, with $R_f = 10^{12}$ Ω, $C_p = 100$ pF, the bandwidth is $1·6 \times 10^{-3}$ Hz, and the risetime $2·2 \times 10^2$ s, which makes measurements rather slow.

For the current-feedback configuration, Fig. 4.6.1(b), there will also be a feedback capacity, C_f, due to circuit strays and that of R_f itself. This may be small, say ≈ 1 pF $= 1·6 \times 10^{11}$ Ω at 1 Hz, but this will be significant when using large values of R_f. The transfer function can be determined from:

$$I = I_1 + I_2 \qquad I_1 = \frac{(E_{in} - E_{out})(1 + sC_f R_f)}{R_f}$$

$$I_2 = sC_p E_{in} \qquad E_{out} = -AE_{in}$$

so
$$\frac{E_{out}}{I} = \frac{-R_f}{1 + s(C_f R_f + C_p R_f/A)}, \qquad \left(\frac{1}{A} \ll 1\right) \qquad (4.6.2)$$

and the bandwidth is now:

$$\omega_b = \frac{1}{\left(C_f R_f + \dfrac{C_p R_f}{A}\right)} \doteq \frac{1}{C_f R_f} \qquad (4.6.3)$$

If $C_p \ll C_f A$, then the bandwidth has been increased by the factor C_p/C_f, i.e., by about 100 times for the figures given above. The effect of C_f can be removed by the modification shown in Fig. 4.6.1(c). Here $R_o \ll R_f$ and $C_o \gg C_f$, but $C_f R_f = C_o R_o$. The

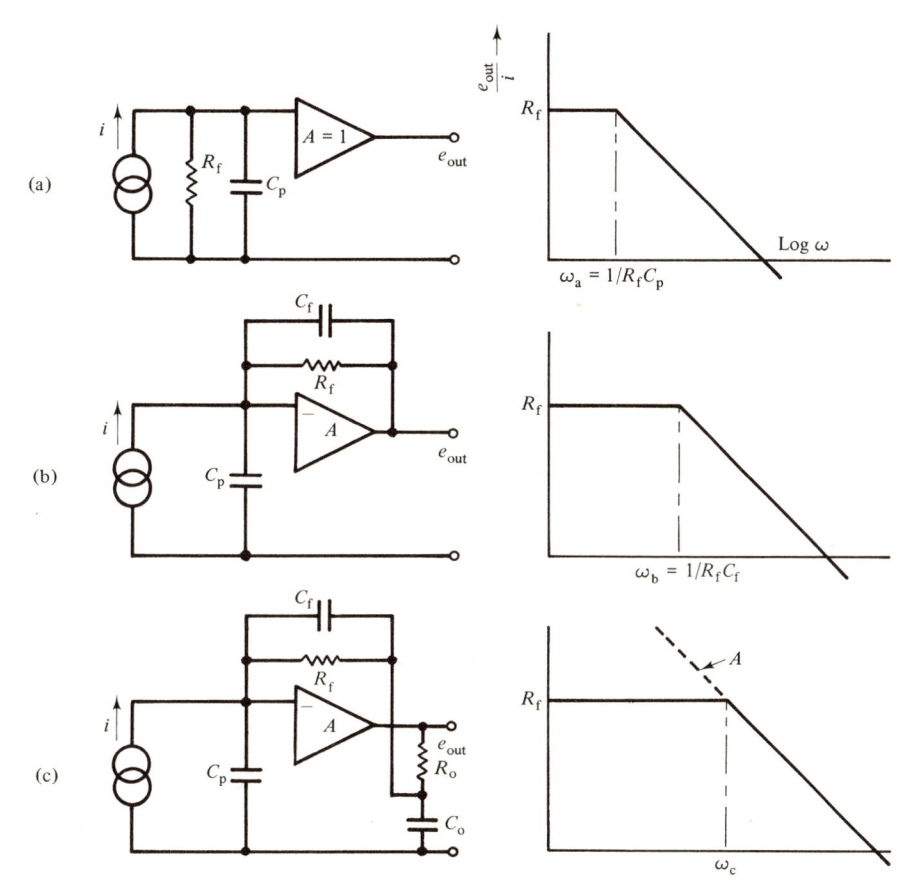

Fig. 4.6.1 Electrometer ammeter circuits

feedback voltage is now $E_{out}/(1+sC_o R_o) = E_{out}/(1+sC_f R_f)$ instead of E_{out}. Thus, ignoring $C_p R_f/A$, the transfer function (4.6.2) reduces to $E_{out}/I = -R_f$. In practice, the amplifier gain A will decrease at high frequencies and $C_p R_f/A$, or the amplifier response itself, will limit the bandwidth. There are, however, other considerations as will become evident below.

The resolution, or the lowest current that can be measured with any system, depends on the noise. This will arise from the Johnson noise (Sec. 1.8) in the measuring resistor, R_f, and from the amplifier input stage. For the resistor, from Eq. (1.8.1):

$$\langle v_{NR}^2 \rangle = 4kTR_f \Delta f \quad \text{or} \quad \langle i_{NR}^2 \rangle = \frac{4kT \Delta f}{R_f} \qquad (4.6.4)$$

185

and for an *RC* circuit the effective noise bandwidth is $\pi/2$ times the -3 dB value, Eq. (1.8.13):

$$\Delta f = \frac{\pi}{2} \cdot \frac{1}{2\pi R_f C} = \frac{1}{4 R_f C} \tag{4.6.5}$$

The signal current produces a voltage:

$$e_S = i_S R_f \quad \text{or} \quad e_S^2 = i_S^2 R_f^2 \tag{4.6.6}$$

so that for the best signal-to-noise ratio, R_f should be as large as possible. The current source resistance $R_{SI} \gg R_f$, so R_{SI} can be neglected. (For a voltage source the source resistance R_{SV} is also in parallel with the input resistance R_{IV} of the voltmeter, but $R_{SV} \ll R_{IV}$ so that R_{SV} determines the Johnson noise.)

The amplifier will also contribute noise. The contributions for bipolar and FET devices are discussed in Secs. 4.1(a), (b), where it is shown that JFET's are superior to bipolar devices particularly for high source resistances, as we have here. MOSFET's are not so good from the noise point of view, but they can provide higher input resistance. Leakage current, I_G, in the FET gate will add shot noise; Sec. 1.8(b):

$$\langle i_{NG}^2 \rangle = 2q I_G \Delta f \tag{4.6.7}$$

and there will be voltage noise represented by a noise generator v_{NA} (Fig. 2.9.4) at the amplifier input. Source noise and gate leakage noise are white, and will contribute white noise at the output. v_{NA} is also white, but will contribute blue noise to the output as a result of the feedback configuration. Since, as far as v_{NA} is concerned, the feedback is attenuated at high frequencies (as for a differentiator, Sec. 2.7), the noise due to v_{NA} at the output will increase with frequency. The noise gain is given by Eq. (2.2.11) with:

$$Z_i = \frac{1}{sC_p}; \quad Z_f = \frac{R_f}{1 + sC_f R_f}; \quad \beta = \frac{1 + sC_f R_f}{1 + sR_f(C_f + C_p)}$$

so
$$G_n = \frac{-A}{1+A} = \frac{A[1 + sR_f(C_f + C_p)]}{1 + A + sR_f(AC_f + C_f + C_p)}$$

$$= \frac{1 + sR_f(C_f + C_p)}{1 + sR_f(C_f + C_p/A)} \quad (A \gg 1) \tag{4.6.8}$$

which has a zero at ω_a and a pole at ω_b:

$$\omega_a = \frac{1}{R_f(C_f + C_p)}; \quad \omega_b = \frac{1}{R_f(C_f + C_p/A)} \tag{4.6.9}$$

The gains below ω_a and above ω_b are given by:

$$G_n(<\omega_a) = 1; \quad G_n(>\omega_b) = \frac{C_f + C_p}{C_f} \tag{4.6.10}$$

The output noise spectrum for v_{NA} is shown in Fig. 4.6.2.

It is clear that v_{NA} contributes an increasing amount of noise as ω increases—hence blue noise. Increasing C_p (dashed lines) will increase the area under the curve, and hence the noise. To cut down this high frequency noise contribution of v_{NA}, C_p must be reduced as far as possible. The effects of varying C_p and C_f are shown in

Figs. 4.6.2 and 4.6.3. While variation of C_p has a large effect on the noise, C_f has rather little effect overall, since a small increase between ω_a and ω_b is compensated by a decrease between ω_b and ω_T. C_f, therefore, can be selected to give the signal bandwidth required, Eq. (4.6.3). Alternatively, if the inherent value of C_f gives a ω_b greater than the desired signal bandwidth ω_d say, an external -12 dB/octave filter

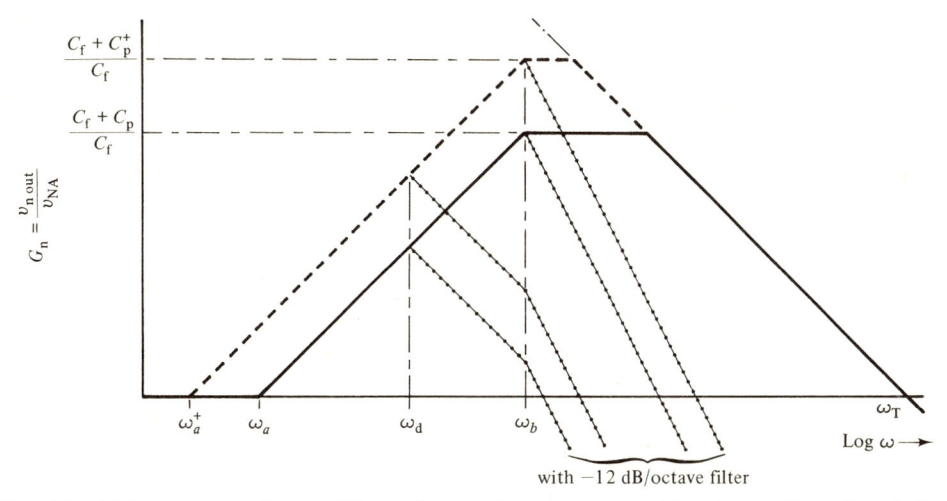

Fig. 4.6.2 Noise spectrum for amplifier voltage noise source v_{NA}. Also shows effect of variation of C_p and -12 dB/octave filter

can be employed to reduce the noise and set the gain bandwidths [k1]. Note that the signal bandwidth will be affected by both ω_b and the filter, if these are close together.

Use of the circuit of Fig. 4.6.1(c) is undesirable from the noise point of view, since there is no noise attenuation at high frequencies until the amplifier open-loop response is reached. The situation is now the same as for the differentiator (Fig. 2.7.2) and there is the possibility of dynamic instability.

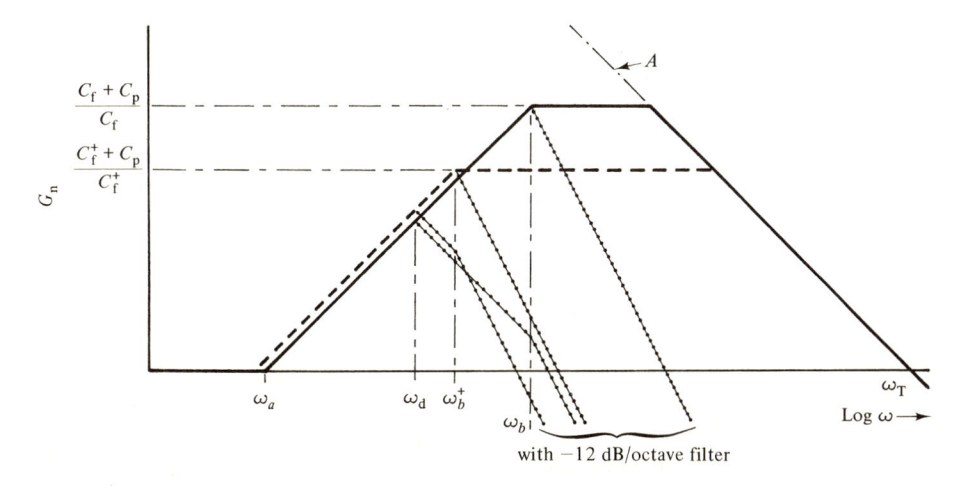

Fig. 4.6.3 Effect on noise spectrum of variation of C_f and -12 dB/octave filter

The vibrating capacitor (or reed) electrometer will only be discussed briefly here, since it is not so readily constructed, and the severe problems arising in measuring the very low currents for which it is best suited make a commercial instrument more attractive [B1, E1, F1, G1, V1, H1, W1, e2]. An outline circuit is shown in Fig. 4.6.4.

A small part, C_v, of the input collecting capacitor, C_c, is varied at a frequency of a few hundred hertz. During the period of one oscillation, the charge Q is essentially

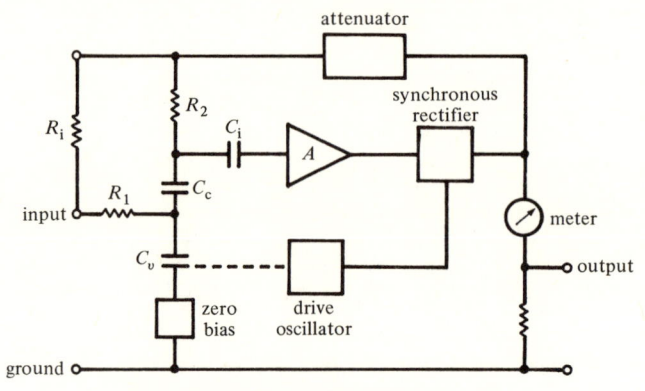

Fig. 4.6.4 Vibrating reed electrometer

constant, R_1 isolating C_c from the source. Thus, a modulated voltage is produced proportional to Q:

$$\delta v = -Q \frac{\delta C}{C^2} \qquad (4.6.11)$$

The varying voltage appears across R_2, is amplified by A and demodulated in the synchronous rectifier (Sec. 10.2). Negative feedback via the attenuator fixes the gain of the system. For voltage or charge measurements R_i is not required. For current measurements either the rate of change of the output, as C_c charges up, is used ($i = dQ/dt$), or the current is passed through the high resistance R_i and the resulting voltage measured.

4.7 Audio and servo power amplifiers

The subject of *audio* amplifiers, particularly high-fidelity, has been so extensively covered that it will not be examined in detail here [v1, w1, x1, y1, u1, B1, C1, D1, E1, F1, G1, H1, I1, J1, K1, M1, Q1, U1, V1, W1, f2, k2].

There are, however, a number of general considerations of particular relevance to *power* amplifiers which are worth discussing here. Power amplifiers are usually classed as A, B, C, or D (or possibly some combination of these, e.g., AB). This nomenclature refers to the location of the quiescent operating point which, in turn, fixes the proportion of a cycle for which the output transistors conduct. In class A, conduction extends over the full cycle and is generally only used for low powers because of the substantial power dissipation in the transistors. Class B stages conduct for just half the cycle and, so, are generally used in push–pull or complementary configurations, where two transistors each supply half the cycle. In class C conduction is for substantially less than half cycle resulting in severe distortion. This class is primarily used for radio frequency (r.f.) applications where high-Q circuits serve to smooth out the waveform. Class D refers to a switched mode system where the output stage is either on or off, passing very rapidly through the intermediate condition. This results in considerable distortion again, but it is of particular use in servo amplifiers.

These classes not only have differences in distortion but, more importantly in power amplifiers, substantial differences in efficiency. This refers to the efficiency of conversion of the d.c. power supplied to useful output power, the remainder being dissipated in the output stage itself. This waste of power may not appear very important in itself (unless working from a battery supply, say), but it also determines the power rating of the transistors, the size of heat sinks, and affects reliability as a result of higher temperatures in both transistors and other components. Efficiencies are given in Table 4.7.1 [Q1].

Table 4.7.1 Efficiencies of power amplifier stages

Class	A	B	D
Theoretical efficiency (%)	50	78	100
Practical efficiency (%)	35	60–65	95

Distortion in class B stages is mainly due to crossover, where one transistor is going off and the other coming on. The current in the load is the difference in collector currents of the two transistors (Fig. 4.7.2). We can thus draw the characteristics of the two transistors as shown in Fig. 4.7.1 to illustrate the non-linearity of the overall

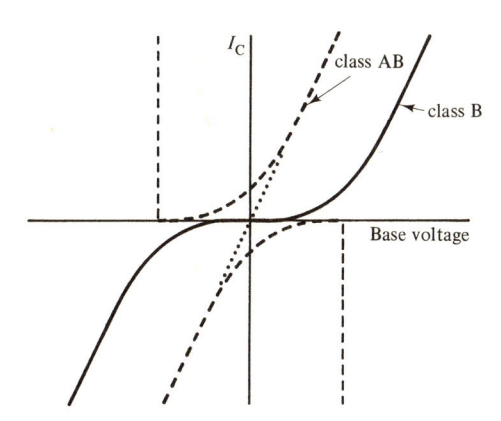

Fig. 4.7.1 Transfer characteristic for class B and class AB operation

characteristic. To reduce this a small standing collector current is introduced, which has the effect of overlapping the two characteristics by the correct amount to give a linear transfer characteristic. This is referred to as class AB operation, and is the condition usually used for high fidelity amplifiers. The efficiency is of course less than that for pure class B, but not much less.

There are many different designs for power amplifiers, but for general use the push–pull complementary type is the most convenient (Fig. 4.7.2).

The output stage is formed by two transistors Q_2 (*NPN*) and Q_3 (*PNP*) each driven by the same signal from the class A driver Q_1. The bias is adjusted to give a linear transfer characteristic, as explained above. The high output resistance (current drive) of Q_1 also helps to reduce crossover distortion. For positive output swings, Q_2 is turned on and supplies current i_+ to the load, since Q_3 is being turned off. On negative swings we have the reverse, and current i_- flows from the load to V_-. The circuit is shown operating between plus and minus rails, so that the load may be d.c. coupled if the quiescent output operating point can be kept at zero. If a.c. coupling is allowed a single power supply may be used (V_- grounded, say) and the load connected via a capacitor; Fig. 4.7.2(b). With the same overall voltage (i.e., $2\,V_+$) the coupling capacitor, C_c, will be charged up to V_+ with the load voltage at zero. On positive swings Q_2 conducts, i_+ flows, and the load voltage rises to nearly V_+. On negative

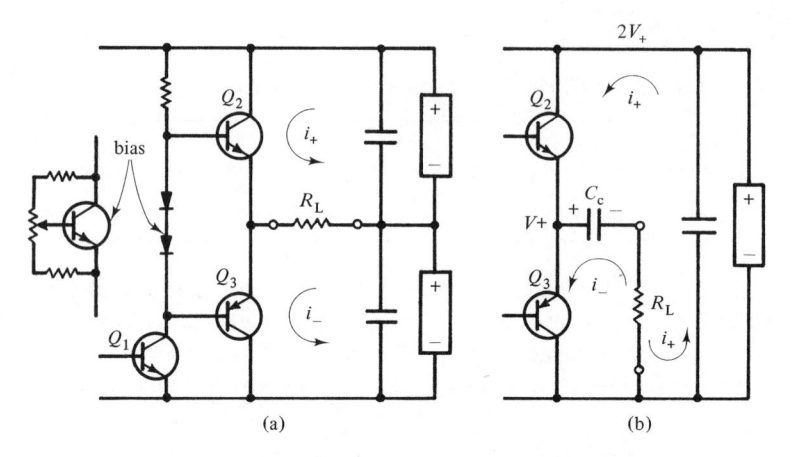

Fig. 4.7.2 Complementary class AB output stage

swings Q_3 conducts, i_- flows discharging C_c through R_L, and the load voltage falls to nearly $-V_+$. Thus, we get the same output as before.

Two methods of generating the bias voltage are commonly used. In the first, two diodes are used to make up for the two V_{BE} voltages of Q_2 and Q_3. These diodes are sometimes mounted on the same heatsink as the output transistors, so that the voltages will track more closely with rise of temperature, which may be quite substantial in a high power circuit. This then compensates for the decrease of V_{BE} as temperature rises, and so keeps the quiescent current fairly constant. If it is required to set the quiescent current to some particular value, then the variable zener (Sec. 1.10(c)) provides the second biasing technique. With a small potentiometer the *zener* voltage can be varied to give the desired quiescent current.

To reduce distortion further, and to gain the usual benefits, overall negative feedback is almost always used. For an audio amplifier the feedback is made frequency dependent, giving the required closed-loop gain over the frequency range of interest, and unity gain at d.c., to give high stability to the quiescent output voltage. This is particularly advantageous in split-supply operation, where d.c. coupling may be used as described above, but it is also useful even if a.c. coupling is used since it will keep the maximum output swing symmetrical.

For higher power amplifiers it may be necessary to add individual drivers to each output transistor in a Darlington or complementary Darlington connection [w1]. This decreases the power dissipation in the single-ended class A driver stage, which otherwise has to run with a substantial quiescent current. The latter can be further reduced by the use of a constant-current load. A circuit using the complementary Darlington configuration is shown in Fig. 4.7.3 [w1, B1, H1, u1].

Q_1, Q_2 form the input stage, and Q_3 is the driver with constant-current load Q_5. Q_4 sets the output stage quiescent current. The two complementary Darlington configurations are formed by Q_6, Q_7 and Q_8, Q_9. Negative feedback is applied via R_1 to the base of Q_2. At high frequencies, where C_1 is negligible relative to R_2, the overall gain is given by $(R_1 + R_2)/R_1$. At low frequencies, C_1 is a high impedance and the system has unity gain. Since substantial feedback is usually applied, and the load Z_L may well be reactive, the problem of dynamic stability is important. The high frequency response is controlled by means of C_2 (Sec. 1.6), the transitional phase

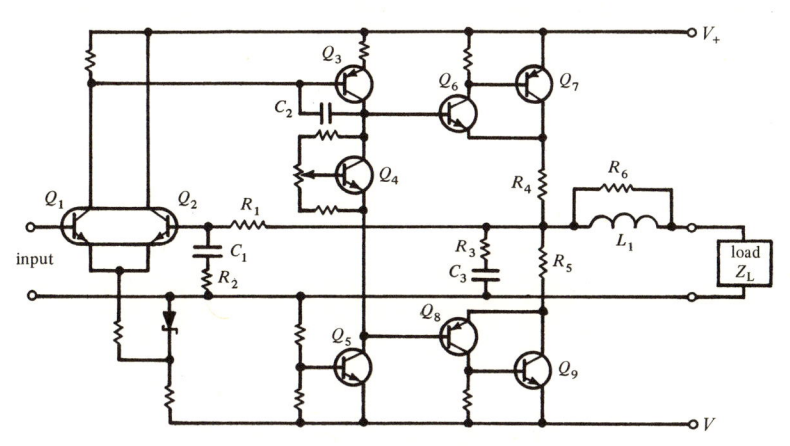

Fig. 4.7.3 Power amplifier using complementary Darlington output stage

network $R_3 C_3$ (Sec. 1.3) and R_6, L_1. L_1 is an inductance of a few microhenry (usually wound on R_6) to compensate for the effects of load capacity, e.g., connecting cables. R_6 is a low resistance (say 10 ohm) to ensure that L_1 has a very low Q, and so avoid any high frequency oscillations. Even though the bandwidth of the amplifier is a few tens of kHz, the unity-gain crossover frequency may be in the MHz region.

For a d.c. amplifier C_1 must be omitted, so that the gain is constant to zero frequency. The circuit is now the same as the power supply/amplifier, Fig. 7.5.5(b), except that it is shown here in the non-inverting configuration (Fig. 2.5.3).

In the past, because of the lack of suitable silicon *PNP* power transistors, quasi-complementary circuits were often used. As can be seen in Fig. 4.7.3, the lower half of the output stage (Q_8, Q_9) uses a *PNP* input and *NPN* power transistor to simulate a power *PNP* transistor. If this arrangement is used with an upper half consisting of a straight *NPN/NPN* Darlington configuration, or even a single *NPN* power transistor, the combination is referred to as quasi-complementary [r1, Q1]. The arrangement shown in Fig. 4.7.3 is true complementary since the upper half simulates an *NPN* power transistor, using an *NPN/PNP* combination, thus matching the lower half. The true complementary is to be preferred, because of the better matching, and silicon *PNP* power transistors are now readily available with matched *NPN* types [H1, D1, u1, x1, r1, I1, J1, w1, B1]. In even earlier circuits, transformers were used both in interstage coupling and for the output. Other than for special requirements, e.g., high voltage output, these are unnecessary and should be avoided, since they are seldom readily available and can introduce large phase shifts making stability difficult to achieve.

The output voltage swing will be determined by the supply voltages and the minimum operating collector voltages of Q_7 and Q_9. Peak output voltage will be $V_+ - 2V_{BE} - V_{R4}$. The power output will depend on the load resistance and the emitter resistors R_4, R_5. These latter resistors serve to limit the maximum output current, and to improve thermal stability and matching of the two halves of the output stage. Though small (≈ 0.5 ohm), they still dissipate substantial power for output currents of several amps, and should be rated accordingly. The power and voltage must depend on the regulation of the supply voltages V_+, V_-. For unregulated supplies there may be a significant drop in voltage for continuous high output, but with reasonable smoothing capacitors this should not happen for transient peaks.

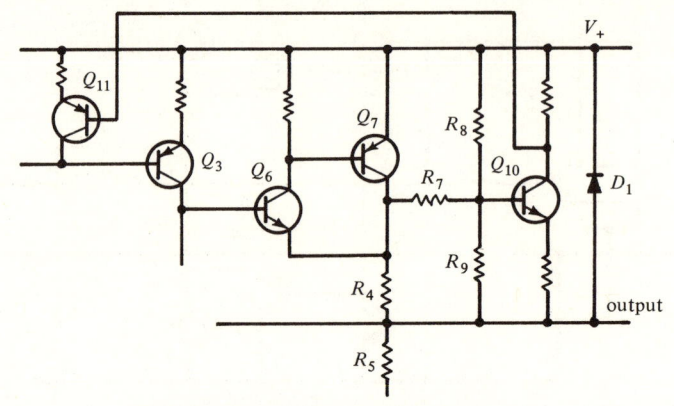

Fig. 4.7.4 Overload protection circuit

This is the main reason for the difference between the several ways in which power ratings are specified [t1, Q1]. For music reproduction there are only occasional large outputs, so the music-power rating can be fixed by the transient capabilities. For continuous sine wave output the rating must be rather less. In practice, the heat-sinking provided in hi-fi amplifiers generally is fixed on the basis of a rather low average power rating so that, if used for continuous sine output, care should be exercised. However, it may be noted that the maximum output transistor dissipation for a class B amplifier occurs when it is delivering about 40 per cent of the maximum possible power output [t1, Q1].

Since large currents flow in the load, the connection of the power supply to the amplifier is important (in a 30 watt amplifier the peak current is 4 A for a 4 Ω load). Leads from the power supply should be of low resistance and connect directly to the output stage, so that these large currents do not circulate in common voltage rails supplying earlier amplifier stages (see Fig. 4.7.2).

In experimental systems, or where changes in load are likely to be made, it is very desirable to have some form of protection against excessive output voltage, current, or power. There are several ways of achieving this [H1, K1, B1, D1, S1, E1, F1, M1, d2, U1, w1]. The protection circuits usually operate by reducing the drive to the output stages, either for the duration of the fault, or by switching and requiring the power supplies to be switched off before reset occurs [K1, D1]. The output current is sensed via R_7 (Fig. 4.7.4) by means of the voltage generated across the emitter resistors R_4, R_5. This is used, via Q_{10}, to switch on Q_{11} and shunt base current from Q_3. By adding to this a signal dependent on the voltage between output and supply V_+, via R_8, R_9, protection against excessive power is achieved. These techniques are fully discussed in [H1]. Reverse diodes D_1, connected between output and the supply lines, will protect against inductive spikes that could cause breakdown in the output transistors.

For moderate power outputs, say up to about 20 W, a number of IC amplifiers can be used (Table 4.7.2). Hybrid and discrete module amplifiers are available up to about 1 kW [N1, E1, F1, q1, s1]. There are also unity-gain buffers to increase the output capability of standard op amps [Z1, Y1, a2] and IC power drivers [z1, O1, X1, v2] for connection to a complementary output stage, which may be either discrete or monolithic [h1, n1]. The latter has integral bias and protection diodes which give excellent quiescent current thermal stability, and eliminate the problem of thermal runaway. Ordinary op amps may also be used as input stages, but will possibly need an intermediate driver stage [o1, c2].

Table 4.7.2 IC power amplifiers

Power amplifiers	Power out (watts)	Supply voltage	Load (ohm)	R_{in} (MΩ)	
MC2870CR	741 op amp plus MC1438 buffer (see below)				
SN76008	10	20	4		
LH0041CJ	200 mA	± 15	100	1	
LH0021CK	1 A	± 15	10	1	
LM379	6	28	8	3	Dual, CL and TH protection
µA791C	1 A	± 15		1	SC and TH protection
TBA810S	7	16	4	5	TH
TBA940	10	16	4		SC and TH protection
TDA2020	20	17	4		
SL415A	5	24	7·5		Includes preamplifier
3571/2	30/60	± 15 to ± 40	0·5 A	10^5	Power op amp, CL and TH protection

Buffers, unity voltage gain
MC1438R: ± 300 mA out, current gain 3000. Bandwidth 1·5 MHz for 20 V peak-to-peak into 300 Ω. Adjustable current limit
LH0033: ± 10 mA into 1 kΩ, ± 100 mA peak, 1500 V/µs slewing, 100 MHz bandwidth
LH0063: ± 250 mA into 50 Ω, ± 500 mA peak, 6000 V/µs slewing, 100 MHz bandwidth large signal, 10^{10} Ω input resistance
3553: ± 200 mA into 50 Ω, 2000 V/µs slewing, 300 MHz bandwidth small signal, 32 MHz large signal, 10^{11} Ω input resistance
821/2: 2·5/5 W output, ± 16 V into 100/50 Ω, 10 MHz bandwidth large signal, 40 MHz small signal, 6 kΩ input resistance, SC protection

Power drivers
NE540: Class AB for 35 W output, 1 MHz bandwidth at 40 dB gain, 200 V/µs slewing, 20 kΩ input resistance, internal CL
MFC4050: Drive 4 W single end class A *PNP* power transistor
MFC8020A: Class B audio driver, 10 mV input for up to 20 W output, input resistance 500 kΩ

CL = current limit, TH = thermal limiting, SC = short circuit

An outstanding example of high power IC amplifier design is the TDA2020, which has hi-fi performance and a number of very useful features [b3, g1, W2]. The circuit is shown in Fig. 4.7.5.

The circuit is designed as a power operational amplifier with differential input (Q_{1-7}) and driver (Q_8) stages in a conventional style. The output is quasi-complementary (Q_{9-12}) with an overall chip geometry carefully chosen to minimize thermal effects on the input stages due to the considerable heat dissipation in the output stages. Since this can be about 10 W good heat sinking is necessary. An R_{th} of only 3°C/W is achieved by mounting the IC chip directly on a copper block which can be clamped to an external heat sink. (The block is connected to the negative supply line so insulation will be necessary.)

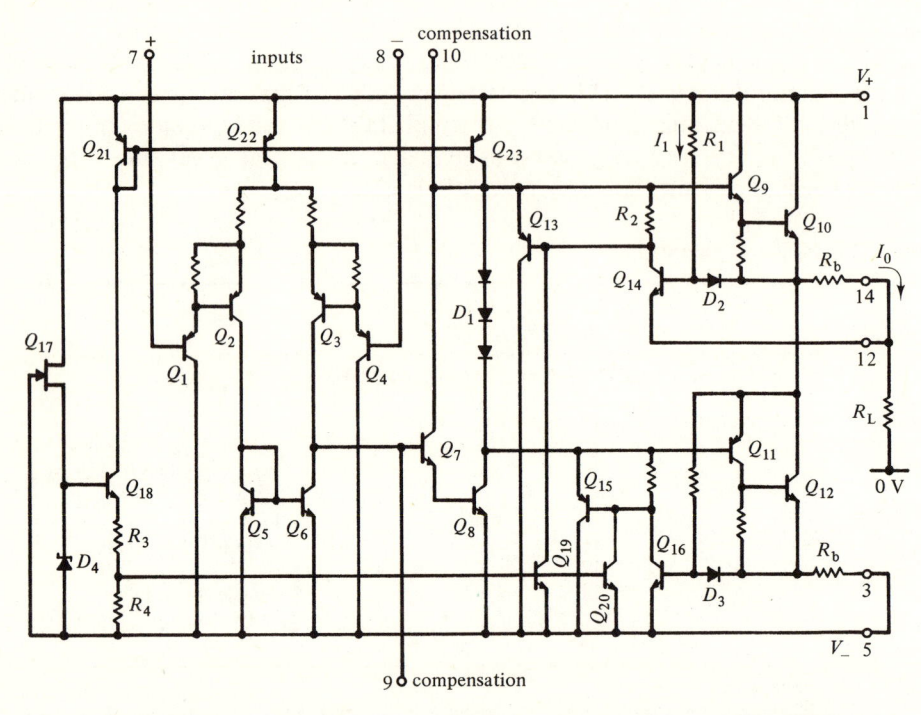

Fig. 4.7.5 Type TDA2020 power amplifier (Adapted courtesy SGS-ATES)

The device is protected against both excess power dissipation and excess temperature. Power limiting is provided by $Q_{13,14}$ and D_2 on the upper half of the output stage, and $Q_{15,16}$, D_3 on the lower. In IC's connections between the silicon chip and the external pins are made with fine gold wires, which are sometimes a limiting factor in current capacity. Here, this is turned to advantage in that the bond wire between Q_{10} and pin 14 (Q_{12} and pin 3), of low but well-defined resistance R_b is used to monitor the output current I_0: $V_b = I_0/R_b$. Normally $I_1 \doteq V_{CEQ10}/R_1$ flows via D_2 to the output, and Q_{14} is off. If I_1 is too large because of excessive V_{CEQ10}, or V_b too large because of excessive I_0, then current is diverted into the base of Q_{14}, which turns on Q_{13} to divert base drive from Q_9 and shut down the output stage. The protection thus depends on both voltage and current (i.e., power) and so the output transistors operate only in their safe operating area: Sec. 1.9(b).

Thermal protection is provided by Q_{17-20} and D_4. The FET current regulator Q_{17}, Sec. 7.10(c), and zener diode D_4 establish a reference voltage at the emitter of Q_{18} which is divided down by $R_{3,4}$ to give 340 mV on the bases of $Q_{19,20}$, the thermal sensing transistors. At 20°C the V_{BE} for conduction is 600 mV, decreasing at a rate of -2 mV/°C. A rise in temperature to 150°C, therefore, decreases V_{BE} to $600 - (130 \times 2) = 340$ mV. $Q_{19,20}$ are turned on and drive current is shunted away from the output stages to close down the system, as before.

The current established in Q_{18} also serves, via Q_{21}, to set the currents in the input and driver stages via $Q_{22,23}$. All the currents are thus related, and the various coefficients are such that they are effectively constant with respect to temperature and supply voltage.

Another development of great potential is that of the power FET [Q2, R2, T2, e3, f3]. This is an enhancement MOSFET (Sec. 8.1) with a voltage rating of 60 V with a

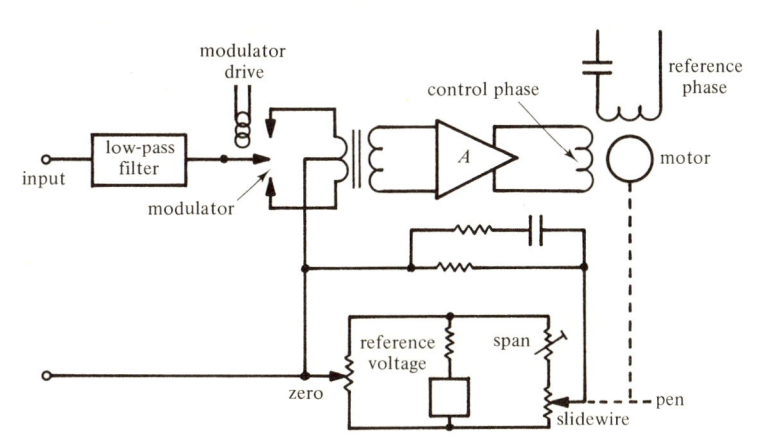

Fig. 4.7.6 Servo system with mechanical chopper

maximum current of 2 A controlled by a gate current of < 1 µA. With a typical f_T of 600 MHz it can switch 1 A in 5 ns, about two orders of magnitude better than a comparable bipolar device. The low input requirements allow it to be driven from almost any source, and the characteristics are such that they may be connected in series/parallel for higher voltage/current operation. The transfer characteristic is highly linear above a certain current, and when complementary devices become available there will be scope for considerable development. From the amplifier protection point of view there is no secondary breakdown (Sec. 1.9) or thermal runaway.

An IC power transistor with current and power limiting and thermal overload protection is available [d2, B2, d1]. At present it is only available in *NPN* form.

For small servos, class B amplifiers are satisfactory. A number of different configurations will be required depending on whether the input and output signals are a.c. or d.c., and on the type of actuator. A very commonly encountered servo actuator is the two-phase a.c. motor. This has a fixed frequency (50 or 60 Hz) reference winding with a fixed amplitude signal of 90° phase, and a control winding of variable amplitude and 0 or 180° phase. The direction of rotation then depends on the phase of the control signal and the torque on its amplitude. The 90° reference phase is obtained by means of an appropriate capacitor in series with the winding inductance. These motors are readily available [N2, P2] and do not have maintenance problems such as associated with brushes in d.c. motors. The latter do however have some advantages [L2] and are also widely used. A more recent development of brushless d.c. motors using Hall-effect switching devices has now eliminated the brush problem [p2, q2, r2] but there remains the possibility of drifts in d.c. amplifiers.

A typical high sensitivity servo system is encountered in chart recorders and x–y plotters. Input signals may be only a few millivolts, so substantial gain is necessary. For stability, a.c. amplifiers are used, the input d.c. signals then being modulated by some form of chopper, either mechanical, optical, or FET. Two typical systems are illustrated in Fig. 4.7.6 [s2, t2].

Figure 4.7.6 shows a mechanical chopper with transformer feeding a square wave to the amplifier. The input low-pass filter is necessary to eliminate any signals approaching the frequency of the chopper, i.e., the modulating frequency must be substantially less than the carrier frequency. In Fig. 4.7.7 an optical chopper is illustrated, and consists of two photoconductors (Sec. 9.3) illuminated by neon

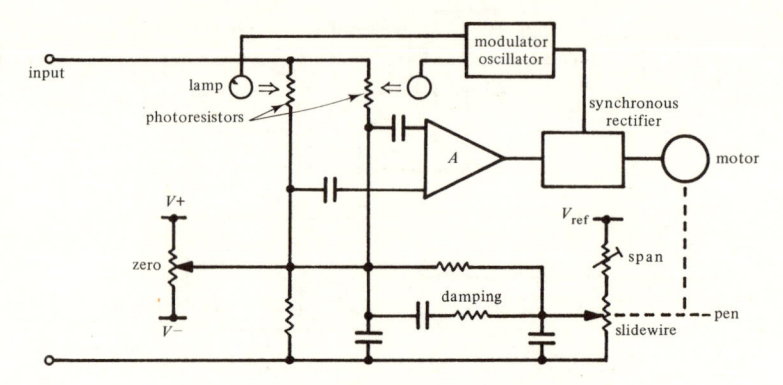

Fig. 4.7.7 Servo system with photochopper

lamps driven off the mains. Each photoconductor is illuminated for alternate half cycles, changing the resistance by many orders of magnitude. The resulting signals are connected via capacitors to the differential amplifier. The output is synchronously demodulated and fed to a d.c. motor.

In servo applications distortion is generally of little concern but efficiency is, especially when large powers are concerned. To reduce the output stage dissipation it is operated as class D, where the transistors are either saturated or cut-off. If the transition time between these two states is kept short the dissipation will be a minimum. This form of drive is used with inductive loads such as a motor which averages the pulse waveform to give a smoothed drive [r1, M2, g2, h2, i2, H2, I2, J2, j2].

The system is run at a high frequency, f_1, say at least ten times greater than the highest frequency it is desired to amplify. With no width modulation the average output is zero; Fig. 4.7.8(a). When an input signal of frequency f_2 is applied, the pulse width is modulated to give an averaged output at f_2 plus harmonics of f_1 and sidebands due to intermodulation products of f_1 and f_2 [i2]. The unrequired high frequency components are filtered out by the load or a smoothing inductance. Systems of this type can operate at efficiencies of greater than 95 per cent and distortion as low as a few per cent. To achieve this sort of performance, it is necessary to use good high frequency transistors as otherwise transition times will be excessive. Consideration should also be given to the suppression of inductive transients that may destroy the transistors and cause interference.

For a fixed frequency a.c. servo system it is not necessary to reproduce the a.c. input error signal. If the error is fed to a symmetrical dual comparator (Sec. 6.1) the output will be a series of pulses at the same frequency, the width being determined by the amplitude of the error signal. Thus, the larger the error the wider the pulses and the more power supplied to the motor.

With such high efficiencies, IC devices can be used to control large powers, e.g., an output power of 200 W from a TO-3 device [R1, M1, i2].

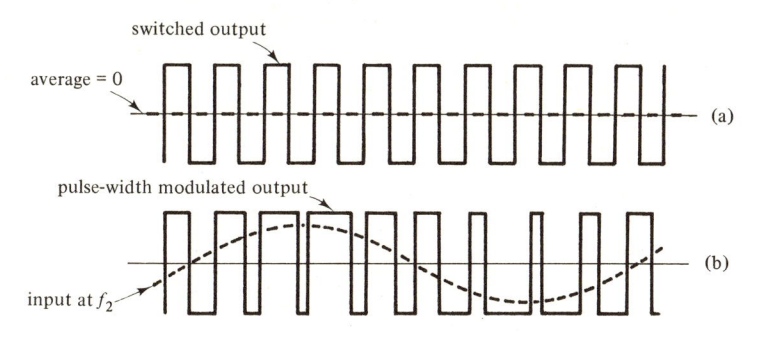

Fig. 4.7.8 Output of class D amplifier

4.8 Miscellaneous amplifiers

4.8(a) *Operational transconductance, programmable, micropower, and Norton*

In contrast to the common operational voltage amplifier, the operational transconductance amplifier has a high output impedance, i.e., a current output, i_{out}, related to the input voltage, e_{in}, by a transconductance g_m [x1, w1]:

$$i_{out} = g_m e_{in} \tag{4.8.1}$$

When connected to a load, R_L, the output voltage is $i_{out} R_L$, and with feedback applied the performance is essentially the same as that of the operational voltage amplifier. However, the transconductance g_m and power consumption in particular, can be varied over a wide range by means of an externally supplied set (or bias) current. The offset voltage, maximum output current, output resistance, and input bias current are also affected. The circuit of the CA3060 amplifier is shown in Fig. 4.8.1 [x1, y1, v1, M1], and it is interesting to note that no resistors are used. The CA3060 actually contains 3 separate amplifiers, a single similar amplifier being available in the CA3080.

The set current, I_b, via the current mirror Q_1, Q_2 (Sec. 1.10(a)), controls the current in the differential amplifier Q_3, Q_4 and hence their transconductance, Eq. (6.2.8). The output is taken from the collector of Q_{14}, while Q_{10}, Q_{11} form an active load and differential to single-ended converter; Sec. 1.10(b). The operation of Q_{13}, Q_{14} in the grounded-base configuration results in high output resistance, which varies from 1 MΩ at $I_b = 200$ μA to 200 MΩ at $I_b = 1$ μA. This high impedance makes it a current source and allows the output load to be referenced to any voltage within the limits of the supply voltages. This, together with the differential input means that there is no ground terminal. The IC also contains a bias regulator to provide a stable source for I_b. The control terminal can be used in three ways:

(i) To set the basic operating parameters, e.g., an amplifier with automatic gain control.
(ii) As an analogue signal input, e.g., as a modulator or multiplier.
(iii) As a digital control input, e.g., as a multiplexer or a sample-hold amplifier (Sec. 6.5).

Addition of a Darlington power output stage to the CA3080 gives the CA3094T with a maximum output current of 100 mA [n1, j1]. Both collector and emitter of the output stage are accessible so that it can sink or source, i.e., accept or provide, current. This also provides a high or low output impedance.

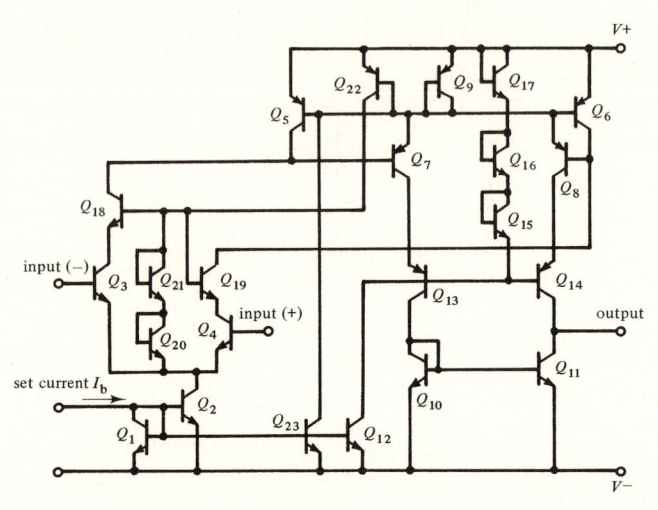

Fig. 4.8.1 Operational transconductance amplifier CA3060 (Reprinted by permission of RCA Solid State Division)

Amplifiers utilizing the same technique of transconductance control, but with the more usual low output impedance are referred to as programmable operational amplifiers. Examples of this type are the μA776 [h1, p1], CA3078 [o1, y1], LM4250 [l1] and L144 [t1]. The gain, bandwidth, slew rate and quiescent power dissipation are all controllable by means of the set current, I_b. For example, operation with a voltage supply as low as 1·2 V is possible with a power consumption of only 0·6 μW [h1]. It should be noted that, for low I_b, the output resistance becomes significant and should be allowed for.

A number of non-programmable micropower amplifiers are also available [a1, b1, c1]. These operate with very low standby power dissipation, with quiescent currents of a few hundred microamperes. As a consequence of the low currents, the input bias and offset currents are very low and input impedance high (tens of megohm). The price is paid principally in reduced output current, slewing rate and large-signal frequency response.

The LM3900 amplifier has been designed particularly for operation from a single rather than dual power supply, and uses the current mirror technique, Sec. 1.10(a), to obtain a differential input [q1, r1]. While the usual differential operational amplifier *differences* input voltages, the LM3900 differences input currents. Hence, it is referred to as a Norton amplifier, a name derived from the Norton equivalent circuit, Sec. 1.2(c). There are four amplifiers in the IC, the circuit of one being shown in Fig. 4.8.2. Bias and input protection circuits are omitted, bias voltages being represented by V_N, V_P.

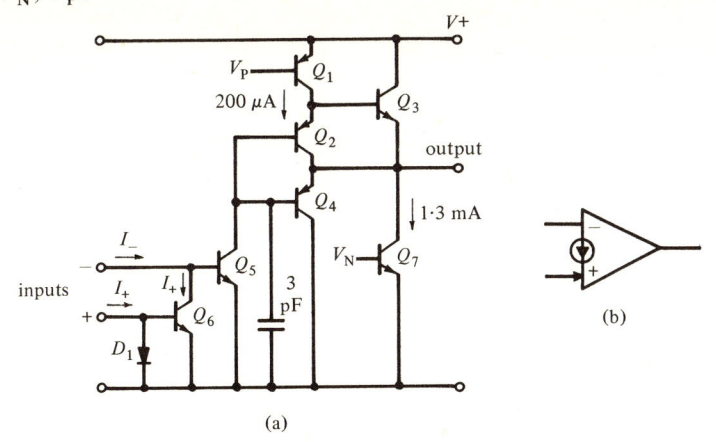

Fig. 4.8.2 (a) Current differencing or Norton amplifier LM3900, (b) circuit symbol (Reproduced by courtesy of National Semiconductor)

The current mirror D_1, Q_6 reflects the input current, I_+, by the collector current of Q_6. Thus, the input current to the base of Q_5 is the difference $I_- - I_+$, giving the current differencing required. The two inputs $(+)$ and $(-)$ always remain one diode drop above ground. Thus, voltage inputs must first be converted to currents using appropriate resistors, in which case there is no limit to the input common-mode voltage range. As the amplifier operates from a single power supply, it is necessary to bias the output to a suitable voltage, for example, to give a symmetrical maximum output swing. A number of techniques may be used to bias the output, one example being shown in Fig. 4.8.3 for an a.c. coupled amplifier.

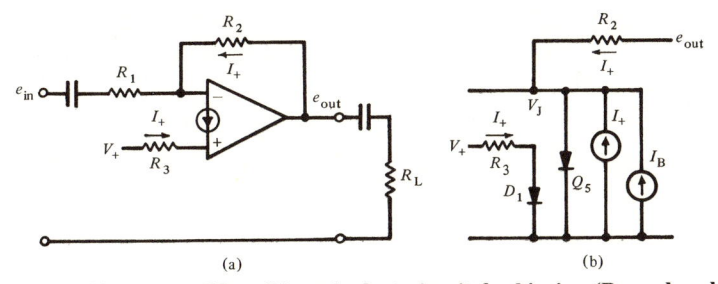

Fig. 4.8.3 (a) LM3900 a.c. amplifier, (b) equivalent circuit for biasing (Reproduced by courtesy of National Semiconductor)

In this case, the d.c. input current is zero so that the current in the feedback resistor R_2 is equal to the $(+)$ input current I_+, neglecting the very small Q_5 base current I_B. If V_J is the forward voltage of D_1, the quiescent output voltage is:

$$e_{out}(\text{d.c.}) = V_J + I_+ R_2$$

$$\doteq 0.5 + \frac{V_+ R_2}{R_3}, \quad \left(I_+ = \frac{V_+}{R_3} \text{ for } V_+ \gg V_J\right) \quad (4.8.2)$$

The a.c. gain is, as before, $G = R_2/R_1$. The LM3900 can be used in a very wide range of circuits as illustrated in a comprehensive application note [q1].

4.8(b) *Low-drift amplifiers*

Drift and low-drift amplifiers have been discussed in chapter 2. A problem with low-drift amplifiers is that performance depends considerably on external effects and components, as well as on the amplifier itself. Mere selection of an amplifier classed as low-drift is no guarantee that you will get the performance you require. The difficulties are primarily confined to d.c. amplifiers, so that if it is possible to convert the system to operate at some suitable a.c. frequency this should be seriously considered.

For lowest drift, chopper amplifiers have the best performance, and in very carefully designed and constructed systems have reached stabilities of about 10^{-9} V/day [x1, Z1]. (Note that drift figures are usually *referred to input*). This sort of amplifier is rather expensive and, for many applications, unnecessary even if the very limited frequency response is acceptable. The latter is set by the chopping frequency and for mechanical choppers with reasonable lifetimes, operating at say 50 Hz, the usable bandwidth is at best a few Hz [d1]. A means of overcoming this limitation by paralleling amplifiers is described in [o1]. The chopper stabilized amplifier, Sec. 2.3(b), also overcomes this problem and a number of high performance types are available. These use solid-state choppers (Sec. 8.2) and are generally constructed of discrete components potted in a small block [s1, t1, A1, B1, C1]. IC types are now also available though these have not as yet produced a lowering of cost [b1, R1]. With these devices a drift of 0·1 μV/°C, 1 μV/month is possible.

Straight amplifiers rely on balanced differential configurations to obtain low drift [D1, E1, F1, G1, H1, I1, O1] and the performance of some devices now approaches that of chopper stabilized types [l1, m1, r1, K1]. The drift of amplifiers with more modest drift specifications may be improved by addition of a carefully matched dual transistor [h1, M1, L1, N1], with an IC preamplifier [a1] or with an *on chip* temperature stabilized differential pair [e1, p1, g1, w1] or preamplifier [q1, v1].

As mentioned above, the realization of a low-drift system is not just a matter of choosing a suitable amplifier—there are external factors that can overwhelm the apparently low drift [n1, t1, W1]. To determine the effective drift even for the ideal circuit, i.e., ignoring thermocouple effects, resistor drift, and tracking, etc., all contributions must be combined [P1, Q1, J1]. These include bias currents flowing in external resistors, common-mode effects, and power supply variation. External effects can be considerable [n1]. Thermojunction voltages, arising from the connection of different metals, can produce voltages of hundreds of microvolts per °C difference between the two junctions of the thermocouple loop. To minimize such effects requires careful layout, good thermal coupling between junctions, and shielding from external temperature changes or air currents. Dissimilar metal junctions arise in many places: copper conductors, solder, kovar leads on semiconductor devices, resistor materials (carbon, metal oxides, metal film, resistance wires), gold- or nickel-plated connectors, and so on.

A further important source of drift is the non-tracking of resistors with change in temperature. This may occur for two nominally equal resistors, but is much more pronounced for resistors of widely differing value, even of the same type, since it is common to use different material for widely differing resistances. For these critical applications matched film networks are available, which can give excellent performance with tracking to 1 p.p.m./°C [S1, i2, j2].

Offset voltage and techniques for balancing this are also important in determining drift [n1, E1, V1, H1]. For a transistor differential amplifier there is, theoretically, a drift of 3·6 µV/°C for each millivolt of offset voltage. Many amplifiers have offset correction terminals which allow the input differential amplifier to be unbalanced to cancel the offset of the amplifier as a whole, and this will generally degrade the drift performance substantially. Alternative techniques are available [E1] for cancelling offset without increasing drift, while some devices using different circuit configurations are not degraded in this way [a1, n1].

4.8(c) *Wide-band amplifiers*

As one of the earliest requirements for wide-band amplifiers was for amplification of the video signals in television systems, the term video is often used in general to refer to wide-band amplifiers. In those early days, a bandwidth of a few MHz presented problems and special configurations such as distributed amplifiers were invented to improve performance. The advent of high frequency transistors has meant an increase of ten to a hundred times in the bandwidth obtainable compared with valve circuits. The design of discrete wide-band amplifiers is discussed in [q1, K1, g1, K2]. We are concerned here with standard IC or hybrid amplifiers rather than the design of discrete amplifiers. A number of available types are listed in Table 4.8.1, which illustrates the performance now obtainable.

Two important requirements for wide bandwidth are minimum capacity, either inherent in active devices or stray, and substantial output current capability. The former affects the bandwidth directly, and the latter is necessary to obtain significant voltage across the low impedances commonly used in high frequency systems, e.g., the 50 ohm characteristic impedance of coaxial cable. Integrated circuits gain in terms of reduced capacities, but have greater problems in providing large signal high frequency response, because of power dissipation problems in the output stage. Thus, any bandwidth figures must be qualified as small-signal or large (power) since the latter may be orders of magnitude less. Recent developments in technology [z1, l1, j1] and of hybrid devices [J1, B1] have given considerable improvement, and all but the most extreme requirements can now be met.

The desirable shape of the passband depends on the particular requirements. For sinusoidal signals the maximum bandwidth flat response is appropriate, and the shape of the cut-off region is not important. Thus, the flat region can be extended at the cost of a much sharper cut-off. For pulse amplifiers the requirements are more critical. As discussed in Sec. 1.4 the droop in the constant parts of the pulse is controlled by the low frequency response, and the risetime by the high frequency response. However, a sharp cut-off at high frequency will have, as a consequence, a rapid change of phase with frequency, giving overshoots and ringing. Thus, for high fidelity pulse amplification it is better to have a more gradual fall-off even at the expense of some constancy of in-band gain. This is of importance in oscilloscopes, for example.

In some situations it is necessary to amplify and then measure pulse height very accurately, as in nuclear spectroscopy. Here, the problems of undershoot and pulse pile-up become critical [M2] and, since the pulses are random, correction is difficult.

Table 4.8.1 IC and hybrid wide-band amplifiers

	Bandwidth (MHz)	Slewing (V/µs)	Output	Comments
LH0024C	70	400	± 12 V; 1 kΩ; 15 MHz	Op amp
LH0032C	70	500	± 10 V; 1 kΩ; 10 MHz	FET input op amp, 8 ns rise at UG
LH0033C	100	500	± 13 V; 1 kΩ; 100 MHz	FET input UG buffer
LH0063C	100	6000	± 250 mA; 50 Ω	FET input UG buffer
LH0061	10	75	± 12 V; 0.5 A; 1 MHz	Op amp
LM318	15	50	± 3 V; 2 kΩ	Op amp
µA733	20	—	4 V p–p; 20 MHz	DIDO, fixed gains 10/100/400
AD509	20	120	± 10 V; 2 kΩ	Op amp, fast settling 0.1 per cent in 500 ns
3507	20 (GB)	120	± 12 V; 1 kΩ; 1.6 MHz	Op amp, fast settling 0.1 per cent in 200 ns
NE501A	150	—	1 V; 600 Ω	Adjustable gain, 2 ns rise
HA2530/5	70 (GB, 0 dB)	320	± 10 V; 2 kΩ; 5 MHz	Op amp
CA3100	38	70 (20 dB)	± 30 mA; 1 MHz	FET op amp
L115	10 (40 dB)	100 ($\times 1$)	± 12 V; 2 kΩ; 1.5 MHz	Op amp, 30 ns rise
SL550	125 (40 dB)	—	0.5 V; 200 Ω	Low noise, gain control by external current
SL541C	100 (20 dB)	175	± 3 V; 6 mA	Op amp, fast settling 1 per cent in 50 ns
SN7510	100	—	4.5 V p–p; 5 kΩ; 10 MHz	DIDO, 10 ns rise
825	40	1000	± 10 V; ± 100 mA; 10 MHz	Op amp, settling 0.1 per cent in 100 ns

Bandwidths are unity gain (UG) small signal unless otherwise indicated. Output shows voltage into load over large signal bandwidth. See also Table 4.7.2 for some power amplifiers

Techniques for overcoming these problems by means of double differentiation, delay-line clipping, and pole–zero cancellation are discussed in [M2, N2, O2, P2, Q2]. In this application, and others, where the pulse height is to be sampled or digitized, the problem of settling time is important. This is the time required for the output to settle to within some specified percentage of the final value. Even with a simple single time-constant system, it requires a time equal to nearly 5 time constants to reach say within 0.1 per cent of the final value (Sec. 1.4). For a complex amplifier with overshoots and non-linear operation, prediction of settling time is liable to considerable error [F1, M1, l1, L1, j1]. It is worth noting that an amplifier with a high slewing rate does not necessarily have a shorter settling time than one with a more moderate rate.

Most of the standard IC operational amplifiers have rather limited bandwidth for large signals. This may be several orders of magnitude less than the small-signal bandwidth usually shown in data sheets, and will be load dependent as a result of output current limitations. To extend their capabilities, a number of unity voltage gain boosters are available that can be connected to the amplifier output and included in the feedback loop [B1, N1, P1, O1, Q1]. Inclusion within the feedback loop will, as usual, decrease output impedance, and reduce distortion, which is more significant for large outputs.

An excellent examination of monolithic operational amplifiers has been given by Solomon [y1]. We follow his treatment of bandwidth limitation here. It is readily shown that the high frequency gain, $A_v(\omega)$, and unity-gain frequency, ω_T, are given by:

$$A_v(\omega) = \frac{g_m}{\omega C_c}, \qquad \omega_T = \frac{g_m}{C_c} \qquad (4.8.3)$$

where g_m is the transconductance of the input stage, and C_c the compensation capacity. The corresponding maximum slewing rate is then:

$$S_{max} = \left(\frac{de_{out}}{dt}\right)_{max} = \frac{2\omega_T I_1}{g_m} = \frac{2I_1}{C_c} \qquad (4.8.4)$$

where I_1 is the quiescent current in one side of the input differential amplifier. For a given ω_T, set primarily by the technology available, the slewing rate is set by the ratio I_1/g_m. For a simple differential amplifier, see Sec. 1.9(b):

$$g_m = \frac{qI_1}{kT} \quad \text{or} \quad \frac{I_1}{g_m} = \frac{kT}{q} = 26 \text{ mV at } 300 \text{ K} \qquad (4.8.5)$$

and, thus, for a bipolar amplifier the maximum slewing rate is:

$$S_B = 2\omega_T \frac{kT}{q} = 5\cdot 2 \times 10^{-8}\, \omega_T \quad \text{V/}\mu\text{s} \qquad (4.8.6)$$

Even for quite high values of ω_T the corresponding full-power-output bandwidth (Sec. 2.9(p)) is rather modest. For example, with $f_T = 10$ MHz and for a peak output $E_0 = 10$ V, we have from Eq. (2.9.3):

$$f_{max} \text{ (full power)} = \frac{S_B}{2\pi E_0} = 50 \text{ kHz} \qquad (4.8.7)$$

The slewing rate can be increased by an order of magnitude by addition of emitter resistors in the input stage which reduce g_m, but at the expense of increased offset and noise. The alternative of increasing I_1 is not effective since $g_m \propto I_1$, and it is usually required that input bias and offset currents (Secs. 2.9(q), (t)) be low. The answer is to use a FET input stage. The ratio of I_1 to g_m is much greater, and there is little problem with bias currents. From Eq. (8.1.2) the minimum value of g_{fs}/I_D occurs when $I_D = I_{DSS}$, giving:

$$\left(\frac{g_{fs}}{I_D}\right)_{min} = -\frac{2}{V_P} \qquad (4.8.8)$$

If we call the unity-gain frequencies for the FET and bipolar cases ω_{TF} and ω_{TB}, then the ratio of the maximum slewing rates is:

$$\frac{S_F}{S_B} = \frac{qV_P}{2kT} \cdot \frac{\omega_{TF}}{\omega_{TB}} \qquad (4.8.9)$$

Taking $V_P = 2$, typically, and $\omega_{TF} = \omega_{TB}$ for comparison, then the ratio is about 40. With other modifications an improvement of two orders of magnitude is possible.

A useful technique, applicable to some amplifiers, for increasing bandwidth is to use feedforward, Sec. 3.5(c). Here the limiting input stages are bypassed for high frequencies [A1] and some devices are now made with this in mind [j1, R1].

Prediction of the closed-loop response from the open-loop performance using the Nichols Chart is discussed in [h1, j1].

Non-operational IC video amplifiers are also available. These may be single-ended types [S1, X1, U1, e1, b1, f1] or of the differential input, differential output (DIDO) configuration [a1, d1, Y1, T1, V1, W1] (Sec. 4.2). The latter have advantages when units are cascaded for higher gain, and have improved dynamic stability since the differential configuration can be used to neutralize the inherent feedback [d1].

One of the main bandwidth limiting factors is that to change a voltage the capacity at that point must be charged, and this takes time. An attractive alternative technique is to use current gain with minimal voltage variations. Using circuits very much like the multiplier circuit of Fig. 6.2.1, this has proved to be most effective, but devices based on this principle do not appear to be generally available as yet [m1].

References section 4.1: Low noise amplifiers

a1   Doyle N: A Low-Noise Tape Preamplifier; Fairchild Semiconductor Application Note APP-180, Sep. 1969.
b1   SGS: TBA231 Dual Low-Noise Operational Amplifier; SGS Data Sheet, Sept. 1970.
c1   Evangelisti F: Low-Noise FET Input Amplifier for Low Frequency Applications: Rev. Sci. Instrum. 43, 338–341, 1972.
d1   Kopp M K: Wide Band Low Noise Voltage Sensitive Preamplifier with Temperature Compensation; Rev. Sci. Instrum. 42, 714–715, 1971.
e1   Griffiths D: Low Noise, Constant Loop Gain, AC Amplifier Details; J. Phys. E Sci. Instrum., 3, 243–245, 1970.
f1   Riva G M: Low Noise High Input Impedance Preamplifier using the BFX82 Field Effect Transistor; SGS Application Report AR174, 1967.
g1   Riva G M: Low-Noise High Input Impedance Preamplifier; SGS Application Report AR159, 1966.
h1   Fairchild: A Low-Drift, Low Noise Monolithic Operational Amplifier for Low Level Signal Processing (μA725); FCH Application Brief APP136, 1969.
i1   Conti M, Cini C: Low Noise Parametric Preamplifier for Electroencephalography; SGS Application Report AR160, 1966.
j1   Cantarano S, Pallottino G V: A Low Noise FET Amplifier for a Spaceborne Magnetometer; Electronic Eng. 42, 57–60, 1970.
k1   Smith L, Sheingold D H: Noise and Operational Amplifier Circuits; Analog Dialogue, 3, No. 1, 1, 5–16, March 1969.
l1   Faulkner E A, Harding D W: Some Measurements on Low Noise Transistors for Audio Frequency Applications; Radio Electronic Engr. 36, 31–33, 1968.
m1   Faulkner E A: The Design of Low-Noise Audio Frequency Amplifiers; Radio Electronic Engnr. 36, 17–30, 1968.
n1   Robinson F N H: Noise in Transistors; Wireless World 76, 339–340, July 1970.
o1   Sutcliffe H: Equivalent Circuit for Noise in Bipolar Transistors; J Elec. Eng. Education 6, 371–374, Oct. 1968.
p1   Nielsen E G: Behaviour of Noise Figure in Junction Transistors; Proc IRE 45, 957–963, 1957.
q1   van der Ziel A: Noise in Junction Transistors; Proc IRE 46, 1019–1038, 1958.
r1   Watson J: An Introduction to Field Effect Transistors; Siliconix Ltd.
s1   Faulkner E A: Optimum Design of Low Noise Amplifiers; Electronic Lett. 2, 426–427, 1966.
t1   Knott K F: Comparison of Varactor-Diode and Junction FET Low-Noise LF Amplifiers; Electronic Lett. 3, 512, 1967.
u1   du Bois J L: Conditions for Optimum Noise Performance of Transistor Amplifiers with Reactive Source; IEEE Trans AU-13, 15–22, 1967.
v1   Miyoshi D S, Cotts R M: Helium Cooled Radiofrequency Preamplifier for Use in NMR; Rev. Sci. Instrum. 39, 1881–1884, 1968.
w1   Emmer T L: Low Noise Transistor Amplifiers for Solid State Detectors; IRE Trans NS-8, 140–146, 1961.

x1   Clayton G B: Operational Amplifiers; Butterworths, 1971.

y1   Robe T J: Measurement of Burst (Popcorn) Noise in Linear Integrated Circuits; RCA Application Note ICAN-6732 (Data Book SSD-202, 249–256, 1972).

z1   Fairchild: Applications of the μA739 and μA749 Dual Preamplifier ICs in Home Entertainment Equipment; Fairchild Complete Linear Book 1, 609–615.

A1   Nielsen E G: Amplifier Noise, Chapter 7 of Amplifier Handbook, Shea R F (Ed); McGraw-Hill, 1966.

B1   Buckingham M J, Faulkner E A: The Principles of Pulse Signal Recovery from Gravitational Antennas; Radio Electronic Engr. 42, 163–171, 1972.

C1   Livezey J A, Holden R: IC Operational Amplifier Noise Measurements; Eimbinder J (Ed), Linear Integrated Circuits Theory and Applications, Chap. 6; Wiley, 1968.

D1   Teeling J: An Integrated Circuit Stereo Preamplifier (MC1303); Motorola Application Note AN-420, 1968.

E1   Hamstra R H, Wendland P: Noise and Frequency Response of Silicon Photodiode Operational Amplifier Combination; Applied Optics 11, 1539–1547, 1972.

F1   van der Ziel A: Noise in Solid State Devices and Lasers; Proc IEEE 58, 1178–1206, 1970.

G1   Kasser R: A New Noise Equivalent Circuit for the Junction FET with Uncorrelated Noise Sources; Proc IEEE 58, 1171–1172, 1970.

H1   Teledyne: Low Noise FETs—A Challenge to Low Noise Bipolars; Teledyne Semiconductor, JFET Applications and Specifications, June 1972, 105–109.

I1   Byerly J E, Long E L: LM381 Low Noise Dual Preamplifier; National Semiconductor Application Report AN-64, 1972.

J1   Byerly J E: LM381A Dual Preamplifier for Ultra-Low Noise Applications; National Semiconductor Application Note AN-70, 1972.

K1   Robinson F N H: Noise in Field Effect Transistors at Moderately High Frequency; Electronic Eng. 41, Mar. 1969, 353–355.

L1   Radeka V: Field Effect Transistors for Charge Amplifiers; IEEE Trans NS-20, 182–189, 1972.

M1   Krycuk G, Walling J D: Miniature Charge Sensitive Preamp-Amplifier for use with Silicon Surface Barrier Detectors; IEEE Trans NS-20, 228–231, 1972.

N1   Mullard: Field-Effect Transistors in a Preamplifier for use with Solid State Radiation Detectors; Mullard Technical Publication TP1106, 1969.

O1   Smith R A, Jones F E, Chasmar R P: The Detection and Measurement of Infra-Red Radiation; Oxford University Press, 1960.

P1   Kennedy E J, De Lorenzo J T, Brashear H R: A Versatile Voltage Sensitive Preamplifier for use with Photomultiplier Tubes; Rev. Sci. Instrum. 40, 1504–1505, 1969.

Q1   Hardcastle I: A High Fidelity Preamplifier; Texas Instruments Application Report B68, 1969.

R1   Thorig J: High Quality Preamplifier; Mullard Tech. Comm. 11, Sept. 1970, 153–155.

S1   Walker H P: Low-Noise Audio Amplifiers; Wireless World 78, May 1972, 233–237, and Nov. 520.

T1   Sesnic S S, Craig G R: Thermal Effects in JFET and MOSFET Devices at Cryogenic Temperatures; IEEE Trans ED-19, 933–942, 1972.

U1   Haslett J W, Kendall E J M: Temperature Dependence of Low Frequency Excess Noise in Junction-Gate FETs; IEEE Trans ED-19, 943–950, 1972.

V1   Rogers C G: MOSTs at Cryogenic Temperatures; Solid State Elect. 13, 1519–1526, 1970.

W1   Anderson P T, Pipes P B: A Low Noise Amplifier with Application to Noise Thermometry Between 300 and 4K; Rev. Sci. Instrum. 45, 42–44, 1974.

X1   Smith K F, Cline J E: A Low-Noise Charge Sensitive Preamplifier for Semiconductor Detectors Using Paralleled Field-Effect-Transistors; IEEE Trans NS-13, June 1966, 468–476.

Y1   Johnson L O, Heath R L: A Direct-Coupled Gamma-Ray Spectrometer for High Counting Rates; IEEE Trans NS-17, 276–284, 1970.

Z1   Gore W G, Smith G W: An Ultralow Noise Preamplifier and Bias Supply for Photoconductive Infrared Detectors; J Phys. E Sci. Instrum. 7, 644–646, 1974.

a2   Davidson A, Newbower R S, Beasley M R: An Ultra-Low-Noise Preamplifier Using Superconducting Quantum Devices; Rev. Sci. Instrum. 45, 838–846, 1974.

b2 Mullard: Use of Field Effect Transistors with Capacitor Microphones; Mullard Application Note TP1104, 1969.
c2 Solomon J E: Cascade Noise Figure of Integrated Transistor Amplifiers; Motorola Application Note AN-223, 1966.
d2 Fabian M: Selecting FETs for Low Noise Applications; Siliconix Application Note 43, Dec. 1972.
e2 Bell R: The Noise Problems Encountered in Integrated Circuits; Electronic Equip. News Jan. 1975, 20–22.
f2 Watson F B: Find the Quietest JFETs by Testing them with Some Simple Circuits; Electronic Design 8 Nov. 1974, 98–102.
g2 Itoh H, Knudsen K L: Direct Measurement of Transistor Noise Voltage, Noise Current and Noise Figure; Hewlett-Packard J 21, No.2, Oct. 1969, 2–7.
h2 Mantena N R: Sources of Noise in Transistors; Hewlett-Packard J 21, No.2, Oct. 1969, 8–11.
i2 Motchenbacher C D, Fitchen F C: Low-Noise Electronic Design; Wiley 1973.
j2 Alderman D W: Liquid Helium Temperature CW NMR S/N Improvement Using a MOSFET RF Amplifier; Rev. Sci. Instrum. 41, 192–197, 1970.
k2 Yerbuny M J: A Gain-Stabilizing Detector for Use in Radio Astronomy; Rev. Sci. Instrum. 46, 169–179, 1975.
l2 Maxwell B: Specifying and Measuring a Low Noise FET-Input IC Op Amp, the AD514; Analog Dialogue 8, No.2, 6, 7, 19.
m2 Faulkner E A: The Principles of Impedance Optimization and Noise Matching; J. Phys. E Sci. Instrum. 8, 533–540, 1975.
n2 National Semiconductor: LH0044 Series Precision Low Noise Operational Amplifiers; National Semiconductor Data Sheet Dec. 1974.
o2 National Semiconductor: LF156 Monolithic JFET Input Operational Amplifier; National Semiconductor Data Sheet.
p2 Klaassen F M: Characterization of Low 1/f Noise in MOS Transistors; IEEE Trans ED-18, 887–891, 1971.
q2 Lengeler B: Semiconductor Devices Suitable for Use in Cryogenic Environments; Cryogenics Aug. 1974, 439–447 (Kernforschungsanlage Julich, Institut fur Festkorperforschung, Jul-1021-FF, Nov. 1973.)
r2 Texas Instruments: SN76131N Low Noise Stereo Preamplifier; Texas Instruments Data Sheet Dec. 1971.
s2 Llacer J: Optimum Filtering in the Prescence of Dominant 1/f Noise; Nuc. Instr. Meth. 130, 565–570, 1975.
t2 Watson B: Audio-Frequency Noise Characteristics of Junction FETs; Siliconix Application Note AN74-4.
u2 Intersil: FET Input Operational Amplifier; Intersil Data Sheet Mar. 1972.
v2 Fairchild: The µA776, an Operational Amplifier with Programmable Gain, Bandwidth, Slew-Rate and Power Dissipation; Fairchild Application Note.
w2 RCA: Four Independent AC Amplifier Array CA3048; RCA Data Sheet 1969.
x2 Motorola: Dual Low-Noise Stereo Preamplifier MC1339P; Motorola Data Sheet 1972.
y2 Stefanovitch D: Ultralow Noise Preamplifier for High Impedance Infrared Bolometer; Rev. Sci. Instrum. 47, 239–240, 1976.
z2 Maxwell J: Hold Noise Down with JFETs; Electronic Design 16 Feb. 1976, 146–152.
A2 Brookdeal: Your Easy Guide to Low Noise AC Amplifiers; Ortec/Brookdeal 1975.
B2 SGS-ATES: Preamplifier for Casette Recorders with ALC, TDA1054; SGS-Ates Data Sheet 1975.
C2 Soderquist D: Minimization of Noise in Operational Amplifier Applications; Precision Monolithics Application Note AN-15, Apr. 1975.

References section 4.2: Differential and instrumentation amplifiers

a1 Demrow R I: Evolution from Operational Amplifier to Data Amplifier; Analog Devices Application Note 1968.
b1 Wu C C, Brandt R: Dual High-Gain Differential Amplifiers, Chap. 5 Designing with Linear IC's, Eimbinder (Ed); Wiley 1969.

c1 Krabbe H: Using a Monolithic Instrumentation Amplifier (AD520); Electronic Eng. 44, 22–23, 1972.

d1 Krabbe H: Monolithic Data Amplifier (AD520). Differential Instrumentation Amplifier on a Single Chip has High Input Impedance, Single Resistor Gain Adjustment, Adjustable Output Bias, Output Current Sensing; Analog Dialogue 6, No.1, 3–5, 1972.

e1 Shales J: A General Purpose IC Differential Output Operational Amplifier (MC1420); Motorola Application Note AN-475, 1967.

f1 Borlase W H: AD520 Monolithic Instrumentation Amplifier; Analog Devices Application Note 1973.

g1 Smith D R: Boost CMR in Differential Applications with a Special Transformer that Cancels Common-Mode Currents but Permits Differential Signals to Pass Unhampered; Electronic Design 27 Sep. 1973, 94–95.

h1 Pouliot F: Amplifiers for Instrumentation; Electron 23 May 1974, 30, 32, 36, 39, and 1 Aug. 1974, 30.

i1 Mortensen H H: A Fully Differential Input Voltage Amplifier (Instrumentation Amplifier); National Semiconductor Linear Brief LB-19, Dec. 1972.

j1 Graeme J G: Applications of Operational Amplifiers: Third Generation Techniques, 2.4 Instrumentation Amplifiers; McGraw-Hill 1973.

k1 Cooper E: Matched Dual Operational Amplifiers (Mono OP-10); Electronic Equipment News Sep. 1973, 58–59.

l1 Burr-Brown: Isolated Operational Amplifiers 3450/1/2; Burr-Brown Data Sheet, Sep. 1974.

m1 Analog Devices: Instrumentation Isolating Amplifier; Electron 20 Apr. 1972, 41–42.

n1 Burr-Brown: FET Input Instrumentation Amplifier 3660/3670; Burr-Brown Bulletins PDS-316/7, Jan. 1975.

o1 Zicko P: Designing with Chopper-Stabilized Operational Amplifiers; Design Electronics Sep. 1970, 66, 68, 70, 73, 74, 131.

p1 Miller B: For Tough Measurements, Try IA's; Electronic Design 2 Aug. 1974, 84–87.

q1 Gross T A O: Baluns for Instruments; Electronic Products Sep. 1963, 38–39.

r1 Analog Devices: Good Circuit Practice Gets Best Results from Isolation Amplifiers; Analog Dialogue 5, No.3, Apr.–Jun. 1971, 12.

s1 Analog Devices: Integrated Circuit Precision Instrumentation Amplifier AD521; Analog Devices Data Sheet 1974.

t1 Breuer D R: Some Techniques for Precision Monolithic Circuits Applied to an Instrumentation Amplifier; IEEE J SC-3, 331–341, 1968.

u1 Seino K C: Low-Drift IC's Form Instrumentation Amplifier; Electronics 1 May 1975, 99, 101.

v1 Analog Devices: Precision, Low Drift, Low Noise, Wide Band Instrumentation Amplifier Model 606; Analog Devices Data Sheet 1974.

w1 Analog Devices: Economy, Low Noise, Low Drift Instrumentation Amplifier Model 610; Analog Devices Data Sheet 1974.

x1 Ott W E: Instrumentation Amplifiers, Versatile Differential Input Gain Blocks; Burr-Brown Application Note AN-75, Aug. 1974.

y1 Tinko M, Maxwell B, Brokaw A P: Monolithic Differential Instrumentation Amp (AD521); Analog Dialogue 9, No.1, 1975, 3–5.

z1 Dobkin R C: Instrumentation Amplifiers; National Semiconductor Linear Brief LB-21, June 1973.

A1 Smith J I: Modern Operational Circuit Design; Wiley-Interscience 1971.

B1 van den Boorn J H, van Etten W C: Feedback Improves the Stability of Difference Amplifiers; Electronic Eng. 42, Dec. 1970, 48–51.

C1 Burr-Brown: Low Offset Voltage Instrumentation Amplifier 3662; Burr-Brown Data Sheet PDS-344, Oct. 1975.

D1 Dobkin R C: Instrumentation Amplifier; National Semiconductor Linear Brief LB-1, 1969.

E1 National Semiconductor: Quadzilla—National Linear Quad Application Book (LM324, LM3900); National Semiconductor Data Book.

F1 Raytheon: Quad Op Amps, Amplifiers, Comparators, Combinations (4136, 324, 3900, 3301, 339, 3302, 4137, 4142); Raytheon Halbleiter Databook.
G1 Pouliot F: Isolation Amplifiers for Effective Data Acquisition; Analog Dialogue 9, No.2, 1975, 10–12.
H1 Burr-Brown: Low Drift Instrumentation Amplifier 3626; Burr-Brown Data Sheet PDS-350, Feb. 1976.
I1 Harris: Quad Operational Amplifier HA-4741 (741); Harris Semiconductor Data Sheet 1975.
J1 Ferranti: Triple Wideband Amplifier with 5V Regulator ZN417E; Ferranti Data Sheet Nov. 1974.
K1 Erdi G: Instrumentation Operational Amplifier with Low Noise, Drift, Bias Current; Precision Monolithics Application Note 1973.

References section 4.3: Logarithmic amplifiers

a1 Gibbons J F, Horn H S: A Circuit with Logarithmic Transfer Response Over 9 Decades; IEEE Trans CT-11, 378–384, 1964.
b1 McDowell W P, Paul J M, Bobis J P: Accurate 9 Decade Temperature Compensated Logarithmic Amplifier; Rev. Sci. Instrum. 39, 1068–1069, 1964.
c1 Paterson W L: Multiplication and Logarithmic Conversion by Operational Amplifier-Transistor Circuits; Rev. Sci. Instrum. 34, 1311–1316, 1963.
d1 Borlase W, David E: Design of Temperature Compensated Log Circuits Employing Transistors and Operational Amplifier; Analog Devices Application Note 1969.
e1 Fairchild: An Arithmetic Analog Computer Using µA735 Logarithmic Amplifiers; Fairchild Application Brief APP-131, 1969.
f1 Dobkin R C: Logarithmic Converters; National Semiconductor Application Note AN-30, 1969.
g1 Ehrsam W: Transistor Logarithmic Conversion Using an Integrated Operational Amplifier; Motorola Application Note AN-261, 1967.
h1 Spicer D, Mann R: Simple Logarithmic and Exponential Amplifiers; Texas Instruments Application Report N73, 1969.
i1 Gledhill B: Nonlinear Elements Offer Analogue Solutions; Electronic Eng. 43, 70–73, 1971.
j1 Philbrick Nexus: Transconductors (Logarithmic, Trigonometric and Arbitrary); Philbrick Nexus Research.
k1 Analog Devices: Log of Current Ratio; Electronic Eng. 43, Feb. 1971, 73, 76, 77.
l1 Texas Instruments: Logarithmic Amplifier SN76502; Texas Instruments Data Sheet and Application Note 1971.
m1 Analog Devices: NPN Log Conformance Transistors AD818; Analog Devices Data Sheet.
n1 Analog Devices: Precision Logarithmic Module 751P/N; Analog Devices Data Sheet.
o1 Philbrick: Transconductors: Non-Linear Circuits for Generation of Exponential, Transcendental, and High-Order Mathematical Functions (Module PPL4P/N); Philbrick Nexus Research.
q1 Cholet J: L'Amplification Logarithmique SN76502; Texas Instruments Application Note.
r1 Jadouille C: Logarithmic Detector for Low Frequencies; Orbit Apr. 1970, 53.
s1 Ahrenkiel R: Wide-Bandwidth Logarithmic Amplifier for Analyzing Decay Kinetics; Rev. Sci. Instrum. 40, 78–81, 1969.
t1 Sheingold D, Pouliot F: The Hows and Whys of Log Amps; Electronic Design 1 Feb. 1974, 52–59.
u1 Intersil: Monolithic Log Amplifier 8048. Monolithic Antilog Amplifier 8049; Intersil Data Sheet Aug. 1973.
v1 Kennedy E J: Low-Current Measurement Using Transistor Logarithmic DC Electrometers; IEEE Trans NS-17, 326–334, 1970.
w1 Rochelle J M, Kennedy E J: Miniaturized Logarithmic Count-Rate Circuit; Rev. Sci. Instrum. 44, 1638–1642, 1973.

x1 Fowler E P: Logarithmic DC Amplifiers Using All Solid State Components; UK Atomic Energy Establishment Report AEEW-R484, 1966.
y1 Radeka V: Logarithmic Charge Amplifier for Scintillation Detectors; Nuc. Instr. Meth. 113, 401–412, 1973.
z1 Sheingold D H: Nonlinear Circuits Handbook; Analog Devices 1974.
A1 Intersil: A Log/Antilog Op Amp; Electronic Eng. 44, Dec. 1972, 43.
B1 Sheingold D: Bipolar Operation of Paired Log Transistors; Proc IEEE 58, 1855–1856, 1970.
C1 Musal H: Transient Response of an Operational Amplifier with Logarithmic Feedback; Proc IEEE 57, 206–208, 1969.
D1 Graeme J G: Applications of Operational Amplifiers: Third Generation Techniques, 3.3 Logarithmic Amplifiers; McGraw-Hill 1973.
E1 Data Device Corp.: Monolithic Log 1451 and Antilog 1452 Amplifiers; ILC Data Device Corp. Data Sheet.
F1 Gilbert B: Current Inverter with Wide Dynamic Range—A Useful Adjunct to Integrated-Circuit Log Devices; Analog Dialogue 9, No.1, 1975, 17.
G1 Hyde F J: Thermistors; Iliffe Books 1971.
H1 Texas Instruments: Temperature Compensation with Sensistor Resistors; Texas Instruments Application Report CA-125.
I1 Hahn C E W: The P–N–P Transistor used Exponentially to Linearize the Voltage Output of the P(CO_2) Physiological Electrode; Rev. Sci. Instrum. 42, 1164–1168, 1971.
J1 Ghelfan P: Log Converters Speed High-Accuracy Calibration of Operational Devices; Electronic Eng. 45, Jan. 1973, 47–49.
K1 Clayton G B: Operational Amplifiers; Butterworths 1971.
L1 Jeremiasen R: Logarithmic Amplifier Accepts 100dB Signal Range; Hewlett-Packard J 25, 16–17, 1974.
M1 Teledyne Philbrick: Temperature Compensated Logarithmic Modules 4537/4538; Teledyne Philbrick Data Sheet 1972.
N1 Analog Devices: 6-Decade, High Accuracy Log Ratio Module Model 757; Analog Devices Data Sheet 1975.
O1 Burr-Brown: Logarithmic Amplifier 4127; Burr-Brown Data Sheet PDS-346, Jan. 1976.
P1 Grimbergen C A, Kohnke G H P: Fast-Response Apparatus for 11-Decade Logarithmic Current-Voltage Measurements; Rev. Sci. Instrum. 47, 854–858, 1976.

References section 4.4: Active filters

a1 Girling E J, Good, E F: Active Filters. A Practical Approach on Feedback Amplifier Theory; Wireless World, (1) Survey of Circuits; Aug. 1969, 348–352. (2) Basic Theory: 1st and 2nd Order Responses; Sep. 1969, 403–408. (3) Properties of Passive and Non-Feedback CR Networks; Oct. 1969, 461–465. (4) Basic Theory: Active Circuits; Nov. 1969, 521–525. (5) An Integrator and a Lag in a Loop; Dec. 1969, 568–572. (6) Lead-Lag Network and Positive Gain; Jan. 1970, 27–31. (7) The Two Integrator Loop; Feb. 1970, 76–80. (8) The Two Integrator Loop, Continued; Mar. 1970, 134–139. (9) Synthesis by Factors; Apr. 1970, 183–188. (10) Uses of the Parallel-T Network; May 1970, 231–234. (11) More on the Parallel-T Network; June 1970, 285–287. (12) The Leapfrog or Active Ladder Synthesis; July 1970, 341–345.
b1 Mitra S K: Active Inductorless Filters (Selected Reprints); Institute of Electrical and Electronic Engineers, New York, 1971.
c1 Stremler F G: Simple Arithmetic: an Easy Way to Design Active Bandpass Filters; Electronics, 7 June 1971, 86–89.
d1 Stephenson F W: ICs Encourage RC Active Filter Design; Electronic Eng. 42, Sep. 1970, 63–67.
e1 Faulkner E A, Viscount Downe: A Second-Order Active Filter Circuit for Tuned Amplifiers and Sinusoidal Oscillators; Electronic Eng. 39, May 1967, 287–290.
f1 Sutcliffe H: Tunable Filter for Low Frequencies Using Operational Amplifiers; Electronic Eng. 36, June 1964, 399–403.
g1 Burr-Brown: Handbook of Operational Amplifier Active RC Networks; Burr-Brown Research Corp. 1966.

h1 White G: Design and Use of RC Parallel-T Networks; IRE Trans. AU-8, 26–33, 1960.
i1 Cowles L G: The Parallel-T Resistance-Capacitance Network; Proc. IRE, 40, 1712–1717, 1952.
j1 Tavares S E: A Comparison of Integration and Low-Pass Filtering; IEEE Trans. IM-15, 33–38, 1966.
k1 Ionnides P G: RC Elements Improve Active-Filter Performance; Electronic Eng. 44, May 1972, 43–46.
l1 Rowe N B: Designing A Low-Frequency Active Notch Filter; Electronic Eng. 44, Apr. 1972, 43–45.
m1 Roberts J: N-Path Filter Techniques; Electron, 1 June 1972, 18–19.
n1 Broeker B: Commutating Filter Techniques; Motorola Application Note AN-534, 1970.
o1 Haussman H: Variable Filter Characteristics with an Op Amp; Electronic Eng. 44, Feb. 1972, 41–42.
p1 Hall A M, Holland M: Filter Design Simplified with Active Filter Modules; Electronic Eng. 44, Feb. 1972, 48, 50, 52.
q1 Fairchild: Active Filters with Gain; Electronic Eng. 44, Feb. 1972, 56.
r1 Kesner D: An Op Amp RC Bandpass Filter; Motorola Application Note AN-452, 1968.
s1 Welling B: Analysis and Design of Active Filters Using Operational Amplifiers; Motorola Application Note AN-438, 1968.
t1 Huelsman L P: Active Filters: Lumped, Distributed, Integrated, Digital and Parametric; McGraw-Hill, 1970.
u1 Fairchild: Active Filters with Gain Using the uA725; Fairchild Application Brief 132, 1969.
v1 Fairchild: Low-Pass Active Filter for Electronic Imaging Using the μA715; Fairchild Application Brief 129, 1969.
w1 Sabbadini G F, Riva G M: RC Active Filters Using Integrated Operational Amplifiers; SGS-Fairchild Application Report 162, 1967.
x1 May F T, Dandl R A: Active Filter Element and its Application to a Fourier Comb; Rev. Sci. Instrum. 32, 387–391, 1961.
y1 Battes R J: Impedance-Lowering Op Amp Speeds Filter Response; Electronics, 44, 10 May 1971, 82.
z1 Ghausi M S: Electronic Circuits: Devices, Models, Functions, Analysis and Design; Van Nostrand Reinhold, 1971.
A1 Sallen R P, Key E L: A Practical Method of Designing RC Active Filters; IRE Trans CT-2, 74–85, 1955.
B1 Mattera L: Active Filters Get More of the Action; Electronics, 45, 19 June 1972, 104–106.
C1 Beckman Instruments: Model 881 Universal Active Filter; Beckman Instruments Data Sheet, July 1972.
D1 Lee M R: Active Filters Simplified; Electron, 9 Nov. 1972, 33–34.
E1 Kerwin W J, Huelsman L P, Newcomb R W: State-Variable Synthesis for Insensitive Circuit Transfer Functions; IEEE J. SC-2, 87–92, 1967.
F1 Thomas L C: The Biquad: Part I—Some Practical Design Considerations; IEEE Trans. CT-18, 350–357, 1971.
G1 Tow J: A Step-by-Step Active-Filter Design; IEEE Spectrum, 6, 64–68, 1969.
H1 Tarmy R, Ghausi M S: Very High-Q Insensitive Active RC Networks; IEEE Trans. CT-17, 358–366, 1970.
I1 Tow J: Design Formulas for Active RC Filters Using Operational Amplifier Biquad; Electronic Letters, 24 July, 1969, 339–341.
J1 Henderson K W, Kautz W H: Transient Responses of Conventional Filters; IRE Trans CT-5, 333–347, 1958.
K1 Olsen D E: Speed Active Multipole Filter Design with a Flexible Computer Program that Calculates the Component Values for Optimum Performance; Electronic Design, 23 Nov. 142–147, 1972,
L1 Zicko C P: Optimize Second-Order Active Filters; Electronic Design, 17 Feb. 70–73, 1972.
M1 Hansen P D: New Approaches to the Design of Active Filters; Lightning Empiricist, 13, Jan.–July 1965, 3–16, and July–Oct. 2–12.

N1 Farrer W: A Simple Active Filter with Independent Control Over the Pole and Zero Locations; Electronic Eng. 39, Apr. 1967, 219–222.
O1 Scott H H: A New Type of Selective Circuit; Proc. IRE 26, 226–235, 1938.
P1 Valley G, Wallman H: Vacuum Tube Amplifiers; MIT Radiation Laboratory Series Vol. 18, 1948, McGraw-Hill.
Q1 Inigo R M: Active Filter Realization Using Finite-Gain Voltage Amplifiers; IEEE Trans. CT-17, 445–448, 1970.
R1 Pease R: An Easily Tunable Notch-Pass Filter; Electronic Eng. 43, Dec. 1971, 50.
S1 Guyton R D: Active RC Network has Two Movable Zeros, Fixed Poles; Electronics, 44, 26 Apr. 1971, 58.
T1 Melen R: Tunable Active Filter Maintains Constant Q; Electronics, 44, 19 July, 1971, 72.
U1 Jenkins J: Active Filter has Separate Band and Frequency Controls; Electronics, 45, 11 Sep. 1972, 110.
V1 Edge G M: Tunable Filter and Oscillator; Instrument Review, July 1967.
W1 Good E F: Selective Amplifiers with Parallel-T Feedback; Electronic Eng. 35, May 1963, 330–331.
X1 Dobkin R: High-Q Notch Filter; National Semiconductor Linear Brief LB-5, 1969.
Y1 Dobkin R: High-Q Active Twin-T; EEE Sep. 1969, 46–48.
Z1 Lamden R J: Network-Tuned Amplifiers with variable Bandwidth; Electronic Eng. 35, Feb. 1963, 109–112.

a2 McQuown A N: Stagger Tuned Low Frequency Selective Amplifiers; White Instrument Labs, Network Notes No.4, Nov. 1957.
b2 White Laboratories: Applications of the Twin-T Network; White Instrument Labs. Network Notes No.5, Dec. 1958.
c2 Urquart R: A New Microwave Link Analyzer with High Frequency Test Tones; Hewlett-Packard J. 24, Sep. 1972, 8–16.
d2 Fairchild: A Voltage Tuned Active Filter; Electronic Eng. 44, Feb. 1972, 45.
e2 Motorola: Bandpass and Notch Filter; Motorola Data Sheet MC3401P, 1972.
f2 Buckerfield P S T: The Parallel-T DC Amplifier: A Low Drift Amplifier with Wide Frequency Response; Proc. IEE 99, Pt.II, 497–506, 1952.
g2 Macken W J: FETs as Variable Resistances in Op Amps and Gyrators; Electronic Eng. 44, Dec. 1972, 60–61.
h2 Brandt R: Active Resonators Save Steps in Designing Active Filters; Electronics, 45, 24 Apr. 1972, 106–110.
i2 Rolfe J, Moore S E: The Efficient Use of Photomultiplier Tubes for Recording Spectra; Applied Optics, 9, 63–71, 1970.
j2 Schoonaert D H, Kretzschmer J: Realization of Operational Amplifier All-Pass Networks; Proc. IEEE 59, 953–955, 1969.
k2 Aronhine P, Budak A: An Operational Amplifier All-Pass Network; Proc. IEEE, 57, 1677–1678, 1969.
l2 Genin R: Realization of an All-Pass Transfer Function Using Operational Amplifiers; Proc. IEEE, 56, 1746–1747, 1968.
m2 Dutta Roy S C: RC Active All-Pass Network Using Differential Input Operational Amplifiers; Proc. IEEE, 57, 2055–2056, 1969.
n2 Sen Roy N: Realization of All-Pass Characteristics by Dual Inputs; Proc. IEEE 57, 836, 1969.
o2 Ghausi M S: Principles and Design of Linear Active Circuits; McGraw-Hill, 1965.
p2 Frederiksen T M, Howard W M, Sleeth R S: The LM-3900—A New Current Differencing Quad of +/− Input Amplifiers; National Semiconductor Application Note AN-72, and Electron, 28 June 1973 42–43.
q2 Wilson D R, Burl M: Design and Application of Active Compensation Circuits for Servo Control Systems; Radio and Electronic Eng. 43, 379–383, 1973.
r2 Storey D J, Cullyer W J: Active Low-Pass Linear-Phase Filters for Pulse Transmission; Proc IEE 112, April 1965, 661–668.
s2 Active Filter Modules: Burr-Brown, Analog Devices, Barr and Stroud, Beckman Instruments, Tranchant Electronique.

t2 Teledyne: The JFET Active Filter; Teledyne Semiconductor JFET Applications and Specifications, June 1972, 144–148.

u2 Bachman A E: Transistor Active Filters Using Twin-T Rejection Networks; Proc. IEE, 106B, 170–112, 1959.

v2 Grebene A B, Camenzind H R: Frequency Selective IC Using Phase-Lock Techniques; IEEE J. SC-4, 216–225, 1969.

w2 Penn T C: Simple Tunable RC Null Networks; Electronic Eng. 36, 849, 1964.

x2 Wolf A: A Note on the Parallel-T Resistance-Capacitance Network; Proc. IRE, 34, 659, 1946.

y2 Burr-Brown: Universal Active Filters; Burr-Brown Data Sheet, UAF Series PDS-295A, 1974.

z2 Tobey G E, Graeme J G, Huelsman L P: Operational Amplifiers, Chapter 8: Active Filters; McGraw-Hill, 1971.

A2 Lewis C P, Mathew M I: The Design of Digital Filters in the W-Plane; Electronic Eng. 46, 12, 13, 15, 1974.

B2 Steiner N A: Voltage-Tunable Active Filter Features Low, High and Bandpass Modes; Electronic Design, 6 Dec. 1972, 96, 98.

C2 Ellern F: Active Notch Filters for Eliminating Noise; Electronic Eng. 44, Sep. 1972, 65–67.

D2 Heinlein W E, Holmes W H: Active Filters for Integrated Circuits; Prentice-Hall 1974.

E2 Williams A B: Active Filter Design; Artech House Books, 1975.

F2 Beauchamp K G: Signal Processing Using Analog and Digital Techniques, Chapter 7 Digital Filtering; George Allen and Unwin, 1973.

G2 Schauman R: Low-Sensitivity High-Frequency Tunable Active Filter Without External Capacitors; IEEE Trans. CAS-22, 39–44, 1975.

H2 Srinivasagopalan R, Martens G O: A Comparison of a Class of Active Filters with Respect to the Operational Amplifier Gain-Bandwidth Product; IEEE Trans. CAS-21, 377–381, 1974.

I2 Geffe P R: Exact Synthesis with Real Amplifiers; IEEE Trans. CAS-21, 369–376, 1974.

J2 Hilburn J L, Johnson D E: Manual of Active Filter Design; McGraw-Hill,

K2 Markus J (Ed): Electronic Circuits Manual, Chapter 28 Filter Circuits—Active; McGraw-Hill, 1971.

L2 Burr-Brown: Universal Active Filter UAF-31; Burr-Brown Data Sheet PDS-318, Dec. 1974.

M2 Burr-Brown: Active Filter Design Examples Using Universal Active Filters; Burr-Brown Application Note AN-61, July 1973.

N2 Freeny S L: Special-Purpose Hardware for Digital Filtering; Proc. IEEE, 63, 633–648, 1975.

O2 DeFalco J A: Apply Topological Graphs to Active Filter Analysis; Electronic Design, 26 Apr. 1975, 84–87.

P2 Graeme J G: Applications of Operational Amplifiers: Third Generation Techniques; McGraw-Hill 1975.

Q2 Gazin J F: Filtres Actifs à Amplificateurs Opérationels; Thomson-CSF/Sescosem Manuel de'Applications CIL, Tome 3, 1974.

R2 Bronzite M: Simple Active Filters. Design Procedure; Wireless World 76, 117–118, Mar. 1970.

S2 Brookdeal Electronics: Signal Recovery Improved by Two Orders of Magnitude (Type 467 Coherent Filter); Electronic Eng. 42, 100, 1970.

T2 Faulkner E A, Grimbleby J B: Active Filters and Gain-Bandwidth Product; Electr. Lett. 6, 549–550, 1970.

U2 Geckle W A: Breadboard Active Filters at a Computer; Electronic Design 21, 21 June 1973, 104–110.

V2 McDermott J: Unusual Filter Concept Promises High Q, Low Frequency Device; Electronic Design 21, 16 Aug. 1973, 22, 24.

W2 Beauchamp K G: A Twin-T Filter Design Having an Adjustable Centre Frequency; Electronic Eng. 39, June 1967, 384–387.

X2 Posel K: A New Treatment of the RC Parallel-T Network; Proc. IEEE 110, 126–138, 1963.

Y2 Wilson D R, Corrall D R, Mathias R F: The Design and Application of Digital Filters; IEEE Trans. I ECI-20, 68–74, 1973.

Z2 Hamilton T A, Sedra A S: A Single-Amplifier Biquad Active Filter; IEEE Trans. CT-19, 398–403, 1972.

a3 Stanton L: Theory and Application of Parallel-T Resistance-Capacitance Frequency-Selective Networks; Proc. IRE 34, 447–456, 1946.

b3 Dutta Roy S C: A Versatile Second Order Active Filter; Electronic Eng. 46, Feb. 1974, 64–66, 68.

c3 Lloyd A: Transform the Biquad into a Biquartic and Reap Bonuses. Biquartic Filters Allow Easy Low-Pass to Band-Pass Transformations with Few Calculations; Electronic Design 22, 4 Jan. 1974, 120–127.

d3 McDermott J: Unusual Filter Concept Promises High Q, Low-Frequency IC Device; Electronic Design 21, 16 Aug. 1973, 22, 24.

e3 Baril M: Three-Mode Network is Filter or Oscillator; Electronics 12 Apr. 1973, 105–106.

f3 Kincaid R, Shirley F: Active Bandpass Filter Design is Made Easy with Computer Program; Electronics 16 May 1974, 123–128.

g3 Faulkner E A, Grimbleby J B: The Effect of Amplifier Gain-Bandwidth Product on the Performance of Active Filters; Radio Electronic Engnr. 43, 547–552, 1973.

h3 Constanides A G, Bogner R E: Introduction to Digital Filtering; Wiley 1975.

i3 Attikiouzel J: Simulation of Inductance; Electron 9 May 1974, 90–91.

j3 Paull C J, Evans W A: The Application of a Commutated Filter to the Design of a Frequency Response Analyzer; Radio Electronic Engnr. 43, 369–378, 1973.

k3 Lloyd A: Sharpen Active Null Networks by use of Pole-Shift Techniques; Electronic Design 21 June 1974, 102–104.

l3 Burr-Brown: Universal Active Filters; Burr-Brown Data Sheet PDS-295A, July 1974.

m3 Burr-Brown: Active Filter Design Examples Using Universal Active Filters; Burr-Brown Application Note AN-61, July 1973.

n3 Kaufman M: Get Notch Q's in the Hundreds; Electronic Design 2 Aug. 1974, 96–101.

o3 Evans W A, Paull C J: High Frequency Voltage/Current Switching Techniques Related to the Design of Multi-Path Filters; IEE Conference Pub. 106, 1973, 145–153.

p3 Todd C D: Silicon Epitaxial FETs, Part 7: FET Active Filters; Electronic Components Aug. 1966, 746–750.

q3 Shepard I: Which Filters?; Electron 21 Nov. 1974, 27, 31, 32, 47.

r3 Attikiouzel J, Linggard R: Ring of Two Active Network; Electron 5 Dec. 1974, 41, 42, 44.

s3 Feller D W: Design CMOS Commutative Filters with Q's that Rival Quartz; Electronic Design 8 Nov. 1974, 116–120.

t3 Visel T A: Narrowband Digital Filter Achieves High Q's; Electronics 22 Nov. 1973, 118.

u3 Ranks E, Sandberg I W: An Alternative Approach to the Realization of Network Transfer Functions: The N-Path Filter; Bell Syst. Tech. J 39, Sep. 1960, 1321–1350.

v3 Mittleman J: Active Filters: Part 1 The Road to High Q's; Electronics 27 May 1968, 109–114.

w3 de Pian L: Active Filters: Part 2 Using the Gyrator; Electronics 10 June 1968, 114–120.

x3 de Pian L, Meltzer A: Active Filters: Part 3 Negative Impedance Converters; Electronics 2 Sep. 1968, 82–93.

y3 de Pian L, Meltzer A: Active Filters: Part 4 Approaching the Ideal NIC; Electronics 16 Sep. 1968, 105–108.

z3 Moschytz G S, Wyndrum R W: Active Filters: Part 5 Applying the Operational Amplifier; Electronics 9 Dec. 1968, 98–106.

A3 Welling B: Active Filters: Part 6 The Op Amp Saves Time and Money; Electronics 3 Feb. 1969, 82–90.

B3 Salerno J: Active Filters: Part 7 Analog Blocks Ensure Stable Design; Electronics 17 Feb. 1969, 100–105.

C3 Hurtig G: Active Filters: Part 8 Positive Results from Negative Feedback; Electronics 31 Mar. 1969, 96–102.

D3 Marsocci V A: Active Filters: Part 9 Applying Nonlinear Elements: Electronics 14 Apr. 1969, 116–121.
E3 Aaronson G: Active Filters: Part 10 Synthetic Inductors from Gyrators; Electronics 7 July 1969, 118–125.
F3 Mullaney J W: Active Filters: Part 11 Varying the Approach; Electronics 21 July 1969, 86–93.
G3 Shepard R R: Active Filters: Part 12 Short Cuts to Network Design; Electronics 18 Aug. 1969, 82–91.
H3 Meltzer A: Activating the Passive RC Network; Electronics 27 May 1968, 114–118.
I3 Johnson E C: Take a Shortcut to Filter Design; Electronics 25 Oct. 1971, 90–92.
J3 Microsystems International: Active Filter Design Using Quad Operational Amplifiers; Microsystems International Application Note 1974.
K3 Al-Nasser F: Tables Shorten Design Time for Active Filters; Electronics 23 Oct. 1972, 113–118.
L3 Budak A, Petrela D M: Frequency Limitations of Active Filters Using Operational Amplifiers; IEEE Trans CT-19, July 1972, 322–328.
M3 Soderstrand M A, Mitra S K: Gain and Sensitivity Limitations of Active RC Filters; IEEE Trans CT-18, Nov. 1971, 600–609.
N3 Attikiouzel J: Operational Amplifiers: Limitations Due to Finite Gain and Phase Shift; Electron 31 Jan. 1974, 13, 15–16.
O3 Harden W R: Digital Filters with ICs Boost Q Without Inductors; Electronics 24 July 1967, 91–100.
P3 National Semiconductor: Quadzilla—National Linear Quad Application Book (LM324, LM3900); National Semiconductor Data Book.
Q3 Raytheon: Quad Op Amps, Amplifiers, Comparators, Combinations (4136, 324, 3900, 3301, 339, 3302, 4137, 4142); Raytheon Halbleiter Databook.
R3 Motorola: Monolithic Quad Operational Amplifier MC3401P; Motorola Data Sheet 1972.
S3 Siliconix: Micropower Triple Operational Amplifier L144; Siliconix Data Sheet 1974.
T3 Fairchild: Differential Video Amplifier µA733; Fairchild Data Sheet.
U3 Motorola: Gate Controlled Two-Channel-Input Wideband Amplifier MC1445; Motorola Data Sheet 1972.
V3 RCA: Video and Wide-Band Amplifier CA3040; RCA Data Sheet 1972.
W3 Delagrange A D: It Could Be the 'Ideal' Filter; Electronic Design 16 Feb. 1976, 156–161.
X3 Mullard: Integrated Gyrator Circuit TCA580; Mullard Data Sheet Apr. 1976.
Y3 Edwards G: Digital Filters Can Simplify Signal Processing; Electronic Eng. June 1976, 53–55.
Z3 Harris: Quad Operational Amplifier HA-4741 (741); Harris Semiconductor Data Sheet 1975.
a4 Ferranti: Triple Wideband Amplifier with 5V Regulator ZN417E; Ferranti Data Sheet Nov. 1974.
b4 National Semiconductor: Quad 741 Op Amps LM148/149; National Semiconductor Data Sheet Nov. 1975.
c4 Linsley-Hood J L: The 'H' or 'Bootstrap' LF Circuit Filter; Electronic Eng. July 1976, 55–58.
d4 Wireless World: Circard Series 1: Basic Active Filters; Wireless World Circard Series.
e4 Cutler D S: Active Filter with controlled Phase Shift; Electronic Eng. Sep. 1975, 18–19.
f4 Waddington D E O'N: Narrow Band Crystal Filter Design; Marconi Instrumentation 15, No.1, 10–13, 1975.

References section 4.5: Servo amplifiers and systems

a1 Mazur T: A ROM-Digital Approach to PWM-Type Speed Control of AC Motors; Motorola Application Note AN-733, 1974.
b1 McDonnell D: Microcomputers for Digital Servo Systems; New Electronics 14 Oct. 1975, 74, 78.
c1 Cutler D S: Torque Control Circuits for a Miniature DC Motor; New Electronics 14 Oct. 1975, 48, 54.

d1 DeRoy B E: Automatic Control Theory; Wiley 1966.
e1 Thaler G J, Brown R G: Analysis and Design of Feedback Control Systems; McGraw-Hill 1960.
f1 James H M, Nichols N B, Phillips R S: Theory of Servomechanisms; McGraw-Hill 1974.
g1 Ahrendt W R, Taplin J F: Automatic Feedback Control; McGraw-Hill 1951.
h1 Savant C J: Basic Feedback Control System Design: McGraw-Hill 1958.
i1 Chestnut H, Mayer R W: Servomechanisms and Regulating System Design; Wiley 1959 (2 Vols.).
j1 D'Azzo J J, Houpis C H: Feedback Control System Analysis and Synthesis; McGraw-Hill 1960.
k1 Miller C A: Temperature Control Using Commercially Available DC Amplifiers; J Phys. E Sci. Instrum. 44, 573–574, 1967.
l1 Merrill H L, Warp R A: A Go-Anywhere Strip-Chart Recorder that has Laboratory Accuracy; Hewlett-Packard J 25, Dec. 1973, 2–8.
m1 Pipes L A: Applied Mathematics for Engineers and Physicists; McGraw-Hill 1964.
n1 West J C: Textbook of Servomechanisms; English Universities Press 1957.
o1 Sargunar J E T: Designs for Servo Amplifiers; Electron 7 Dec. 1972, 35–37.
p1 Williams F C, West J C: The Position Synchronisation of a Rotating Drum; Proc IEE 98 Pt.II, 29.
q1 Computing Techniques: Servo Amplifier Type A11–2; Computing Techniques Data Sheet 1973.
r1 Fay G V, Freyling N: Pulse-Width Modulation for DC-Motor Speed Control; Motorola Application Note AN-445, 1968.
s1 Hewlett-Packard: Feedback Loop and Servomechanism Measurements Using HP Fourier Analyzers; Hewlett-Packard Application Note 140–2, June 1971.
t1 Campbell D L, Westlake R T: Build a High-Current Servo Amplifier with IC's; Control Eng. 16, Dec. 1969, 91–94.
u1 Spalla L J: DC Servo Design Made Simple: Control Eng. 18, Feb. 1971, 56–59.
v1 Wilson D R (Ed): Modern Practice in Servo Design: Pergamon 1970.
w1 Bates B, Conway J K, Courts G R, McKeith C D, McKeith N E: A Stable High Finesse Scanning Fabry-Perot Interferometer with Piezoelectric Transducers: J Phys. E Sci. Instrum. 4, 899–901, 1971.
x1 Bleuler E, Haxby R O (Ed): Methods of Experimental Physics Vol.2 Electronic Methods, Chapter 8 Gould L A: Servomechanisms, Regulation and Feedback; Academic Press.
y1 Hicks T R, Reay N K, Scadden R J: A Servo Controlled Fabry-Perot Interferometer Using Capacitance Micrometers for Error Detection: J Phys. E Sci. Instrum. 7, 27–30, 1974.
z1 Electro-Craft: DC Motors, Speed Controls, Servo Systems; Electro-Craft Handbook 2nd Edn. 1973.
A1 Moore A W: Precision Control of Motor Speed with Phase-Locked-Loops; New Electronics 19 Mar. 1974, 42, 44, 47, 57, 61.
B1 Burri M: Digitally Controlled Ramp Generator for Variable Duty Cycle Regulators; Semiconductors (Motorola) 1974 No.1, 8–13.
C1 Humphries D: Thyristor Control of Electric Furnace Temperature; Mullard Tech. Comm. 9, July 1967, 182–190.
D1 Williamson K H: Speed Control of Two-Phase AC Induction Motors; Mullard Tech. Comm. 9, Sep. 1967, 214–238.
E1 Grant R P: Electronic Speed Control for Electric Drills and Food Mixers; Mullard Tech. Comm. 9, Sep. 1967, 252–255.
F1 Wilson D R, Burl M: Design and Application of Active Compensation Circuits for Servo Control Systems; Radio Electronic Engnr. 43, 379–383, 1973.
G1 Brown J M, Towill D R, Payne P A: Predicting Servomechanism Dynamic Errors from Frequency Response Measurements; Radio Electronic Engnr. 42, 7–20, 1972.
H1 Gutzwiller F W (Ed): Regulating Systems Using Thyristors; General Electric SCR Manual (4 Edn.) Chapter 12, 1967.
I1 Dratler J: A Proportional Thermostat with 10 Microdegree Stability; Rev. Sci. Instrum. 45, 1435–1444, 1974.

J1 Graeme J G: Applications of Operational Amplifier: Third Generation Techniques, 6.3 Controllers; McGraw-Hill 1973.
K1 Stanbury A C: Some Design Criteria for Proportional Temperature Control Systems; J Phys. E Sci. Instrum. 42, 787–790, 1965.
L1 Markus J (Ed): Electronic Circuits Manual, Chapter 76 Servo Circuits, Chapter 87 Temperature Control Circuits; McGraw-Hill 1971.
M1 Ferranti: Pulse Proportional Servo ZN403E; Ferranti Data Sheet Aug. 1970.
N1 Freyling N: High-Performance all Solid-State Servo Amplifier; Motorola Application Note AN-225, 1966.
O1 Bews J: Potentiometer Performance is Vital to Servosystem Accuracy; Electronic Eng. 44, 27–29, May 1972.
P1 Shinners S M: Control System Design; Wiley 1964.
Q1 Philbrick/Nexus: Applications Manual for Operational Amplifiers; Philbrick/Nexus Research 1968.
R1 Bunbury D St P: The Design of Apparatus for the Measurement of Mossbauer Spectra; J Sci. Instrum. 43, 783–790, 1966.
S1 D'Azzo J J, Houpis C H: Linear Control System Analysis and Design: Conventional and Modern; McGraw-Hill 1975.
T1 Hulbert J K: A Field Tracking Digital NMR Magnetometer for In-Situ Use with Superconducting Solenoids; J Phys. E Sci. Instrum. 9, 283–286, 1976.
U1 Fairchild: Motor Speed Control System uA7391; Fairchild Data Sheet 1976.

References section 4.6: High input impedance and electrometer amplifiers

a1 Sherwin J S: Build Better Source Followers 10 Ways; Electronic Design 7 June 1970, 80–84.
b1 Teledyne: Dual FET Applications; Teledyne Applications and Specifications June 1972, 140–144.
c1 Underwood R K: New Design Techniques for FET Op Amps; National Semiconductor Application Note AN-63, 1972.
d1 Barker R W J, Hart B L: An Ultra-High Input Impedance Amplifier and its Drift Performance; Electronic Components 27 Oct. 1972, 1007–1009.
e1 Smith D H: High Performance Flame-Ionization Detector System for Gas Chromatography; Hewlett-Packard J 24, Mar. 1973, 2–10.
f1 Demrow R I: Op Amps as Electrometers or—The World of fA; Analog Dialogue 5, Feb./Mar. 1971, 6–7.
g1 Widlar R J: IC Op Amp Beats FETs on Input Current; National Semiconductor Application Note AN-29 1969.
h1 Fullagar D: The 8007—a High Performance FET-Input Op Amp; New Electronics 31 Oct. 1972, 24–25.
i1 Pieau J F: Compact Electrometer has Automatic Range Switching; Electronic Eng. 44, Oct. 1972, 71–73.
j1 Analog Devices: Choosing and Using N-Channel Dual J-FETs; Analog Dialogue 4 Dec. 1970, 4–9.
k1 Cath P G, Peabody A M: High-Speed Current Measurements; Anal. Chem. 43 Sep. 1971, 91A–99A.
l1 Underwood R: New Techniques with FET Op Amps Challenge the Designer (LH0052 series); Electron 14 Sep. 1973, 31–33.
m1 Analog Devices: Model 301/302/303 Ultra Low Bias Current Varactor Bridge Operational Amplifiers; Analog Devices Data Sheet 1969.
n1 Analog Devices: Models 310/311 Ultra Low Bias Current Varactor Bridge Operational Amplifiers; Analog Devices Data Sheet 1969.
o1 Chater W T: A Logarithmic Electrometer for Space Flight Application; Rev. Sci. Instrum. 40, 529–532, 1969.
p1 Taylor D J: A Current-to-Frequency Converter for Astronomical Photometry; Rev. Sci. Instrum. 40, 559–562, 1969.
q1 Wing W H, Sanders T M: FET Operational Amplifiers as Fast Electrometers; Rev. Sci. Instrum. 38, 1341–1342, 1967.

r1 Praglin J, Nichols W A: High-Speed Electrometers for Rocket and Satellite Experiments; Proc IRE 48, 771–779, 1960.

s1 Pelchowitch I, Zaalberg Van Zelst J J: A Wide-Band Electrometer Amplifier; Rev. Sci. Instrum. 23, 73–75, 1952.

t1 Electrometers: Keithley Instruments, Princeton Applied Research, Cary Instruments, H W Sullivan.

u1 Kipp and Zonen: Supersensitive Galvanometers (A54); Kipp and Zonen Data Sheet.

v1 Kendall B R F, Zabielski M F: Compensated Resistors for High-Frequency Electrometer Applications; Electrometer Lett. 6, 776–778, 1970.

w1 Chater W C: A Digitizing Electrometer System Using an Integrating Circuit Preamplifier; Rev. Sci. Instrum. 42, 129–134, 1971.

x1 Dow P C: An Analysis of Certain Errors in Electronic Differential Analyzers. II Capacitor Dielectric Absorption; IRE Trans EC-7, 17–22, 1958.

y1 Habermel P D: Plastic Film Capacitors; Radio Electronic Engnr. 40, 259–264, 1970.

z1 Waller W F (Ed): Electronics Design Materials; Macmillan 1971.

A1 Kemp L A W, Woodall J E: Evaluation of a High-Insulation Dry-Reed Switch for Electrometer Applications; Electronic Eng. 40, May 1968, 236–239.

B1 Cary Instruments: 401 Vibrating Reed Electrometer; Cary Instruments Data Sheet.

C1 Resistors: Welwyn Electric, Victoreen Instrument, Eltec Instrument.

D1 Stata R: Operational Integrators; Analog Dialogue 1 No.1 Apr. 1967, 6–11.

E1 Riegler H: The Vibrating Capacitor, Theory and Application; Nachrichtentechnik 10, No.11, 501–505, 1960.

F1 Palevsky H, Swank R K, Grenchik R: Design of Dynamic Condenser Electrometers; Rev. Sci. Instrum. 18, 298–314, 1947.

G1 Keithley J F: Electrometer Measurements; Instruments and Control Systems 35, 74–81, Jan. 1962.

H1 H W Sullivan: Vibron Electrometer 33C-2/33B-2; H W Sullivan Data Sheet.

I1 Dagpunar S S: Electrometer Valves; Mullard Tech. Comm. 7, Aug. 1963, 194–199.

J1 Yair R: Charge Sampling Method for Low Current Measurement; Rev. Sci. Instrum. 45, 395–399, 1974.

K1 Samuelson G, Bengtsson L G: Precise and Rapid Measurements of Small Currents from High Impedance Sources; Rev. Sci. Instrum. 44, 920–921, 1973.

L1 Kendall B R F, Reiter R F: Three-Terminal Shielded Resistors for Fast Electrometers; Rev. Sci. Instrum. 45, 850–852, 1974.

M1 Wanlass F: Low Current Measurement Using Metal Oxide Silicon Field Effect Transistor (MOSFET) Electrometer Circuits; General Microelectronics Application Note Vol. 1 No.1.

N1 Siliconix: High-Input-Impedance UNIFET Amplifiers; Siliconix Application Note File 606, 1973.

O1 Crawford R H: High Input Impedance Techniques for Transistor Circuits; Texas Instruments Application Report Aug. 1962.

P1 Tumber A J: Design of High-Impedance Common Collector Input Stages; Electronic Applic. (Neth.) 24, No.1, 1–6, 1963–4.

Q1 Burwen R S, Sullivan D: AD503, AD506 IC FET Input Operational Amplifiers; Analog Devices Tech. Bulletin Aug. 1971.

R1 Burwen R S, Sullivan D: AD513, AD516 IC FET Input Operational Amplifiers; Analog Devices Tech. Bulletin Aug. 1971.

S1 Thomas R: FETs for Op-Amps; Electron 5 Apr. 1973, 63, 65–67.

T1 Russell R D, Ahern T K: Economical Mass Spectrometer Ion Current Measurement with a Commercial Parametric Amplifier (Philbrick 1702); Rev. Sci. Instrum. 45, 1467–1469, 1974.

U1 Fishman J: Beware those FET Op Amp Specs!; Electronic Design 4 Jan. 1975, 104–107.

V1 Van Nie A G, Zaalberg Van Zelst J J: A Vibrating Capacitor Driven by a High Frequency Electronic Field; Philips Tech. Rev. 25, 95–103, 1963–4.

W1 Klein G, Zaalberg Van Zelst J J: Precision Electronics; Philips Technical Library 1967.

X1 Miles F: Low Bias Current Amplifiers; Electronic Equipment News 10 Oct. 1971, 26–33.

Y1 Frantz R: Voltage Measurements in Biomedical Research. How FET-Input IC Op Amps Can Help—A Brief Summary; Analog Dialogue 8, No.2, 18–19, 1974.
Z1 Philbrick/Nexus: Applications Manual for Operational Amplifiers; Philbrick/Nexus Research 1968.
a2 Smith J I: Modern Operational Circuit Design; Wiley-Interscience 1971.
b2 Keithley Instruments: Electrometer Measurements; Keithley Instruments Handbook 1972.
c2 Scott W D: Details for Constructing a Miniature Solid State Electrometer Probe; Rev. Sci. Instrum. 43, 152–153, 1972.
d2 Siegel B: Applications for a High Speed FET Input Op Amp LH0062; Electronic Components 4 May 1973, 378–381.
e2 Mullard: Vibrating Capacitor XL7900; Mullard Data Sheet Apr. 1968.
f2 Analog Devices: Precision Power FET-Input Electrometer Op Amp AD515; Analog Devices Data Sheet 1975.
g2 National semiconductor: LF155/LF156/LF157 Monolithic JFET Input Operational Amplifiers; National Semiconductor Data Sheet Sep. 1975.
h2 Oliver J P: Fast Electrometer Amplifier for Astronomical Photometry; Rev. Sci. Instrum. 47, 581–582, 1976.
I2 Witten S: Designing Junction FET Input Op Amps; Siliconix Application Note AN74-3, Aug. 1974.
j2 Fullagar D, Hendry R: The 8043—a Low Cost Dual FET-Input Operational Amplifier; Intersil Application Note Sep. 1973.
k2 Fullagar D: Better Understanding of FET Operation Yields Viable Monolithic J-FET Op Amp; Electronics 6 Nov. 1972, 98–101.
l2 Phelan J: The 8500—Ultra Low Bias Current Operational Amplifier; Intersil Application Bulletin Nov. 1970.

References section 4.7: Power amplifiers

a1 National Semiconductor: P–I–N Diode Drivers; Electronic Eng. 44, Oct. 1972, 18–19.
b1 Gray P R: A 15W Monolithic Power Operational Amplifier; IEEE J SC-7, 474–480, 1972.
c1 Burr-Brown: High Voltage Operational Amplifiers Models 3580/1/2; Burr-Brown Data Sheet PDS-313, Oct. 1974.
d1 Dance J B: Power IC Gives High Gain (LM395); Electronic Components 28 Jan. 1975, 15–16.
e1 Texas Instruments: Current Amplifier Type HIC037; Texas Instruments Data Sheet Jan. 1971.
f1 Signetics: Servo Amplifier Type NE543; Signetics Data Sheet 1974.
g1 Matthews P L, Watts A J: Advances in Power Linears; New Electronics 18 Feb. 1975, 76, 79, 80.
h1 SGS-ATES: Monolithic Complementary Darlington Pair TDA1410/1420; SGS-ATES Data Sheet.
i1 Texas Instruments: SN6008 10Watt Audio Amplifier; Texas Instruments Data Sheet Apr. 1975.
j1 RCA: High-Reliability Multi-Purpose 7-Ampere Operational Amplifier; RCA Data Sheet File 789, 1974.
k1 Burr-Brown: High Current—High Power Operational Amplifiers 3571/2; Burr-Brown Data Sheet PDS-334, May 1975.
l1 Tijou J A: High Quality 25W Audio Amplifier; Mullard Tech. Comm. 13, 280–288, 1975.
m1 National Semiconductor: Dual 6Watt Audio Amplifier LM379; National Semiconductor Data Sheet Feb. 1975.
n1 Palara S, Corsi F: Monolithic Dual Darlington for Power Boosting TDA1420/10; New Electronics 28 Oct. 1975, 18, 20, 21.
o1 Nelson-Jones L: Ultra-Low Distortion Class-A Amplifier; Wireless World 77, Mar. 1970, 98–103.
p1 Greenburg R (Ed): Power Transistor Handbook; Motorola 1961.
q1 Dale R G, Fay G V, Freyling E N, Haver R J: Semiconductor Power Circuits Handbook; Motorola 1968.

r1 RCA: Power Circuits, DC to Microwave; RCA Electronic Components Technical Series SP-51, 1969.
s1 RCA: RF Power Transistor Manual; RCA Solid State Division Technical Series RFM-430, 1971.
t1 RCA: High-Speed, High-Voltage, High-Current Power Transistors for Amplification, Switching and Control; RCA Solid State Division Technical Series PM-80, 1970.
u1 Norris B (Ed): Semiconductor Circuit Design, Section 3 Audio Circuits; Texas Instruments 1972.
v1 Ferranti: High Fidelity Audio Designs; Ferranti Application Note ESA 340468, Apr. 1968.
w1 Becciolini B: Audio Circuit Design with Silicon Complementary Pairs; Motorola Aug. 1970.
x1 Fisher M S: A High-Quality, Low Cost, 15-Watt, Complementary-Symmetry Power Amplifier; RCA Application Note AN-3185, 1966.
y1 Dale R G (Ed): Semiconductor Power Circuits Handbook, Chapter 5 Servo and Audio Power Amplifiers; Motorola 1968.
z1 Van Allen R: Applying the Power Driver NE540; Electronic Eng. 45, June 1973, 18.
A1 Mullard: TAA300 Integrated One-Watt Class B AF Amplifier; Mullard Application Note TP1050, Sep. 1968.
B1 Ruehs R G: High Power Audio Amplifiers with Short Circuit Protection; Motorola Application Note AN-485, 1969.
C1 Wickens J: 15W Class A Audio Amplifier; Mullard Tech. Comm. 11, Nov. 1970, 177–178.
D1 Webster S W: All Silicon Complementary-Symmetry 35W(RMS) Audio Power Amplifier with Short Circuit Protection; Texas Instruments Application Report CA105, 1968.
E1 Peterson W R: General Application Considerations for the RCA-HC1000 Hybrid Linear Power Amplifier; RCA Application Note AN-4483, 1970.
F1 Peterson W R: Audio Applications for the RCA-HC1000 Hybrid Linear Power Amplifier; RCA Application Note AN-4474, 1970.
G1 Peters A (Ed): Transistor Audio and Radio Circuits; Mullard TP1069/1 1970.
H1 Hardcastle I: Audio Power Amplifier Design, 1–100Watt; Texas Instruments Application Report B107, 1971.
I1 Teeling J: Medium Power Audio Amplifiers using Complementary Plastic Transistors; Motorola Application Note AN-484, 1969.
J1 Freyling N: Complementary Solid-State Audio Amplifiers; Motorola Application Note AN-230, 1966.
K1 Blaser L: Short-Circuit Protection in a 25-Watt Audio Amplifier; SGS-Fairchild Application Note AR105, 1963.
L1 Burr-Brown: Wideband/Fast Slewing Buffer Amplifier 3553; Burr-Brown Data Sheet PDS-329, May 1975.
M1 Thorig J, Peters W A M: High Quality Audio Amplifiers; Mullard Tech. Comm. 11, Sep. 1970, 147–152.
N1 Analog Devices: 400 Series Power Operational Amplifiers; Analog Devices Data Sheet.
O1 Signetics: Power Driver NE540; Signetics Data Sheet 1972.
P1 Byerly J E, Van der Kooi M: LM380 Power Audio Amplifier; National Semiconductor Application Note AN69, 1972.
Q1 RCA: Solid-State Power Circuits Designer's Handbook; RCA Technical Series SP-52, 1971.
R1 TRW: Power Switching Amplifiers MCA/B 2001/2; TRW Semiconductors Data Sheet 1970.
S1 Nappe J: General Application Considerations for the RCA-HC2000 Power Hybrid Operational Amplifier; RCA Application Note AN-4782, 1971.
T1 Fairchild: Power Operational Amplifier µA791; Fairchild Data Sheet 1973.
U1 Becker R B H: High-Power Audio Amplifier Design Obtaining 100W and More from a Fully-Protected Class-B Circuit; Wireless World 78, Feb. 1972, 79–84.
V1 Johnson K C: Class-B Audio Amplifier Circuits; Wireless World 76, Apr. 1970, 159–161.
W1 Blomley P: New Approach to Class B Amplifier Design; Wireless World 77, Feb. 1971, 57–61, and Mar. 1971, 127–131, Apr. 1971, 180.

X1 Opalinsky G, Hoeft W: Build Power Amplifiers with IC Drivers (AD540); Electronic Design 21, 2 Aug. 1973, 72–77.
Y1 Beckman: Models 821/822 Unity Gain Power Booster; Beckman Data Sheet 1968.
Z1 Motorola: MC1438R Power Booster; Motorola Data Sheet 1972.

a2 National Semiconductor LH0021C/LH0041C Power Operational Amplifiers; National Semiconductor Data Sheet Apr. 1972.
b2 Long E L, Frederiksen T M: High-Gain 15-W Monolithic Power Amplifier with Internal Fault Protection; IEEE J SC-6, 35–44, 1971.
c2 Campbell D L, Westlake R T: Build a High-Current Servoamplifier with ICs; Control Eng. 18, Feb. 1971, 56–59.
d2 Dobkin R C: IC with Load Protection Simulates Power Transistor (LM395); Electronics 7 Feb. 1974, 119–123.
e2 Hoeft W: A Monolithic Power Driver for Complementary Power Transistors; IEEE Trans BTR-18, 59–64, Feb. 1972.
f2 Lohstroh J, Otala M: An Audio Power Amplifier for Ultimate Quality Requirements; IEEE Trans AU-21, 545–551, Dec. 1973.
g2 Miller C H: High Efficiency Amplification Using Width Modulated Pulses; Proc IREE (Aust) 25, 314–323, 1964.
h2 Venning B H: A High-Efficiency Low-Frequency Power Source for Vibration Excitation Radio Electronic Engnr. 27, 55–63, 1964.
i2 Camenzind H R: Modulated Pulse Audio Power Amplifiers for Integrated Circuits; IEEE Trans AU-14, 136–140, 1966.
j2 Turnbull G F, Townsend J M: A Feedback Pulse Width Modulated Audio Amplifier; Wireless World 71, Apr. 1965, 160–165.
k2 Linsley-Hood J L: A Direct-Coupled High Quality Stereo Amplifier; Hi-Fi News and Record Review Nov. 1972, 2120, 2121, 2123, Dec. 1972, 2380, 2381, 2383, 2385, Jan. 1973, 60, 61, 63, Feb. 1973, 290, 291, 293, 294, Apr. 1974, 75, 77, 79.
l2 Siemens: Electronic Motors 1AD Series; Siemens Data Sheet 1973.
m2 Pshaenich A: Use Pulse Width Modulation to Control DC Motors; Electronic Design 22, 1 Feb. 1974, 68–70.
n2 Logis J, Scheerer R C: Switch High Inductive Loads Fast; Electronic Design 22, 1 Feb. 1974, 72–74.
o2 Jung W G: Improve Op-Amp Audio Circuits by Mating Op-Amp Dynamic Characteristics and Compensation to the Circuit Application; Electronic Design 21, Sep. 1973, 68–73.
p2 Wieder H H: Hall Generators and Magnetoresistors; Pion Books 1971.
q2 Papst: Brushless DC Motor GA25.06; Papst-Motoren Data Sheet.
r2 Dittrich W, Rainer E: Electronic Motor DMc3, a New Miniature Brushless DC Motor; Siemens Rev. 34, 97–99, Mar. 1967.
s2 Bryans: Model 27000 Chart Recorder; Bryans Handbook.
t2 Hewlett-Packard: Model 7035A X-Y Recorder; Hewlett-Packard Handbook.
u2 Siegel B, Van Der Gaag L: Applications for a New Ultra-High Speed Buffer (LH0033); National Semiconductor Application Note AN-48, Aug. 1971.
v2 Motorola: Class B Audio Driver MFC8020A; Motorola Data Sheet 1970.
w2 SGS: Audio Amplifier Module Type EA1000 (TAA621) User's Handbook; SGS 1971.
x2 Antoniazzi P, Sabbadini G F: TBA641 Power Audio Amplifier; SGS Product Profile 105, Mar. 1971.
y2 Chambers S: A 1000W Solid-State Power Amplifier; Electronic Design 22, 1 Apr. 1974, 58–62.
z2 Wireless World: High Fidelity Designs; Wireless World Reprints 1974.

A2 Frewin P D: Feedback Eliminates Power Loss in High-Current Output Stages; Electronic Eng. 43, June 1971, 62–63.
B2 Henderson R: 3-Terminal Power Integrated Circuit; New Electronics 10 Dec. 1974, 91–92.
C2 Cobbe R: Simple Linear Pulse Width Servo Amplifier; Electronic Eng. 46, Dec. 1974, 31.
D2 Hejhall R C: Solid-State Linear Power Amplifier Design (2-30MHz); Motorola Application Note AN-546, 1971.

E2 Oliver B M: Distortion in Complementary-Pair Class-B Amplifiers; Hewlett-Packard J 22, Feb. 1971, 11–16.
F2 Long E L: Low-Cost High Voltage Servo Amplifiers; Motorola Application Note AN-241, 1966.
G2 Norris B: Super Silect Transistors in Audio Amplifiers; Texas Instruments Application Report B117, 1971.
H2 Eadon-Smith J P: A Direct Current Switching Amplifier; Electronic Eng. 34, 472–475, 1962.
I2 Bell E C, Sergent T: Distortion and Power Output of Pulse Duration Modulated Amplifiers; Electronic Eng. 37, 540–542, 1965.
J2 Loos C H: Time-Proportional Control; Control Eng. 12, May 1965, 65–70.
K2 Subbarao W V: Boost Audio-Amplifier Efficiencies; Electronic Design 12 Apr. 1974, 96–98.
L2 Electro-Craft: DC Motors, Speed Controls, Servo Systems; Electro-Craft Handbook, 2nd Edn. 1973.
M2 Fay G V, Freyling N: Pulse-Width Modulation for DC Motor Speed Control; Motorola Application Note AN-445, 1968.
N2 Servo Motors: Evershed and Vignoles, Honeywell, Kearfott, Servomex, Muirhead, Vatric, Smiths Industries.
O2 Sherwin J: LM377, LM378, LM379 Dual Two, Four, and Six Watt Power Amplifiers; National Semiconductor Application Note AN-125, Jan. 1975.
P2 Mitchell W S E: Motors for Servo Applications; Design Electronics Dec. 1967, 18–21, 24–25.
Q2 Fabian M: Performance in Power FETs; New Electronics 24 Feb. 1976, 54, 56, 58.
R2 Siliconix: N-Channel Enhancement Mode Power MOSFET VMP-1; Siliconix Data Sheet.
S2 Plessey: 3W and 5W Audio Amplifiers SL414A/415A; Plessey Data Sheet Aug. 1973.
T2 Shaeffer L: Use FETs to Switch High Currents; Electronic Design 26 Apr. 1976, 66–72.
U2 Sandoli B: TBA810S/AS Thermally Protected Audio Power Amplifier; SGS-ATES Technical Note 120.
V2 DiBert R, Petrelli G: TCA940 Fully Protected Audio Power Amplifier; SGS-ATES Technical Note 119.
W2 Romano A, Murari B: TDA2020, TDA2010 Hi-Fi Monolithic Amplifiers; SGS-ATES Report.
X2 Mullard: Integrated 6W Audio Amplifier TDA1004; Mullard Data Sheet Nov. 1974.
Y2 Mullard: Audio Power Amplifier TDA2610; Mullard Technical Note 35 (TP1541) 1976.
Z2 National Semiconductor: LH0033/63 Fast and Damn Fast Buffer Amplifiers; National Semiconductor Data Sheet Aug. 1973.
a3 Motorola: Class A Audio Driver MFC4050; Motorola Data Sheet Dec. 1972.
b3 SGS-ATES: 20W Hi-Fi Audio Power Amplifier with Short Circuit Protection and Thermal Shutdown TDA2020; SGS-ATES Data Sheet 1975.
c3 Pshaenich A: Servo Motor Drive Amplifiers; Motorola Application Note AN-590, 1972.
d3 Zinder D: Pulse Width Modulation for Small DC Motor Control; Motorola Application Note AN-705, 1973.
e3 Shaeffer L: VMOS—A Breakthrough in Power MOSFET Technology; Siliconix Application Note AN76-3, 1976.
f3 Shaeffer L: The MOSPOWER FET Audio Amplifier; Siliconix Design Aid DA76-1, 1976.
g3 Vander Kooi M, Ragle L: MOS moves into Higher Power Applications; Electronics 24 June 1976, 98–103.

References section 4.8a: Operational transconductance, programmable, micropower and Norton amplifiers

a1 National Semiconductor: LM312 Micropower Operational Amplifier; National Semiconductor Data Sheet 1973.
b1 Fairchild: uA735C Micropower Operational Amplifier; Fairchild Data Sheet.

c1   Microsystems International: ML4202C Programmable Quad Operational Amplifier; Microsystems International Data Sheet 1974.

d1   Signetics: NE533 Micropower Operational Amplifier; Signetics Data Sheet 1972.

e1   Texas Instruments: Dual Low-Power Operational Amplifier SN72L022; Texas Instruments Data Sheet.

f1   Texas Instruments: Quad Low-Power Operational Amplifier SN72L044; Texas Instruments Data Sheet.

g1   Grebene A B: Analog Integrated Circuit Design, Chapter II Micropower Circuits; Van Nostrand Reinhold 1972.

h1   Fairchild: The µA776, an Operational Amplifier with Programmable Gain, Bandwidth, Slew-Rate and Power Dissipation; Fairchild The Complete Linear Book 637–641.

i1   RCA: Transconductance Amplifiers for Multiplexing; Electronic Eng. 44, May 1972, 70.

j1   Campbell L R, Wittlinger H A: Some Applications of a Programmable Power Switch/Amplifier (CA3094); RCA Application Note ICAN-6048, 1972.

k1   Fairchild: A Micropower Operational Amplifier (µA735); Fairchild Application Brief APP-123, 1969.

l1   Van der Kooi M K, Cleveland G: Micropower Circuits Using the LM4250 Programmable Op Amp; National Semiconductor Application Note AN-71, 1972.

m1   RCA: Operational Transconductance Amplifiers CA3080; RCA Data Sheet, File 475, 1971.

n1   RCA: Programmable Power Switch/Amplifier CA3094T; RCA Data Sheet, File 598, 1972.

o1   RCA: Micropower Operational Amplifier CA3078T; RCA Data Sheet.

p1   Fairchild: Multi-Purpose Programmable Operational Amplifier µA776; Fairchild Data Sheet.

q1   Frederiksen T M, Howard W M, Sleeth R S: The LM3900—A New Current Differencing Quad of +/− Input Amplifiers; National Semiconductor Application Note AN-72, Sep. 1972.

r1   National Semiconductor: LM3900 Quad Amplifier; National Semiconductor Data Sheet.

t1   Van der Kooi M K: L144 Programmable Micropower Triple Op Amp; Siliconix Application Note Dec. 1973.

u1   Vlcek P: Norton Quad Amplifier can be a Low-Cost Function Generator; Electronics 16 May 1974, 98.

v1   RCA: Ideas for 101 Uses of Op Amps, Part 3, Micropower Op Amps; RCA Application Note SUN-906, 1974.

w1   Wittlinger H A: Applications of the CA3080 and CA3080A High-Performance Operational Transconductance Amplifiers; RCA Application Note ICAN-6668.

x1   RCA: Linear Integrated Circuits; RCA Technical Series IC-42, 1970.

y1   Avery L R: Recent Advances in the Design of Micropower Operational Amplifiers (CA3060, 3080, 3078); RCA Application Note. See also Electronic Components 20 Apr. 326–330, 4 May 373–376, 1973.

References section 4.8b: Low-drift amplifiers

a1   Dobkin R C: IC Preamp Challenges Choppers on Drift (LM121); National Semiconductor Application Note AN-79, Feb. 1973.

b1   Harris: HA-2900/4/5 Chopper Stabilized Operational Amplifier; Harris Data Sheet Aug. 1973.

c1   Analog Devices: AD-506L High Accuracy Low Drift IC Fet-Input Op Amp; Analog Devices Data Sheet 1973.

d1   DuBois J L: Choppers—Solid State or Electromechanical?; Electronic Products Jan. 1968, 43–47.

e1   Lieux J D: Applying a Temperature Stabilized Transistor Pair (µA726); Electronic Products May 1967, 84, 86, 87.

f1   Altschuler S: Add Chopper Stabilization to Any Op Amp; Electronic Products Feb. 1967, 71, 72, 74, 76, 77.

g1   Fitchen F C: Electronic Integrated Circuits and Systems; Van Nostrand Reinhold 1970.

h1 Precision Monolithics: MAT-01 Ultra-Matched Monolithic Dual Transistor Series; Precision Monolithic Data Sheet, Nov. 1973.

i1 Jones D: A Monolithic Chopper Stabilized Amplifier (HA-2900); New Electronics 13 Nov. 1973, 55, 56, 61, 63, 65.

j1 Shepherd I E: Sources of Lost Gain in Chopper Amplifiers; Electron 28 Dec. 1972, 11–13.

k1 Mann R: A Chopper Amplifier; Texas Instruments Application Report B33, 1968.

l1 Analog Devices: AD504 IC Ultra-Stable Operational Amplifier; Analog Devices Data Sheet 1973.

m1 Analog Devices: AD508 IC Chopperless Low Drift Operational Amplifier; Analog Devices Data Sheet 1973.

n1 Dobkin R C: Low Drift Amplifiers; National Semiconductor Linear Brief LB-22, June 1973.

o1 Buckerfield P S T: The Parallel-T DC Amplifier: A Low-Drift Amplifier with Wide Frequency Response; Proc. IEE 99 Pt.II, 497–506, Oct. 1952.

p1 Fairchild: Temperature-Controlled Differential Pair μA726; Fairchild Data Sheet.

q1 Fairchild: Temperature-Controlled Differential Preamplifier μA727; Fairchild Data Sheet.

r1 Precision Monolithics: Mono OP-07 Ultra-Low Offset Voltage Op Amp Series; Precision Monolithics Data Sheet June 1974.

s1 Analog Devices: Chopper Stabilized Operational Amplifiers 201/2/3/10; Analog Devices Application Manual.

t1 Zicko P: Designing with Chopper-Stabilized Operational Amplifiers; Design Electronics Sep. 1970, 66, 68, 70, 73, 74, 131, and Analog Devices Application Note 1970.

u1 National Semiconductor: LM321 Precision Preamplifier; National Semiconductor Data Sheet Aug. 1973.

v1 SGS-Fairchild: The Application of Linear Microcircuits; SGS-Fairchild Handbook, Aug. 1967.

w1 SGS: The Application of Linear Microcircuits Volume 2; SGS Handbook May 1969.

x1 Hoell P C: Low-Level DC Amplifier with Whole-Loop Feedback; Rev. Sci. Instrum. 29, 1120–1124, 1958.

y1 Bhola S K, Murphy R H: Design of Low Level DC Chopper Amplifiers; Electronic Eng. 39, 318–322, 1967.

z1 Ricks R: A High Speed Zero Input Current Chopper Amplifier; Fairchild Application Brief 111, Aug. 1969.

A1 Analog Devices: Low Voltage Drift Chopper Stabilized Amplifiers Models 210/231/233/234/260/261; Analog Devices Product Guide 1973.

B1 Burr-Brown: Chopper Stabilized Amplifiers Models 3291/3354/3480/3271; Burr-Brown Catalogue LI-205F, Mar. 1974.

C1 Computing Techniques: Low Drift Chopper Stabilized Amplifier A8-7; Computing Techniques Catalogue Apr. 1974.

D1 Graeme J G: Operational Amplifiers—Design and Applications, Chapter 2 Input Error Signals and Thermal Drifts of a Differential Stage; McGraw-Hill 1971.

E1 Graeme J G: Applications of Operational Amplifiers—Third Generation Techniques; McGraw-Hill 1973.

F1 Beneteau P J: The Design of High Stability DC Amplifiers; SGS-Fairchild Application Report APP-23/AR11.

G1 National Semiconductor: Drift Compensation Techniques for Integrated DC Amplifiers; National Semiconductor Application Note AN-3, 1967.

H1 Hoffait A H, Thorton R D: Limitations of Transistor DC Amplifiers; IEEE Proc 52, 179–184, 1964.

I1 Widlar R J: Drift Compensation Techniques for Integrated DC Amplifiers; EDN 10 June 1968.

J1 Harris S: How to Really Look at Low-Drift IC Op Amps; Electronics 45, 9 Oct. 1972, 120–121.

K1 Computing Techniques: Ultra-Low Drift Differential Amplifier D4-1; Computing Techniques Data Sheet 1974.

L1 Analog Devices: TDN: Temperature-Drift Nonlinearity—A New Dual-FET Specification; Analog Dialogue 6, No.1, 13–14, 1972.

M1 Analog Devices: AD810 Dual NPN Transistors; Analog Devices Product Guide 1973.

N1 Analog Devices: Low Voltage Drift Differential Input High CMR Amplifier Model 184; Analog Devices Product Guide 1973.

O1 Fairchild: A Low-Drift, Low Noise Monolithic Operational Amplifier for Low Level Signal Processing μA725; Fairchild Application Brief APP-136, July 1969.

P1 Harris S: Not by Drift Alone . . . . . .; Analog Dialogue 6, No.2, 12, 1972.

Q1 Harris S: Not by Drift Alone . . . Chapter 2. The 741 Op Amp Family; Analog Dialogue 7, No. 1, 11–12, 1973.

R1 Texas Instruments: Chopper Stabilized Operational Amplifier SN72088; Texas Instruments Data Sheet.

S1 Clegg L: High Precision Thin-Film Resistance Networks; Analog Dialogue 8, No.1, 6–9, 1974.

T1 Analog Devices: Long-Term Drift Measurements on Op Amps; Analog Dialogue 5, No.2, 13, 1971.

U1 Analog Devices: RTI vs RTO. How to Compute the Drift of Instrumentation Amplifiers; Analog Dialogue 6, No.2, 14, 1972.

V1 Graeme J G: Offset Null Techniques Increase Op Amp Drift; EDN 1 Apr. 1971.

W1 Fishman J: Beware Those FET Op-Amp Specs!; Electronic Design 4 Jan. 1975, 104–107.

X1 Murari B, Evangelisti A: Direct Coupled Amplifier for Thermocouples and Strain-Gauges; SGS-Fairchild Application Report AR156, Aug. 1966.

Y1 Stata R: Operational Amplifiers, Part IV: Offset and Drift in Operational Amplifiers; Analog Devices Application Note.

Z1 Erdman R: Precision Digital Measurement of Low DC Voltage Using a Nanovolt Amplifier; Keithley Instruments Product Notes.

a2 Fullagar D: Dual FET-Input Operational Amplifier; New Electronics 18 Mar. 1975, 79, 86.

b2 Williams J: Prevent Low-Level Amplifier Problems; Electronic Design 15 Feb. 1975, 62–67.

c2 Maidique M A: Monolithic Operational Amplifier with 1 μV/degree C Drift (AD504); Analog Dialogue 5, No.3, 3–5, Apr. June 1971.

d2 Fairchild: A New Approach to Low Drift Amplifiers (μA727); Fairchild Application Note.

e2 Kalinski J: A Modified Chopping Method of Drift Elimination in Direct Coupled DC Amplifiers; J Phys. E Sci. Instrum. 8, 414–416, 1975.

f2 Baldwin G L, Rigby G A: New Techniques for Drift Compensation in Integrated Differential Amplifiers; IEEE J SC-3, 325–330, 1968.

g2 Sundquist B, Backstrom G: Low Noise and Drift by Parallel Amplifiers; Rev. Sci. Instrum. 46, 928–929, 1975.

h2 Analog Devices: Low Cost, Laser Trimmed Precision IC Op Amp AD510; Analog Devices Data Sheet 1975.

i2 Analog Devices: Precision General Purpose Resistor Networks; Analog Devices 1974.

j2 Analog Devices: The Analog Devices Resistor Book; Analog Devices 1975.

k2 Precision Monolithics: Ultra-Low Offset Voltage Operational Amplifier OP-07; Precision Monolithics Data Sheet.

l2 Beneteau P J, Riva G M, Murari B, Quinzio G: Drift Compensation in DC Amplifiers; SGS-Fairchild Application Report AR121, Aug. 1964.

m2 Fairchild: Low Offset Voltage Operational Amplifier μA714; Fairchild Data Sheet 1976.

n2 Soderquist D, Erdi G: The MonoOP-07 Ultra-Low Offset Voltage Op Amp—A Bipolar Op Amp that Challenges Choppers, Eliminates Nulling; Precision Monolithics Application Note AN-13, Aug. 1974.

References section 4.8c: Wide-band amplifiers

a1 Theriault G E: Application of the RCA-CA3001 Integrated Circuit Video Amplifier; RCA Application Note ICAN-5038.

b1 Theriault G E, Campbell T H, Leidich A J: Application of the RCA CA3021, CA3022, and CA3023 Integrated Circuit Wideband Amplifiers; RCA Application Note ICAN-5338.

c1 Austin W M, Kleinman H M: Application of the RCA CA3020 and CA3020A Integrated Circuit Multi-Purpose Wide-Band Power Amplifiers; RCA Application Note ICAN-5766.

d1 Austin W M: Principal Features and Applications of the RCA-CA3040 Integrated Circuit Wideband Amplifier; RCA Application Note ICAN-5977.

e1 RCA: Linear Integrated Circuits Handbook; RCA Technical Series IC-41, 1967.

f1 RCA: Linear Integrated Circuits; RCA Technical Series IC-42, 1970.

g1 Millman J, Taub H: Pulse, Digital and Switching Waveforms; McGraw-Hill 1965.

h1 Thibodeaux E: Predict Wideband Amplifier Response with a Simple Graphical Procedure; Electronic Design 6 Dec. 1974, 68–71.

i1 Welling B, Russell R: Using the MC1545, a Monolithic Gated Video Amplifier; Motorola Application Note AN-475, 1969.

j1 Thibodeaux E: The HA-2530/2535 Wideband High Slew Inverting Amplifier; Harris Semiconductor Application Note 516, Feb. 1974.

k1 Hejhall R C: Solid-State Linear Power Amplifier Design (2–30MHz); Motorola Application Note AN-546, 1971.

l1 Thibodeaux E: A Wideband High Slew Inverting Amplifier (HA-2530/2535); New Electronics 16 Apr. 1974, 40–41.

m1 Gilbert B: A New Wide-Band Amplifier Technique; IEEE J SC-3, 353–365, 1968.

n1 SGS: L115 Wide Band Operational Amplifier; SGS Product Profile Feb. 1971.

o1 Fairchild: The μA715. A Versatile High Speed Operational Amplifier; Fairchild Application Brief APP-121, June 1969.

p1 Fairstein E, Hahn J: Nuclear Pulse Amplifiers—Fundamentals and Design Practice; Nucleonics 23, July 1965, 56–61; 23, Sep. 1965, 81–86; 23, Nov. 1965, 50–55; 24, Jan. 1966, 54–60; 24, Mar. 1966, 68–72.

q1 Kolk P: Design of Wideband Transistor Amplifiers; RCA Application Note SMA-7, 1963.

r1 Sijtstra S: Vertical Deflection Amplifier for 150MHz Oscilloscope; Mullard Tech. Comm. 10, 158–166, 1968.

s1 Hart K, Oude Moleman F G: Horizontal Deflection Amplifier for 150MHz Oscilloscope; Mullard Tech. Comm. 10, Sep. 1968, 167–174, 10, 158–166, 1968.

t1 Mullard: FET Vertical Deflection Pre-Amplifier for a Wide-Band Oscilloscope; Mullard Application Note TP1067, May 1969.

u1 Beneteau P J: A 120 Volt 40 Nanosecond Transistor Video Amplifier; SGS-Fairchild Application Note APP-27, Sep. 1961.

v1 Reddi V G K: Transistor Pulse Amplifiers; SGS-Fairchild Application Note APP-32/2, Sep. 1961.

w1 Beneteau P J, MacIntosh J A: A 2 Nanosecond Video Amplifier; SGS-Fairchild Application Note APP-38.

x1 Jackson H G: A 1ns Risetime Amplifier with Direct Coupling; Nuc. Instr. Meth. 33, 161–163, 1965.

y1 Solomon J E: The Monolithic Op Amp: A Tutorial Study; IEEE J SC-9, 314–332, 1974.

z1 Haynes G: Higher Performance Analogue IC's; New Electronics 18 Feb. 1975, 61, 62, 64.

A1 Dobkin R C: LM118 Op Amp Slews 70V/us; National Semiconductor Linear Brief LB-17, Sep. 1971.

B1 National Semiconductor: High Speed Buffers (LH0033); Electron 29 June 1972, 31–32.

C1 Welling B: An IC Wideband Video Amplifier with AGC (MC1550); Motorola Application Note AN-299, 1967.

D1 Adley D L: Design Considerations in High Voltage Video Output Circuitry; Motorola Application Note AN-171, 1965.

E1 Union Carbide: Video Amplifiers Utilizing the Field Effect Transistor; Union Carbide Application Note AN-12, Apr. 1967.

F1 Demrow R I: Settling Time of Operational Amplifiers; Analog Dialogue 4, No.1, 1–11, 1970.

G1 Intronics: Design Guide for Wideband Operational Amplifiers; Intronics Design Guide 1970.
H1 Motorola: Using ECL Gates as Wideband Amplifiers; Electronic Eng. 45, June 1973, 24.
I1 Reinert J, Renschler E: Gated Video Amplifier Applications: The MC1545; Motorola Application Note AN-491, 1969.
J1 National Semiconductor: Applications for a New Ultra-High Speed Buffer (LH0033, LH0063); National Semiconductor Application Note AN-48, Aug. 1971.
K1 Gray P E, Searle C L: Electronic Principles. Physics, Models and Circuits; Wiley 1969.
L1 Fishman J G: High Speed Op Amps—How Fast is Fast?; New Electronics 11 June 1974, 51, 56, 60.
M1 Pease R, Maddox E: The Subtleties of Settling Time; New Lightning Empiricist (Teledyne Philbrick) July 1971, 1–9.
N1 Beckman: Model 821 Miniaturized Power Amplifier; Beckman Data Sheet 68266, Sep. 1968.
O1 Harris: HA-2630/2635 High Performance Current Booster; Harris Semiconductor Data Sheet Feb. 1974.
P1 Motorola: MC1438R Power Booster; Motorola Data Sheet Dec. 1972.
Q1 Texas Instruments: HIC037 Hybrid Microcircuit Current Amplifier; Texas Instruments Data Sheet July 1971.
R1 Ott W: Combine Two Op Amps to Avoid the Speed Accuracy Compromise; Electron 27 Feb. 1975, 42.
S1 Signetics: Video Amplifier NE501A; Signetics Data Sheet 1972.
T1 Signetics: Video Amplifier NE592K; Sigmetics Data Sheet 1972.
U1 RCA: Low Power Video and Wideband Amplifiers CA3021/2/3; RCA Data Sheet 1972.
V1 RCA: Video and Wideband Amplifier CA3040; RCA Data Sheet 1972.
W1 RCA: Video and Wideband Amplifier CA3001; RCA Data Sheet 1972.
X1 Motorola: Monolithic Video Amplifier MC1552G; Motorola Data Sheet 1972.
Y1 Fairchild: Differential Video Amplifier μA733; Fairchild Data Sheet 1973.
Z1 Shillito P: Slew Rate Limiting Nomograph; Electron 24 Oct. 1974, 55.
a2 Read C: Settling Time in Op Amps; New Electronics 22 Jan. 1974, 25.
b2 Harris: High Slew Rate, Wideband Inverting Amplifier HA-2530/2535; Harris Semiconductor Data Sheet Sep. 1972.
c2 Harris: Wide Band, High Impedance Operational Amplifiers HA2620/2622/2625; Harris Semiconductor Data Sheet.
d2 Plessey: Low Noise Wideband Amplifier with External Control SL550; Plessey Data Sheet Dec. 1974.
e2 Beckman: FET Input Wideband Operational Amplifier 825; Beckman Data Sheet Nov. 1973.
f2 Analog Devices: High Speed Operational Amplifier AD505; Analog Devices Data Sheet 1972.
g2 Analog Devices: Fast Settling IC Op Amp AD509; Analog Devices Data Sheet 1975.
h2 Analog Devices: High Speed, Low Cost IC Operational Amplifier AD518; Analog Devices Data Sheet 1975.
i2 Analog Devices: High Speed, Precision, FET-Input Operational Amplifier AD528; Analog Devices Data Sheet 1974.
j2 RCA: Wideband Operational Amplifier CA3100; RCA Data Sheet 1973.
k2 RCA: COS/MOS Operational Amplifiers CA3130; RCA Data Sheet 1974.
l2 Burr-Brown: Wideband Operational Amplifiers 3506/3508; Burr-Brown Data Sheet PDS-298, Apr. 1973.
m2 Teledyne Philbrick: 200ns to 0.01% Settling, FET Operational Amplifier 1430; Teledyne Philbrick Data Sheet 1974.
n2 Motorola: Video Amplifier MC1510; Motorola Data Sheet June 1967.
o2 Analog Devices: Low Cost, High Speed IC Op Amps ADX218; Analog Devices Data Sheet 1975.
p2 Sansen W M C, Meyer R G: An Integrated Wide-Band Variable Gain Amplifier with Maximum Dynamic Range; IEEE J SC-9, 159–166, 1974.

q2 Roberts J A, Taylor M: High-Level Instrument Output Amplifier; Design Electronics Jan. 1970, 46–47.

r2 Davidson C W: Wideband Voltage Amplifiers; Intertext Publishing.

s2 Apfel R J, Gray P R: A Fast-Settling Monolithic Operational Amplifier Using Doublet Compression Techniques; IEEE J SC-9, 332–340, 1974.

t2 Davis P C, Moyer S F, Saari V R: High Slew Rate Monolithic Operational Amplifier Using Compatible Complementary PNP's; IEEE J SC-9, 340–347, 1974.

u2 Kamath B Y, Meyer R G, Gray P R: Relationship Between Frequency Response and Settling Time of Operational Amplifiers; IEEE J SC-9, 347–352, 1974.

v2 Meyer R G, Eschenbach R, Edgerly W M: A Wide-Band Feedforward Amplifier; IEEE J SC-9, 422–428, 1974.

w2 Cherry E M, Hooper D E: The Design of Wide-Band Transistor Feedback Amplifiers; Proc IEE 110, 375–389, 1963.

x2 Addis J: Three Technologies on One Chip Make a Broadband Amplifier; Electronics 5 Jun. 1972, 103–107.

y2 Datel: FET Input Wideband IC Amplifier AM-405-2; Datel Systems Product Handbook 1974.

z2 Datel: Bipolar Input Wideband IC Amplifier AM-452-2; Datel Systems Product Handbook 1974.

A2 Fairchild: High Slew Rate Operational Amplifier μA772; Fairchild Data Sheet.

B2 Krabbe H, Burwen R S: Stable Monolithic Op Amp Slews at 130V/μs (AD505); Analog Dialogue 5, No.4, 3–5, 1971.

C2 Towers T D: Elements of Linear Microcircuits, Chapter 8 Wide Band Amplifiers; Iliffe 1973.

D2 Markus J (Ed): Electronic Circuits Manual, Chapter 95 Video Circuits; McGraw-Hill 1971.

E2 Trout B: RF Designs with a Linear IC (MC1590); EEE 17, Dec. 1969, 64–68.

F2 Grebene A B: Analog Integrated Circuit Design, Chapter 8 Wideband Amplifiers; Van Nostrand Reinhold 1972.

G2 Van Kessel T J: An Integrated Operational Amplifier with Novel HF Behaviour; IEEE J SC-3, 348–352, 1968.

H2 Plessey: High Speed Video Amplifier SL541C; Plessey Data Sheet Publication PS1438, Jan. 1975.

I2 Datel: High Speed Monolithic Operational Amplifiers AM-400 Series; Datel Systems Data Sheet 1974.

J2 Ghausi M S: Electronic Circuits; Van Nostrand Reinhold 1971.

K2 Eimbinder J (Ed): Linear Integrated Circuits: Theory and Applications, Chapter 10 Bogusz J F, Ekiss J A, Herman P E: Integrated-Circuit Broadband Amplifiers, Chapter 12 Johnson B T: Integrated Wideband Amplifier; Wiley 1968.

L2 Eimbinder J (Ed): Application Considerations for Linear Integrated Circuits, Chapter 6 Krabbe H: High-Frequency Characteristics of Wideband Inverter Operational Amplifiers, Chapter 8 Welling B: The Versatile Wideband IC Amplifier; Wiley-Interscience 1970.

M2 Delaney C F G: Electronics for the Physicist; Penguin Books 1969.

N2 Siegel B: Applications for a High Speed FET Input Op Amp LH0062; Electronic Components 4 May 1973, 378–381.

O2 Nowlin C H, Blankenship J L: Elimination of Undesirable Undershoot in the Operation and Testing of Nuclear Pulse Amplifiers; Rev. Sci. Instrum. 36, 1830–1839, 1965.

P2 Blankenship J L, Nowlin C H: New Concepts in Nuclear Pulse Amplifier Design; IEEE Trans NS-13, 495–507, 1966.

Q2 Fairstein E: Considerations in the Design of Pulse Amplifiers for Use with Solid State Radiation Detectors; Trans IRE NS-8, 129–139, 1961.

R2 National Semiconductor: High Speed Buffers (LH0033); Electron 29 June 1972, 31–32.

S2 Aria R: FETs for Video Amplifiers; Siliconix Application Note 70/2, Oct. 1970.

T2 Beason J: Better Bipolar-MOS Process Yields Linear ICs with Good AC and DC Specs (HA2530); Electronics 31 Oct. 1974, 65–70.

U2 Burr-Brown: Fast Slewing Externally Compensated Operational Amplifier 3507; Burr-Brown Data Sheet Jan. 1976.
V2 National Semiconductor: High Slew Rate Operational Amplifier LH0024; National Semiconductor Data Sheet Aug. 1973.
W2 National Semiconductor: Ultra Fast FET Operational Amplifier LH0032; National Semiconductor Data Sheet Aug. 1973.
X2 National Semiconductor: Damn Fast Buffer Amplifier LH0063; National Semiconductor Data Sheet Aug. 1973.
Y2 National Semiconductor: 0.5Amp Wide Band Operational Amplifier LH0061; National Semiconductor Data Sheet Aug. 1973.
Z2 Texas Instruments: Differential Video Amplifier SN7510; Texas Instruments Data Sheet Sep. 1973.
a3 National Semiconductor: Wideband Monolithic JFET Input Operational Amplifier (LF356/7); National Semiconductor Data Sheet Sep. 1975.

5 Oscillators

5.1 Sinusoidal RC oscillators

Oscillators in the frequency range 1 Hz to 1 MHz most commonly use the Wien RC network as the frequency determining element. This has been analysed in Sec. 1.11 [f1, a1] where it was found that at a frequency:

$$f_0 = \frac{1}{2\pi RC} \qquad (5.1.1)$$

the network has a gain of 1/3 and the phase shift is zero (Fig. 5.1.1).

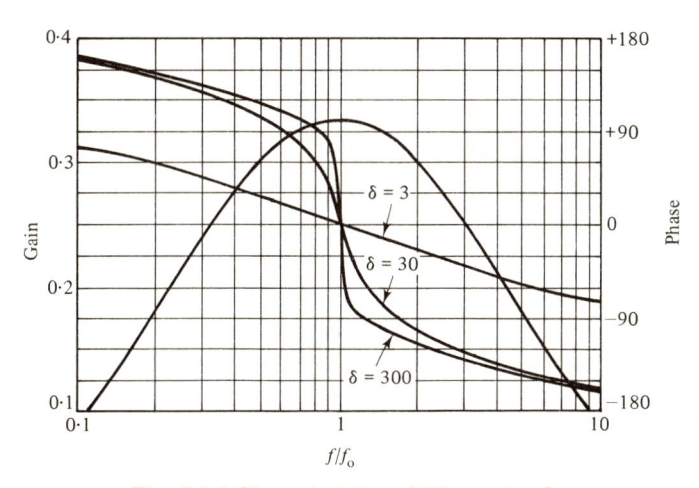

Fig. 5.1.1 Characteristics of Wien network

To obtain oscillations of constant amplitude, i.e., keep the pole exactly on the $j\omega$ axis, an amplifier gain of $+3$ is required. Since it is impossible to keep the gain exactly at this value, some form of automatic control is necessary. This is provided by the other half of the bridge, consisting of resistors R_t and R_b (Fig. 5.1.2).

R_t is a negative temperature coefficient thermistor [x1] such that at ambient temperature the ratio $\beta_r < 1/3$, say:

$$\beta_r = \frac{R_b}{R_b + R_t} = \frac{1}{3} - \frac{1}{\delta} \quad (\delta \geqslant 3) \qquad (5.1.2)$$

Then the negative feedback via the β_r network is less than the positive feedback β_ω via the CR network. The gain A is high, so the poles are in the right half-plane

(RHP) and oscillations grow. Increasing the current through R_t causes a fall in resistance and, hence, increases negative feedback until eventually equilibrium is reached at some constant amplitude e_o (i.e., δ increases as R_t decreases). It must be arranged that e_o is within the linear region of the amplifier A for low harmonic distortion.

The selectivity of the Wien network itself is poor [f1, pp. 671, 689] and would provide unsatisfactory frequency stability and harmonic rejection. The bridge

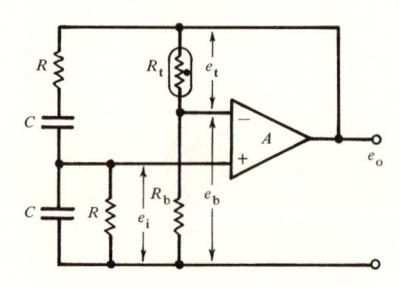

Fig. 5.1.2 Wien-bridge oscillator

combination operating at (or near) null, however, considerably increases selectivity. If the overall feedback factor is β, then:

$$\beta = \beta_\omega - \beta_r = \beta_\omega - \left[\frac{1}{3} - \frac{1}{\delta}\right] \tag{5.1.3}$$

where $\quad \beta_\omega = [3 + j(\omega/\omega_0 - \omega_0/\omega)]^{-1} = 1/3 \quad$ at $\quad \omega_0$

Since the oscillation condition is $A\beta = 1$, then at ω_0:

$$\beta = \frac{1}{\delta} \quad \text{or} \quad A = \delta \tag{5.1.4}$$

If A were infinite, the bridge balance would be exact ($\delta = \infty$), but for finite gain some imbalance must remain. It is shown in [f1] that, relative to the Wien network only, the harmonic discrimination is improved by a factor $\delta/3$, and that the stability factor against changes in oscillation frequency is given by:

$$S_f = \frac{\Delta\phi}{\Delta(\omega/\omega_0)} = -\frac{2\delta}{9} \quad \text{at} \quad \omega_0 \tag{5.1.5}$$

Thus, a high value of δ and, hence, of A is of considerable importance. Since common IC operational amplifiers have gains of 10^5 or 10^6, this is readily achieved. Remember, however, the 20 dB/decade fall off with frequency. Curves for several values of δ are shown in Fig. 5.1.1. For the simple Wien network (i.e., $\delta = 3$) a phase change of 20° ($\frac{1}{3}$ radian) would change ω_0 by a factor 2. For the same phase change with $A = \delta = 10^3$ the relative change would be only 10^{-3}.

Frequency is varied by changing both R's or both C's simultaneously. For low frequencies it is generally simpler to vary R and switch C for various ranges, since suitable double-gang potentiometers are more readily available than capacitors. However, if the amplifier has high input impedance so that high value resistors can be used for R, varying C will give a smoother variation than resistors, in many cases.

Note also that frequency is directly proportional to C rather than $C^{1/2}$ as in the case of an LC oscillator. This means that a 10:1 variation of frequency may be covered with C. There is also a lower limit on R, to avoid loading the amplifier output.

Imbalance in the C's, R's, or variations of gain, phase, or load impedance with frequency can result in changes in e_o. These changes cause changes in loop-gain so that the negative feedback divider gain, β_r, must alter to maintain stable oscillation. By adjustment of the slope of the thermistor characteristic the variation of e_o can be eliminated [e1]. Figure 5.1.3 shows the current–voltage characteristics of R_b and R_t.

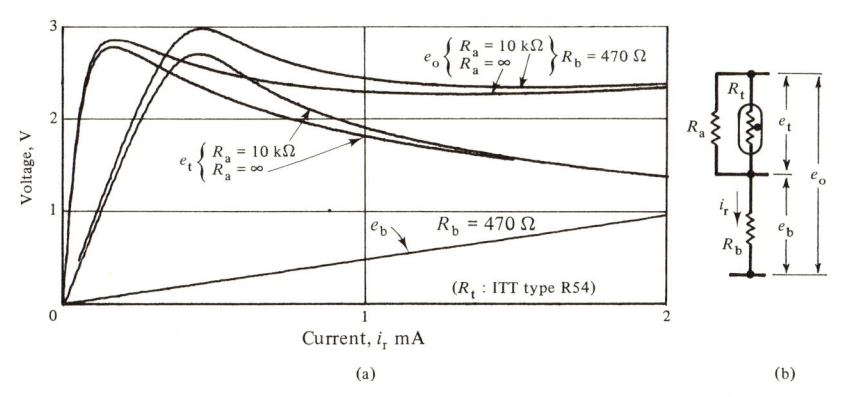

Fig. 5.1.3 Compensation of thermistor characteristics for Wien bridge

In the vicinity of the operating current, i_r, the slope of the thermistor characteristic is made equal but opposite to R_b. This may require the addition of R_a. The resulting sum of R_b and R_t has a region where e_o is independent of i_r, but the ratio e_b/e_o is free to change to maintain the loop-gain at unity. The thermistor should be operated near the maximum allowed temperature to reduce the effects of ambient variations. Thermal insulation will help in reducing rapid changes.

In some cases, amplitude *bounce* is found when changing frequency. This occurs when the amplifier is operating in a linear mode and disappears when a small amount of non-linearity is present [g1].

An interesting feature of these oscillators is that they may be readily locked to an external frequency [e1, j1]. A suitable voltage of nearly the same frequency is injected into the inverting input of the amplifier. The oscillator then operates at the frequency of the input signal, and filters it to reduce noise and harmonic distortion substantially.

In some low frequency applications it is convenient to use a two phase (0 and 90°) oscillator. This makes a variable phase signal easy to obtain, as well as starting and stopping the oscillation at particular phases. These requirements are readily met by the electronic analogue simulation of simple harmonic motion, the computer being shown in Fig. 5.1.4 [d1, h1, i1, v1].

Assuming perfect integrators (Sec. 2.6) we have:

$$E_1 = RCsE_2 = R^2C^2s^2E_3 = -R^2C^2s^2E_1$$

or $\quad e_1 = B \sin(t/RC) \qquad e_2 = -BRC \cos(t/RC) \qquad$ (5.1.6)

$$f = \frac{1}{2\pi RC}$$

The amplitude, B, will be set by the initial conditions of the integrators [d1]. In practice, the amplifiers have finite gain and the phase shift is slightly less than 90° or, including the phase inversion of the amplifier, just greater than 90°, Fig. 5.1.4(b), i.e., $-e_3$ is not quite equal to e_1. Addition of a fraction (e_4) of e_2 to e_3 will achieve this. The angle θ is fixed by the gains A_1 and A_2 and is, thus, effectively constant. Variation of e_4, therefore, will control the magnitude of all the other phasors, and stabilization of e_4 by means of a limiter, will give a constant amplitude output.

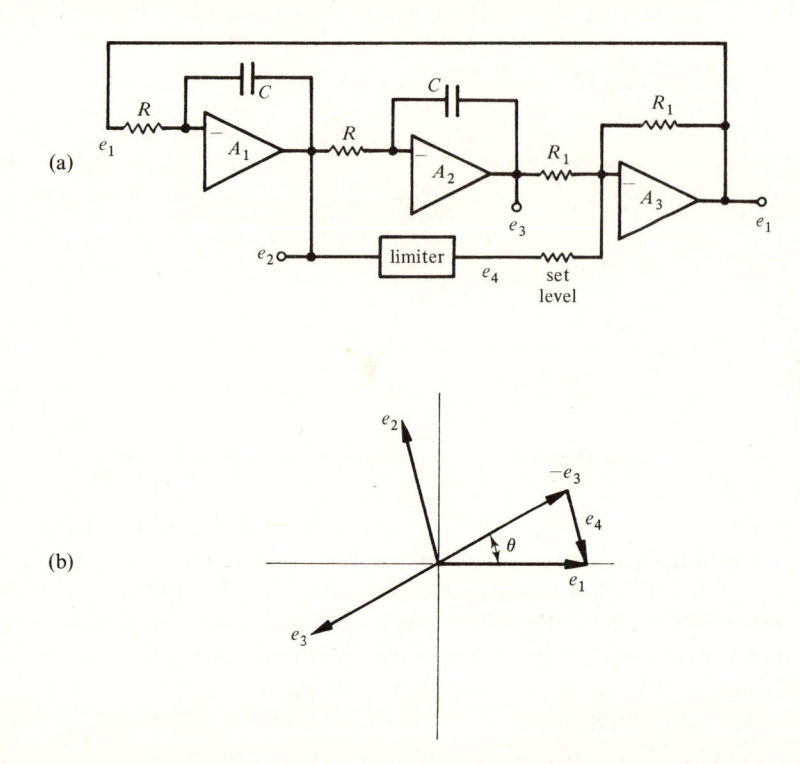

Fig. 5.1.4 (a) Low frequency two-phase oscillator, (b) phasor diagram showing gain control

5.2 Function generators

The term *function generator* is used to describe oscillators generating non-sinusoidal waveforms. The basic waveform is usually a triangle from which ramp, sawtooth, square, pulse, or approximate sinusoids may be derived. (The latter is particularly important at very low frequencies, say <1 Hz, as discussed below.) The basic circuit is shown in Fig. 5.2.1.

A current source supplies a current, $-i$, to an operational integrator to give a positive going ramp at the output. When the output voltage reaches a preset value the comparator switches and turns on a second current source $2i$, causing the output ramp to reverse slope. When this reaches a preset value the comparator again switches, turning the $2i$ generator off, and the process is then repeated. This produces a symmetrical triangular wave from the integrator and square wave from the comparator. Frequency is varied by controlling the value of i. In practice, a range of 100:1 is easily achieved and 1000:1 if special attention is given to eliminating leakage currents at the low current end. Thus wide range sweeps are readily obtained. The range is extended by switching C. The frequency range is from 0·001 Hz (0·0001 Hz with special care) to 100 kHz easily, 1 MHz with some performance degradation, and 10 MHz with some difficulty.

Sawtooth and ramp waveforms are obtained by changing the 2:1 current ratio fed to the integrator, by the appropriate factor. Trigger pulses are derived by differentiating the square wave and clipping one polarity. These pulses can be used to trigger a

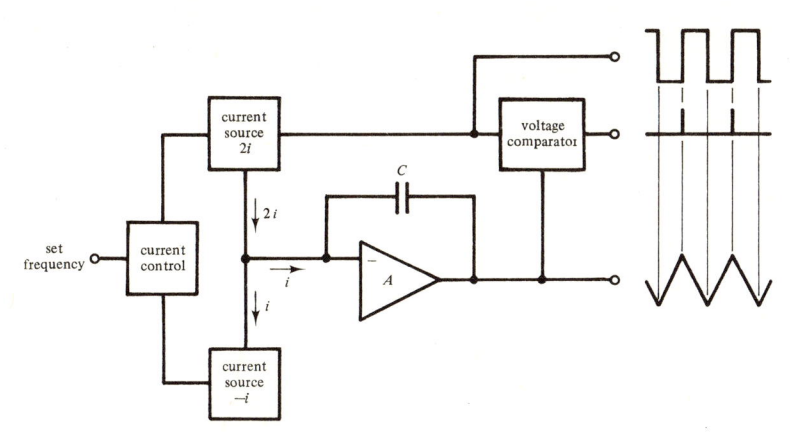

Fig. 5.2.1 Basic function generator

pulse generator of variable duration, such as a monostable, to give variable pulse waveforms.

In a sinusoidal generator, employing a high-Q resonator, a significant number of cycles must elapse after the frequency is changed to allow the amplitude of oscillation to settle. At high frequencies this is usually not significant, but at very low frequencies considerable time must elapse. Since the function generator does not use high-Q circuits, but relies on non-linear techniques, this problem does not arise. It would, thus, be of considerable use if sine waves could be derived from the basic function generator outputs. This cannot be done simply by filtering out higher harmonics, as

(a)   (b)

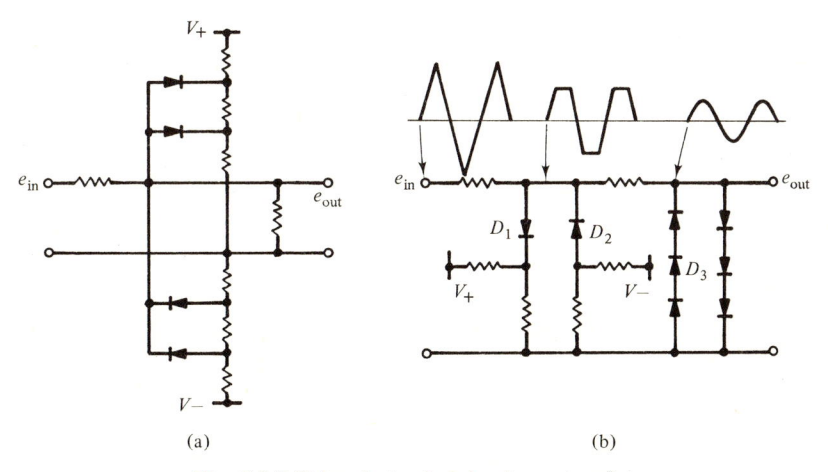

Fig. 5.2.2 Triangle to sine shaping networks

this again requires high-Q filters. However, by using non-linear approximation techniques, low-distortion sine waves may be readily derived from the basic triangular wave. This is commonly done by approximating the sine wave by a number of straight line segments, or by using inherently non-linear elements such as diodes. Two simple schemes are illustrated in Fig. 5.2.2 [a1, b1, e1, G1, K1].

In Fig. 5.2.2(a) a number of diodes are biased at selected voltages. As the triangular wave rises they conduct successively, so increasing the attenuation of the waves and rounding it to an approximate sine wave. Symmetrical halves are required for the positive and negative parts of the triangle. With only four breakpoints on each side, a distortion of less than 1 per cent may be realized. In Fig. 5.2.2(b) the curvature of diode characteristics is used. This also improves the performance of the arrangement in Fig. 5.2.2(a). The first set of diodes D_1, D_2 clip the triangular wave to give a trapezoidal shape, which is then further shaped by the more rounded characteristics of germanium diodes (as compared with silicon) [e1]. The various parameters, clipping level, signal amplitude, resistance values, and number of diodes, must of course be carefully proportioned, but again less than 1 per cent distortion is possible. This level of distortion is not discernable by eye.

Though standard circuits may be assembled to form a function generator, a number of IC's are available which provide various facilities. Brief characteristics of some of these are given in Table 5.2.1.

Table 5.2.1 IC function generators

	Frequency control	Tuning range	Frequency (max) MHz	Outputs	Sinewave distortion, per cent	
NE566V [j1]	voltage (resistance)$^{-1}$	10:1	1	triangle, square	—	
8038 [G2]	voltage	10^3:1	1·5	triangle, square, sine, sawtooth	<1	
XR-2206 [w2]	voltage	2000:1	1	triangle, square, sine, sawtooth	2·5 (0·5)	Includes multiplier and buffer amplifier. FM, AM, FSK (frequency shift keying)
XR-2307 [L2]	voltage	10^3:1	1	triangle, square	—	4 digitally-switched frequency ranges
XR-S200 [x2]	voltage	10:1	30	triangle, square, sine, sawtooth	2	Includes multiplier and op amp
SN74S124 [T1]	voltage	2:1	60	square	—	

The NE566 [j1] uses the principles described above but does not include a sine shaper. The XR-S200 [x2, 11] is a rather different arrangement in that it includes a voltage controlled oscillator, balanced modulator (Sec. 6.3), and buffer amplifier. The inclusion of the modulator, which is essentially a multiplier, makes it possible to generate many complex amplitude and frequency modulated waveforms. These are illustrated in the data sheet [x2, 11]. Matching of components in the IC's is close so that, with stable external components, good frequency stability is obtained

(0·01%/°C). The XR-2206 [w2] has a very wide timing range, but lower maximum frequency.

The 8038 is a versatile form of Fig. 5.2.1 with variable current ratios, a wide tuning range, and a good sine shaper [f1, F2, G2]. The advantages of circuit integration are well illustrated by the circuit diagram shown in Fig. 5.2.3. Transistors Q_{1-13} form the current sources that charge and discharge the capacitor C_{ext}. The frequency of oscillation depends on the voltage at pin 8, the external resistors $R_{A,B}$ and C_{ext}. For fixed frequency operation (e.g., pin 7 connected to 8) the fixed voltage on the bases of $Q_{2,3}$ determines the current $i_{A,B}$ in the inverse ratio of the external resistors, $i_A/i_B = R_B/R_A$. The magnifying current mirror (Sec. 1.10(a)) produces the current $2i_B$, which can be switched on and off by Q_{25}. The voltage levels on C_{ext} are sensed by two comparators Q_{15-18}, referenced to $\frac{2}{3}V_{CC}$ by chain R_{8-10}, and Q_{19-22} referenced to 1/3. At these two reference levels the comparators switch and trigger the control bistable $Q_{26,27}$, which in turn controls the current $2i_B$ via Q_{25}. The bistable and associated transistors are held in an unsaturated condition by Schottky diodes (Sec. 1.9) to obtain high-speed operation.

C_{ext} charges and discharges at rates dependent on R_A and R_B, but the frequency is not dependent on V_{CC}, since the comparator reference voltages and the voltage on pin 8 are both directly proportional to V_{CC}. As the voltages at pins 4 and 5 are equal to that at pin 8 (=pin 7), the voltages across $R_{A,B}$ are 0·2 V_{CC}, so $i_{A,B}$ and the times for C_{ext} to charge and discharge are readily determined. The bistable square wave is available at pin 9, which requires an external load which may be connected to any voltage within the device ratings. The triangle waveform across C_{ext} should not be used directly, as loading may affect the waveform particularly for small charging currents. The waveform is taken via Q_9 to a buffer amplifier Q_{35-40} with a complementary output stage. As the comparator reference levels are accurately 1/3 and $\frac{2}{3}V_{CC}$, the average output at pin 3 will be $\frac{1}{2}V_{CC}$. The supply voltage may be either $+V_{CC}$ or $\pm\frac{1}{2}V_{CC}$; in the latter case the average value at pin 3 is 0 volt.

The right-hand side of the circuit, Q_{41-56}, is the sine shaper, the upper set for the positive half-cycle and the lower for the negative. Reference voltages set by the chain R_{32-40} and buffered by even-numbered transistors, determine when the odd-numbered transistors start conducting as the triangle wave varies in amplitude. This variable resistance in series with R_{44} and shunting the output at pin 2 shapes the triangular wave to a sine wave with total harmonic distortion of only 1 per cent. The usable frequency range for triangle and sine outputs is from 0·001 Hz to about 200 kHz, while the square wave is usable up to about 1 MHz.

The proportionality of the currents $i_{A,B}$ to the voltage at pin 8 allows the generation of frequency sweeps with a ramp input, or frequency modulation with a sine wave. For small deviations the modulating signal is fed (via a capacitor if necessary) directly to pin 7, 8, or to pin 8 with an additional resistor between 7 and 8 if higher input resistance is required. For sweeps, a voltage must be provided between pin 8 and V_{CC} with a range down to about $\frac{2}{3}V_{CC}$. In principle, it is possible to obtain a sweep range of 1000:1, but to cover the complete range may require a voltage, V_8, a few hundred millivolt above V_{CC}, owing to transistor matching tolerances. This is most readily achieved by using a forward conducting diode between V_{CC} and the device supply input (pin 6) and referencing the sweep to V_{CC} directly.

A number of additional facilities are readily added to the standard function generator circuit. These include phase-locking to an external signal, generation of

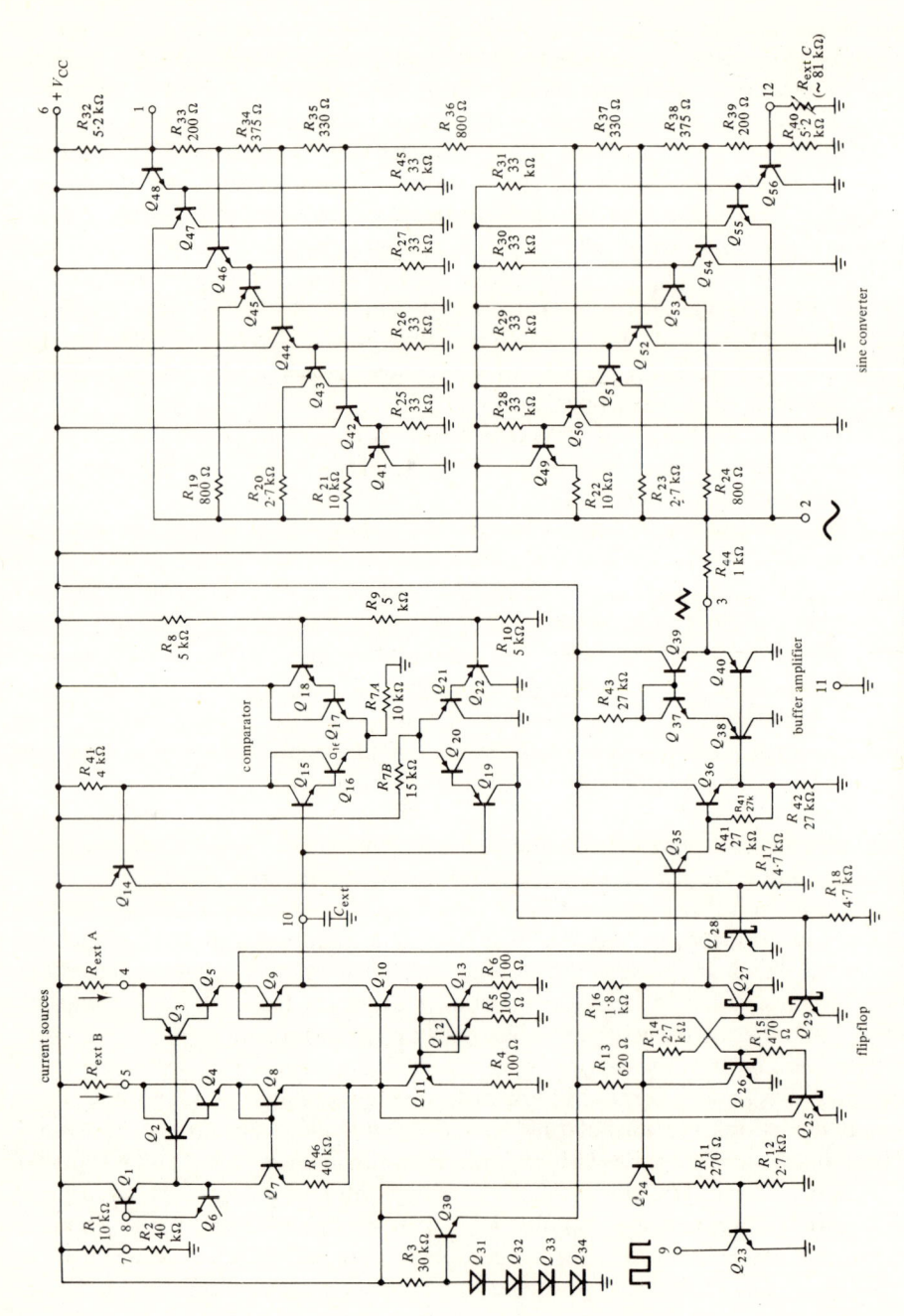

Fig. 5.2.3 8038 IC function generator (Intersil Inc., with permission)

single or given multiple number of cycles, or offsetting the zero level. An arrangement for phase-locking is shown in Fig. 5.2.4 [c1].

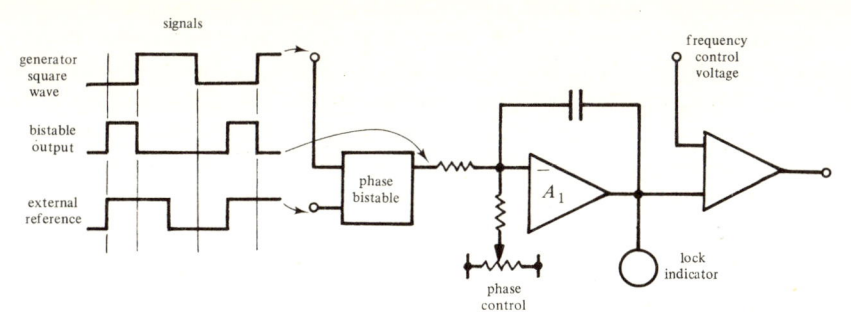

Fig. 5.2.4 Phase-lock function generation

The external reference and generator square wave are compared by the phase bistable to give the output shown. This is filtered by the low-pass filter to give the appropriate correction voltage to the frequency control voltage. The system is, in fact, just a phase-locked loop (Sec. 6.4). The phase control shifts the d.c. level which allows an offset of $\pm 90°$.

Figure 5.2.5(a) shows a system for generating single whole cycles.

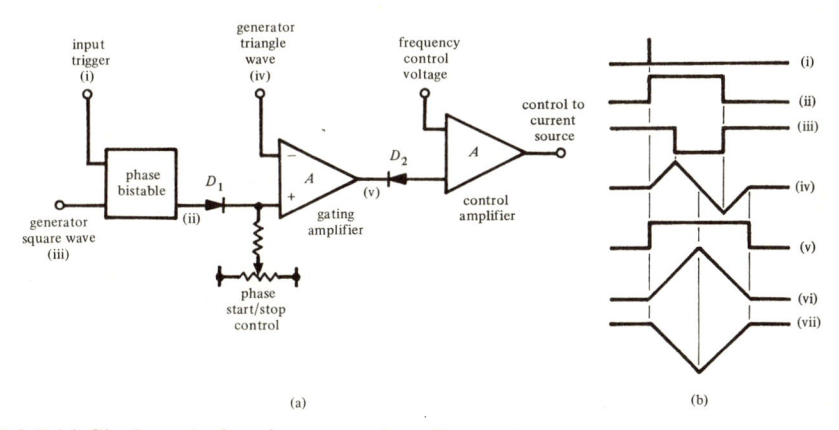

Fig. 5.2.5 (a) Single cycle function generation, (b) waveforms. (vi) and (vii) show output waveforms with phase control $\pm 90°$

In the stable state the phase bistable holds D_1 reverse biased. D_2 is forward biased and completes a negative feedback loop from the output of the triangle generator, which stops oscillations. An input trigger switches the phase bistable, causing the gating amplifier to reverse bias D_2, so removing the negative feedback and the oscillator starts. The generator square wave resets the phase bistable, but the triangle waveform keeps the gating amplifier and D_2 off until the waveform returns to the initial voltage level. Thus, one complete cycle is generated. The start/stop phase may be varied by adding the appropriate voltage to the input of the gating amplifier, as shown. This gives $\pm 90°$ phase variation and output waveforms as shown in Fig. 5.2.5(b). If a given number of cycles is required, a presettable counter is inserted in the square wave input line to the phase bistable.

A simple wide-range function generator can be made with the µA776 programmable amplifier [i1]. The slewing rate is proportional to the set bias current. Applying a square wave to the input gives a triangle wave out, since the µA776 slews at its maximum set value charging its internal 30 pF compensation capacitor. The triangle wave is fed to a high impedance comparator to generate the square wave for the µA776 input. Changing the set bias current changes the frequency, over a range of 10^5 to 1 from 0·1 Hz to over 10 kHz. The high input impedance comparator is particularly necessary at low set bias currents (low frequencies) since the µA776 output impedance is large here.

A waveform useful in generating a display raster, i.e., stepping a voltage through a number of equal steps, is produced by the staircase generator [B1, p. 73; z2, p. 712; y2; H1]. The basic circuit is shown in Fig. 5.2.6.

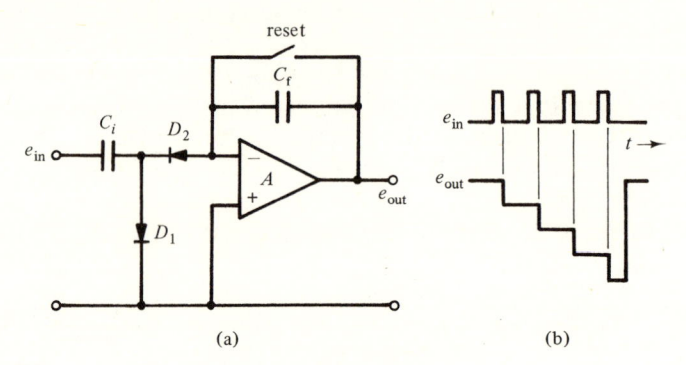

Fig. 5.2.6 Staircase generator

A train of fixed amplitude (e_{in}) pulses is applied via input capacitor, C_i, to a diode pump, D_1, D_2. On the positive going edge of the pulse, D_1 conducts and C_i is charged to voltage e_{in}. On the negative going edge, D_1 is reverse biased and D_2 conducts, discharging C_i into the integrator. Because of the virtual ground, the charge on C_i ($Q_i = C_i e_{in}$) is transferred to C_f, irrespective of the charge already on C_f. This gives an output voltage step δe_{out}:

$$\delta e_{out} = \frac{Q_f}{C_f} = \frac{Q_i}{C_f} = e_{in}\frac{C_i}{C_f} \qquad (5.2.1)$$

To terminate the staircase some form of reset is required. This can be either a switch (mechanical or electronic) as shown, or a pulse generator feeding a pulse of appropriate amplitude and polarity to the virtual ground, to cancel the charge on C_f.

If C_f is shunted with a resistor R_f, then the charge on C_f will leak away between the input pulses. If the average output voltage is e_{out} for a given input pulse repetition rate f_{in}, then the average current i_f through R_f is equal to the charge input per unit time, $e_{in} C_i f_{in}$, and:

$$e_{out} = i_f R_f = e_{in} C_i f_{in} R_f \qquad (5.2.2)$$

Thus, for constant e_{in}, the output voltage is proportional to the input frequency. This provides a convenient analogue frequency meter or a pulse ratemeter. It should be noted that C_f does not enter the expression for e_{out}. However, it does control the amplitude of the fluctuations in the output, Eq. (5.2.1), and should be chosen to suit the application. A long time-constant, $R_f C_f$, gives a smooth output but a slow response to input frequency changes, and vice versa [F1, V1, W1, i2]. If f_{in} is constant, the circuit may be used as a capacitance meter.

The reverse process of voltage-to-frequency conversion is illustrated in Fig. 5.2.7 [Q1, n1, p1, t1, u1, D1, E1, O1, U1, d2, j2]. Application of a voltage, e_{in}, to the integrator produces a ramp, e_{out}. When this reaches a present level, $-V_{ref}$, the comparator switches and triggers the pulse generator. This supplies a pulse of appropriate polarity to reset the integrator to zero. If e_{in} is still present the whole process is repeated to give sawtooth and pulse outputs of repetition frequency proportional to the input voltage. A larger e_{in} will cause the integrator output to reach the reference level sooner and, hence, increase the repetition frequency. If inputs of either polarity are used a further pulse generator and comparator with reference voltage $+V_{ref}$ must be added.

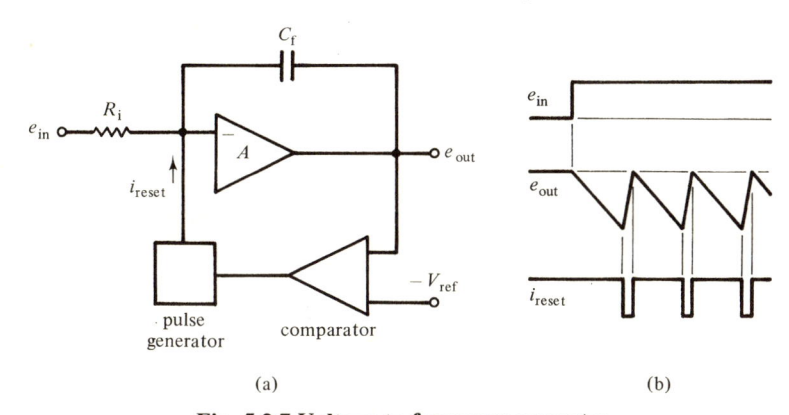

Fig. 5.2.7 Voltage-to-frequency converter

With the advent of cheap digital IC's the synthesis of complex waveforms by digital methods has become more attractive [z1, A1, x1, f2, g2, S1]. The desired function can be stored in a memory and read out repeatedly. If necessary, smoothing may be added to reduce the digital steps.

5.3 Relaxation and negative resistance oscillators

5.3(a) *Multivibrators*

This term usually covers a number of similar circuits, i.e., monostable, bistable, and astable circuits, and Schmitt triggers [d1, A2] but their applications are basically different. However, because of their similar circuit operation it is instructive to consider them together. Detailed design of such circuits is considered in [d1, E2], so here we will deal only with the basic principles and some of the IC forms available. Simple circuits for the four types are shown in Fig. 5.3.1.

The bistable circuit, Fig. 5.3.1(a), has two stable states, with either of the two transistors cut-off and with the other conducting or even saturated. Since the transistors are d.c. coupled, either state can last indefinitely unless some external signal causes a change to the other. These circuits illustrate the application of positive feedback with a pole on the positive real axis (Sec. 3.2) which gives fast regenerative switching between states [d1, p. 368]. Thus, if the circuit is pushed in one direction it will flop over into a limiting state and remain there. Though commonly referred to as a *flip-flop*, it would be more appropriate to call it a *flop-flop*. The system may be triggered in many ways, one symmetrical form being shown. Here the two diodes D_1

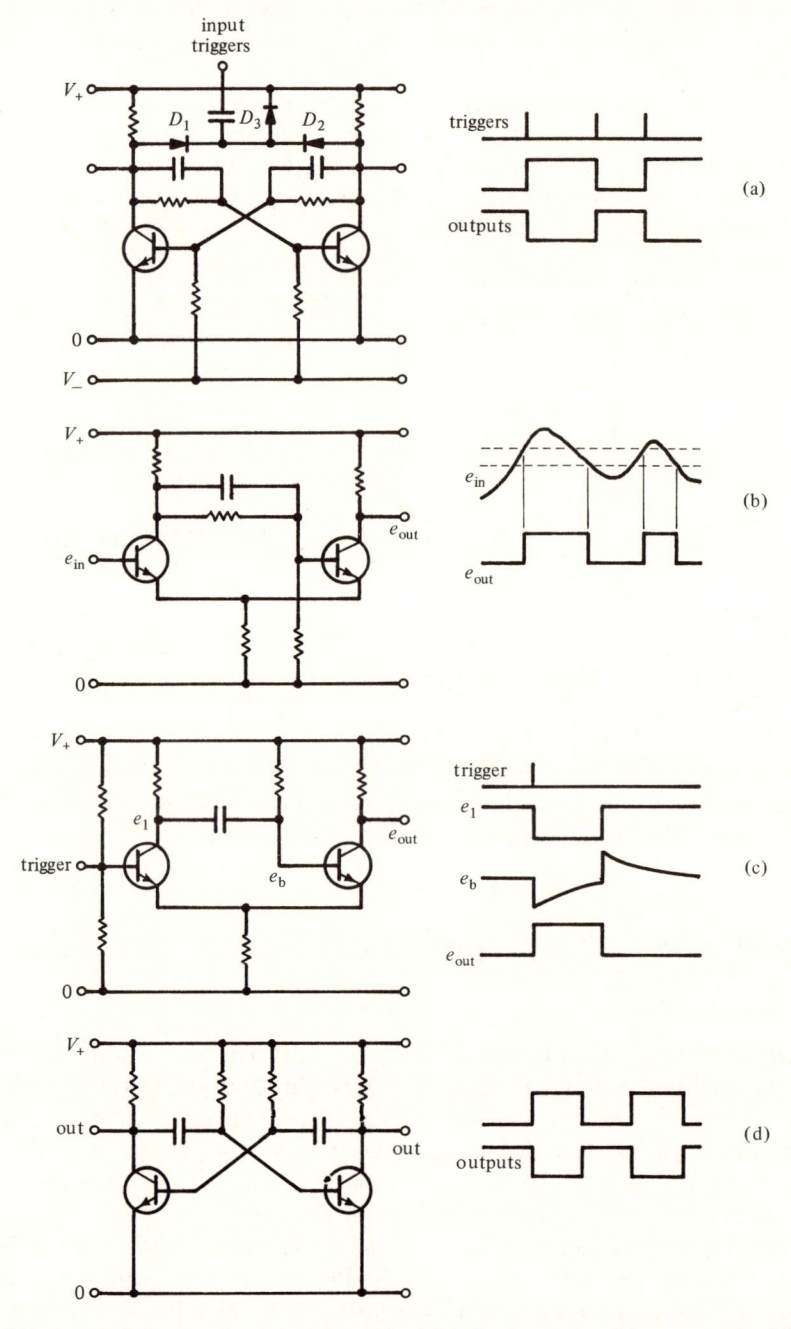

Fig. 5.3.1 Basic multivibrator circuits, (a) bistable, (b) Schmitt trigger, (c) monostable, (d) astable

or D_2 route the negative trigger pulse to the OFF device collector, and via the coupling to the ON side base. The other diode will be reverse biased and so will not pass the trigger. D_3 serves to clamp the positive excursion of the trigger pulse to the supply rail. Successive triggers cause the system to change alternately between the two states. Application of separate triggers to the two sides allows the circuit to be set (S) into one state or reset (R) to the original. Hence it is often referred to as an RS flip-flop, particularly in logic applications. The capacitors shown shunting the coupling resistors are commutating or speed-up capacitors, and serve to transmit the fast edges from the collectors to the bases. If these were not present, slow transitions between states would be obtained because of the integrating action of the coupling resistor and the transistor base capacity. The optimum value of capacity is as for a slightly overcompensated attenuator (Sec. 1.4). Note that it is more effective to apply a trigger to turn OFF the conducting device than vice-versa [A2, p. 380].

The Schmitt trigger, Fig. 5.3.1(b), also has two stable states but the state depends on the d.c. level of the input. It is thus the same as a comparator with positive feedback (Sec. 6.1) and exhibits the same hysteresis in switching levels. It is useful in deriving fast edges from slowly varying waveforms. The hysteresis avoids chatter when the input waveform remains close to the switching levels. The existence of an unused collector provides a convenient output point that is not involved in the switching process, so that loading will not affect its operation. Again there are two d.c. connections, the second being the common emitter connection.

The monostable circuit, Fig. 5.3.1(c), has only one stable state. When triggered it goes into a temporary state for a time dependent on the *RC* time constant, and then returns to the original stable state. It is useful, therefore, for generating a longer pulse from a short trigger, or a time delay. This circuit is also referred to as a one-shot circuit.

The astable circuit, Fig. 5.3.1(d), has two a.c. couplings and hence no stable state, flipping back and forth between two states (a flip-flip). This is, then, an oscillator generating square waves with a mark-space ratio dependent on the time constants of the two sides.

Notwithstanding what has been said about the type of coupling and the stability of states, marginal or extreme conditions can cause improper operation.

All these circuits may be constructed from discrete components [A2, d1, q2, a1, h1], but there are many IC forms that are more convenient and may have a number of useful additional features. Few astable circuits are made, but they can be readily assembled using standard logic gates [e1, L1]. A type with voltage control of frequency is made [C1] and monostable circuits can be connected as astables [B1, f1]. Bistable circuits are made in a number of forms, some of considerable complexity, particularly those for use in logic systems. These are discussed in [i2].

There are many types of monostable or timing circuit, some of which are listed in Table 5.3.1. They may be divided into two types, lockout and those able to be retriggered. In the former, after the trigger is applied, further triggers have no effect until the monostable cycle is completed, i.e., the inputs are locked-out. In the latter, application of a further trigger during the cycle will cause the cycle to start over again, i.e., the system is retriggerable. Figure 5.3.2 illustrates the waveforms obtained in both cases, including the effect of a clear pulse.

Where provided the clear input will reset the outputs to their original state, irrespective of the state. In some cases it is possible to connect an output back to one of several available inputs, to convert a retriggerable type to a lockout configuration [f1].

The delay time of a monostable is set by an $R_t C_t$ time constant, and can be varied over a wide range from tens of nanoseconds to hours. Limits on R_t are set by leakage currents and current limitations in the IC, and those on C_t by the stray capacity and by leakage in the capacitor, particularly for large capacities where electrolytic types are necessary.

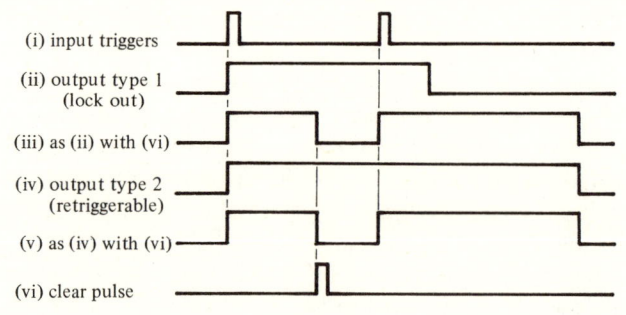

(i) input triggers
(ii) output type 1 (lock out)
(iii) as (ii) with (vi)
(iv) output type 2 (retriggerable)
(v) as (iv) with (vi)
(vi) clear pulse

Fig. 5.3.2 Waveforms for retriggerable and lockout monostables

For very short delays the bipolar logic types are suitable. However, they usually have a limited R_t range and so cannot be varied over a wide range without capacitor switching (Table 5.3.1 types (a) to (e)). For wide range and low power dissipation the MOS types, (f) and (g), are useful [D1, B1]. There are several devices specially designed as timers with delays up to hours; (h) to (j) [X1]. The NE555 is a low cost

Table 5.3.1 Monostable and timing IC's

		Lockout/ retrigger	Inputs	Clear	Timing range	Minimum time (ns)	Supply voltage	Comments
(a)	9603	L	±Schmitt −edge	no	10:1 40 kΩ max	50	5	TTL, SN74121, SN74221 Dual
(b)	9600 (96L02)	R	±edge	yes	10:1 50 kΩ max	50	5	TTL, SN74122, 9602 and SN74123 duals, MIC74123A and AM26123 improved, MM74C123 MOS
(c)	N8T20B	—	±edge	yes	—	8 MHz input	±5	4 mV comparator with logic and monostable
(d)	H117	L	−edge	no	10:1 100 kΩ max	1 μs	20	HLL, separate inverter
(e)	342CJ	L	+edge	no	2–62 kΩ	100	10–16	HLL, expander input, dual. SN15342
(f)	CD4047AE	R	±edge	yes	large 10 kΩ min		5–15	MOS, mono-astable logic, divide by 2 circuit
(g)	MC14528CP	R	±edge	yes	large 5 kΩ min	300	5–16	MOS, dual
(h)	NE555V	R/L	−edge	yes	large 1 kΩ–20 MΩ	1 μs	5–18	200 mA output/sink
(i)	XR-320	L	±edge	yes	10^3:1 2 kΩ min	1 μs	4·5–20	100 mA output, TTL output, linear ramp timing
(j)	LM322	L	+edge	no	large 3 kΩ–10^9 Ω	3 μs	4·5–40	Floating output 50 mA 40 V. 50:1 voltage control

Timing range refers to variation with R_t for fixed C_t. Large implies limitation by leakage currents, e.g., of C_t.

Equivalents shown are not necessarily identical and data sheets should be consulted.

general purpose timer [k1 to w1, C2] and the XR-320 [j1] uses a current source to charge C_t, and so generates a linear timing ramp rather than the usual exponential. The LM322 [t2, r2, s2] has a versatile floating output and the timing is voltage controllable over a 50:1 range. A number of specialized devices are available, such as light blinkers [y2] and tachometers [w2, x2, B2, F2, S2].

A good example of the range of logic monostables is the 9602, which contains two separate retriggerable circuits, each as shown in Fig. 5.3.3 [O2, i2]. The simple circuit of Fig. 5.3.1(c) has become considerably more complex. Figure 5.3.3(b) shows a block diagram of the circuit together with the numbers of the associated transistors. Timing is controlled by the external R_t, C_t. The letters refer to the state sequence diagram, Fig. 5.3.3(c), which indicates the detailed sequence of events.

In the stable or quiescent state, $Q_{5,7,9}$ are off and $Q_{6,12}$ are on. Current through the external timing resistor R_t holds Q_{10} of the Schmitt trigger on, while Q_{11} via Q_{13B} and the base-collector junction of Q_{14}, holds the Q output low and $\bar{Q}$ high. Positive or negative edges may be used to trigger the monostable as shown. These are TTL inputs which means that the circuit driving the inputs must be able to sink 1·6 mA at $\leqslant 0.4$ V (0·8 V maximum) at low level and supply 40 µA at $\geqslant 2.4$ V (2 V minimum) at high level. The sequence of events following a trigger is then as follows.

(i) Q_5 triggers the differentiator producing a fast negative edge at Q_7 collector which (via Q_{14}) sets Q high ($\bar{Q}$ low) and (via D_8) sets the discharge monostable to its unstable state (Q_{12} off).

(ii) The discharge monostable resets the Schmitt (Q_{11} on) which takes over control of Q, $\bar{Q}$ from the differentiator, resets the differentiator (via Q_8), and starts the discharge of C_t through R_d and Q_9. The differentiator output pulse at Q_7 collector is about 50 ns wide, and largely determines the minimum overall delay time of about 70 ns.

(iii) When C_t has discharged sufficiently the discharge monostable resets (Q_{12} on), and C_t begins charging via R_t and Q_{12} base–emitter. As R_d is usually $\ll R_t$, the discharge period is only a small fraction of the total timing interval.

(iv) Time-out occurs when RC reaches the threshold of the Schmitt which switches, Q_{11} goes off taking Q, $\bar{Q}$ back to the quiescent state.

(v) Retrigger inputs have no effect during the C_t discharge period (ii) and (iii).

(vi) After (v) but before time-out a retrigger will cause C_t to discharge as before, but the Schmitt is unaffected so that the outputs remain in the triggered state (Q high, $\bar{Q}$ low). Note that a constant input level ($\bar{I}_0$, I_1) will not cause retriggering—the appropriate transition must occur.

(vii) The reset input $\overline{CD}$ is normally high. A negative pulse during a timing period overrules the Schmitt control and resets the outputs (Q low, $\bar{Q}$ high), but does not affect the timing cycle itself which proceeds to its normal conclusion, i.e., $\overline{CD}$ only inhibits the outputs from reflecting the timing cycle and does not prevent a cycle from being triggered.

The mode of operation has several consequences for the timing elements R_t, C_t. The minimum value of R_t is set by the requirement that during the discharge (ii) Q_9 does not come out of saturation because of excess collector current; the maximum value is set by the need for Q_{10} to receive sufficient base current to remain on in the quiescent state. The voltage across C_t will be reversed during the cycle, which has consequences if electrolytic capacitors are used. Though the reverse voltage is small

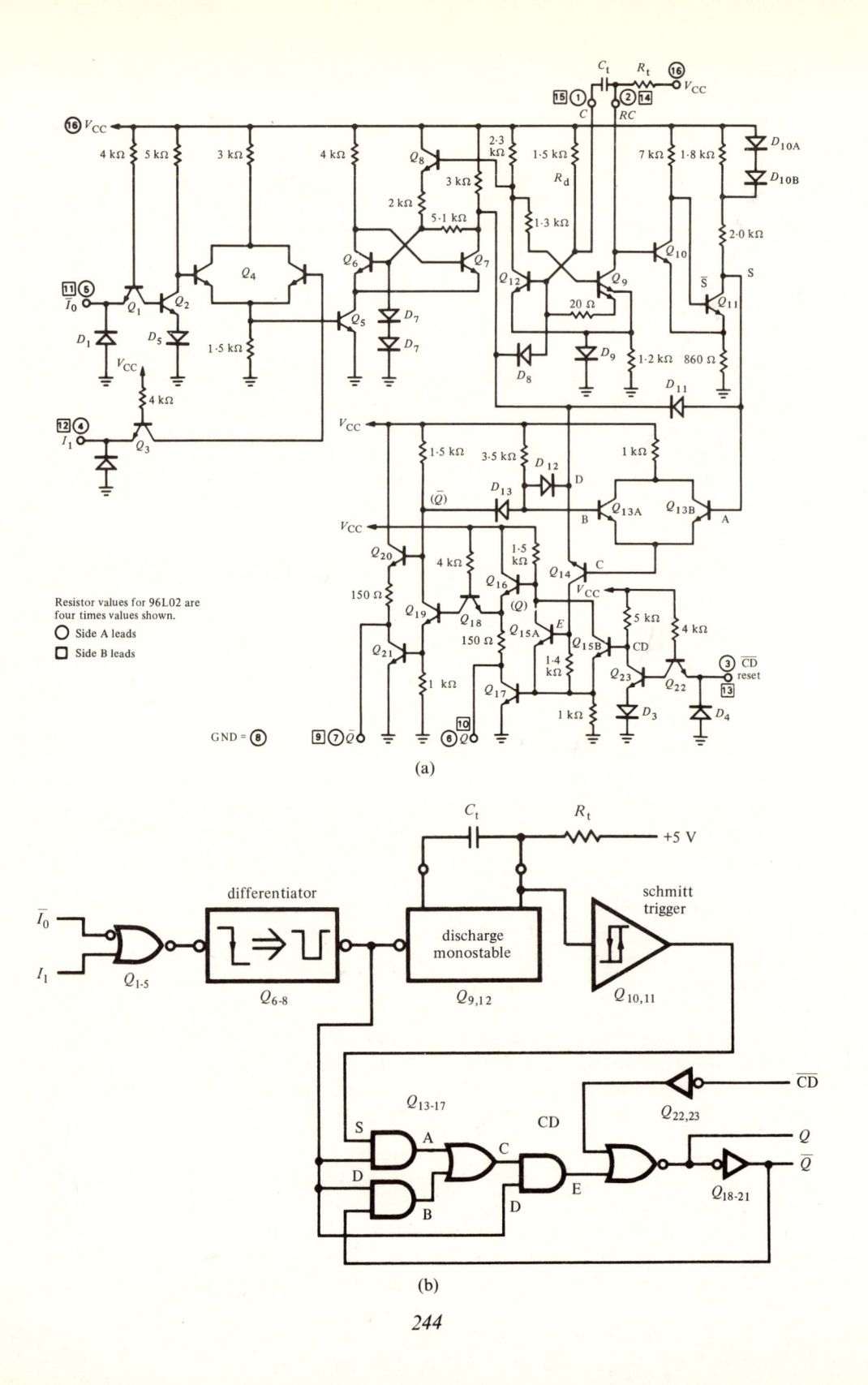

(a)

(b)

	Reference points in (b)
	D S A B C E Q Q̄
Circuit in quiescent state	H H H H H H L H
Input trigger, differentiator starts	(L) H H H H H L H
Start discharge period	L H (L)(L) H (L) L H
50ns negative pulse at Q_{7C}	L H L L (L) L (H) H
	L H L L L L H (L)
Schmitt trigger turns off	L (L) L L L L H L
Differentiator restores	(H) L L L L L H L
Schmitt takes over control of outputs from differentiator	Charging period
Schmitt trigger turns on	H (H) L L L L H L
	H H (H) L L L H L
	H H H L (H) L H L
	H H H L H (H) H L
	H H H L H H (L) L
	H H H L H H L (H)
Returned to quiescent state	H H H (H) H H L H

H = high, L = low, ◯ shows changes, → consequential flow, CD = L

(c)

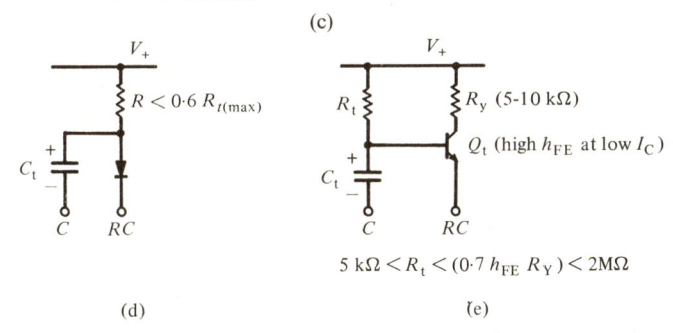

(d)   (e)

$R < 0.6\, R_{t(max)}$

$5\,k\Omega < R_t < (0.7\, h_{FE}\, R_Y) < 2M\Omega$

R_y (5-10 kΩ)

Q_t (high h_{FE} at low I_C)

Fig. 5.3.3 9602 IC monostable, (a) circuit diagram, (b) block logic diagram, (c) state sequence, (d) timing with electrolytic capacitor, (e) extended timing using capacitance multiplier (Courtesy Fairchild Semiconductor)

(≈ 1 V, which suitable electrolytics can withstand) there are low limits on reverse leakage currents if timing is not to be affected. Alternative arrangements for electrolytic capacitors are shown in Fig. 5.3.3(d) and (e) which eliminate the voltage reversal. However, these circuits have reduced timing predictability and temperature stability and do not operate predictably when retriggered.

For $C_t > 1000$ pF the timing equation is:

$$t = AR_t C_t \left(1 + \frac{B}{R_t}\right) \qquad (5.3.1)$$

	A	B
9602	0·31	1
96L02	0·33	3
96S02	0·30	0·11

with an accuracy of ± 10 per cent and a temperature stability of $10^{-3}/°C$ for the IC alone. R_t is in kilohms and, for C_t in microfarads, t will be in microseconds. For values of $C_t < 1000$ pF the device parameters become important and t tends to independence of C_t. The 96L02 operates on $\frac{1}{5}$ the power and has 4 times the allowable range of R_t, while a Schottky version [M2] extends the timing range down to 30 ns.

An example of the verstile timer IC's is the LM322 shown in Fig. 5.3.4 [t2, r2, s2]. The circuit can be divided into a number of sections as shown in Fig. 5.3.4(b). The voltage regulator Q_{18-26} provides a reference voltage $V_{ref} = 3.15$ V, and the current sources Q_{27-31}, set by the constant current from Q_{23} through diode Q_{28}, supply the various parts of the circuit. The comparator Q_{11-17} compares the voltage across the timing capacitor C_t with the internal reference at the junction of R_{16} and R_{17}. This voltage is set at 2 V $=(1-1/e)$ 3.15 V so that the timing equation is just $\tau = R_t C_t$ (Sec. 1.4). (The comparator input bias current is very small (300 pA) so the drop across R_{15} is negligible.) When equality is detected, the comparator, via the logic and latch section Q_{4-10}, switches the floating output stage Q_{32-36}, the output current being limited by Q_{32} to about 120 mA. The floating output stage allows the system to drive ground or supply referred loads, using if desired a separate supply, up to 40 V. The logic also turns on the discharge transistor Q_1 which rapidly discharges C_t ready for the next cycle. The trigger input Q_{2-3} has a threshold of 1.6 V and triggers on positive inputs. It is locked-out after triggering and is protected to ± 40 V. If the trigger input is high when time-out occurs the output is switched as usual, but C_t is not discharged. The logic input allows the choice of whether the output stage is on (logic low) or off (logic high) during the timing interval, and has a threshold of only 150 mV.

The V_{adj} terminal allows variation of the internal comparator reference voltage, and this facility can be used to trim to a particular period, to provide timing variation over a range of $> 50:1$ [r2] or to reset the timer before time-out. In the latter application, a negative pulse or a level below the voltage on C_t, produces the same effect as if C_t had reached the normal switching point. However, as indicated above, if the trigger input is high at the time only the output switches, and C_t is not discharged. A similar reset action may be obtained with positive pulses at the R/C terminal, two possibilities being illustrated in Fig. 5.3.4(c).

To obtain the longest possible timing intervals, the comparator is operated at very low currents so as to minimize the input bias current. For short timing intervals greater currents are required in the comparator to enable faster transitions to be achieved. By connecting the boost terminal to V_+, the operating currents of $Q_{14,17}$ are increased substantially via Q_{30}, which is otherwise off. This allows minimum times of a few μs compared with about 1 ms in the unboosted condition. The longest period is of the order of hours, in which case due attention must be given to leakage both in C_t and anything in contact with the R/C pin.

A number of Schmitt trigger IC's are available, usually members of standard logic series. These include several TTL types [G1, M1], CMOS [N1, P1] and HLL [J2]. A precision type with high input impedance and large output current is described in [J1]. Very high input impedance can also be obtained by using standard CMOS gates [y1].

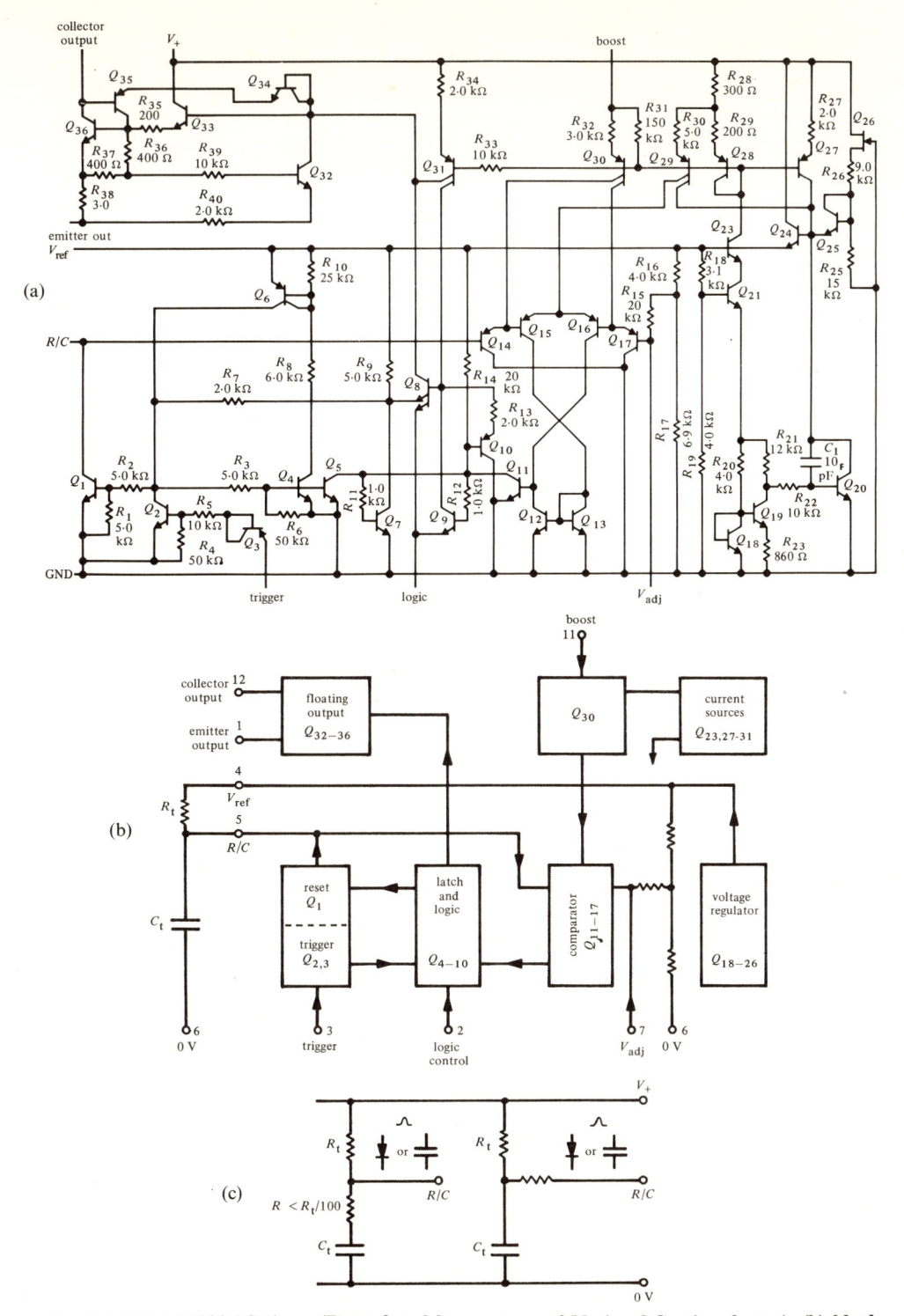

Fig. 5.3.4(a) LM322 IC timer (Reproduced by courtesy of National Semiconductor), (b) block diagram, (c) reset using R/C terminal

5.3(b) Unijunction transistor

The unijunction transistor (UJT) is a three terminal device which exhibits a region of current-controlled negative resistance. This allows the construction of very simple oscillators with a high current pulse output waveform, particularly suitable for triggering other devices. Figure 5.3.5 shows the unijunction, an equivalent circuit and a schematic characteristic curve [c1, b1, e1, f1, j1].

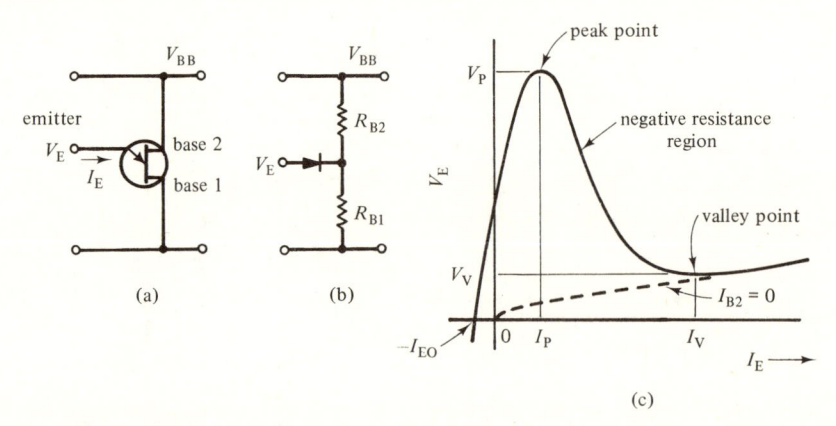

Fig. 5.3.5 (a) Unijunction transistor, (b) equivalent circuit, (c) characteristic curve

The region between base 1 and base 2 is resistive and is represented by $R_{B1} + R_{B2} = R_{BB}$. The ratio $R_{B1}/R_{BB} = \eta$, the intrinsic stand-off ratio, which lies between 0.5 and 0.85 in commercial devices. R_{BB} ranges between 5 kΩ and 10 kΩ, and the emitter has a P–N junction to the bases. The characteristic curve shown has been distorted for the sake of clarity. In practice, typical values are $I_{E0} \approx 5$ nA, $I_P \approx 1$ μA, $I_V \approx 3$ mA, $V_V \approx 1.5$ V. The peak point voltage depends on the applied voltage V_{BB} and the forward drop across the emitter–base diode V_J:

$$V_P = \eta V_{BB} + V_J \doteq 0.6 V_{BB} + 0.4 \text{ volt} \quad (5.3.2)$$

When $V_E = V_P$, the emitter diode starts conducting, injecting holes into the B_1 region. The increase in charge density causes R_{B1} to decrease, leading to the negative resistance region between I_P and I_V. Above this is the saturation region where I_{B2} may be neglected, and the characteristic approaches that of a simple P–N junction.

General considerations in the use of negative resistance devices are discussed in [c1, p1]. To produce an astable system the simple circuit of Fig. 5.3.6 can be used. Here R_1 and R_2 are small resistors and can be ignored for the present. The capacitor C_t charges up through R_t until $V_E = V_P$. If V_E just exceeds V_P then a rapid transition is made to a point depending on the load line, Fig. 5.3.6(b) [b1, c1].

Load line I does not allow V_P to be reached, so there will be no transition. Load line III leads to a stable state at P_3, and the unijunction remains conducting. This leads to maximum and minimum values for R_t:

$$R_{t(max)} < \frac{V_{BB} - V_P}{I_P}, \quad R_{t(min)} > \frac{V_{BB} - V_V}{I_V} \quad (5.3.3)$$

Load line II can also lead to a stable state at P_2, unless we consider the effect of the presence of C_t. This causes the dynamic operating path to be quite different from the characteristic curve. When the emitter starts conducting, E_E cannot fall immediately because of the charge on C_t. As I_E increases, V_E falls more rapidly and the operating path follows a curve somewhat as shown in Fig. 5.3.6(b). When the path meets the UJT characteristic it tries to follow it to P_2. This requires an increase in V_E which is resisted by the capacity of C_t, and the operating path continues as shown until it meets the UJT characteristic again in the cut-off region. This completes one cycle, and C_t starts charging via R_t for the next.

The peak current that can flow in the emitter–base 1 junction during discharge of C_t can be very large (maximum peak ratings ≈ 1 A), so that a small resistor R_1 of a few tens of ohms can give a large positive pulse at output 1. Since R_{B1} decreases

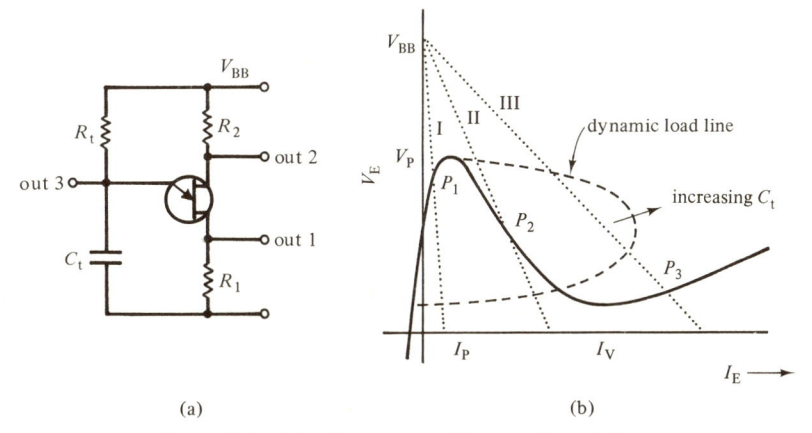

Fig. 5.3.6 (a) Unijunction oscillator, (b) load lines

during this period, the current I_{B2} will increase to I_{B2} (mod) (≈ 10 mA typically), so that a resistor R_2 of a few hundred ohms will give a negative pulse at output 2. The waveform at output 3 will be of the usual exponential sawtooth form. Frequencies up to about 100 kHz are obtainable with this circuit. A complementary unijunction is also available [h1].

The programmable unijunction transistor is of rather different internal construction, being a 4-layer *PNPN* structure, but it has the same characteristics as the standard type. The difference is that the parameters η, R_{BB}, I_P, and I_V can be set by means of two external resistors [g1, d1, l1, k1].

A tunnel diode has a characteristic of similar shape to the UJT, except that it is voltage rather than current controlled. Its particular advantage is its very high speed of operation since it switches in tens of picoseconds. Applications are rather specialized, so it will not be discussed here [c1, q1, i1, b1].

5.4 Crystal oscillators

Crystal oscillators are used to obtain greater frequency stability than can be obtained with conventional types. They use quartz crystal resonators which have high Q (up to $\approx 10^5$) and small frequency change with temperature. The range of frequencies is from a few hundred Hz to 100 MHz, but the most readily available fall in the range 50 kHz to 20 MHz. Popular frequencies are 100 kHz, 1 MHz, and 5 MHz. The equivalent circuit of a crystal and a response curve are shown in Fig. 5.4.1 [i1, g1, f1].

It is seen that there is a series (low impedance) resonance depending on L and C, and a parallel (high impedance) resonance depending on L, C, and C_o. The frequencies of these two resonances are quite close, say a few parts in 10^5. The crystal can be used in either mode, but the circuits will differ. When used in the series mode the crystal appears as a pure resistance at resonance, while in the parallel mode it will appear as inductive and resonate with the load capacity presented by the oscillator circuit. Thus, in the latter case, the frequency is lowered towards the series resonance. When

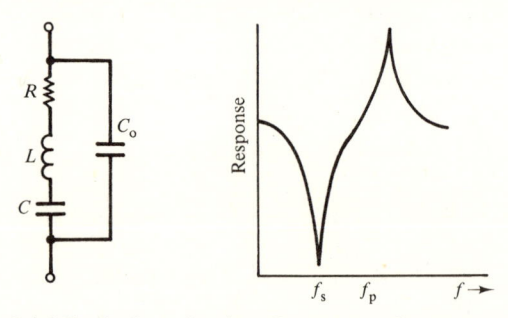

Fig. 5.4.1 Equivalent circuit and response of quartz crystal

specifying a crystal for a very precise frequency, therefore, it is necessary to say whether it is to be used in series or parallel and to state the load capacity. However, a small trimmer capacitor in series or parallel may be used to *pull* the frequency by up to about 1 part in 10^5. Phase shifts in the amplifier driving the crystal will also cause a change of frequency, since the resonator must then be slightly reactive to ensure the correct feedback phase to maintain oscillation. The properties of a balanced bridge as discussed in Sec. 5.1 are useful in this connection. A very high stability circuit, using this, is the Meacham Bridge oscillator [p1, q1].

A simple oscillator may be constructed using an appropriate amplifier with suitable gain at the frequency of interest. A comparator (Sec. 6.1) may be used since these are essentially wideband amplifiers, but internally compensated amplifiers are unsuitable because of phase shifts. The crystal is used as the positive feedback impedance, Fig. 5.4.2 [r1, a1, b1, j1, t1].

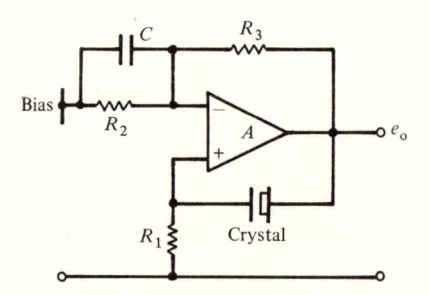

Fig. 5.4.2 Simple crystal oscillator (series resonance)

The positive feedback will be a maximum at series resonance of the crystal since it has minimum (resistive) impedance here. Negative feedback, due to R_3 and R_2, serves to stabilize the operating point and is only effective at d.c. and low frequencies, as a result of the bypass capacitor C. The bias is adjusted to set the mean output voltage, e_o, to the centre of the amplifier output swing to allow maximum symmetrical output. R_1 is chosen to give sufficient positive feedback depending on the crystal type (try 10 kΩ). It should not be too small, as this will load the amplifier output and allow excessive current in the crystal. The three resistors should be related in the usual way (Sec. 2.9(v)) to reduce the effect of offset currents.

Many crystal oscillator modules are available commercially [s1]. Some have built-in temperature compensation, and others produce square wave outputs suitable for driving logic systems.

References section 5.1: Sinusoidal RC oscillators

a1   Williams P: Wien Oscillators; Wireless World 77, 541–547, 1971.
b1   Fairchild: Application of the μA716 Fixed Gain Amplifier as a Wien-Bridge Oscillator; Fairchild Application Brief 45, 1967.
c1   Dobkin R: Easily Tuned Sine Wave Oscillators; National Semiconductor Linear Brief LB-16, 1971.
d1   Earls J C: Generation of Low Frequency Sinusoidal Voltages of Given Phase, Amplitude and Frequency by Means of a Two-Integrator Loop; J. Sci. Instrum. 39, 73–74, 1962.
e1   Owen R E: A Modern, Wide Range, RC Oscillator; General Radio Experimenter 39, Aug. 1965, 3–12.
f1   Strauss L: Wave Generation and Shaping; McGraw-Hill 1970.
g1   Oliver B M: The Effect of μ-Circuit Non-Linearity on the Amplitude Stability of RC Oscillators; Hewlett-Packard J 11, No.8–10, 1–8, 1960.
h1   Good E F: A Two-Phase Low Frequency Oscillator; Electronic Eng. 29, 164–169 and 210–213, 1957.
i1   Howe R M, Leite R J: A Low-Frequency Oscillator; Rev. Sci. Instrum. 24, 901–903, 1953.
j1   Owen R E: RC Oscillator Synchronisation; General Radio Experimenter 41, Feb. 1967, 3–11.
k1   Bailey A R: Low Distortion Sine-Wave Generator; Electronic Technology 37, Feb. 1960, 64.
l1   Philbrick/Nexus: Applications Manual for Operational Amplifiers; Philbrick/Nexus Research 1968, 68–73.
m1   Smith J I: Modern Operational Circuit Design; Wiley/Interscience 1971.
n1   Edson W A: Vacuum Tube Oscillators; Wiley 1953.
o1   SGS-Fairchild: The Application of Linear Microcircuits; SGS-Fairchild 1967.
p1   Mehta V B: Distortion in RC Bridge Feedback Oscillators; Electronic Eng. 39, Sep. 1967, 582–585.
q1   Mehta V B: Comparison of RC Networks for Frequency Stability in Oscillators; Proc IEEE 112, 296–300, 1965.
r1   Bernstein S: An Improved RC Bridge Circuit with High Selectivity; Electronic Eng. 38, May 1966, 288–293.
s1   Savant C J, Savant C A: Notch Network Design; Electronics 28, Sep. 1955, 172.
t1   Savant C J: Basic Feedback Control System Design; McGraw-Hill 1958. Appendix IX Design of Bridged and Parallel-T Networks.
u1   Vanderkooy J, Koch C J: Generate Low-Distortion Sinewaves; Electronic Design 21, 5 July 1973, 70–73.
v1   Foord A: Two-Phase Low-Frequency Oscillator; Electronic Eng. 46, Dec. 1974, 19, 21.
w1   Tucker D G: The History of Positive Feedback; Radio Electronic Engr. 42, 69–80, 1972.
x1   Hyde F J: Thermistors; Iliffe Books 1971.
y1   Ghausi M S: Electronic Circuits. Chapter 6 Feedback Amplifiers and Oscillators; Van Nostrand Reinhold 1971.

z1   Giddy J H: Transistor Wien Bridge Oscillators for 20c/s to 300kc/s; Mullard Technical Publication TP537.

A1   Darwood N: Continuous Sinewave Oscillator with Any Period; Electronic Eng. Apr. 1976, 29, 31.

References section 5.2: Function generators

a1   Cowan W T: Sweeping Four Decades at Low Frequencies; Hewlett-Packard J 19, No.9, May 1968, 2–7.

b1   Dudley R L: A Voltage Programmable Low-Frequency Function Generator with Plug-In Versatility; Hewlett-Packard J 17, No.3, Nov. 1965, 2–5.

c1   Dudley R L: The Trigger/Phase-Lock Plug In; Hewlett-Packard J 17, No.3, Nov. 1965, 6–9.

d1   Hanson R C: Compact Function Generator Covers 0.0005Hz to 5MHz; Hewlett-Packard J 20, No.10, June 1969, 10–13.

e1   Heflin E H: Compact Function Generator with Enhanced Capability/Cost Ratio; Hewlett-Packard J 24, No.11, July 1973, 15–20.

f1   Intersil: A Precision Waveform Generator and Voltage Controlled Oscillator (8038); Intersil Application Bulletin A012, Oct. 1972.

g1   Harris Semiconductor: A Simple Square-Triangle Waveform Generator; Electronic Eng. 44, Oct. 1972, 29.

h1   Bracho S, Civit A: Vary Both Slopes in Novel Triangle Generator; Electronic Eng. 45, Feb. 1973, 29.

i1   Fairchild: Five Decade, Current-Controlled Oscillator without External Capacitors (μA776); Fairchild Application Report.

j1   Signetics: Linear Phase-Locked Loops Applications Book; Signetics 1972, 37–38.

k1   Exact Electronics: Instruction Manual Model 7060 VCF/Sweep Generator; Exact Electronics 1972.

l1   Exar: Monolithic Waveform Generator XR-205; Exar Integrated Systems Data Sheet July 1972.

m1   Botos R A: A Low-Cost, Solid State Function Generator; Motorola Application Note AN-510, 1969.

n1   Unsworth P J: An Accurate Voltage-to-Frequency Converter; J Phys. E Sci. Instrum. 2, 407–410, 1969.

o1   Mann R: A Voltage Controlled Square Wave–Triangular Wave Generator; Texas Instruments Application Report B37, Jan. 1968.

p1   Bombi F: High Performance Voltage-to-Frequency Converter has Improved Linearity; Electronic Eng. 42, Dec. 1970, 61–64.

q1   Durcansky G, Matula S: Minimising Error in Fast V-F Converter; Electronic Eng. 44, May 1972, 35–37.

r1   Flynn A: Improving the Linearity of Voltage-to-Frequency Converter; Electronic Eng. 45, Apr. 1973, 22–23.

s1   Lindsay N M: Reducing Reset Errors in V-F Converters; Electronic Eng. 45, May 1973, 17.

t1   Civit A, Bracho S: ICs Simplify V-F and V-T Conversion; Electronic Eng. 43, Dec. 1971, 36–38.

u1   Hood R B: Simple 1% Voltage-to-Frequency Converter; Electronic Eng. 44, Dec. 1972, 36–37, also A Minimum Component μA749 Voltage-to-Frequency Converter with 1% Accuracy; Fairchild Application Brief APP-144, Feb. 1970.

v1   Bussolati C: A Linear Voltage-Controlled Oscillator; Fairchild Application Report AR-58, Apr. 1963.

w1   Sobajic M V, Veselinovic D I, Danilovic D Z: IGFETs Improve the Linearity of Bootstrap Sweep Generators; Electronic Eng. 45, May 1973, 63–65.

x1   Grzybowski W, Wagner F: Nonlinear Functions from Digital-to-Analogue Converters; Electronic Eng. July 1971, 48–51.

y1   Botos R A, Newmire L J: A Synchronously Gated N-Decade Sweep Oscillator; Motorola Application Note AN-540.

z1 Huehne K: Digital Waveform Synthesis; Semiconductors (Motorola) 4, No.1, 1973, 28–29, and Electron 28 Sep. 1972, 37–38.
A1 Powner E T, Green D H, Taylor G T: Digital Waveform Synthesis; Electronic Eng. 41, Aug. 1969, 50–54.
B1 Philbrick/Nexus: Applications Manual for Operational Amplifiers; Philbrick/Nexus Research 1968, 68–73.
C1 Tobey G E, Graeme J G, Huelsman L P: Operational Amplifiers: Design and Applications; McGraw-Hill 1971.
D1 Korytkowski J: Accurate Current-to-Frequency Converter; Electronic Eng. 39, 568–570, 1967.
E1 Smith K C, Sedra A: Simple Wide Band Linear Voltage to Frequency Converter; Electronic Eng. 40, 140–143, 1968.
F1 Ahad E, Smith K C: Frequency-to-Voltage Converter has Rapid Response to Frequency Changes; Electronic Eng. 43, July 1971, 42–46.
G1 Smith J I: Modern Operational Circuit Design; Wiley-Interscience 1971.
H1 Cadwallader M: Linear-Staircase Generator; Electronic Eng. 39, Nov. 1967, 682–685.
I1 Klein G, Hagenbeuk H: Accurate Triangle-Sine Converter; Electronic Eng. 39, Nov. 1967, 700–704.
J1 Klein G, Hagenbeuk H: An Accurate Triangular-Wave Generator with Large Frequency Sweep; Electronic Eng. 39, June 1967, 388–390.
K1 Ritchie C C, Young B W: The Design of Biased-Diode Function Generators; Electronic Eng. 31, 347–351, 1959.
L1 Burr-Brown: Low-Frequency Function Generator; Electronic Eng. 42, May 1970, 99.
M1 Piper J A, Sandle W J, Williams O M: A Simple Saturation Amplifier to Produce 2A, 100V, 40ns Rise-Time Pulses; J Phys. E Sci. Instrum. 2, 903–905, 1969.
N1 MacLennan D N, Wells F H: A Wide Range Digitizer for Direct Coupled Analogue Signals; J Phys. E Sci. Instrum. 1, 284–288, 1968.
O1 Taylor D J: A Current-to-Frequency Converter for Astronomical Photometry; Rev. Sci. Instrum. 40, 559–562, 1969.
P1 Miler G: Simple Function Generator; Electronic Components 11 Dec. 1973, 17.
Q1 Andersen R A: A Voltage-to-Frequency Converter for Greater Flexibility in Data Handling; Hewlett-Packard J 12, Oct. 1960, 1–6.
R1 Kurahashi Y: Less than 1.5% Distortion Over 1000:1 Range Provided by Swept-Frequency Oscillator; Electronic Design 22, 4 Jan. 1974, 154.
S1 Texas Instruments: A Precision Triangular Function Generator using Programmable Counters; Texas Instruments Applications Brief B143.
T1 Texas Instruments: The SN74S124 TTL Compatible Voltage Controlled Oscillator; Texas Instruments Applications Brief B145.
U1 Shapiro E G: Linear Seven-Decade Current/Voltage-to-Frequency Converter; IEEE Trans NS-17, 335–344, 1970.
V1 Karlovac N: Logarithmic Ratemeter Response to a Step Change in Frequency; Rev. Sci. Instrum. 43, 1540–1541, 1972.
W1 Rochelle J M, Kennedy E J: Miniaturized Logarithmic Count-Rate Circuit; Rev. Sci. Instrum. 44, 1638–1642, 1973.
X1 Ross P J: A Simple, Accurate Voltage to Frequency Converter; J Phys. E Sci. Instrum. 7, 706–707, 1974.
Y1 Griffing B: A High Voltage Pulse Generator for Acoustoelectric Studies; Rev. Sci. Instrum. 45, 964–965, 1974.
Z1 Tyler I L, Denenstein A, Langenberg D N: Infinite-Hold-Time Electric Ramp Generator; Rev. Sci. Instrum. 45, 1007–1008, 1974.
a2 Minnis T: Accurate 10MHz Reference Obtained from Counter's 1MHz Internal Standard; Electronic Design 1 Sep. 1974, 98.
b2 Dobkin R C: Precise Tri-Wave Generation; National Semiconductor Linear Brief LB-23, June 1973.
c2 Tribolet J-P: Original Sawtooth Generator; Electronic Eng. 44, Dec. 1972, 40.
d2 Hood R B: Simple 1% Voltage-to-Frequency Converter; Electronic Eng. 44, Dec. 1972, 36–37.

e2 Sample P: The Frequency Synthesizer as a Signal Generator; Electronic Eng. 46, Dec. 1974, 39–43.

f2 Huehne K: Generate Custom Waveforms Digitally; Motorola Application Note AN-589, 1972.

g2 Tierney J, Rader C M, Gold B: A Digital Frequency Synthesizer; IEEE Trans AU-19, 48–56, 1971.

h2 Ginstrup O: An Exponential Current Generator; IEEE Trans IM-22, 222–225, 1973.

i2 Cohen D, Tiroshi I, Eylon S: High-Speed Frequency-to-Voltage Converter with 0.01% Accuracy; IEEE Trans IM-22, 108–113, 1973.

j2 Zuch E L: How to Use a Universal Voltage-to-Frequency Converter; New Electronics 21 Jan. 1975, 24, 25, 27, 28, 33.

k2 Riedel R J, Danielson D D: The Dual Function Generator: A Source of a Wide Variety of Test Signals; Hewlett-Packard J 26, Mar. 1975, 18–24.

l2 Teledyne Philbrick: Need a 1kHz Full Scale V-F?; Teledyne Philbrick Bulletin AN-2, Jan. 1974.

m2 Teledyne Philbrick: Magnitude Plus Sign ADC Using a V-to-F Converter; Teledyne Philbrick Bulletin AN-6.

n2 Teledyne Philbrick: V-F's as Long-Term Integrators; Teledyne Philbrick Bulletin AN-9, Jan. 1974.

o2 Teledyne Philbrick: V-F's, F-V's and Audio Tape Recorders; Teledyne Philbrick Bulletin AN-11.

p2 Pease R A: Voltage-to-Frequency Module Serves Diverse Applications; Teledyne Philbrick Application Note AN-1.

q2 Graeme J: Use V/F Converters for Analog Data Transmission; Electronic Design 1 Apr. 1975, 110–114.

r2 Zuch E L: Voltage-to-Frequency Converters: Versatility Now at Low Cost; Electronics 48, 15 May 1975, 91–95.

s2 Wills L J, Denby E F: Logarithmic Time Base Generator; Rev. Sci. Instrum. 46, 1030–1031, 1975.

t2 Mellor D J, Woodcraft C P: Field Generator for a Monopole Mass Spectrometer; J Phys. E Sci. Instrum. 4, 1084–1085, 1970.

u2 Limuti D: Pulse Amplifier can Deliver Over 500V with Frequencies to 100kHz; Electronic Design 27 Sep. 1973, 102.

v2 Milne R, Maas P: A Digital Very Low Frequency Function Generator; J Phys. E Sci. Instrum. 8, 863–865, 1975.

w2 Exar: Monolithic Function Generator XR-2206C; Exar Integrated Systems Data and Application Sheet June 1974.

x2 Exar: Multi-Function Integrated Circuit XR-S200; Exar Integrated Systems Data and Application Sheet June 1974.

y2 Frederiksen T M, Howard W M, Sleeth R S: The LM3900—A New Current Differencing Quad of +/− Input Amplifiers; National Semiconductor Application Note AN-72, Sep. 1972, 18–25.

z2 Millman J, Taub H: Pulse, Digital and Switching Waveforms; McGraw-Hill 1965.

A2 Jenks E, Powner E T: Digital Waveform Synthesis; IEE Conference Publication 106, Digital Instrumentation, 1973, 49–55.

B2 Sheingold D H: Nonlinear Circuits Handbook; Analog Devices 1974.

C2 Moran P L: A Phase Continuous Programmable Oscillator; Microelectronics 7, 40–44, 1975.

D2 O'Neill W: Waveform Generator Chips Help the Circuit Designer (8038); Electronics 20 Nov. 1972, 123–124.

E2 Hewlett-Packard: Frequency Synthesizers; Hewlett-Packard Application Note 96, Jan. 1969.

F2 O'Neill W: Everything You Always Wanted to Know About the 8038; Intersil Application Bulletin A013, May 1973.

G2 Intersil: Precision Waveform Generator/Voltage Controlled Oscillator 8038; Intersil Data Sheet Dec. 1972 (Earlier issues in error).

H2 Pouliot F: Have You Considered V/F Converters?; Analog Dialogue 9, No.3, 1975, 6–9.

I2   O'Neill W: Waveform Generator Chips Help the Circuit Designer (8038): Electronics 20 Nov. 1972, 123–124.

J2   Bruggink G: Triangle-Wave Generator has High Accuracy; Electronic Eng. June 1976, 32.

K2   Armstrong D R, Katzir A, Yariv A: Fast, High-Current Pulse Generator with Variable Amplitude and Width; Rev. Sci. Instrum. 47, 767–769, 1976.

References section 5.3a: Multivibrators

a1   Tucker M J, Hunter C A: A Stable Very Low-Frequency Multivibrator; Electronic Eng. 41, Sep. 1969, 37–39.

b1   Beneteau P J, Blaser L: A Simple Method of Temperature Stabilizing Monostable Multivibrators; Fairchild Application Report AR-33, 1961.

c1   Alderisio P, Evangelisti A: A Fast Switching Emitter-Coupled Astable Multivibrator; Fairchild Application Report AR170, 1966.

d1   Millman J, Taub H: Pulse, Digital and Switching Waveforms; McGraw-Hill 1965.

e1   Dean J A, Rupley J P: Astable and Monostable Oscillators Using RCA COS/MOS Digital Integrated Circuits; RCA Application Note ICAN-6267 and RCA Data Book SSD-203, 207–214, 1972.

f1   Gray T, Anderson J, Walker R: The 9601, a Second Generation Retriggerable One-Shot; Fairchild Application Note APP-173, Mar. 1969.

g1   Byers C: Fast Monostable Multivibrators Using ECL Gates; Electron 27 July 1972, 17–18.

h1   Brown J P: IC Monostables can be Economical; Electronic Eng. 44, Apr. 1972, 30–33.

i1   Lyons W, Whitworth H: Compact 5MHz True Double Pulse Generator Incorporating ICs; Design Electronics Jan. 1971, 69–71, 103.

j1   Exar: XR-220/320 Monolithic Timing Circuit; Exar Integrated Systems Data Sheet Sep. 1972.

k1   Signetics: Some Devices Based on a Monolithic Timing Circuit; New Electronics 6 June 1972, 24–25.

l1   Signetics: Novel Timer IC for Only 85p; Electronic Eng. 44, Dec. 1972, 75.

m1   Trotman D: Timer Microcircuit Makes Useful Pulse Generator; Electronic Components 9 Mar. 1973, 211–212, and 274.

n1   Signetics: Applications of the SE/NE555 Timer; Signetics Application Note.

o1   Motorola: MC1455 Timing Circuit; Motorola Data Sheet 1973.

p1   De Kold D: IC Timer Plus Thermistor can Control Temperature (555); Electronics 21 June 1973, 128–129.

q1   Robbins M S: IC Timer's Duty Cycle Can Stretch Over 99% (555); Electronics 21 June 1973, 129.

r1   Orrel S A: IC Timer Plus Resistor can Produce Square Waves (555); Electronics 21 June 1973, 130.

s1   McGowan E J: IC Timer Automatically Monitors Battery Voltage (555); Electronics 21 June 1973, 130–131.

t1   Harvey M L: Pair of IC Timers Sounds Auto Burglar Alarm (555); Electronics 21 June 1973, 131.

u1   De Kold D: IC Timer Converts Temperature to Frequency (555); Electronics 21 June 1973, 131–132.

v1   Pate J G: IC Timer can Function as a Low-Cost Line Receiver (555); Electronics 21 June 1973, 132.

w1   Mattera L: IC Timers Make the Most of Delay (555); Electronics 21 June 1973, 142–143.

x1   Exar: XR-2556 Dual Timing Circuit; Exar Integrated Systems Data Sheet May 1973.

y1   Halloran J: A Schmitt Trigger with CMOS Gates; Electronic Components 14 Sep. 1973, 724–725, Electron 3 May 1973, 37.

z1   Parsons R, Slomkowski J: Applications of the SN74121N TTL IC Monostable; Texas Instruments Application Report B50, 1968.

A1   Texas Instruments: Type SN74121N High Performance TTL Monostable; Texas Instruments Report 1968.

B2 RCA: COS/MOS Low Power Monostable/Astable Multivibrator CD4047; RCA Data Sheet 1972.

C1 Motorola: Dual Voltage-Controlled Multivibrator MC4324/4024P; Motorola Data Sheet Apr. 1970.

D1 Motorola: Dual Retriggerable/Resetable Monostable Multivibrator MC14528CP; Motorola Data Sheet 1972.

E1 Elremco: LR171E Linear/Digital LSI Timing Integrated Circuit, and Applications and Design Data List 171F; Electrical Remote Control Co., 1973.

F1 SGS/Fairchild: The Application of Linear Microcircuits; SGS/Fairchild 1967.

G1 Parsons R: Characteristics and Applications of the SN7413N Dual Schmitt Trigger; Texas Instruments Application Report B81, 1969.

H1 Calvin T J, Greiner R A, Swift W B: Switching Levels in Transistor Schmitt Circuits; IRE Trans 1–9, 309–313, 1960.

I1 Brown J P: Practical Approach Simplifies IC Oscillator Design; Electronic Eng. 44, Nov. 1972, 76–78.

J1 General Electric: Precision Threshold Detector with Hysterisis PA494; General Electric Data Sheet 1970.

K1 Motorola: Emitter-Coupled Oscillator MC1684; Motorola Data Sheet 1972.

L1 RCA: COS/MOS Integrated Circuits Manual (Astable and Monostable Oscillators 108–122); RCA Technical Series CMS-270, 1971.

M1 Texas Instruments: Schmitt-Trigger Positive-Nand Gates and Inverters, SN7413 Dual 4-Input, SN7414 Quad 2-Input, SN74132 Hex Inverter; Texas Instruments Data Sheets.

N1 Motorola: Dual Schmitt Trigger MC14583; Motorola Data Sheet 1973.

O1 National Semiconductor: Dual Schmitt Trigger MM74C13; National Semiconductor Data Sheet 1973.

P1 National Semiconductor: Dual Monostable Multivibrator MM74C123; National Semiconductor Data Sheet 1973.

Q1 National Semiconductor: LM375 Oscillator and Buffer with TTL Output; National Semiconductor Data Sheet 1972.

R1 Potton A: An Introduction to Digital Logic; Macmillan 1973.

S1 Metz A J, Howard R H: True Random Ratemeter with Automatic Dead-Time Correction for Duty Factors up to 99%; Rev. Sci. Instrum. 40, 16–20, 1969.

T1 Signetics: Dual Solid-State Timer NE556; New Electronics 5 Feb. 1974, 13, 16, 17.

U1 Marconero R, Pallotino G V: Wide-Range Current-to-Frequency Converter; Electronic Eng. 40, May 1968, 264–266.

V1 Smith-Saville R J, Ness S: Charge Feedback Increases Pulse-Rate Meter Accuracy; Electronics 7 Feb. 1966, 85–86.

W1 Exar: XR-2240 Programmable Timer/Counter; Exar Integrated Systems Data Sheet and Application Notes, Nov. 1973.

X1 Grebene A B: Which IC Timer to Buy?; Electronic Design 1 Feb. 1974, 62–66.

Y1 ITT: Universal Pulse Generator MIC74124; ITT Semiconductors Data Sheet Aug. 1972.

Z1 Mitchell K: A Versatile Universal Pulse Generator Monolithic Integrated Circuit 74124; New Electronics 5 Feb. 1974, 32, 33, 35, 36.

a2 ITT: Cut Down on Logic Devices with Versatile Pulse Generator MIL74124; Electronic Eng. 44, Nov. 1972, 23.

b2 Texas Instruments: Dual Voltage-Controlled Oscillators SN74S124; Texas Instruments Data Sheet.

c2 Exar: Voltage Controlled Oscillator XR-2307; Exar Integrated Systems Data Sheet 1973.

d2 Mostek: MOS counter Time-Base Circuit MK5009P; Mostek Data Sheet Oct. 1973.

e2 Mostek: Using the MK5009P MOS Counter Time-Base Circuit; Mostek Application Note AN-104, Oct 1972, New Electronics 28 May 1974, 31–32.

f2 Alex T K: Frequency Doubler Covers Wide Frequency Range for Unsymmetric Square Waves; Electronic Design 2 Aug. 1974, 114, 116.

g2 Siliconix: FETs in Solid-State Timers; Siliconix Application Note File 104, May 1965.

h2 Microsystems International: The Operational Amplifier as a Relaxation Oscillator; Microsystems International Application Note 1974.

i2 Alfke P, Larsen I (Eds): The TTL Applications Handbook, Chapter 13 Monostable Multivibrators; Fairchild Aug. 1973.

j2 Davis W F, Frederiksen T M: A Precision Monolithic Time-Delay Generator for use in Automotive Electronic Fuel Injection Systems; IEEE J SC-7, 462–469, 1972.

k2 Hoover M V, Packover P A, Jones H: High-Accuracy Long-Period Timer; New Electronics 10 June 1975, 18, 20.

l2 Aldridge D, Mouton A: Industrial Clock/Timer Featuring Back-Up Power Supply Operation; Motorola Application Note AN-718A, 1974.

m2 Ponting I: Milliseconds to Months (LR171E); Electron 3 Jan. 1974, 23–25.

n2 Blandford D J: A COS/MOS Schmitt Trigger Circuit (CD4093B); New Electronics 11 Nov. 1975, 50, 52, 54.

o2 Analog Devices: Low Cost, High Performance, 10/20kHz Voltage to Frequency Converters Models 450, 454, 456; Analog Devices Data Sheet 1975.

p2 Intersil: Programmable Timers/Counters 8240, 8250, 8260; Intersil Data Sheet Aug. 1975.

q2 Ghausi M S: Electronic Circuits. Devices, Models, Functions, Analysis, and Design, Chapter 6 Feedback Amplifiers and Oscillators, Chapter 10 Regenerative, Switching, and Wave Shaping Circuits; Van Nostrand Reinhold 1971.

r2 Dance J B: Accurate Long Period Analogue Timers (LM322N); Electronic Components 10 Sep. 1974, 13.

s2 Nelson C: Versatile Timer Operates from Microseconds to Hours (LM122/322); National Semiconductor Application Note AN-97, Dec. 1973.

t2 National Semiconductor: LM122/LM222/LM322 Precision Timer; National Semiconductor Data Sheet Apr. 1973.

u2 Heath F R: Low Cost Precision Timing (ZN1034E); Electronics Industry Nov. 1975, 42.

v2 Signetics: Quad Timer 553/554; Signetics Data Sheet.

w2 Texas Instruments: General Purpose Monostable/Tachodriver SN76810P; Texas Instruments Data Sheet Oct. 1971.

x2 Stewart-Warner: Tachometer Driver SW780; Stewart-Warner Data Sheet Feb. 1971.

y2 National Semiconductor: LM3909 LED Flasher/Oscillator; National Semiconductor Data Sheet Jan. 1975.

z2 Delaney C F G: Electronics for the Physicist, Chapter 7 Circuits with Positive Feedback; Penguin Books 1969.

A2 Ghausi M S: Electronic Circuits. Chapter 10 Regenerative, Switching, and Wave Shaping Circuits; Van Nostrand Reinhold 1971.

B2 Markus J (Ed): Electronic Circuits Manual. Chapter 89 Timer Circuits; McGraw-Hill 1971.

C2 Bockstahler R W: Bistable Action of 555 Varies with Manufacturer; Electronics 19 Feb. 1976, 131.

D2 Sherrod P: Comparator Circuit Makes Versatile Schmitt Trigger; Electronics 19 Feb. 1976, 128–129.

E2 Strauss L: Wave Generation and Shaping; McGraw-Hill 1970.

F2 Philips/Mullard: Revolution Counter SAK140; Philips/Mullard Data Sheet July 1974.

G2 SGS: One-Shot Multivibrator H117 (High Level Logic); SGS Data Sheet Mar. 1971.

H2 Penttinen A: Pulse Generator with Linearly Changing Frequency; Electronic Eng. 48, Apr. 1976, 25.

I2 Walter D J: Integrated Circuit Systems; Iliffe 1971.

J2 Teledyne: HiNIL Quad Schmitt Trigger 367; Teledyne Data Sheet Dec. 1972.

K2 Siemens: Schwellwertschalter TCA105 (Threshold Switch); Siemens Data Sheet.

L2 Texas Instruments: Precision Level Detectors SN72560/72D560; Texas Instruments Data Sheet.

M2 Advanced Micro Devices: Dual Retriggerable, Resettable Schottky Monostable Multivibrator Am26S02; Advanced Micro Devices Data Sheet.

N2 National Semiconductor: Dual CMOS Monostable Multivibrator MM74C123; National Semiconductor Data Sheet 1973.

O2 Fairchild: Dual TTL IC Retriggerable Resettable Monostable Multivibrator 9602; Fairchild Data Sheet.

P2   Delhom L A: The Field-Effect Transistor in a Schmitt Trigger Circuit; Texas Instruments Application Report C30, 1968.
Q2   Morrison J M: Op. Amp. Increases RC Time Constants; Electronic Eng. June 1972, 62–63.
R2   Tuthill R D: Schmitt Trigger Design with Op Amps; Wireless World July 1976, 32–33.
S2   National Semiconductor: Tachometer-Speed Switch LM2907/2917; National Semiconductor Data Sheet Feb. 1976.
T2   Blandford D J: Applications of the RCA-CD4093B COS/MOS Schmitt Trigger; RCA Application Note ICAN-6346, 1975.
U2   RCA: Programmable Schmitt Trigger CA3098; RCA Data Sheet 1975.

References section 5.3b: Unijunction oscillators

a1   Motorola: Unijunction Transistor Timers and Oscillators; Motorola Application Report AN-294, 1972.
b1   Cleary J F (Ed): Transistor Manual (7th Edn.) Chapter 13 Unijunction Circuits; General Electric 1964.
c1   Millman J, Taub H: Pulse, Digital and Switching Waveforms; McGraw-Hill 1965.
d1   Coers G: Programmable Unijunction Transistors; Texas Instruments Application Report CA-169, Oct. 1972.
e1   Crawford R H, Dean R T: The How and Why of Unijunction Transistors; Texas Instruments Application Report CA-68, Mar. 1969.
f1   Pamplin B F: Unijunction Transistors—How to Use Them; Electronic Components Jan. 1967, 59–63.
g1   General Electric: Programmable Unijunction Transistor D13T1/2; General Electric Data Sheet 1967.
h1   General Electric: Complementary Unijunction Transistor D5K1; General Electric Data Sheet 1967.
i1   Lowry H R, Giorgis J, Gottlieb E, Weischedel R C: Tunnel Diode Manual; General Electric 1961.
j1   Norris B (Ed): Semiconductor Circuit Design, Chapter VI Unijunction Transistors Theory, Operation and Circuits; Texas Instruments 1972.
k1   Coers G: Programmable Unijunction Transistors; New Electronics 6 Mar. 1973, 23, 25.
l1   Haver R J, Shiner B C: Theory, Characteristics and Applications of the Programmable Unijunction Transistor (MPU131–3); Motorola Application Report AN-527, 1971.
m1   Greiter O: The Unijunction Transistor; Wireless World 77, July 1970, 333–336.
n1   Hoberman S: Understanding and Using Unijunction Transistors; Foulsham-Sams Technical Books 1969.
o1   Delaney C F G: Electronics for the Physicist. Chapter 7 Circuits with Positive Feedback; Penguin Books 1969.
p1   Strauss L: Wave Generation and Shaping; McGraw-Hill 1970.
q1   Smith-Saville R J: Variable Frequency Tunnel Diode Relaxation Oscillator; Nuc. Instrum. Meth. 55, 120–124, 1967.
r1   Spofford W R: Applications for the New Low Cost TD700 Series Tunnel Diodes; General Electric Application Note 90.66, 1967.
s1   Todd C D: Measurement of Tunnel Diode Negative Resistance; Rev. Sci. Instrum. 32, 338–342, 1961.
t1   Gottlieb E: Tunnel Diode Sinewave Oscillators; General Electric Application Note 90.33, 1965.
u1   RCA: Tunnel Diode Manual; RCA Technical Manual TD-30, 1963.

References section 5.4: Crystal oscillators

a1   Eaton S S: Micropower Crystal-Controlled Oscillator Design Using COS/MOS Inverters; RCA Application Note ICAN-6539.
b1   Byers C: IC Crystal Controlled Oscillators; Motorola Application Note AN-417, 1968.
c1   Metcalf W S: Crystal Frequency Control: Electron 28 Sep. 1972, 15–17.

d1   Motorola: A 200MHz Crystal Oscillator with ECL Gates; Electronic Components 28 July 1972, 721.

e1   Page P B: Wide Range Temperature Compensation of Miniature Quartz Crystal Oscillators; Electronic Components 14 Jan. 1972, 21, 24–26, 5 May 1972, 429–431.

f1   — —: Guide to the Specification and Use of Quartz Oscillator Crystals; Radio Communication and Electronic Engineering Association.

g1   Fairweather D, Richards R C: Quartz Crystals as Oscillators and Resonators; Marconi Ltd.

h1   Smith W L: Miniature Transistorized Crystal-Controlled Precision Oscillators; IRE Trans 1–9, 1–8, 1960.

i1   Gerber E A, Sykes R A: State of the Art—Quartz Crystal Units and Oscillators; Proc IEEE 54, 103–116, 1966.

j1   RCA: COS/MOS Integrated Circuits Manual; RCA Technical Series CMS-270, 1971.

k1   Motorola: Crystal Oscillator MC12060/1; Motorola Data Sheet 1974.

l1   Hewlett-Packard: Fequency Synthesizers; Hewlett-Packard Application Note 96, Jan. 1969.

m1   Althouse J: IC Timer, Stabilized by Crystal, Can Provide Subharmonic Frequencies; Electronic Design 8 Nov. 1974, 148.

n1   Driscoll M M: Two-Stage Self-Limiting Series Mode Type Quartz-Crystal Oscillator Exhibiting Improved Short-Term Frequency Stability; IEEE Trans IM-22, 130–138, 1973.

o1   Driscoll M M, Healey D J: Voltage-Controlled Crystal Oscillators; IEEE Trans ED-18, 528–535, 1971.

p1   Straus L: Wave Generation and Shaping; McGraw-Hill 1970.

q1   Edson W A: Vacuum Tube Oscillators; Wiley 1953.

r1   SGS/Fairchild: The Application of Linear Microcircuits; SGS/Fairchild 1967.

s1   Oscillator Modules: Cathodeon Crystals, Salford Electrical Instruments, Marconi, Mullard.

t1   National Semiconductor: LM375 Oscillator and Buffer with TTL Output; National Semiconductor Data Sheet 1972.

u1   Delaney C F G: Electronics for the Physicist; Penguin Books 1969.

v1   Matistic A S: Quartz-Crystal Timing Accuracy is Hard to Beat; Electronic Design 19 Jan. 1976, 74–79.

w1   Bajeu G: Design Transistor Oscillators with Either Bipolar or Field-Effect Transistors, Using Admittance Data from Spec Sheets; Electronic Design 12 Apr. 1976, 98–102.

x1   Noble F W: Need an Adjustable Crystal Oscillator?; Electronic Design 29 Mar. 1976, 88–90.

6 Circuit functions

6.1 Comparators and discriminators

6.1(a) *Comparators*

Comparators are designed to compare the magnitude of two signals, the output being in one of two well-defined states depending on whether one signal is greater or less than the other. The comparison takes account of the sign so that $+V$, or even zero, is greater than $-V$. Both input signals may be varying, or one may be a pre-selected reference level. The two output states may be more or less well defined by the active circuit, but it is often necessary or desirable to define these more sharply by means of external components [j1, k1, g1, l1, i1].

The basic differential input operational amplifier will perform the comparator function, where the system is used open-loop to obtain sensitivity and discrimination (Fig. 6.1.1).

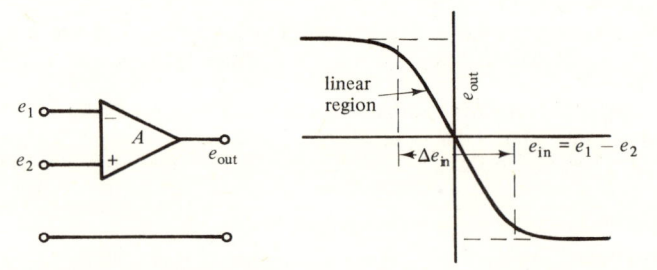

Fig. 6.1.1 Differential amplifier as a comparator, with transfer function

When e_1 is more positive than e_2, e_{out} will be at its negative limit, and vice versa. When $e_1 \doteq e_2$ there will be a small range of $e_1 - e_2$ where this is linearly related to e_{out}. The smaller the range Δe_{in} of the linear regime the better the discrimination of the comparator: the steeper the slope the greater the sensitivity. It is clear that the two are related through the maximum output voltage. Although the output levels are shown equal, and they would often be for many operational amplifiers, they may be made any convenient value. A common figure for open-loop gain in IC amplifiers is, say, 10^5, so for an $e_{o(max)}$ of 10 V, the range $\Delta e_{in} = 200\ \mu\text{V}$, and for inputs of a few volts the discrimination would be about 1 part in 10^4. This ignores the existence of amplifier input drift which is important at these levels (see Sec. 2.9).

Although a differential input is shown in Fig. 6.1.1, a single input amplifier could be used (Fig. 6.1.2). If there is no feedback loop to maintain a virtual ground the system would operate, but there would be interaction between the two signals. By providing a feedback path the virtual ground will (ideally) ensure that the two signals do not interact, and at the same time the feedback circuit can set the output levels.

A disadvantage of this circuit is that the reference signal must be inverted, i.e., e_1 and e_2 must have opposite polarities, otherwise the effective input cannot change sense. Assume e_1 is positive and e_2 is negative. The currents i_1 and i_2 will then flow as shown. As long as $i_1 \neq i_2$ a current i must flow. e_{out} will be at one of the limits set by the limit circuit, depending on the sense of i. The virtual ground will be maintained by the feedback and there will be no interaction between e_1 and e_2. For $i_1 \doteq i_2$ the circuit will be in the linear region, the limit circuit will be inoperative ($i=0$), and the system will be operating open-loop, so there will be no virtual ground. However, the difference between i_1 and i_2 over which this holds is very small for a high gain, A, so that there

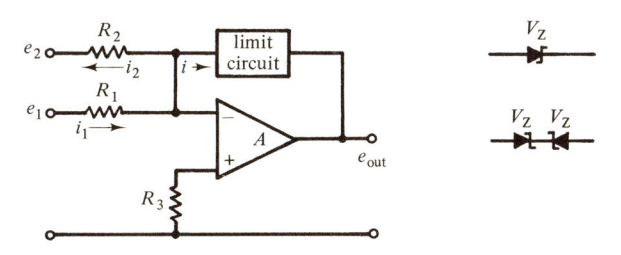

Fig. 6.1.2 Virtual ground comparator with limiter

is still little interaction between the two inputs. The comparison, thus, occurs when $i_1 = i_2$, i.e., when:

$$\frac{e_1}{R_1} = \frac{e_2}{R_2}, \quad \text{or} \quad e_1 = \frac{R_1}{R_2} \cdot e_2 \qquad (6.1.1)$$

This relation makes it simple to scale a fixed reference voltage to suit requirements. It may be noted that the same types of limit circuit may equally well be applied in Fig. 6.1.1 to fix the output levels independently of those of A alone. If the reference voltage is zero, the comparator is sometimes referred to as a zero-crossing detector, but this term will here be used for a more particular application; Sec. 6.1(d).

6.1(b) *Hysteresis*

A difficulty often arises when one or both the inputs are slowly varying functions of time. Because of the fine discrimination, noise on either of the signals can cause undesired switching of the output when in or near the linear region. Unless this can be removed by filtering it is usual to introduce some hysteresis into the circuit, so that the switching point depends on the direction from which it is approached. This is illustrated in Fig. 6.1.3.

The hysteresis is obtained by introducing a small amount of positive feedback via R_f and R_i. As shown, with R_i connected to ground, the nominal reference voltage is zero. With e_1 negative (point a on the transfer curve), e_{out} will be at the positive limit e_{out}^+. Since the negative feedback is operative, the differential input voltage $e_{in} \to 0$, so that the comparator input voltages V are equal, $V_{(-)} = V_{(+)}$, so:

$$e_{out}^+ - V_L^+ = \frac{e_{out}^+ R_i}{R_i + R_f}, \quad \text{or} \quad e_{out}^+ = \frac{V_L^+(R_i + R_f)}{R_f} \qquad (6.1.2)$$

Therefore, the voltage at the comparator inputs are:

$$V_{(-)} = V_{(+)} = \frac{e_{\text{out}}^+ R_i}{R_i + R_f} = V_L^+ \frac{R_i}{R_f} \qquad (6.1.3)$$

Switchover takes place when $i_1 = 0$, i.e., when the negative feedback is no longer operative. This will occur when $e_1 = V_{(-)} = e_h^+$ (point c on the transfer curve):

$$e_h^+ = V_L^+ \frac{R_i}{R_f} \qquad (6.1.4)$$

The positive feedback now takes control and switches the output rapidly to the negative limit (point d). It is important that the transfer be aperiodic (pole on the

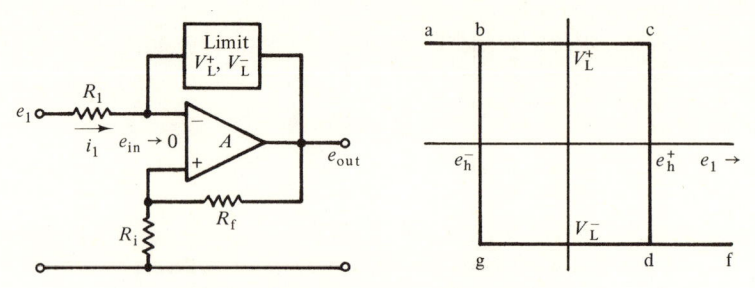

Fig. 6.1.3 Comparator with hysteresis

positive σ axis: see Sec. 1.11 and Fig. 1.11.5) as otherwise oscillations may occur (see Sec. 3.2 and Fig. 3.2.4). Further increase of e_1 produces no change (point f).

If e_1 is now decreased there will be no effect until point g is reached. Then, as above, but with the output at e_{out}^- and the V_L^- limit operating:

$$e_{\text{out}}^- = V_L^- \frac{(R_i + R_f)}{R_f} \quad \text{and} \quad e_h^- = V_L^- \frac{R_i}{R_f} \qquad (6.1.5)$$

Again, the positive feedback carries the system rapidly to point b. The total hysteresis is, thus:

$$e_h = e_h^+ - e_h^- = \frac{R_i(V_L^+ - V_L^-)}{R_f} \qquad (6.1.6)$$

The hysteresis, in principle, can be reduced to zero to have only a fast transition, but two limitations arise: instability of gain and oscillation during transitions. It is instructive to consider the variation of response as a function of positive feedback. For this configuration put $-A$ for A in Eq. (2.2.6) and the gain is given by:

$$G = \frac{+A}{1 - A\beta} \qquad (6.1.7)$$

If the loop-gain $L = A\beta$ is <1, then the gain $G > A$ but still finite. The transfer curve will be similar to that shown in Fig. 6.1.1, only steeper (Fig. 6.1.4).

When $L = 1$, $G = \infty$ and the transfer curve has infinite slope in the active region. The output changeover is now independent of the rate of input change, and the hysteresis is zero. If $L > 1$ the slope changes sign, and the Z-shaped transfer curve results. The sloping segment is not attainable as all points on it are unstable, the output making one or other of the vertical transitions as before. Although a fair approximation is possible it is practically impossible to ensure that L will always remain exactly equal to unity, so the hysteresis cannot be kept equal to zero. In practice, it is desirable to operate with $L > 1$.

As the feedback is positive, the system will oscillate in the transition region unless suitable conditions are arranged. A two pole system is aperiodic, and a three pole system can be aperiodic (see Sec. 3.2). Available IC comparators, generally, do not have accessible compensation points, so little can be done in this respect. In any case, the position of any poles is directly dependent on the loop-gain, Eq. (3.2.2), and this can vary from zero to the nominal value as a result of the curvature of the transfer characteristic (Fig. 6.1.1). In the case of the Z characteristic the corners are still rounded, so that the same problem arises.

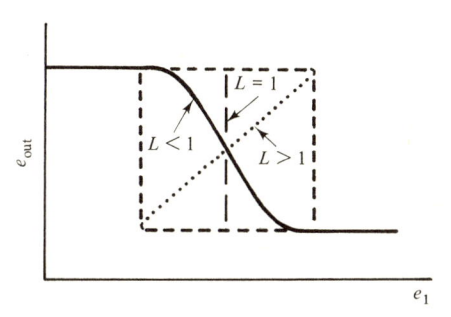

Fig. 6.1.4 Comparator characteristic with positive feedback

A technique for avoiding the oscillation problem is to make the transition as fast as possible, and any potential oscillation frequency low enough so that the transition is complete before the oscillation gets started. The positive feedback speeds up the transition and the requirement $L > 1$ means $A > R_f/R_i$ in Fig. 6.1.3.

In using comparators due consideration must be given to the differential and common-mode voltage ratings of the device (Sec. 2.9). In Fig. 6.1.2, so long as the virtual ground is maintained, these ratings are not significant. By choosing R_1 and R_2 large enough, very high voltages can be compared, the limiting factor being drifts due to variation of offset current in these resistors; Eq. (2.9.12).

6.1(c) *IC comparators*

The switching speed of a comparator is dependent on the bandwidth of the amplifier, the feedback applied, and the amount of overdrive. To obtain the fastest response the circuit must be specifically designed, and this is usually done without consideration of the suitability of the resulting response for feedback. For operational amplifiers feedback is a prime consideration, and speed suffers considerably; therefore, special IC comparators have been designed, the type 710 being a representative device. The circuit is shown in Fig. 6.1.5.

The circuit is a two stage differential input amplifier, Q_{1-4}, of low gain (since small load resistors are used for high speed), with an emitter follower output, Q_7. The signal from Q_2 passes direct to Q_4, while that from Q_1 is inverted by the unity-gain feedback section Q_3, Q_5, R_1 and fed to Q_4 via R_2. The maximum positive output is set by the clamp diode Q_6 together with V_{BE7} and the zener D_2. The maximum negative output is set by the reverse conduction of the collector–base diode of Q_8. The latter also serves to isolate the current source Q_9, Q_{10} from the output. The two zeners D_1, D_2 with V_{CB8} give a quiescent output voltage of about 1·4 V. The performance of the circuit is illustrated in Table 6.1.1. Because of saturation in the circuit there is a

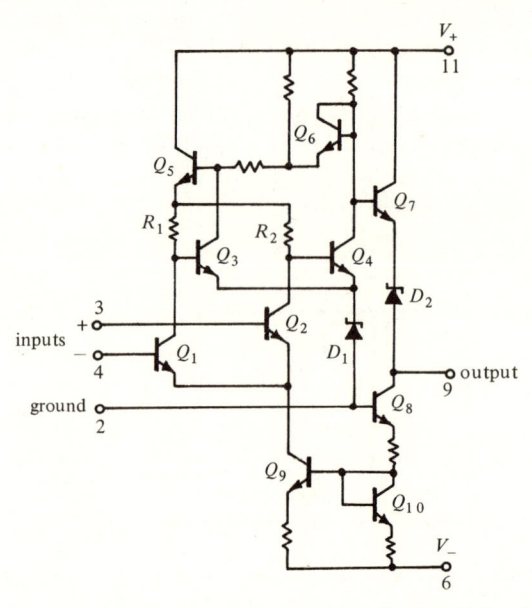

Fig. 6.1.5 Type 710 comparator (Courtesy Fairchild Semiconductor)

recovery time or delay between the application of the input signal and the start of the output transition. The time for the transition itself is specified as response time. Both times are dependent on the amount of input overdrive, which is the amount by which the absolute minimum input change, to cause a transition, is exceeded. Larger overdrive gives shorter times.

Although the term dual comparator might be expected to refer to two comparators on the same IC chip, as for amplifiers, and there are such devices, e.g, 720, the name has also been given to the type 711 which consists of two comparators whose outputs are combined through an OR circuit (Fig. 6.1.6). The actual comparator circuits are very similar to the 710.

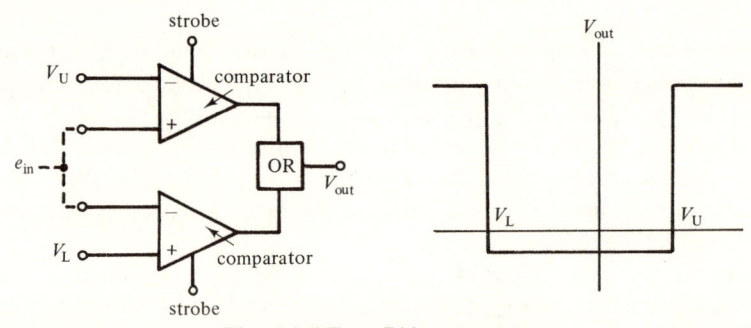

Fig. 6.1.6 Type 711 comparator

Table 6.1.1 IC comparators

	Gain	Output swing	Input CMV	Input DV	Response time	Recovery time	Supply volts	Comments
µA710 [j1]	1500	−0·5/+3·2	±5	±5	40	20	+12, −6	SN72810 improved, SN72820 dual
µA711 [j1]	1500	−0·5/+3·2	±5	±5	40	20	+12, −6	Dual 710 with strobes but common output
µA734 [s1]	6×10^4	0·4/7	±10	±10	120	320	±15	Dual, strobes, variable hysteresis output, protection, synchronous clamps
µA750 [r1]		220 mA	0 to V_+	±5	50	470	+26	
µA760 [q1]		0·2/3·2	±4·5	±5	10	20	±6·5/4·5	
LM311 [c1]	2×10^5	50 mA	±15	±30	200	100	±15	Floating TTL output stage
LM339 [u1]	2×10^5	0/5	V_+ to 1·5	36	250	250	±1 to 18 or 2 to 36	Quad
NE526 [t2]	2000	0·5/3·5	±5	5	10	40	±5	Differential amplifier with separate TTL 2IP Nand gate
NE529 [u2]	5000	0·5/3·3	±6	±5	5	10	±10, 5	Floating dual outputs, strobes, separate output V_+
AM686 [Q1]		0·5/2·7	±4	+6	2·5	10	±5	AM685 for ECL
CA3099E [j2]		50 mA	V_+ to 2	10	500 rise 50 fall	600	12 or ±6	Micropower, hysteresis, programmable operating current and output, memory flip-flop
CMP–01CY [k2]	5×10^5	0/2·4	±13	±11	300 rise 50 fall	50	±18 or 36	

CMV = common-mode voltage; DV = differential voltage.

265

Two reference levels V_U and V_L ($V_U > V_L$ say) which may be positive or negative, are applied to the inputs as shown. The signal e_{in} is connected to the other two inputs in parallel. The two states of the output indicate whether e_{in} is within the reference levels or outside them.

A further feature of the 711, as well as many other comparators, is the provision of strobe input terminals. A suitable logic signal applied to these can inhibit or enable the comparator irrespective of the input conditions.

Although these comparators are not suitable for negative feedback, they can be used to advantage where positive feedback is involved as discussed above, or in the various types of multivibrator and high frequency oscillator where fast switching or good high frequency response is required [a1, b1, c1, e1, f1, n1, q1, r1, s1, t1, u1, B1, D1, I1, K1, N1, P1, Q1].

6.1(d) *Discriminators*

Comparators are frequently used as discriminators which serve to indicate whether a pulse is above or below a preset amplitude. This application is just as described previously. A window discriminator is used if it is required to know whether the pulse

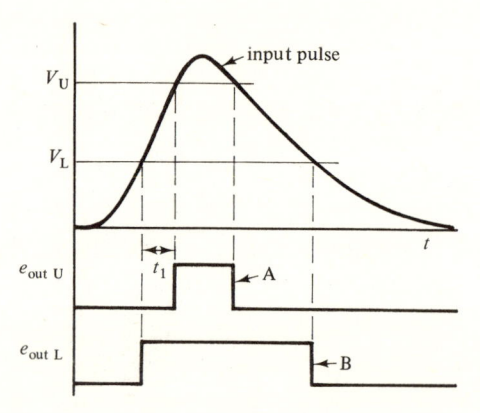

Fig. 6.1.7 Window discriminator pulse shapes

was between two levels, but a difficulty arises here. Since the output from the upper level discriminator changes some time, t_1, after the lower level, a good pulse could be indicated before the upper discriminator vetoes it (Fig. 6.1.7).

By using the falling rather than the rising edges of the discriminator outputs this difficulty can be avoided: the veto due to edge A occurs before the good indication of edge B. For an acceptable pulse, lying between V_U and V_L, only e_{outL} is obtained, while for a pulse below V_L there is no output.

For small window widths, the drifts of the comparators and reference levels become significant. The drifts arise not only from offset voltage changes, particularly with temperature, but also as a result of input bias currents (Sec. 2.9), since it is not simple to maintain equality of source resistance [Y1]. Improved performance is obtained by replacing one of the absolute reference levels by a window-width voltage riding on the other absolute level. Another approach, using an integrator to servo out offsets and drift, is described in [L1].

A further use of comparators is in the detection of coincidence of pulses or measurement of the time delay between them [p2, g1, y1, z1, S1]. Sharp edges are required for accurate measurement. However, if the pulses are not of the same amplitude the time of the output pulse would not have a fixed relationship with the start or the centroid of the pulse; Fig. 6.1.8(a).

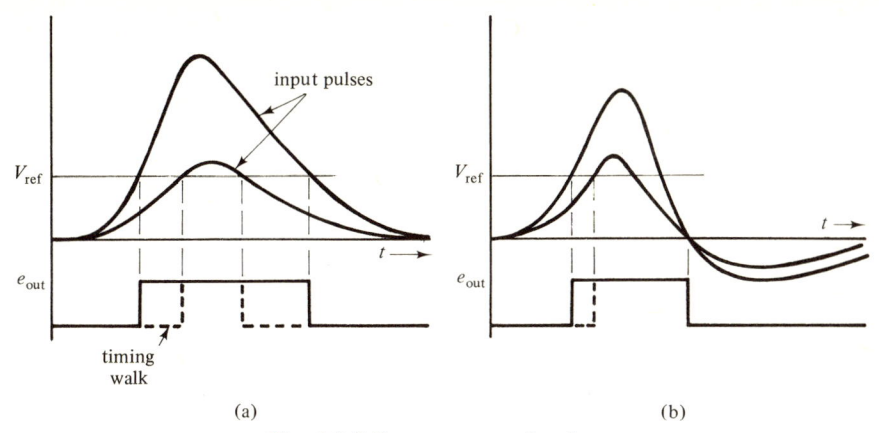

Fig. 6.1.8 Zero-crosser pulse shapes

The technique illustrated is known as a leading-edge discrimination, and the variation as timing walk. If the pulses are always of the same shape then, if they are differentiated twice, the output signal will cross zero at a time independent of the amplitude, Fig. 6.1.8(b). To show this, mathematically, for arbitrary time constants is rather cumbersome, but it can fairly easily be demonstrated for an exponential input $v_i = v_0 (1 - \exp(-at))$ and using two isolated differentiating time constants equal to $1/a$. The output from the first differentiator is $v_1 = v_0 \, at \exp(-at)$, and from the second $v_2 = v_0 \, at (1 - at/2) \exp(-at)$, which crosses zero when $t = 2/a$ irrespective of v_0 [l1, p. 42; g1, p. 228].

A circuit that can detect the zero crossing (after being primed by the initial crossing of some reference level to eliminate spurious crossings), is called a zero-crossing discriminator or crossover pickoff. A simple way to arrange this is to set a comparator reference level equal to its hysteresis, so that the negative edge of the output pulse occurs at the zero crossing; Fig. 6.1.8(b) [d1, T1, n2, S1, o2].

The timing walk in leading-edge timing can be reduced by lowering V_{ref} as far as the noise of the system will allow. In high precision timing applications (e.g., to tens of picoseconds) the source of the signals may have an important effect on the performance. In the case of optical or particle detectors for example (photomultipliers or Ge (Li) detectors), the effect of statistical variation in the time to collect enough charge to reach a low leading-edge threshold can be less than for a zero-crosser with an equivalent threshold of half the pulse [b2, V1]. It has been found that for particular detectors a combination of leading-edge and crossover timing can give improved performance. This is referred to as the constant fraction of pulse height (CFPHT) discriminator [A1, b2, a2, q2, p2]. As suggested by the name, the approach here is to use the pulse itself to provide the reference level. The pulse is attenuated to a fraction, f, and added to the inverted and delayed original pulse. The resultant waveform will be bipolar, crossing zero where the two pulses are of equal amplitude; Fig. 6.1.9.

As the reference level is a constant fraction of the pulse itself, the resultant will in principle always cross zero at the same time irrespective of amplitude or risetime. This is illustrated in the figure for variations of amplitude or risetime (B, C) or both (D). A value of f much less than $\frac{1}{2}$ gives the best timing characteristics, while $f=\frac{1}{2}$ gives a symmetrical output (equal positive and negative areas), that is advantageous in reducing pulse pile-up in subsequent stages; Sec. 4.8(c) [b2].

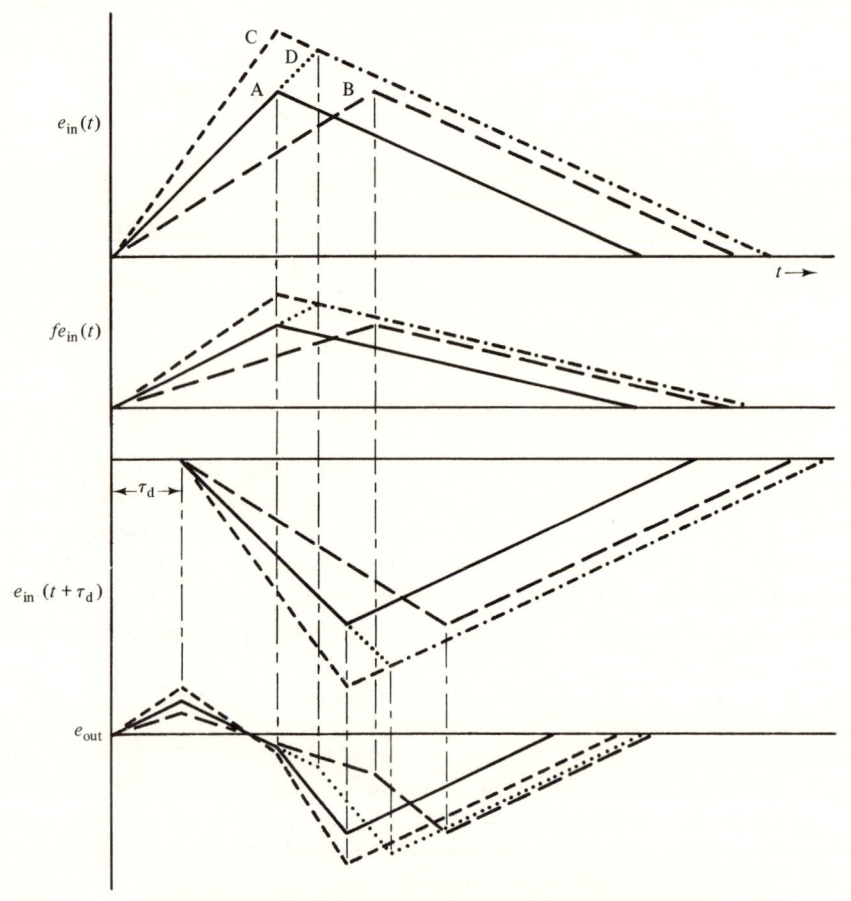

Fig. 6.1.9 **Waveforms for constant fraction discriminator**

Further variants include the use of a snap-off diode to define the crossover point more precisely [s2], and an amplitude-dependent gain and rise-time circuit in which the amplitude induced walk compensates for the effects of variable risetime [M1]. A rather different approach using a tapped delay line estimation method, known as slope reversal processing, allows simultaneous pulse width discrimination [o1].

6.2 Multipliers

From the time of the earliest development of operational amplifiers some means of implementing the one missing basic mathematical operation—multiplication—has been sought. Once this was realized a host of new applications would become possible, and over the years many ingenious systems were tried. However, these were either complex, expensive, unreliable, or slow, or several of these simultaneously and, hence, did not enjoy great popularity or use. The development of cheap dual planar transistors with near ideal characteristics, Sec. 1.9(b), was the key to the realization of cheap and effective discrete, and later integrated, multipliers.

To give some idea of the tremendous potential of the multiplier, some of the possible applications are listed:

extraction of roots	power series generation
raising to powers	trigonometric transformations
division	rectangular–polar conversion
power measurement	modulation
frequency multiplication	demodulation
automatic gain control	variable frequency filters
phase measurement	voltage-controlled function generator
ratio measurement	correlation.

The wide range emphasizes the importance of this element. Before outlining some of these uses, the principles of operation of the present type of IC multiplier will be described. This is based on the variable transconductance transistor amplifier. Other types of multipliers are discussed by Korn and Korn [D1].

6.2(a) *Four-quadrant variable transconductance multiplier*

The development and operation of the wide bandwidth linear four-quadrant multiplier has been described by Gilbert [g1]. This work led to the basic commercial multiplier MC1495 and later to the improved MC1494 [c1, e1, f1, k1]. More recently a further improved type, the AD530, has been introduced which includes an operational amplifier and requires considerably less external circuitry [W1, X1, Y1, Z1, a1, b1]. All these types use the same basic multiplier circuit shown in Fig. 6.2.1 [B1].

The circuit comprises two pairs of transistors $Q_{13,14}$ and $Q_{15,16}$ with cross-coupled collectors, and driven by the signals across the diode connected transistors,

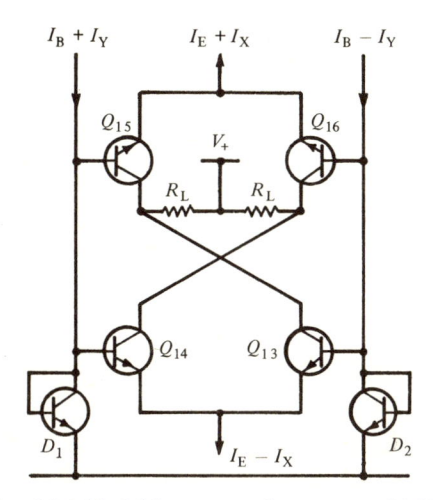

Fig. 6.2.1 Variable transconductance multiplier

$D_{1,2}$. The inputs are in the form of currents I_B+I_Y and I_B-I_Y for the Y input, and I_E+I_X and I_E-I_X for the X input. The output must then be of the form $M=XY$.

$Q_{14,15}$ act with D_1 in the manner of the current mirror, Sec. 1.10(a), and similarly for $Q_{13,16}$ with D_2. Although I_{C15} cannot be put equal to I_B+I_Y (nor $I_{C16}=I_B-I_Y$) as for the current mirror, since the emitter of Q_{15} is not common with that of D_1, the ratio of the collector currents will be equal to the ratio of the input currents [g1]:

$$\frac{I_{C15}}{I_{C16}} = \frac{I_B+I_Y}{I_B-I_Y} \tag{6.2.1}$$

from which

$$\frac{I_{C15}}{I_E+I_X} = \frac{I_{C15}}{I_{C15}+I_{C16}} = \frac{I_B+I_Y}{2I_B}$$

or

$$I_{C15} = (I_E+I_X)(I_B+I_Y)/2I_B$$

similarly,

$$I_{C16} = (I_E+I_X)(I_B-I_Y)/2I_B$$

$$I_{C14} = (I_E-I_X)(I_B+I_Y)/2I_B$$

$$I_{C13} = (I_E-I_X)(I_B-I_Y)/2I_B$$

$$\tag{6.2.2}$$

The differential output, I_{out}, is

$$I_{out} = I_{C15}+I_{C13}-I_{C16}-I_{C14}$$

$$= \frac{2I_X I_Y}{I_B} \tag{6.2.3}$$

i.e., the differential output current is proportional to the product of the signal input currents I_X and I_Y. The validity of the assumptions made, matched emitter diodes, infinite betas, and perfect exponential characteristics, are examined by Gilbert [g1] and found to be well justified. It should be emphasized that Eq. (6.2.3) holds for any combination of signs of I_X and I_Y, so that complete four-quadrant operation is allowed.

For the more usual voltage inputs and outputs, it is necessary to include additional circuitry to perform the voltage/current transformations. The circuit including the X and Y drivers is shown in Fig. 6.2.2, which includes several external resistors. The two R_L's convert the differential output current to voltage, and R_{BX} and R_{BY} fix the current I_B on each side and so set the scale factor $2/I_B$ in Eq. (6.2.3). The scale factor for Fig. 6.2.2 is modified by the action of the drivers and depends on the resistors R_X, R_Y. If these were missing, then if the constant current sources $Q_{5,6,7,8}$ were ideal the collector currents in $Q_{2,3,10,11}$ would be fixed and there would be no response to changes in V_X or V_Y. With R_X, R_Y the difference currents I_X, I_Y flow as shown, and are given by:

$$I_X = \frac{V_X}{R_X+r_{e1,2}+r_{e3,4}}, \quad I_Y = \frac{V_Y}{R_Y+r_{e9,10}+r_{e11,12}} \tag{6.2.4}$$

where r_e is the bulk emitter resistance of the transistors and is given by Eq. (1.9.3). The values are dependent on both temperature and emitter current, which will preclude taking $I \propto V$ in Eq. (6.2.4) unless the r_e terms are much smaller than $R_{X,Y}$, i.e., the variation in emitter current must be kept within some suitable ratio. This ratio is fixed by the maximum values of $R_{X,Y}$ and $V_{X,Y}$:

$$R_{X,Y} = \frac{V_{X,Y(max)}}{I_{X,Y(max)}} \quad \text{(ignoring } r_e\text{)} \tag{6.2.5}$$

and the maximum current chosen as $I_{X,Y(max)} = \frac{2}{3}I_E$ (or I_B), say [e1].

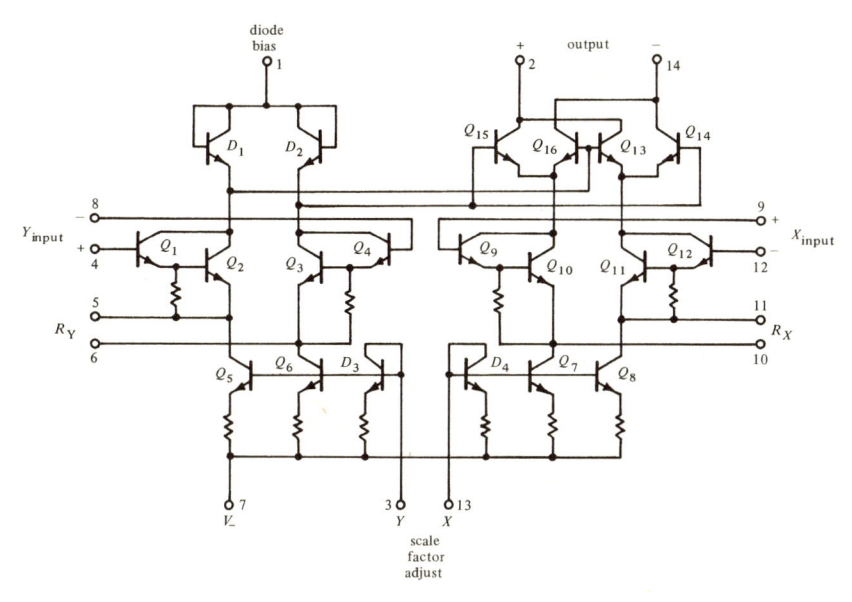

Fig. 6.2.2 Type MC1495 multiplier (Adapted courtesy Motorola Semiconductors)

Using Eq. (6.2.4), with $r_e = 0$, and Eq. (6.2.3), the differential output voltage V_M is given by:

$$V_M = I_{out} R_L = \frac{2R_L V_X V_Y}{I_B R_X R_Y} = K V_X V_Y \tag{6.2.6}$$

where the scale factor

$$K = \frac{2R_L}{I_B R_X R_Y} \tag{6.2.7}$$

For the standard multipliers the maximum input voltages, $V_{X,Y}$, are ± 10 V, so that a scale factor of 0·1 is usually chosen to give a maximum output of ± 10 V. Since there will generally be some small offset voltage independent of V_X and V_Y, one side of each of the inputs is usually connected to a variable potential to allow the zeros to be set.

The circuit shown in Fig. 6.2.2 is that of the MC1495 [e1] (μA795 [F1]). The MC1494 contains in addition various regulators that supply the *diode bias* and *X, Y scale factor adjust* inputs, potentials for the *X, Y* offset adjust potentiometers, and a differential to single-ended current converter for the output. The AD 530 contains further R_X, R_Y, a Z input, and zero, but uses an operational amplifier output stage rather than the current converter. The use of the Z input will be explained in Sec. 6.2(b).

The term *variable transconductance multiplier* arises because the emitter currents of transistors Q_{13-16} control their transconductance g_m. It may be shown that approximately for small ΔV_{BE} (Sec. 1.9(b)) [T1, p. 376; U1, section 11]:

$$g_m = \frac{\Delta I_C}{\Delta V_{BE}} = \frac{1}{r_e} = \frac{qI_E}{kT} \qquad (6.2.8)$$

The present generation of multipliers can provide accuracy and linearity better than 1 per cent, with temperature coefficients of the order of 0·1 per cent/°C. The small signal dynamic frequency response is several MHz for the multiplier section alone, but this will be somewhat reduced if the output devices are included. The accuracy and linearity do not hold to these high frequencies because of additional amplitude (1 per cent at 75 KHz) and vector (phase shift 1 per cent at 5 KHz) errors, and slewing rate limitations (45 V/μs). The relevant data sheets should be consulted for a discussion of these factors (particularly MC1494). For the AD530, error contours as a function of the inputs (*isovers*) are provided. Multipliers described by Gilbert [g1, h1] have operated satisfactorily up to 200MHz. A short guide to multipliers is available from Analog Devices [d1] which gives much useful information and two tables to assist selection.

In the circuits illustrating various applications the multiplier symbol represents the transconductance multiplier only; any following converter or amplifier, whether built-in or not, will be shown separately. For convenience the AD530 configuration will be shown.

6.2(b) *Multiplying and dividing*

The multiplier unit will, of course, multiply directly and it is only necessary to set the required scale factor and the necessary zero trims. In the AD 530 the multiplier scale is preset, but the overall scale can be altered by means of the amplifier gain. Figure 6.2.3 shows the circuit, including the Z input and output zero. Note that this extra input feeds a *differential* virtual ground, and that the multiplier has a high impedance (≈ 300 kΩ) differential current output.

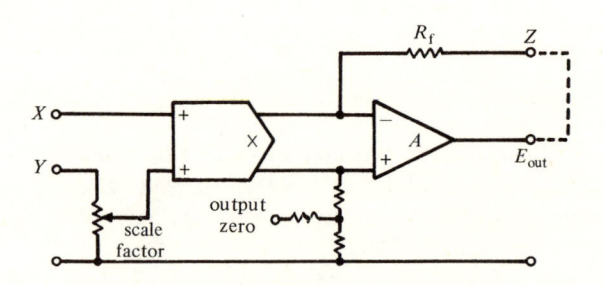

Fig. 6.2.3 Multiplication with AD530

To divide, the multiplier is included in a feedback loop by connecting E_{out} to one of the inputs and feeding the numerator to Z, the denominator being the other input (feedback to Y, which is slightly more linear than X, is recommended for improved accuracy). The arrangement is shown in Fig. 6.2.4.

Since $Y = E_{out}$, and the amplifier input is a differential virtual ground:

$$\frac{XE_{out}}{K_1} + \frac{Z}{K_2} = 0, \quad \text{or} \quad E_{out} = \frac{-KZ}{X} \qquad (6.2.9)$$

where K_2 is a scale factor dependent on R_Z, and $K = K_1/K_2$.

There are two limitations in this type of dividing circuit. Firstly, as X becomes very small the output will increase and eventually limit, i.e., $X \to 0$ is not allowed. In this region there is increased offset, noise, and multiplier error. Secondly, operation is limited to two quadrants only, $\pm Z$ with $-X$. So far it has tacitly been assumed that the input terminals are those that give for $\pm X$ and $\pm Y$, E_{out} positive (or conversely

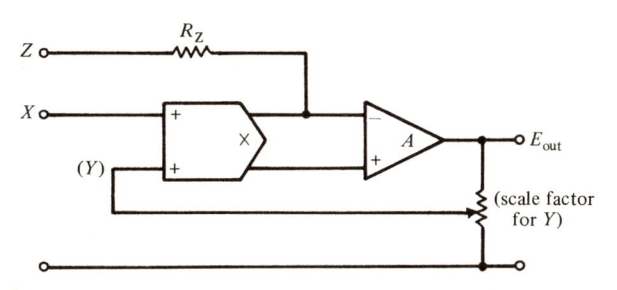

Fig. 6.2.4 Division with AD530

$\pm X$, $\mp Y$, E_0 negative). Hence the $(+)$ on the two multiplier inputs. In the divider connection, for a given value of $Y \equiv E_{out}$, the sign of X determines whether the multiplier plus amplifier is inverting $(-X)$ or non-inverting $(+X)$. In the latter case positive feedback occurs and the system will just lock over at one limit. For operation with $+X$ the normal X input $(+)$ and X zero $(-)$ are simply interchanged (see Fig. 6.2.2). Latch-up can occur if the input common-mode limit is exceeded.

If the product XY is forced to be a constant then a reciprocal, or hyperbolic, relationship is obtained. A hyperbolic sweep would, for instance, be appropriate to give a linear mass scan in a magnetic deflection mass spectrometer. This function is produced by the divide circuit simply by putting $Z = $ constant in Eq. (6.2.9).

6.2(c) *Powers and roots*

If the same signal is fed to both multiplier inputs then:

$$E_{out} = X^2/K \qquad (6.2.10)$$

i.e., a square law or parabolic relationship. If the input signal is sinusoidal, say $E \cos \omega t$, then the output will be:

$$E_{out} = K_1 E^2 \cos^2(\omega t) = \tfrac{1}{2} K_1 E^2 (1 + \cos(2\omega t)) \qquad (6.2.11)$$

using a standard trigonometrical identity. Thus, if the d.c. term is removed by using a.c. coupling on the output, a frequency doubler has been achieved (Sec. 6.3).

Higher integral powers, e.g., X^3, can be obtained by feeding the output of a squarer to the input of a second multiplier together with the original signal, and so on. The errors, however, would need careful examination. A power series can be used to approximate many functions.

The square root function is realized in a similar manner to division (Fig. 6.2.4) by feeding back E_{out} to X and Y, the input being applied at Z. Then in Eq. (6.2.9) $X \equiv E_{out}$ so that:

$$E_{out}^2 = -KZ, \quad \text{or} \quad E_{out} = (-KZ)^{1/2} \tag{6.2.12}$$

The limitation in this case is $Z \leqslant 0$ for similar reasons to those described for the divider, and latch-up is also possible. These latch-up conditions may be avoided by limiting the excursion of the amplifier output.

Connection of a squarer, an averaging filter, and a square-rooter will allow the measurement of r.m.s. values.

Non-integral powers and roots may be obtained if two new units, the ln and $\ln^{-1}$, are introduced. Details of these are given in Sec. 4.3. For powers, the circuit is shown in Fig. 6.2.5.

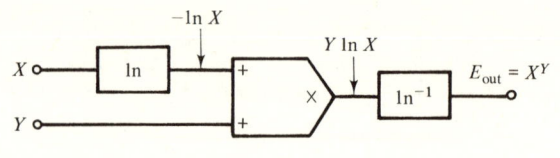

Fig. 6.2.5 Application of a multiplier for raising to a power

Combining this with the divide circuit, as in Fig. 6.2.6, gives roots:

$$E_{out} X = K \ln Z, \quad \text{or} \quad E_{out} = (K/X) \ln Z$$

and
$$E = \ln^{-1} E_{out} = Z^{K/X} \tag{6.2.13}$$

Details of the signs are omitted as these depend on the circuits.

Further important applications are in the field of modulation and demodulation (Sec. 6.3), and as a voltage-controlled gain element, which can be used for automatic gain control, voltage-controlled function generators (Sec. 5.2) or voltage-tunable filters (Sec. 4.4).

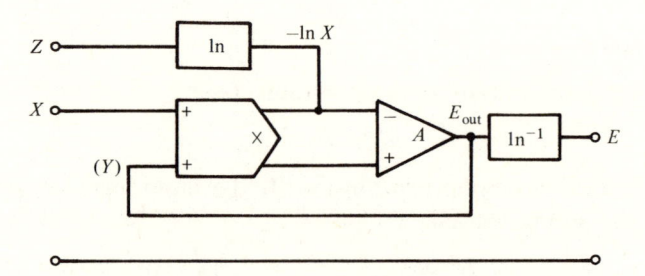

Fig. 6.2.6 Application of a multiplier for extracting roots

6.3 Modulators

Though there are many forms of modulator here we will be concerned only with the cross-coupled differential configuration already discussed in Sec. 6.2. The modulator circuit is basically the same as the multiplier, and is shown in Fig. 6.3.1.

Modulation is essentially a problem of multiplication which is why this circuit is attractive. It is not our purpose to discuss the theory of modulation here [j1, k1, l1] or problems of communication, as these are outside our scope.

The two signals to be multiplied are fed to the two pairs of differential inputs as shown. The linearizing elements used in the multiplier (Fig. 6.2.1) are omitted here.

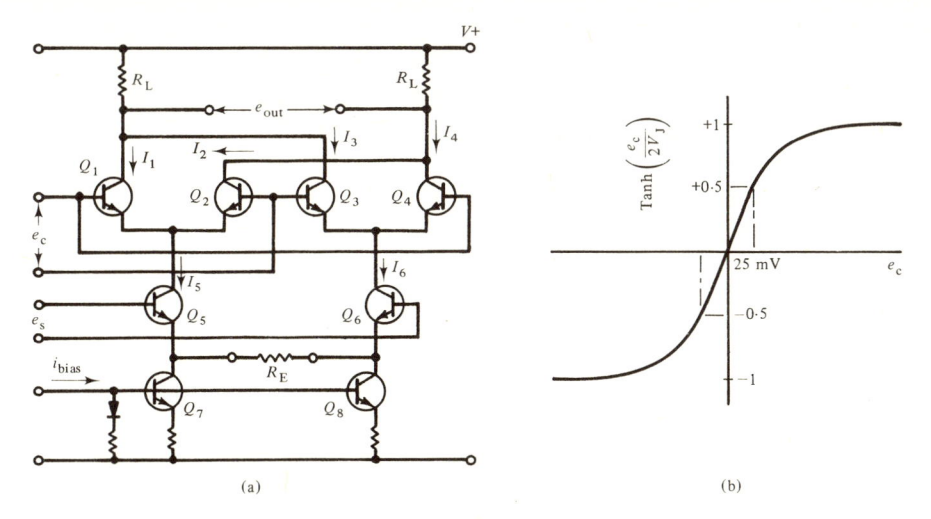

Fig. 6.3.1 (a) Double-balanced modulator, (b) transfer function Tanh $(e_C/2V_J)$

This increases the frequency response and decreases cost, and the resulting non-linearity can usually be reduced by other means. The upper input, to Q_{1-4}, is non-linear so the large amplitude carrier signal e_c is applied here, the modulating signal e_s being applied to $Q_{5,6}$.

$$e_c = E_c \cos(\omega_c t), \qquad e_s = E_s \cos(\omega_s t) \qquad (6.3.1)$$

The output is given by [i1, m1]:

$$e_{out} = \frac{R_L}{R_E} \cdot e_s \tanh\left(\frac{e_c}{2V_J}\right), \qquad 2V_J = \frac{2kT}{q} \doteq 50 \text{ mV} \quad \text{(see Sec. 1.9(a))} \qquad (6.3.2)$$

The form of the tanh function is shown in Fig. 6.3.1(b). If the carrier amplitude E_c is large compared to V_J, the tanh term reduces to a square switching waveform as shown in Fig. 6.3.2.

The output signal will be the product of the modulating signal, e_s, and the separate harmonics of the square wave. However, the effects of the higher harmonics can usually be filtered out. For this balanced configuration there is no output from either input if the other is absent (the product of any quantity and zero is zero). If the carrier amplitude is small then essentially linear operation results, and the output is simply the product of the two inputs. It is seen from Fig. 6.2.1(b) that, for linear operation, the signals must be kept rather small—a few tens of millivolts. Frequency response extends to a few hundred MHz and so should be adequate for most common applications. However, at high frequencies there are increasing problems of feedthrough due to device and stray capacities so good r.f. practice must be observed.

A simple application of the modulator is frequency doubling. The same sinusoidal signal, e_s, is applied to both inputs so that:

$$e_{out} = KE_s^2 \cos^2(\omega_s t)$$
$$= \tfrac{1}{2}KE_s^2[1+\cos(2\omega_s t)] \qquad (6.3.3)$$

where K is a constant and use is made of a standard trigonometrical identity. The output is thus at twice the input frequency. The accompanying constant term may be simply filtered out by using a.c. coupling. There is no limitation to sinusoidal inputs—any waveform may be used. For example a ramp input will give a parabolic output [a1].

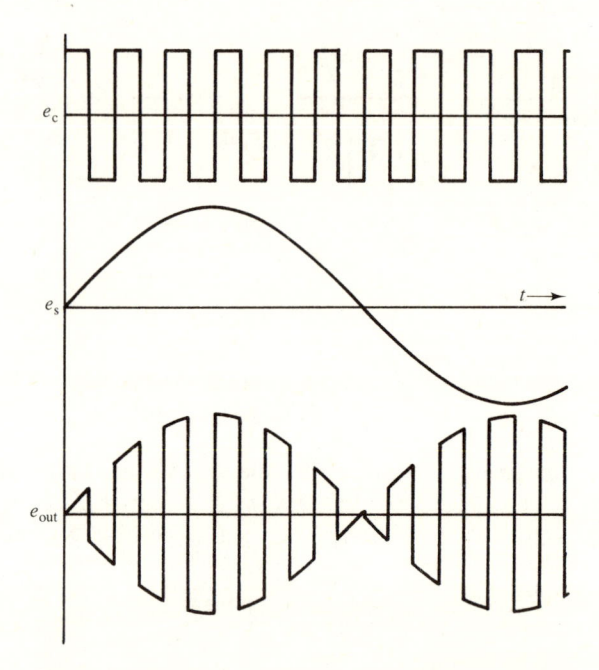

Fig. 6.3.2 Sine-wave modulating switching waveform

Feeding different frequency sine-waves to the two inputs will give a suppressed carrier amplitude modulated output.

$$e_{out} = K[E_s \cos(\omega_s t)] \cdot [E_c \cos(\omega_c t)]$$
$$= \tfrac{1}{2}E_s E_c[\cos(\omega_c + \omega_s)t + \cos(\omega_c - \omega_s)t] \qquad (6.3.4)$$

with waveforms and frequency spectrum as shown in Fig. 6.3.3. In practice, the system will not be perfectly balanced and some adjustable balance control will be required to ensure maximum carrier suppression.

If a constant term is added to the signal we get the standard amplitude modulated waveform, also shown in Fig. 6.3.3.

$$e_{out} = K[E_s(1 + m\cos(\omega_s t))] \cdot [E_c \cos(\omega_c t)]$$
$$= \tfrac{1}{2}KE_s E_c m[\cos(\omega_c + \omega_s)t + \cos(\omega_c - \omega_s)t] + KE_s E_c \cos(\omega_c t) \qquad (6.3.5)$$

where $m \leq 1$ is the degree of modulation. Here we have the two sidebands at $(\omega_c + \omega_s)$ and $(\omega_c - \omega_s)$, as before, but with the addition of the carrier at ω_c.

Feeding signals of identical frequency to both inputs but allowing for a phase difference ϕ between them gives:

$$e_{out} = K[E_s \cos(\omega_s t + \phi)].[E_c \cos(\omega_s t)]$$
$$= \tfrac{1}{2} K E_s E_c [\cos(2\omega_s t + \phi) + \cos \phi] \qquad (6.3.6)$$

which, if filtered to eliminate the high frequency term at $2\omega_s$, gives an output proportional to $\cos \phi$, i.e., a phase detector circuit. Note, however, that it is also proportional

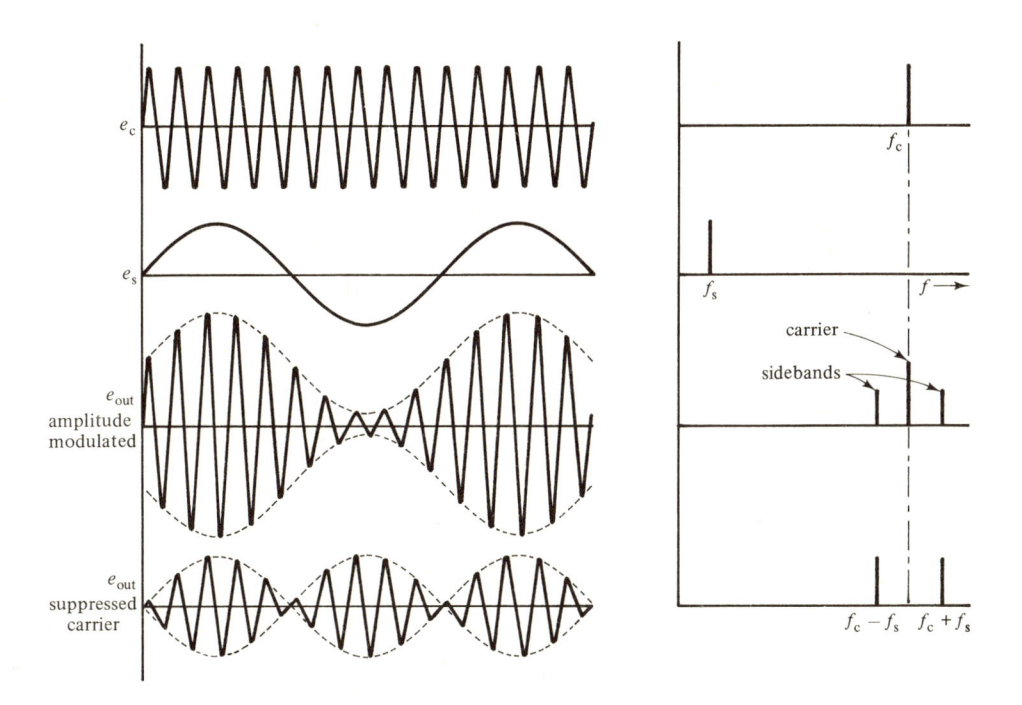

Fig. 6.3.3 (a) Suppressed carrier and amplitude modulated waveforms, (b) frequency spectra

to the two amplitudes E_s, E_c. If both inputs are limited to remove amplitude variations so we have square wave inputs to the modulator, then the output will be a linear function of ϕ [m1, s1, r1].

A useful feature of the double-balanced form of modulator is that the output is independent of any asymmetry of the input waveforms and hence also independent of noise. This can be demonstrated by the waveforms shown in Fig. 6.3.4 where the current designations refer to Fig. 6.3.1 [r1].

It is seen that the sum current in either load resistor, i.e., $(I_1 + I_3)$ or $(I_2 + I_3)$ stays constant irrespective of the asymmetry of the waveforms. The decrease in I_1 (I_2) is just compensated by the increase in I_3 (I_4).

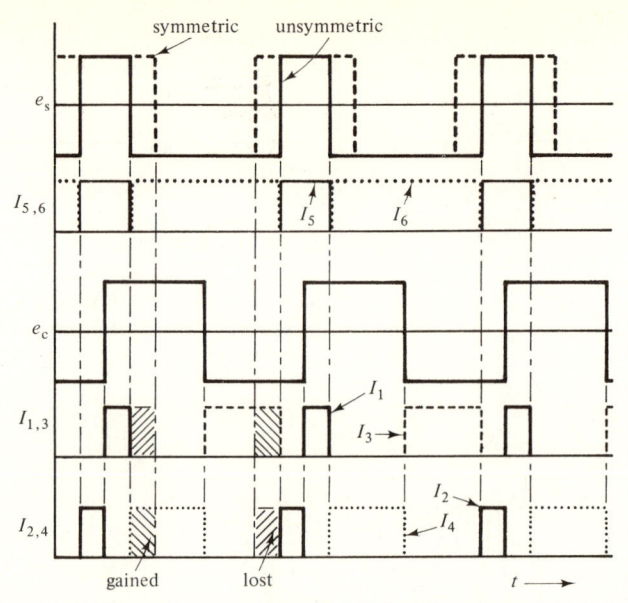

Fig. 6.3.4 Effect of input asymmetry on double-balanced modulator

6.4 Phase-locked loop

Phase-locking is a technique for maintaining the frequency of a local oscillator exactly equal to the average frequency of some input signal. In a conventional automatic frequency control system some difference of frequency is required, to produce the correction signal. In phase-locking the difference is only of *phase*, the averaging taking place within one cycle so that there is an exact correspondence between an input and a local oscillator cycle. Though the technique has been known for some time [r1] it has not been commonly used. However, a number of IC phase-locked loops are now available [k1, l1, m1, n1, o1, s1, t1] which allow this very useful technique to be readily used in many applications [b1, c1, d1, f1, h1, k1, M1, P1].

In essence, the phase-locked loop consists of three parts, a phase detector, a low-pass filter, and a voltage-controlled oscillator (VCO), connected as shown in Fig. 6.4.1. The phase detector is commonly double-balanced, and of the form described in Secs. 6.2 and 6.3 (Fig. 6.3.1). The oscillator is often current rather than voltage controlled, but this is not significant in discussing the operating principles.

The operation of the system is most readily understood if it is first considered to be *in lock*. Then the frequency, f_o, of the local oscillator will be equal to the input

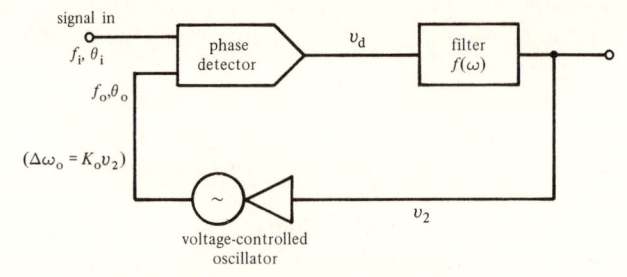

Fig. 6.4.1 Basic phase-locked loop

frequency, f_i, differing only in phase, $\theta_i - \theta_o \neq 0$. This phase difference is detected to give a voltage, v_d, which is filtered and fed to the VCO. Any tendency for either signal f_i or f_o to change frequency gives a change of phase and hence a change of feedback voltage, v_2, in the correct sense to keep f_o equal to f_i. This is a proportional controller with the phase error $\theta_e = (\theta_i - \theta_o)$ inversely proportional to the loop gain. Since phase is the time integral of frequency (or frequency the time derivative of phase, $f = \partial \phi / \partial t$), the system is also an integral controller with respect to frequency, so that there will be no average frequency error in lock (see Sec. 4.5).

When the loop is not in lock there are two possibilities. If f_i and f_o differ substantially, there will be no effective feedback voltage, v_2, and nothing will happen. However, if $(f_i - f_o)$ is less than some value, determined by the parameters of the loop, there will be an effective feedback voltage which will eventually drive the loop into lock. This automatic acquisition of lock is an extremely useful feature.

There are two classes of operation for a phase-locked loop. So far it has been assumed that the input signal is clean and well defined (i.e., high signal-to-noise ratio) so that there is no doubt what f_o is to be compared with. This would arise, for example, if we wished to lock two oscillators together or to provide coherent frequency multiplication or division. At the other end of the scale are signals with a very low signal-to-noise ratio, possibly considerably less than unity. This may arise in the demodulation of weak radio signals, or in a tracking filter used to seek out and extract a weak signal from noise. In these applications the noise performance is obviously of the utmost importance. The ability of a phase-locked loop (PLL) to average out noise and provide a cleaned-up signal of the same frequency as the input, is one of its greatest attractions.

The theoretical basis for the design of phase-locked loops is covered by Gardner [b1] and Viterbi [i1]. Useful résumés are given by Mills [d1] and Nash [e1]. The design of an IC phase-locked loop is discussed by Grebene and Camenzind [a1], and the practical implementation for many standard and unusual applications in [k1].

Following Gardner [b1], the basic transfer function of the loop is readily derived. For the phase detector, filter, and controlled oscillator we have (see Fig. 6.4.1):

$$v_d = K_d(\theta_i - \theta_o), \qquad v_2 = v_d f(\omega)$$
$$\Delta \omega_o = K_o v_2 = \partial \theta_o / \partial t \qquad (6.4.1)$$

Taking Laplace transforms of Eq. (6.4.1) gives:

$$V_d(s) = K_d(\theta_i(s) - \theta_o(s)), \qquad V_2(s) = V_d(s)F(s) \qquad (6.4.2)$$
$$\theta_o(s) = K_o V_2(s)/s$$

the last expression again indicating that θ_o is proportional to the integral (i.e., $1/s$) of V_2. The loop transfer function is, thus:

$$\frac{\theta_o(s)}{\theta_i(s)} = H(s) = \frac{K_o K_d F(s)}{s + K_o K_d F(s)}$$

or
$$\frac{\theta_e(s)}{\theta_i(s)} = \frac{\theta_i(s) - \theta_o(s)}{\theta_i(s)} = 1 - H(s) = \frac{s}{s + K_o K_d F(s)} \qquad (6.4.3)$$

where $\theta_e(s)$ is the phase error. This is limited to $\pm 90°$, otherwise the system would go out of lock. The voltage, v_2, is a cyclic function of phase, being zero for $\theta_e = 0$ and going to maxima of opposite sign for $\theta_e = \pm 90°$. Beyond this the sense reverses and increasing $|\theta_e|$ generates a v_2 in a sense such as to push the system away from lock. The phase discriminator characteristic is similar to the more commonly known frequency discriminator curve, and is illustrated in Fig. 6.4.3.

There is the possibility of some confusion regarding the phase relationships. $\theta_e(s)$, as used by Gardner, refers to the variation of phase relative to some reference, and not to the absolute phase difference $(\theta_i - \theta_o)$. In fact, as can be seen from Secs. 6.3 and 10.2, the output, v_2, of the usual phase detectors is zero when the inputs are at $\pm 90°$. The discussion by Gardner [b1, Figs. 5-4, 5-5] obscures this by taking the two signals to be initially at 90°. Thus, the reference phase for $\theta_e(s)$ is actually 90°, and at lock $(\theta_i - \theta_o) = 90°$ [k1, p. 15].

The performance of the loop, given by $H(s)$, is now dependent on the form of the filter characteristic $F(s)$. Commonly, this consists of a simple lag or a more flexible lag/lead filter (Fig. 6.4.2). Active equivalents of these may also be used [b1, p. 8; N1].

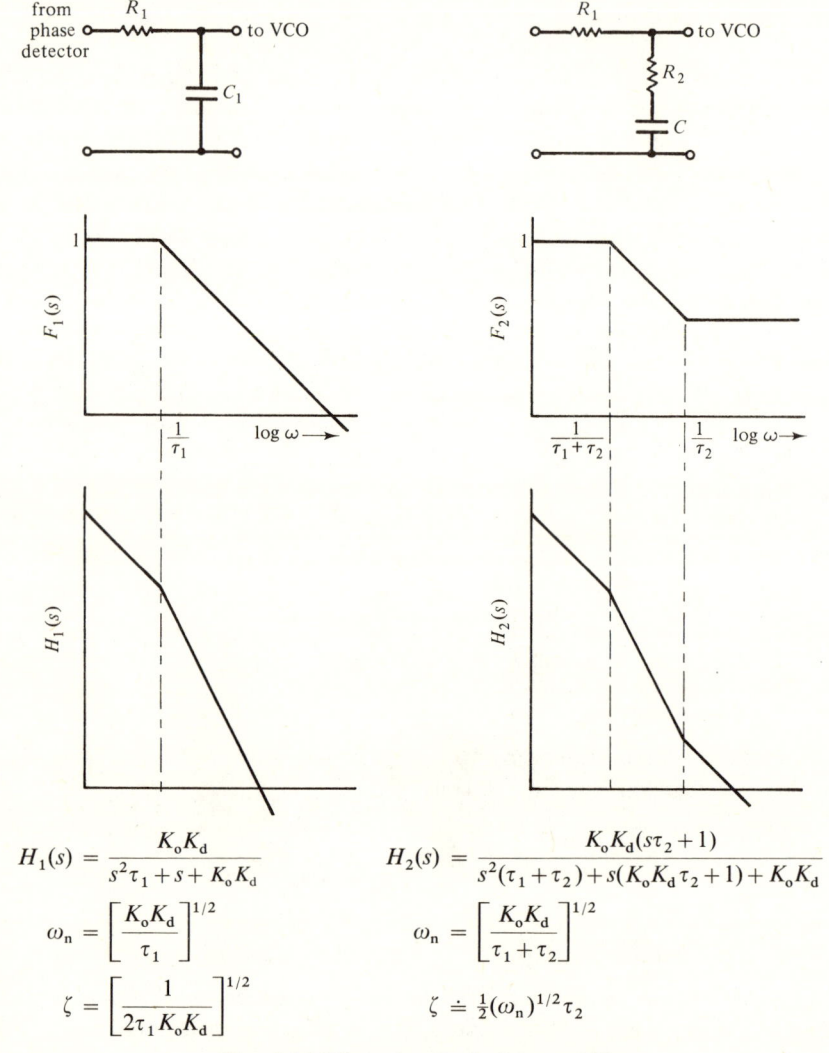

$$H_1(s) = \frac{K_o K_d}{s^2 \tau_1 + s + K_o K_d}$$

$$\omega_n = \left[\frac{K_o K_d}{\tau_1}\right]^{1/2}$$

$$\zeta = \left[\frac{1}{2\tau_1 K_o K_d}\right]^{1/2}$$

$$H_2(s) = \frac{K_o K_d(s\tau_2 + 1)}{s^2(\tau_1 + \tau_2) + s(K_o K_d \tau_2 + 1) + K_o K_d}$$

$$\omega_n = \left[\frac{K_o K_d}{\tau_1 + \tau_2}\right]^{1/2}$$

$$\zeta \doteq \tfrac{1}{2}(\omega_n)^{1/2} \tau_2$$

Fig. 6.4.2 Filter circuits for loop stability

Included with the figure are expressions for the natural frequency, ω_n, and the damping factor, ζ, of the general second order system as described in Secs. 3.2 and 3.7. For the lag filter both ω_n and ζ depend on τ_1 so it is not possible to select these independently. The narrow bandwidth requires a large τ_1 and, hence, the damping ζ is small (Q large). In a truly second order system, instability cannot occur (although the response may be far from desirable, Sec. 3.2), but in practice there will always be additional time constants that could cause instability. With the lag-lead filter, ω_n and ζ can be set independently since there are two time constants τ_1 and τ_2. If τ_1 is substantially greater than τ_2 then the former will control ω_n and the latter ζ.

Choice of bandwidth is dependent on the application, as there are conflicting requirements. To avoid output phase jitter due to noise the bandwidth should be as narrow as possible. To minimize transient error due to signal modulation, and to obtain best tracking and acquisition properties, the bandwidth should be as large as possible [d1]. The low-pass filter acts as a short-term memory, rejecting interference and aiding recapture if lock is lost because of some transient signal or disturbance.

The loop-gain $K_o K_d F(s)$ is a further variable usually denoted by K_v. This controls the phase error, θ_e. If the frequencies are identical there is no phase error. If the frequencies differ by $\Delta\omega$ then the static phase error is:

$$\theta_v = \frac{\Delta\omega}{K_v} \qquad (6.4.4)$$

Note that $F(0) = 1$ for a passive filter, and A_0 for an active filter.

We now define several frequency ranges. Here again there is, unfortunately, a difference of nomenclature which may cause confusion.

(i) $\pm\Delta\omega_L$ is the range over which lock is maintained when the loop is initially in lock. Gardner [b1, d1, o1] calls this the hold-in range $\Delta\omega_H$ and it is given by:

$$\pm\Delta\omega_L = \pm K_o K_d F(0) = \pm K_v \qquad (6.4.5)$$

and at the limits $\theta_e = \pm 90°$. $\Delta\omega_L$, in principle, can be made as large as desired by increasing K_v, but some element will eventually limit and the loop will go out of lock.

(ii) $\pm\Delta\omega_C$ is the capture range, within which lock will be acquired eventually. Gardner calls this the pull-in range $\Delta\omega_p$ and it is given by:

$$\pm\Delta\omega_C \doteq 2^{1/2}(2\zeta\omega_n K_v - \omega_n^2)^{1/2} \qquad (6.4.6)$$

and this is always $\leq \omega_L$. Thus, if the VCO frequency f_o is within $\Delta\omega_C$, then the loop will move towards lock and eventually lock in, a number of beat frequency $(f_i - f_o)$ cycles occurring in this time. An approximate expression for the time required for capture for an initial difference $\Delta\omega$, is given by:

$$T_c \doteq \frac{(\Delta\omega)^2}{2\zeta\omega_n^3} \qquad (6.4.7)$$

but this is not good for $\Delta\omega \approx \Delta\omega_C$ or if it is small, near $\Delta\omega_{IL}$, see (iii). A narrow band loop (τ_1 large, or ω_n small) may require a considerable time to lock in: a sweep may then be necessary to accelerate the process [b1, p. 50].

(iii) $\pm\Delta\omega_{IL}$ is the frequency range within which lock will be acquired immediately without skipping cycles. This is actually denoted by $\Delta\omega_L$ in Gardner [b1, p. 43] but this clashes with (i). For the lag-lead filter it is given by:

$$\Delta\omega_{IL} = \frac{K_o K_d \tau_2}{\tau_1 + \tau_2} \doteq 2\zeta\omega_n \tag{6.4.8}$$

This quantity is not given in the other references quoted. Though Gardner's terms and symbols appear more appropriate, those given above are generally used in the device data sheets and application notes [k1, l1, m1, n1].

The mechanism of pull-in is of interest. A *normal* beat frequency would give a symmetrical phase detector output and, thus, no nett voltage to move the VCO towards lock. The control signal in the loop, v_2, frequency modulates the VCO and this beats with the input frequency to produce a very distorted asymmetrical beat waveform [b1, p. 44]. The d.c. component of this drives the VCO towards lock. It may be noted here that the VCO's in the IC's listed in Table 6.1.1 generate square or triangular waveform rather than sinusoidal.

The effect of noise on a phase-locked loop is complex, and reference should be made to [b1, pp. 17, 148; i1]. Since noise is random, statistical methods should be used. The approximate theory given in [b1] leads to the definition of two loop quantities, the loop-noise bandwidth (in hertz):

$$B_L = \frac{\omega_n}{2}\left(\zeta + \frac{1}{4\zeta}\right) \tag{6.4.9}$$

(where ω_n is in radians/s and ζ should usually have a value in the range 0·25 to 1), and the loop signal-to-noise ratio:

$$(SNR)_L = \frac{P_S}{2B_L W_i} \tag{6.4.10}$$

where P_S = input signal power (watts)
        W_i = input noise power spectral density (watts/Hz)

It is found that a minimum $(SNR)_L$ of about +6 dB is needed for acquisition of lock [d1, p. 5]. This does not conflict with an earlier statement that signals less than noise (S/N < 0 dB) can be demodulated, since the bandwidth of the input noise, B_i, will usually be considerably greater than B_L. The ratio:

$$\frac{(SNR)_S}{(SNR)_L} = \frac{B_i}{B_L}$$

An indication of lock is often of use [b1, p. 52]. This cannot be detected instantaneously, because of the effects of noise, and averaging for some time (of the order of the inverse loop bandwidth, B_L) is necessary. A common technique of detecting lock is shown in Fig. 6.4.3. A further phase detector is included which operates with a quadrature signal from the VCO. The output of the in-phase detector is proportional to sin θ_e (or its equivalent triangular response), and hence is small for θ_e small. The output of the quadrature detector is proportional to cos θ_e, and hence is large for θ_e small, i.e., at lock.

The filtered d.c. output of the quadrature detector provides a lock indication signal, some threshold being set by V_{ref}. When out of lock the outputs of both phase detectors are beat notes with small d.c. components. If the sense of lock is required, the d.c. component of the in-phase detector can be used.

The combination shown in Fig. 6.4.3 can be used to detect tone coded signals, i.e., signals consisting of the presence or absence of a particular frequency or tone. These may be used, for example, in digital signalling or remote control applications. If a signal within the capture range $\Delta\omega_C$ is present for a sufficient time, a lock signal will be generated by the quadrature phase detector. If amplifier A has high gain it will act as a comparator (Sec. 6.1), or a following trigger circuit may be used to obtain a sharp trigger.

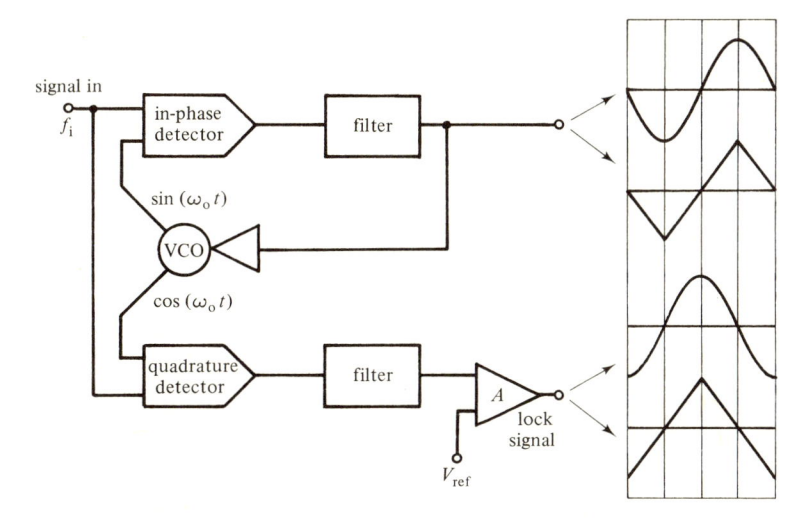

Fig. 6.4.3 Phase-locked loop with quadrature lock detector

6.5 Sample-hold

To measure the amplitude of a signal at some instant it is convenient, and often necessary, to sample the signal at that instant and hold the resulting sample for a period long enough to enable the measurement to be made to the desired accuracy. A common example occurs in the digitizing of a signal at a particular instant, since it takes a significant time—depending on the number of bits or accuracy—to carry out the digital processing. For example, to be able to digitize a sinusoidal voltage to an accuracy of 0·1 per cent (10 bits) in 10 μs (quite a fast converter) the frequency must be limited to about 16 Hz.

A sample-hold may be left to follow the input signal before changing to hold and, therefore, they are also referred to as track-hold circuits.

The technique used for a sample-hold is basically simple, but there are a number of practical difficulties. The essential parts are a switch that may be made for a short interval to sample the signal, and a capacitor to store the sampled voltage (Fig. 6.5.1).

When the switch S is made (see Sec. 8.2) the hold capacitor, C_H, is charged from the source, e_{in}. S is then broken and C_H retains the charge to give the output, e_{out}. There are several important considerations:

(i) The speed with which the switch can be made and broken.
(ii) The charging time-constant, dependent on C_H and the switch (R_s) and source resistances.

(iii) The read-out circuit and the leakage resistance of S and C_H, which cause discharge of C_H.
(iv) Delays in the switch relative to the control signal.

Switches can be of various types, the commonest being FET's (Sec. 8.1) for use from d.c. to medium speeds, and diode bridges for high-speed applications [P1, Q1, S1, D1, C1, B1, A1, x1]. Important requirements are that the switch should have low *on* and high *off* resistance, introduce minimum offset, have low signal feed-through capacity (when off), and couple minimum control voltage into the signal circuit.

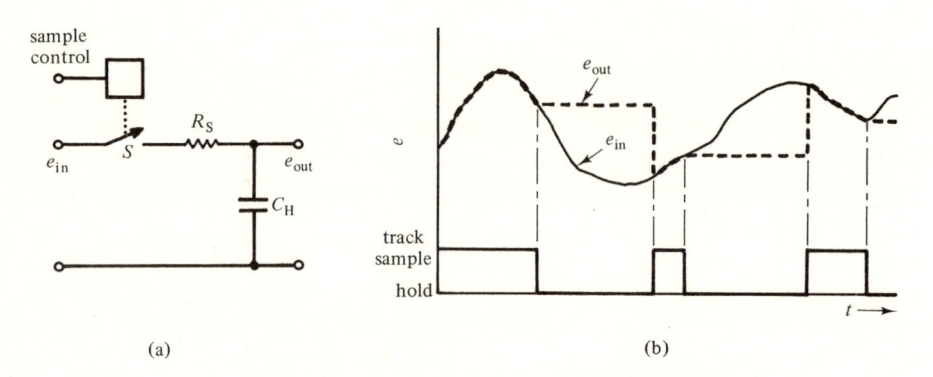

Fig. 6.5.1 (a) Basic sample-hold circuit, (b) idealized waveforms

The minimum sampling time is set by the charging time-constant, and the accuracy to which it is desired to work. For example, it requires about 7 time-constants for 0·1 per cent, and 10 for 0·01 per cent accuracy (Sec. 1.4). Since the circuit will be driven by some source the characteristics of the latter will also be important, particularly with respect to slewing rate, i.e., the ability to supply the current to charge C_H. The acquisition time is the time that elapses before the output settles to within some specified accuracy of the input (Fig. 6.5.2). This may or may not include the delay between the control voltage and closure of the switch.

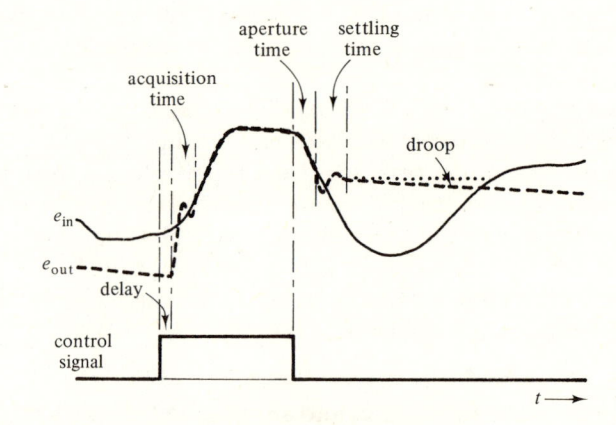

Fig. 6.5.2 Sample-hold parameters

The read-out circuit should have low bias current and high input impedance, so as not to draw current from C_H; Fig. 6.5.3(a). The switch, and the capacitor itself, must also have low leakage, and C_H must have low dielectric absorption (see Sec. 4.6(a), [u2]). These sources of leakage for the charge on C_H cause the stored voltage to decay with time (droop), the time to decay by the required accuracy of the system being called the hold time. The read-out amplifier will also have a certain transient response so there will also be a settling time (Secs. 3.7 and 4.8(c)) before its output is within the required accuracy of the final value.

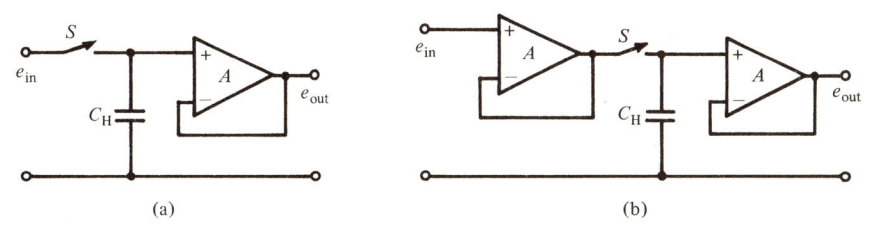

Fig. 6.5.3 (a) Open-loop non-inverting sample-hold, (b) addition of input buffer amplifier

There will always be some delay between the application of the control voltage and the actual operation of the switch. The switch-on delay is generally of less importance and can be allowed for, if it is constant. The switch-off delay is usually called the aperture time, though there is, unfortunately, some difference in the definition of this term [u1, a1]. The meaning used here seems to be the commonest. This delay can again be allowed for, but any uncertainty will cause a wrong value to be stored.

Though open-loop systems are employed for speed (Fig. 6.5.3) there are advantages in using overall feedback (Fig. 6.5.4) [Z1, o2, i1, e1, g1, z1, u1, v1].

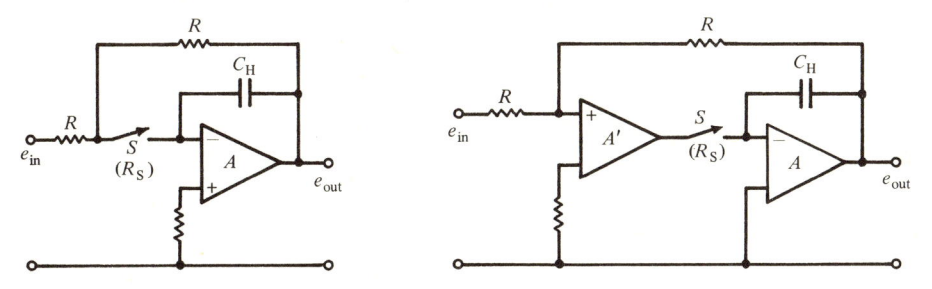

Fig. 6.5.4 (a) Closed-loop inverting sample-hold, (b) circuit with improved response time

The improvement obtained in using closed-loop configurations is primarily in tracking accuracy and aperture-time stability. Because of the large open-loop gain of the amplifier, e_{out} will be forced to be equal to e_{in} irrespective of the switch characteristics. Also, since the input to the amplifier is a virtual ground, the switch will always operate at the same point on the switch control signal, irrespective of the held voltage. This will substantially improve the aperture-time stability. The overall penalty paid is in slower response times. For the circuit of Fig. 6.5.4(a) the transfer function is found to be:

$$G = \frac{E_{out}}{E_{in}} = \frac{-\beta}{s+\beta}, \text{ with } \beta = \frac{1}{(2R_S+R)C_H} \qquad (6.5.1)$$

For a unit step input ($E_{in} \to 1/s$) we have, using standard transforms:

$$e_{out} = 1 - e^{-\beta t}, \quad \text{i.e., a time constant} \quad \tau = 1/\beta = (2R_S + R)C_H \quad (6.5.2)$$

To increase the response speed, a driving amplifier of gain A' can be added, as shown in Fig. 6.5.4(b) [z1]. Assuming A to be large, as before, the transfer function is now:

$$G = \frac{E_{out}}{E_{in}} = \frac{-\alpha}{s+\alpha}, \quad \text{with} \quad \alpha = \frac{A'}{2R_S C_H}$$

so

$$\tau = \frac{1}{\alpha} = \frac{2R_S C_H}{A'} \quad (6.5.3)$$

Fast acquisition and long holding times are generally mutually exclusive. If both are required it is usually simpler to use two cascaded sample-holds. The first samples the signal in a short time, the second samples the output of the first in a more leisurely manner and provides the long hold [h1]. If very long hold times are required an analogue-to-digital conversion is most appropriate [i2].

Decay rates in the hold mode can be estimated by assuming leakage and bias currents (i_1) arise from current sources. The hold voltage on the capacitor then decays at a rate i_1/C_H. For the small droops, of interest here, the exponential decay can be considered to be linear (Sec. 1.4).

A circuit closely related to the sample-hold is the boxcar integrator [h2, i2, j2, z1, k2, w1, y1]. The circuit configuration is essentially the same, but the sampling time is substantially less than the charging time constant of the hold circuit. This means that many samples must be taken before the output reaches its equilibrium value, so that the signal must be repetitive and the sampling instant locked to this in some way. This technique is used to improve the signal-to-noise ratio of weak signals by time averaging, and is just a generalized form of the lock-in amplifier (or phase-sensitive detector). These topics are discussed in Secs. 10.2 and 10.3.

The time relationship between the signal and the sample gate may be varied, to trace out the whole of the signal waveform of interest. This stroboscopic technique is, for example, the basis of sampling oscilloscopes and has allowed the extension of the effective frequency response (for repetitive signals) up to at least 10 GHz, compared with about 500 MHz for the best real time oscilloscopes [A1, B1, C1, D1, Q1]. If the stroboscopic slowing down facility only is required, then it is not necessary to have the long charging time-constant—the shortest time constant will give the fastest risetime of the system. However, since wide-band signals are usually noisy, sampling oscilloscopes generally have an alternative smoothed mode with an effectively longer time constant. When averaging is required the improvement in signal-to-noise ratio will depend on the ratio of charging time-constant to gate time, since this will determine the number N of samples necessary to reach equilibrium (there will still be noise fluctuations of course). The improvement will then be by a factor of approximately $\sqrt{N}$. If large d.c. drifts are present at the input, it may be difficult to separate the slow output *signal* from the drift. A technique for reducing such drifts is described in [z2].

There are important considerations to be made when reconstructing a signal from discrete samples. These are embodied in the sampling theorem [w2, x2, y2, A2]. This says that, for a bandwidth limited signal, i.e., one for which the signal is zero above some frequency, f_{max}, to detect every component of the signal the interval, t_s, between samples must be:

$$t_s \leq \frac{1}{2f_{max}} \qquad (6.5.4)$$

Thus, to detect a given frequency component requires a minimum of two samples within one period of that frequency. If samples are taken at a greater rate, the output will be smoother but will contain no additional information. However, if the signal does not meet the bandwidth limitation condition (or what is, in effect, the same thing, t_s does not meet the criterion of Eq. (6.5.4)), then frequencies above f_{max}, say at $f_{max}+f'$, will contribute to the measured component at $f_{max}-f'$, i.e., the higher frequency masquerades as a lower frequency component. This effect is known as *aliasing* and can cause serious errors.

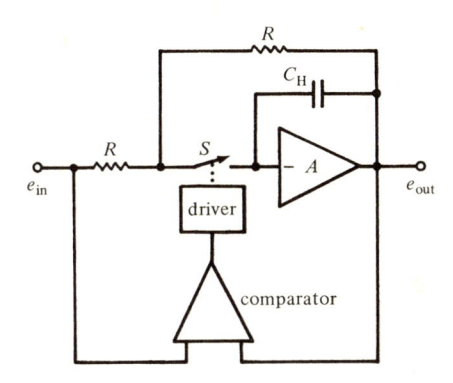

Fig. 6.5.5 Peak detector using sample-hold and comparator

If the switch of a sample-hold is replaced by a diode then the signal itself operates the gate. The hold capacitor will charge up to the peak of the input voltage, and the diode becomes reverse biased when the signal decreases. For a closed-loop system the forward voltage drop and resistance of the diode will be eliminated. This peak-detector will present a d.c. output voltage equal to the maximum past peak input signal. The orientation of the diode will determine whether the positive or negative peak is measured [c2, m2, n2, r1, b1, e2]. An alternative technique is to use a standard sample-hold circuit with the addition of a comparator whose output drives the sample gate; Fig. 6.5.5. The input signals to the comparator are the actual signal and the sample-hold output [u1].

The sense in which the inputs to the comparator are connected, and the required polarity of the gate control voltage, will determine whether the positive or negative peaks of e_{in} are followed. A small hysteresis (Sec. 6.1) should be added to the comparator to minimize false triggering due to noise.

The wide application and interacting design problems have prompted the development of a range of IC and modular sample-hold devices, so most of the detail design is taken care of and use is fairly straightforward [o1, E1, F1, G1, H1, I1, J1, t1, K1, W1, Y1, g2].

References section 6.1: Comparators and discriminators

a1   Chapman E, Cognac R: DC Comparator Operations Utilizing Monolithic IC Amplifiers; Motorola Application Note AN-405, 1967.

b1   Widlar R J: Precision IC Comparator Runs from +5V Logic Supply (LM311); National Semiconductor Application Note AN-41, Oct. 1970.

c1   National Semiconductor: LM311 Voltage Comparator; National Semiconductor Data Sheet Sep. 1970.

d1   Metz A J: Simple Tunnel Diode Circuit for Accurate Zero Crossing Timing; Rev. Sci. Instrum. 38, 1445–1449, 1967.

e1   Bhola S: Transitron Dual Comparators and their Applications; Transitron Application Report MD/AP10-68.

f1   Widlar R J: An IC Voltage Comparator for High Impedance Circuitry; National Semiconductor Linear Brief LB-12.

g1   Delaney C F G: Electronics for the Physicist; Penguin Books 1969.

h1   Gomez A: Designing with Integrated Comparators: Eimbinder J (Ed) Application Considerations for Linear Integrated Circuits; Wiley-Interscience 1970.

i1   Strauss L: Wave Generation and Shaping; McGraw-Hill 1970.

j1   SGS–Fairchild: The Application of Linear Microcircuits; SGS–Fairchild 1967.

k1   Tobey G E, Graeme J G, Huelsman L P: Operational Amplifiers, Design and Applications; McGraw-Hill 1971.

l1   Millman J, Taub H: Pulse, Digital and Switching Waveforms; McGraw-Hill 1965.

m1   Marconi–Elliott: Linear Integrated Circuits Applications Handbook; Marconi–Elliott.

n1   Cole H A: Differential Discriminator Circuits; Wireless World Dec. 1971, 603–604.

o1   Hoge F E, Nelson B E, Hines D E: A Slope Reversal Video Processor Having Amplitude and Pulse Width Discrimination; Rev. Sci. Instrum. 43, 1612–1618, 1972.

p1   Tyler C E: A Light Pulse Demodulator with Large Bandwidth and High Sensitivity; Rev. Sci. Instrum. 40, 1466–1467, 1969.

q1   Fairchild: μA760, A High Speed Monolithic Comparator; Fairchild Application Note APP-311, 1971.

r1   Fairchild: The μA750 Dual High Current Comparator and Some of its Applications; Fairchild Application Note APP-315, 1972.

s1   Fairchild: Voltage Comparator Applications Using the μA734; Fairchild Application Note APP-324, 1972.

t1   Signetics: High Speed Dual Differential Comparator/Sense Amplifier (NE521/522); New Electronics 14 Aug. 1973, 21, 22, 25.

u1   Smathers R T, Frederiksen T M, Howard W M: LM339 A Quad of Independently Functioning Comparators; National Semiconductor Application Note AN-74, 1973.

v1   Porges K G, Rudnick S J: Live-Timer Method of Automatic Dead-Time Correction for Precision Counting; Rev. Sci. Instrum. 40, 1–8, 1969.

w1   Rudnick S J, English J J, Howard R H: Highly Stable High-Rate Discriminator for General Use in Nuclear Counting Applications; Rev. Sci. Instrum. 40, 9–15, 1969.

x1   Signetics: Dual Zero-Crossing Detector 8T363; New Electronics 22 Jan. 1974, 40, 42.

y1   Kirsten F A: Nanosecond Coincidence Measurements; IEEE Trans NS-20, 22–35, 1973.

z1   Porat D I: Review of Sub-Nanosecond Time-Interval Measurements; IEEE Trans NS-20, 36–51, 1973.

A1   Gedcke D A, McDonald W J: Design of the Constant Fraction of Pulse Height Trigger for Optimum Time Resolution; Nuc. Instr. Meth. 58, 253–260, 1968.

B1   Hart M, Siddons P: A Complete Pulse-Height Analyzer on a Single TTL Chip (MIC-74135); J Phys. E Sci. Instrum. 7, 591, 1974.

C1   Griffiths B, Tan Z C: High-Speed Tunnel-Diode Comparator; Proc IEEE 62, 639–640, 1974.

D1   National Semiconductor: Comparing the High Speed Comparators (LM360, LM261, μA760, NE529); National Semiconductor Application Note AN-87, June 1973.

E1   Yamashita M: A Pulser-Controlled Dual Window Unit for Use in Gain Stabilization of Scintillation Detectors; Nuc. Instr. Meth. 114, 75–82, 1974.

F1 Rochelle J M: A Simple Differential Discriminator; Nuc. Instr. Meth. 113, 315–316, 1973.

G1 Church V E: A Versatile Anticoincidence Gate; Nuc. Instr. Meth. 102, 305–307, 1972.

H1 Cole H A: A Single-Channel Pulse-Height Analyzer with 100 Nanosecond Resolution; Nuc. Instr. Meth. 84, 93–101, 1970.

I1 Sattler E: Window Discriminator with Integrated Circuits; Nuc. Instr. Meth. 64, 221–224, 1968.

J1 Cole H A: The Use of Integrated-Circuit Amplifiers to Provide Variable Bias in Single-Channel Pulse-Height Analysers; Nuc. Instr. Meth. 79, 356–358, 1970.

K1 Signetics: High Speed Dual Differential Comparator (NE521/522); Signetics Digital, Linear, MOS Applications Handbook 1974.

L1 Johnson K R: Comparator Detects Volts in Narrow Window and Accurately Nulls to Reference Level; Electronic Design 27 Sep. 1974, 124, 126.

M1 Bui A, Snej G: New Simple Circuits to Eliminate Time Slewing; Rev. Sci. Instrum. 45, 1235–1238, 1974.

N1 Brunner R: A High Speed Dual Differential Comparator. The MC1514; Motorola Application Note AN-547, 1971.

O1 Hunter L P (Ed): Handbook of Semiconductor Electronics; McGraw-Hill 3rd Edn. 1970.

P1 Martiens C: Fast Single Channel Analyzer with Integrated Circuits; Rev. Sci. Instrum. 46, 486–487, 1975.

Q1 Advanced Micro Devices: Voltage Comparator AM686; Advanced Micro Devices Data Sheet 1973.

R1 Offerman R W, Schultz S E, Trimble C R: Active Probes Improve Precision of Time Interval Measurements; Hewlett-Packard J 27, Oct. 1975, 11–16.

S1 Bjerke A E, Kerns Q A, Nunamaker T A: Pulse Shaping and Standardizing of Photomultiplier Signals for Optimum Timing Information using Tunnel Diodes; Nuc. Instrum. Meth. 15, 249–269, 1962.

T1 Nadav E, Kaufman B: A Pulse Shape Discriminator with a Tunnel Diode Zero-Crosser; Nuc. Instrum. Meth. 33, 289–292, 1965.

U1 Hvam T, Smedsal M: A Voltage Sensitive Tunnel Diode Discriminator; Nuc. Instrum. Meth. 24, 55–56, 1963.

V1 Bell R E: Comparison of Leading-Edge and Crossover Timing in Coincidence Measurements; Nuc. Instrum. Meth. 42, 211–212, 1966.

W1 National Semiconductor: Voltage Comparator/Buffers LM361; National Semiconductor Data Sheet.

X1 Cole H A: Pulse Discriminator Takes Advantage of Backlash; Electronic Eng. 42, Sep. 1970, 81–83.

Y1 Widlar R J: Core Memory Sense Amplifier Designs Using an Integrated Dual Comparator (μA711); Fairchild Application Bulletin APP-123, Feb. 1966.

Z1 Gray P E, Searle C L: Electronic Principles, Physics, Models, and Circuits; Wiley 1969.

a2 Gedcke D A, McDonald W J: Constant Fraction of Pulse Height Trigger for Optimum Time Resolution; Nuc. Instrum. Meth. 55, 377–380, 1967.

b2 Jones G, Orth P H R: Time Resolution and Pulse Shapes in Zero Crossover Timing; Nuc. Instrum. Meth. 59, 309–313, 1968.

c2 Hazoni Y: A Tunnel Diode Univibrator and Pulse Height Discriminator; Nuc. Instr. Meth. 10, 231–233, 1961.

d2 Franzini P: Tunnel Diode Nanosecond Coincidence Circuit; Rev. Sci. Instrum. 32, 1222–1223, 1961.

e2 Whetstone A, Kounosu S: Nanosecond Coincidence Circuit Using Tunnel Diodes; Rev. Sci. Instrum. 33, 423–428, 1962.

f2 Texas Instruments: Differential Comparators with Strobe SN72510 (Improved 710); Texas Instruments Data Sheet July 1971.

g2 Texas Instruments: Dual Differential Comparators SN72720 (Dual 710); Texas Instruments Data Sheet.

h2 Texas Instruments: Dual Differential Comparators SN72820 (Improved 720); Texas Instruments Data Sheet 1971.

i2 Transitron: Dual Schottky Differential Comparators TSC2711/5711 (711 type); Transitron Data Sheet.

j2 RCA: Programmable Comparator with Memory CA3099E; RCA Data Sheet 1973.

k2 Precision Monolithics: Fast Precision Comparator Series CMP-01; Precision Monolithics Data Sheet Dec. 1971.

l2 Precision Monolithics: Low Input Current Precision Comparator Series CMP-02; Precision Monolithics Data Sheet Feb. 1972.

m2 Plessey: High Speed Comparator SP750B (100MHz, ECL); Plessey Publication P.S.1490.

n2 Wieber D L, Lefevre H W: An Amplitude-Independent Nanosecond Timing Discriminator for Fast Photomultipliers; IEEE Trans NS-13, Pt. 1, Feb. 1966, 406–412.

o2 Gedcke D A, McDonald W J: A Fast Zero-Crossing Discriminator for Time Pickoff with Pulsed Beams; Nuc. Instrum. Meth. 56, 148–150, 1967.

p2 England J B A: Techniques of Nuclear Structure Physics; Macmillan 1974.

q2 Karlsson L: On Compensated Leading Edge Timing with Fast Photomultipliers; Nuc. Instrum. Meth. 100, 193–199, 1972.

r2 Kinbara S, Kumahara T: A Leading-Edge Time Pickoff Circuit; Nuc. Instrum. Meth. 67, 261–266, 1969.

s2 Sinai R: A New Concept: The Elscint Snap-Off Timing Discriminator; Elscint Ideas in Nuclear Instrumentation, 1972.

t2 Signetics: High Speed Analog Voltage Comparator NE526; Signetics Data Sheet 1972.

u2 Signetics: High Speed (Schottky) Analog Voltage Comparator NE529 with Complementary TTL Nand Gates with Separate Strobes; Signetics Data Sheet 1972.

v2 Motorola: Quad High Speed Voltage Comparator MC3430/33; Motorola Data Sheet 1974.

w2 National Semiconductor: Quad Comparators LM339; National Semiconductor Data Sheet Aug. 1973.

References section 6.2: Multipliers

a1 Burwen R S: A Complete Multiplier/Divider on a Single Chip; Analog Dialogue 5, 3–5, 1971.

b1 Harris S: A Choice, Not an Echo: The AD530 vs . . . . .; Analog Dialogue 5, 8–9, 1971.

c1 Renschler E: The Monolithic Four-Quadrant Multiplier; Semiconductors (Motorola) 1970, 46–49.

d1 Analog Devices: Evaluating, Selecting and Using Multiplier Circuit Modules for Signal Manipulation and Function Generation; Analog Devices 1970.

e1 Renschler E: Analysis and Basic Operation of the MC1595; Motorola Application Note AN–489, 1969.

f1 Welling B, Kinsey L: Using the MC1595 Multiplier in Arithmetic Operations; Motorola Application Note AN–490, 1969.

g1 Gilbert B: A Precise Four-Quadrant Multiplier with Subnanosecond Response; IEEE J SC–3, 365–373, 1968.

h1 Gilbert B: A New Wide-Band Amplifier Technique; IEEE J SC–3, 353–365, 1968.

i1 Silicon General: The Wide-Band Multiplier—A New System Building Block; Silicon General Applications Bulletin No. 2.

j1 Burr-Brown: Quarter-Square Multiplier/Dividers; Burr-Brown Data Sheet PDS–201C, 1969.

k1 Renschler E L: The Linear Four-Quadrant Multiplier; Chapter 12 Eimbinder J (Ed) Application Considerations for Linear Integrated Circuits; Wiley-Interscience 1970.

l1 Micro Consultants: The Hybrid Multiplier; Micro Consultants Application Note AN-101.

m1 RCA: Four-Quadrant Multiplier CA3091D; RCA Data Sheet 1971.

n1 Parsons R: SN7497 Binary Rate Multiplier; Texas Instruments Application Report B82, Sep. 1970.

o1 O'Neill B: A Precision Four Quadrant Multiplier; Intersil Application Bulletin A011, 1972.

p1 Pouliot F, Counts L: Versatile New Module: Y(Z/X) at Low Cost; Analog Dialogue 6, No. 2, 3–6, 1972.
q1 Comins N R, Grant P D: A Simple Electronic Divider for Use with a Differential Reflectometer; J Phys. E Sci. Instrum. 6, 751–754, 1973.
r1 Faulkner E A, Grimbleby J B: New Type of Analogue Multiplier with Wide Dynamic Range; Electr. Lett. 8, 145–146, 1972.
s1 Counts L, Pouliot F: Computational Module Stresses Applications Versatility (AD433); Electronics 17 July 1972, 93–94.
t1 Topp J A, Schmid W J: Compensation of Source Fluctuation in Raman Spectroscopy by Quick Analog Dividing; Rev. Sci. Instrum. 42, 1683–1686, 1971.
u1 Jung W G: Get Gain Control of 80 to 100 dB by Using a Two-Quadrant Multiplier; Electronic Design 21 June 1974, 94–99.
v1 Burr-Brown: Multifunction Converter Model 4301; Burr-Brown Data Sheet PDS-307B, June 1974.
w1 Burr-Brown: A Primer on Analog Multiplier Specifications; Burr-Brown Application Note AN-51, Dec. 1972.
x1 Burr-Brown: Analog Modules Multiply User's Options; Burr-Brown Application Note AN-55, May 1973.
y1 Johannsen Chr R: Analog Pulse Divider; Rev. Sci. Instrum. 45, 1017–1021, 1974.
z1 Ferendici A M: A Simple Method of Automatic Optical Transmission Plotting; Rev. Sci. Instrum. 45, 1166–1168, 1974.
A1 Dobkin R C: True RMS Detector; National Semiconductor Linear Brief LB-25, June 1973.
B1 Sheingold D H: Nonlinear Circuits Handbook: Analog Devices 1974.
C1 Counts L: Reducing Multiplier Linearity Errors. Cross-Feed Reduces 2nd Harmonic Distortion and Feed through; Analog Dialogue 8, No. 1, 16, 1974.
D1 Korn G A, Korn T M: Electronic Analog and Hybrid Computers; McGraw-Hill 1964.
E1 Bredenkamp G: A Precision Current Multiplier/Divider; Proc IEEE 60, 1440–1441, 1972.
F1 Fairchild: The µA795, a Low-Cost Monolithic Multiplier; Fairchild Application Note 211.
G1 Gilbert B: A High Performance Monolithic Multiplier Using Active Feedback; IEEE J SC-9, 364–373, 1974.
H1 Bilotti A: Applications of a Monolithic Analog Multiplier; IEEE J SC-3, 373–380, 1968.
I1 Rastra: XR-2208 Operational Multiplier; New Electronics 1 Apr. 1975, 27, 28, 31.
J1 Philbrick/Nexus: Miniature Multiplier 4450; Electronic Eng. 43, Jan. 1971, 52–53.
K1 Analog Devices: High Accuracy, Two Quadrant Analog Divider Model 436; Analog Devices Data Sheet 1974.
L1 Ljung E: Accurate Wide Range Analog Multiplier; Electronic Eng. 47, July 1975, 35–39.
M1 Tobey G E, Graeme J G, Huelsman L P: Operational Amplifiers—Design and Applications; McGraw-Hill 1971.
N1 Frater R H: Accurate Wideband Multiplier-Square-Law Detector; Rev. Sci. Instrum. 35, 810–813, 1964.
O1 Burr-Brown: Analog Multiplier/Divider 4206; Burr-Brown Data Sheet PDS-330, June 1975.
P1 Stevens R T A: Ultraprecision Wide Range Division; New Electronics 11 Nov. 1975, 20, 24.
Q1 Burr-Brown: Analog Divider 4291; Burr-Brown Data Sheet PDS-336, Aug. 1975.
R1 Burr-Brown: Multifunction Converter $E_0 = V_y (V_z/V_x)^m$ (4301); Burr-Brown Data Sheet PDS-307D, May 1975.
S1 Burr-Brown: Low Cost Multifunction Converter $E_0 = V_y (V_z/V_x)^m$ (4302); Burr-Brown Data Sheet PDS-326A, July 1975.
T1 Gray P E, Searle C L: Electronic Principles, Physics, Models, Circuits; Wiley 1967.
U1 Hunter L P (Ed): Handbook of Semiconductor Electronics; McGraw-Hill 3rd Edn. 1970.
V1 Analog Devices: 6-Decade, High Accuracy Log Ratio Module Model 757; Analog Devices Data Sheet 1975.

W1 Analog Devices: Integrated Circuit Multiplier, Divider, Squarer, Square Rooter AD530; Analog Devices Data Sheet 1972.
X1 Analog Devices: IC Programmable Multiplier Divider Computation Circuit AD531; Analog Devices Data Sheet 1973.
Y1 Analog Devices: Internally Trimmed Integrated Circuit Multiplier AD532; Analog Devices Data Sheet 1973.
Z1 Analog Devices: Low Cost IC Multiplier, Divider, Squarer, Square Rooter AD533; Analog Devices Data Sheet 1973.
a2 Exar: Monolithic Operational Multiplier XR-2208/2308; Exar Integrated Systems Data Sheet Oct. 1972.
b2 Intersil: Four Quadrant Analog Multiplier 8013; Intersil Data Sheet Dec. 1971.

References section 6.3: Modulators

a1 Smith M: Numerous Applications of the SN56/76514 Double Balanced Mixers; Texas Instruments Application Report B84, Apr. 1970.
b1 Hejhall R: MC1596 Balanced Modulator; Motorola Application Note AN-531, 1971.
c1 Murari B, Bondini A: L025 Double-Balanced Modulator; SGS Product Profile 103, Apr. 1971.
d1 Motorola: HF Signal Processing IC (MC1596); Electron 31 Aug. 1972, 33–34.
e1 Beckley J C: Integrated Sound Intercarrier Amplifier and Transformerless Audio Stage for Colour TV Receiver; Mullard Tech. Comm. 11, Sep. 1969, 2–5.
f1 SGS: TAA661-IF/FM Amplifier and Detector; SGS Technical Bulletin 101, May 1969.
g1 Mullard: Dual Balanced Modulator/Demodulator TCA240; Mullard Data Sheet Oct. 1974.
h1 Signetics: Balanced Modulator-Demodulator N5596; Signetics Data Sheet 1972.
i1 Grebene A B: Analog Integrated Circuit Design; Van Nostrand Reinhold 1972.
j1 Goodyear C C: Signals and Information: Butterworths 1971.
k1 Betts J A: Signal Processing, Modulation and Noise; English Universities Press, 1970.
l1 Connor F R: Modulation; Edward Arnold 1973.
m1 Bilotti A: Applications of a Monolithic Analog Multiplier; IEEE J SC-3, 373–380, 1968.
n1 Bryant J M: Design Aids for Double Balanced Modulators; Electronic Equipment News Jan. 1972, 51–52.
o1 Renschler E, Weiss D: The Monolithic Multiplier as a Versatile A.C. Design Tool; Design Electronics Mar. 1971, 41, 42, 45, 46, 49, 50.
p1 Fairchild: Applications of the μA796 Modulator/Demodulator in Communication Circuits; Fairchild Application Brief APP163.
q1 Mullard: Applications of the TCA240; Mullard Technical Note 18 (TP1489), 1975.
r1 Smith K L: The Ubiquitous Phase Sensitive Detector; Wireless World 78, 367–370, 1972.

References section 6.4: Phase-locked loop

a1 Grebene A B, Camenzind H R: Frequency-Selective Integrated Circuits Using Phase-Lock Techniques; IEEE J SC-4, 216–225, 1969.
b1 Gardner F M: Phaselock Techniques; Wiley 1966.
c1 Roulston J F: Applying the Phase-Locked Loop in Communications and Instrumentation; Radio and Electr. Engnr. 41, 315–320, 1971.
d1 Mills T B: The Phase Locked Loop IC as a Communication System Building Block; National Semiconductor Application Note AN-46, 1971.
e1 Nash G: Phase-Locked Loop Design Fundamentals; Motorola Application Note AN-535, 1970.
f1 Renschler E, Welling B: An Integrated Circuit Phase-Locked Loop Digital Frequency Synthesizer; Motorola Application Note AN-463, 1969.
g1 Leonhardt R, Fleischmann H A: Pull-In Range of Phase-Lock Circuits with Arbitrary Feedback Factor; Radio and Electr. Engnr. 36, 101–110, 1968.
h1 Moschytz G S: Miniaturized RC Filters Using Phase-Lock Loop; Bell Syst. Tech. J44, 823–870, 1965.

i1   Viterbi A: Principles of Coherent Communication; McGraw-Hill 1966.
j1   Jakowatz C V, White G M: Self-Adaptive Filter Finds Unknown Signal in Noise; Electronics 34 No.7, 17 Feb. 1961, 117–119.
k1   Signetics: Phase Locked Loops Applications Handbook; Signetics 1972.
l1   RCA: COS/MOS Micropower Phase-Locked Loop CD4046A; RCA Data Sheet 1972.
m1   Exar: XR-215 Monolithic Phase-Locked Loop; Exar Data Sheet 1XR04, 1972.
n1   Exar: XR-S200 Multi-Function Integrated Circuit; Exar Data Sheet 1XR01, 1972.
o1   National Semiconductor: LM565 Phase Locked Loops; National Semiconductor Data Sheet 1971.
p1   Fahrenkrug C F: A Second-Order Phaselock Modulation Technique; Microwave J Oct. 1971, 40, 42, 44, 56.
q1   Goldstein A J: Analysis of the Phase-Controlled Loop with a Sawtooth Comparator; Bell Syst. Tech. J 41, 603–633, 1963.
r1   de Bellescize H: La Reception Synchrone; Onde Elect. 11, 230–240, June 1932.
s1   Morgan D K: The RCA COS/MOS Phase-Locked-Loop; New Electronics 20 Feb. 1973, 18–19.
t1   Connelly J A: The HA-2820/2825 Low Frequency Phase Locked Loop; Harris Semiconductor Application Note 605, Jan. 1973.
u1   Connelly J A: Interfacing the High Frequency Phase Locked Loop; Harris Semiconductor Application Note 606, Jan. 1973.
v1   Connelly J A: A General Analysis of the Phase Locked Loop; Electronic Equipment News July/Aug. 1973, 37–41.
w1   Kesner D: Phase Lock Loops; Electron 28 June 1973, 37–39, 12 July, 54, 55, 58, 26 July 31–32.
x1   Motorola: Digital Mixer/Translator, Phase-Locked Loop Component MC12000; Motorola Data Sheet 1972.
y1   Motorola: Emitter-Coupled Oscillator MC1648; Motorola Data Sheet 1972.
z1   Charles F J, Lindsey W C: Some Analytical and Experimental Phase-Locked Loop Results for Low Signal-to-Noise Ratios; Proc IEEE 54, 1152–1166, 1966.
A1   Moore A W: Precision Control of Motor Speed with Phase-Locked-Loops; New Electronics 19 Mar. 1974, 42, 44, 47, 57, 61.
B1   Schowe L F: Build a Wideband Phase-Locked Loop; Electronic Design 21, 1 Sep. 1973, 112–116.
C1   Signetics: PLL Applications; New Electronics 11 June 1974, 38, 41, 43, 46.
D1   Kesner D: Dynamic Peculiarities and Spurious Outputs in Phase-Locked-Loops; Semiconductors (Motorola) 1974/2, 8–14.
E1   Minnis T: Accurate 10MHz Reference Obtained from Counter's 1MHz Internal Standard; Electronic Design 1 Sep. 1974, 98.
F1   Isbell T D, Mishler D S: LM1800 Phase Locked Loop FM Stereo Demodulator; National Semiconductor Application Note AN-81, June 1973.
G1   Signetics: Digital, Linear MOS Applications; Signetics 1974.
H1   Raphael H A: Motor Control by PLL can be Achieved with a Microprocessor; Electronic Design 26 Apr. 1975, 54–57.
I1   Buckmaster H A, Dering J C: The Application of Phase-Lock Microwave Frequency Stabilizers to Electron Paramagnetic Resonance Spectrometers; J Sci. Instrum. 43, 554–557, 1966.
J1   Narath A, Gwinn W D: Phase Stabilized Klystron System and its Application to Microwave Spectroscopy and Microwave Frequency Standards; Rev. Sci. Instrum. 33, 79–82, 1962.
K1   Benjaminson A: Phase-Locked Microwave Oscillator Systems with 0.1cps Stability; Microwave J Dec. 1964, 65–69.
L1   Anderson A T, Sanders D E, Gordy R S: Dual-Bandwidth Loop Speeds Phase Lock; Electronics 48, 9 Jan. 1975, 116–117.
M1   Gupta S C: Phase-Locked Loops; Proc IEEE 63, 291–306, 1975.
N1   Connelly J A: Active Filter Improves Tracking and Capture Range of PLL; Electronic Design 1 Apr. 1975, 128–129.

O1 Dance J B: Hi-Fi Demodulator Circuit (NE563); Electronic Equipment News Jan. 1975, 71.
P1 Grebene A B: Analog Integrated Circuit Design: Chapter 9 Part II Phase-Lock Techniques; VanNostrand Reinhold 1972.
Q1 Veto K: Phase-Locked Loop Generates Clock from Nonreturn-to-Zero Data; Electronic Design 26 Apr. 1975, 90.

References section 6.5: Sample-hold

a1 Rouhof H: High Performance Sample and Hold Circuit; Texas Instruments Application Report B45, 1968. Design Electronics Jan. 1970, 40–45, 72.
b1 Bloyet D, Piejus P, Varoquaux E: A Sampling Linear Detector for Accurate RF Pulse Amplitude Measurement; Rev. Sci. Instrum. 44, 383–390, 1973.
c1 Hart B L, Barker R W J: 'Zero' Decay Analogue Store Using Guarded Gate MOSFETs; Radio and Electr. Engr. 42, 114–116, 1972.
d1 Fairchild: A High Speed Sample and Hold Using the μA715; Fairchild Application Brief 128, June 1969, Electronic Eng. 43, May 1971, 76.
e1 Chacko E, Bargh J K: Inexpensive Sample-and-Hold Unit is Fast and Accurate; Electronic Eng. 45, June 1973, 58–59.
f1 RCA: Bilateral Switch as Sample-Hold Element; Electronic Eng. 44, Oct. 1972, 31.
g1 Roberts J: Sample and Hold Circuits; Electron 22 Feb. 1973, 27, 29.
h1 Marshall F G: A Solid-State Sampling Circuit for Use at Low Pulse Repetition Frequencies; J Phys. E Sci. Instrum. 2, 347–350, 1969.
i1 Dixon G: Analog Switches in Sample and Hold Circuits; Siliconix Application Note AN74-2, May 1974.
j1 Shrum E V, Stephens W A, Ziock K O H: A Highly Linear Fast Sampling System for Non-Recurring Pulses; Nuc. Instr. Meth. 114, 87–91, 1974.
k1 Gordon B M: Digital Sampling and Recovery of Analog Signals; EEE May 1970.
l1 Dunlop J: MOSTs Store Analog Voltages for Long Periods; Electronic Eng. 43, Nov. 1971, 34–35.
m1 Shepherd I: Sampling Techniques in Practical Systems; Electron 22 Nov. 1973, 24, 29.
n1 Haynes G: A New Approach to the Sample-and-Hold; New Electronics 1 Oct. 1974, 17, 21, 22.
o1 Intersil: Low Cost General Purpose Sample and Hold IH5110/5111; Intersil Data Sheet.
p1 Yamashita M: A Precision Sampling Circuit; Rev. Sci. Instrum. 44, 638–639, 1973.
q1 Powner E T, O'Shea A F J: FET Sample and Hold Circuit Using Error-Corrective Feedback; Electronic Eng. 41, Feb. 1969, 209–211.
r1 McDonald J, Pinkerton A: 2 Stage Peak-Holding Circuit Stores Submicrosecond Pulses; Electronics 10 Nov. 1969, 105.
s1 Williams W H: Simplified Sample and Hold Design; Electronic Design 30 Sep. 1971.
t1 Stafford K R, Gray P R, Blanchard R A: A Complete Monolithic Sample/Hold Amplifier; IEEE J SC-9, 381–387, 1974.
u1 Sheingold D H (Ed): Analog-Digital Conversion Handbook: III.4 Sample-and-Hold Modules; Analog Devices June 1972.
v1 Bruck D B: Data Conversion Handbook: Chapter 4 Sample/Holds; Hybrid Systems 1974.
w1 Harris P E, Simmons B E: DC Accuracy in a Fast Boxcar Circuit Via a Comparator; IEEE Trans EC-13, 285–288, 1964.
x1 Kinniment D J, Aspinall D, Edwards D B G: High-Speed Analogue-Digital Converter; Proc IEE 113, 2061–2069, 1966.
y1 Friday R G, Mauro K D: A Computer System for Multi-Parameter Pulse Height Analysis and Control; IEEE Trans NS-19, 726–730, 1972.
z1 Reichert J, Townsend J: Gated Integrator for Repetitive Signals; Rev. Sci. Instrum. 35, 1692–1697, 1964.
A1 Carlson R, Krakauer S, Magleby K, Monnier R, Van Duzer V, Woodbury R: Sampling Oscillography; Hewlett-Packard Application Note 36, 1959.

B1 Tektronix: Sampling Notes; Tektronix Application Note 061-557, 1962.
C1 Zimmerman H A: Nanosecond Measurements with a Sampling Oscilloscope; Electro-Technology Jan. 1965.
D1 Carlson R: A Versatile New DC-500MC Oscilloscope with High Sensitivity and Dual Channel Display; Hewlett-Packard J 11, Jan. Mar. 1960, 1–8.
E1 Harris: Sample and Hold Gated Operational Amplifier HA-2420/2425; Harris Semiconductor Data Sheet Aug. 1974.
F1 National Semiconductor: Sample and Hold Amplifier LH0023CG; National Semiconductor Data Sheet Aug. 1973.
G1 Analogic: High Performance, Low Cost General Purpose Sample and Hold MP240; Analogic Data Sheet 1974.
H1 Burr-Brown: Sample-Hold Amplifiers SHC23; Burr-Brown Data Sheet PDS-29,A, June 1974.
I1 Zeltex: Sample/Hold Amplifiers ZD450 Series; Zeltex Bulletin ZD452, 1972.
J1 Hybrid Systems: Economy Sample/Hold Amplifiers S/H725; Hybrid Systems Data Sheet.
K1 Teledyne Philbrick: Economy Sample-Hold Amplifier 4854; Teledyne Philbrick Data Sheet 1974.
L1 National Semiconductor: Linear Application Handbook; National Semiconductor Feb. 1973.
M1 Fairchild: Multi-Purpose Programmable Operational Amplifier μA766; Fairchild Data Sheet Feb. 1973.
N1 Smith J I: Modern Operational Circuit Design; Wiley Interscience 1971.
O1 Tobey G E, Graeme J G, Huelsman L P: Operational Amplifiers. Design and Applications; McGraw-Hill 1971.
P1 Millman J, Taub H: Pulse, Digital, and Switching Waveforms, Chapter 17 Sampling Gates; McGraw-Hill 1965.
Q1 Hewlett-Packard: Characteristics and Use of HP Sampling Oscilloscope and Probe Accessories; Hewlett-Packard Application Note 44D, 1964.
R1 Faulkner E A, Grimbleby J B: High-Speed Linear Gate; Electronic Eng. 39, 565–567, 1967.
S1 Bosshard R: Feedthrough Induced Distortions in Sampling Oscilloscopes and Their Compensation; Rev. Sci. Instrum. 42, 85–88, 1971.
T1 Fairchild: An Improved Sample-and-Hold Circuit Using the μA740; Fairchild Application Report 297, 1970.
U1 Fairchild: The μA776, an Operational Amplifier with Programmable Gain, Bandwidth, Slew-Rate, and Power Dissipation; Fairchild Application Report 218, 1971.
V1 DePerna R A: Signal is Sampled and Held for 1 Minute; Electronics 1 May 1967, 71–72.
W1 National Semiconductor: Sample and Hold Circuit LH0043C; National Semiconductor Data Sheet Aug. 1973.
X1 Wheeler E E: Precision Peak-Reading Circuit; Electronic Eng. 39, Oct. 1967, 648–649.
Y1 Teledyne Philbrick: Microcircuit Sample-Hold Amplifier; Teledyne Philbrick Data Sheet Oct. 1974.
Z1 Datel Systems: Integrated Circuit Sample and Hold SHM-IC-1; Datel Systems Data Sheet 1974.
a2 Champeney D C: Fourier Transforms and Their Physical Application: 10.4 The Boxcar Detector; Academic Press 1973.
b2 Sanchez A: Understanding Sample-Hold Modules—A Guide to Their Specifications and Application; Analog Dialogue 5, No.4, 6–9, 1971.
c2 Graeme J: Getting Inside a Peak Detector to Make it Do the Job; Electronics 14 Nov. 1974, 145–149.
d2 Markus J (Ed): Electronic Circuits Manual: Chapter 74 Sampling Circuits; McGraw-Hill 1971.
e2 Baker H J: A Peak Hold Energy Readout Circuit for Use with Pyroelectric Laser Energy Monitors; J Phys. E Sci. Instrum. 8, 261–262, 1975.
f2 Teledyne Philbrick: Using the 4130 ADC Series, 4855 Sample-Hold, and 4550 Multi-

f2   plexer in High Speed Data Acquisition Systems; Teledyne Philbrick Applications Bulletin AN-19, Apr. 1975.
g2   Micro Networks: Sample and Hold Amplifiers MN343; Micro Networks Data Sheet July 1974.
h2   Blume R J: 'Boxcar' Integrator with Long Holding Times; Rev. Sci. Instrum. 32, 1016–1018, 1961.
i2   Ware D, Mansfield P: High Stability 'Boxcar' Integrator for Fast NMR Transients in Solids; Rev. Sci. Instrum. 37, 1167–1171, 1966.
j2   Swain D W: Boxcar Integrator Attachment for Oscilloscopes; Rev. Sci. Instrum. 41, 545–547, 1970.
k2   Collins F G, Katchinoski R: 'Boxcar' Attachment for Oscilloscopes Useful for Low Level Signals; Rev. Sci. Instrum. 44, 1178–1181, 1973.
l2   Clark W G, Kerlin A L: Solid State Gated Integrator; Rev. Sci. Instrum. 38, 1593–1596, 1967.
m2   Philbrick/Nexus: Applications Manual for Operational Amplifiers; Philbrick/Nexus Research 1968.
n2   SGS-Fairchild: The Application of Linear Microcircuits; SGS-Fairchild Aug. 1967.
o2   Widlar R J: Designing with Super-Beta Transistor Op-Amp ICs; EEE 17 Dec. 1969, 70–73.
p2   Farnbach W: A Scrutable Sampling Oscilloscope; Hewlett-Packard J 23, 2–8, Nov. 1971.
q2   Best A I, Howard D L, Umphrey J M: An Ultra-Wideband Oscilloscope Based on an Advanced Sampling Device; Hewlett-Packard J Oct. 1966.
r2   Smith J H: High Resolution Time-Domain Reflectometry with a Portable 301b Instrument; Hewlett-Packard J 21, 8–14, Sep. 1969.
s2   Hanson R C: How to Recover Weak Signals Buried in Noise; Hewlett-Packard J 18, 11–15, May 1967.
t2   Patstone W, Dunbar C: Choosing a Sample-and-Hold Amplifier is Not as Simple as it Used to Be; Electronics 2 Aug. 1973, 101–104.
u2   Lefferts P: Is There an Ideal Capacitor?; Electronic Eng. 47, May 1075, 62–64.
v2   Jones D: Application of a Monolithic Sample-and-Hold/Gated Operational Amplifier HA-2420/2425; Harris Semiconductor Application Note 517, Mar. 1974.
w2   Betts J A: Signal Processing, Modulation and Noise; English Universities Press 1970.
x2   Goodyear C C: Signals and Information: Butterworths 1971.
y2   Soucek B: Minicomputers in Data Processing and Simulation: Wiley Interscience 1972.
z2   Hidaka T: Time Domain Difference Amplifier; Rev. Sci. Instrum. 46, 152–154, 1975.
A2   Schwarz M: Information Transmission, Modulation and Noise; McGraw-Hill 1959.
B2   Porchet J P, Gunthard H H: Optimum Sampling and Smoothing Conditions for Digitally Recorded Spectra; J Phys. E Sci. Instrum. 3, 261–264, 1970.
C2   Lee Y W: Statistical Theory of Communication, Chapter 11, Sampling Theory; Wiley 1967.
D2   Hodby J: A Ratio-Measuring System for Use in Pulsed Spectroscopic Measurements; J Phys. E Sci. Instrum. 3, 229–233, 1970.
E2   Hayes S: Video Detector Stores Peak for Minutes; Electronics 19 Feb. 1976, 112–113.
F2   Analog Devices: Low Cost Sample/Hold Amplifier AD582; Analog Devices Data Sheet 1975.
G2   Tozer R C: Sample and Hold Gates Using Field Effect Transistors; Electronic Eng. Mar. 1976, 47, 49.
H2   Marshall S W, Pruitt R A: Digital Pulse-Shape Analysis of Repetitive and Nonrepetitive Pulses; Rev. Sci. Instrum. 38, 1622–1623, 1967.
I2   Grove W M: A DC to 12.4GHz Feedthrough Sampler for Oscilloscopes and other RF Systems; Hewlett-Packard J 18, Oct. 1966, 12–15.
J2   Analog Devices: IC Sample and Hold Gated Op Amp AD583; Analog Devices Data Sheet 1975.
K2   Andrews J R, Lawton R A: Electrically Strobed Oprical Waveform Sampling Oscilloscope; Rev. Sci. Instrum. 47, 311–313, 1971.

7 Power supplies

Almost all electronic systems will require some form of power supply, and performance of the system will often depend on the quality of this. Simple systems such as a thermocouple or photovoltaic cell driving a meter, are examples with inherent power supplies. The source of power will be either the alternating mains supply, or a battery. In the former case, it is necessary to rectify the input to obtain a d.c. output (Sec. 7.1), and in both cases it will often be required to regulate the output to be independent of variations in the source or load (Sec. 7.2). Although most power supplies are voltage regulated, it is sometimes necessary to regulate current (Sec. 7.3). As will be seen, power supplies are not limited to being *little black boxes* with two output terminals, but can be applied in a number of very useful ways (Secs. 7.4 and 7.5).

The development of IC regulators (Sec. 7.7) makes it simple to use several regulators in a system and to place these close to the load. High efficiency can be achieved with switching regulators (Sec. 7.8), portability and isolation with battery operation (Sec. 7.9), and simplicity with regulator diodes (Sec. 7.10) [y1].

7.1 Rectifiers

7.1(a) *Rectifier circuits and transformers*

To obtain d.c. from the a.c. mains, some form of rectifier circuit is necessary. The three elements required are transformer, rectifier, and smoothing filter. The transformer serves to isolate the output from the mains and to transform the voltage to the required value. There are three basic forms of secondary circuit, the half-wave, the full-wave centre-tap, and the full-wave bridge (Fig. 7.1.1).

The half-wave circuit is used only for low currents, as it has low efficiency and large ripple. The two full-wave circuits have greater efficiency, less than half the ripple voltage (at twice the frequency so making smoothing easier), and cause negligible d.c. magnetization of the transformer core. The bridge circuit has the advantages of a smaller transformer than the centre-tap for the same output power, and that the peak-inverse voltage applied to the rectifiers is only half, so that higher voltages may be obtained with the same rectifiers. This is somewhat unfair to the centre-tap circuit, since the bridge uses twice the number of rectifiers, and the former could do the same with two rectifiers in series in each leg. However, with rectifiers in series it is difficult to ensure that they share the inverse voltage equally, while in the bridge this is automatically achieved (E_T and E_C are, effectively, in parallel across either inverse diode). The bridge has two forward voltage drops as two rectifiers conduct in series, but if there are to be several voltage taps on the transformer secondary, the bridge has the advantage.

The relationship between the required output voltage and the r.m.s. transformer voltage is given in Table 7.1.1. If the rectifier circuit is to feed a regulator, then to allow for rectifier drop and negative ripple peaks it is more appropriate to use a value of 1·0 rather than 1·2, especially for low voltage supplies. For these there is also little to choose between the two full-wave circuits.

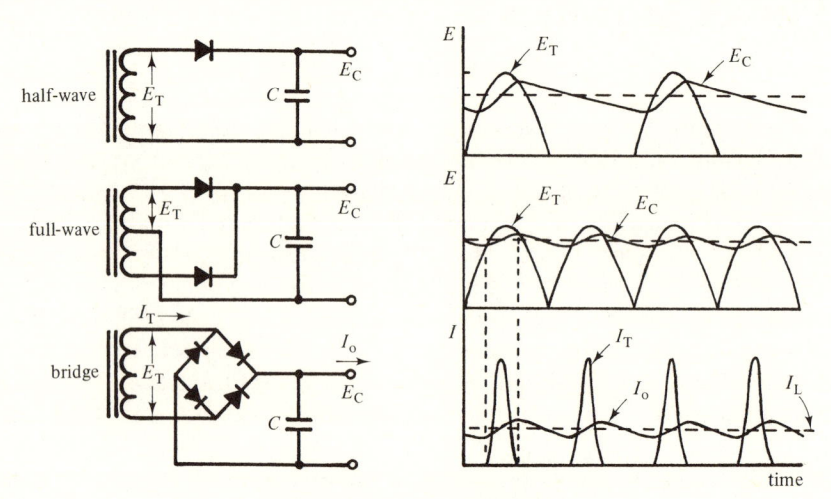

Fig. 7.1.1 Rectifier circuits

A higher voltage than that available from the transformer may be obtained, at the expense of output current, by means of various types of voltage multiplying circuit. In these, capacitors are charged in parallel and discharged in series to give the multiplied voltage. Addition of another rectifier and capacitor to the half-wave circuit, Fig. 7.1.1, gives a voltage doubler, Fig. 7.1.2(a), but this does not have a common input and output line. The cascade circuit does, and may readily be stacked to give any order of multiplication; Fig. 7.1.2(b).

Between the primary and secondary windings of the transformer there will generally be a significant capacity. To prevent mains-borne interference from reaching the output, it is highly desirable that an electrostatic screen be included between the two windings, and that this screen should be connected to earth. This also serves as a

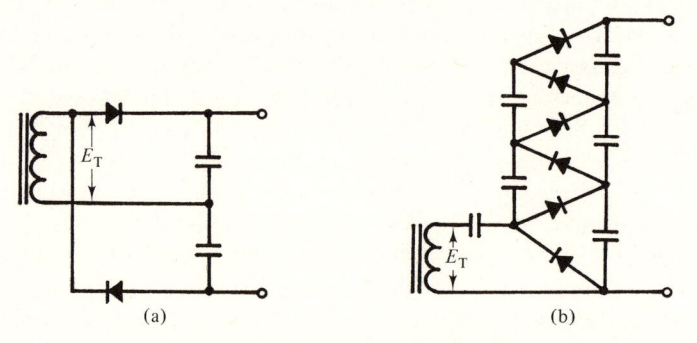

Fig. 7.1.2 Voltage doubler circuits

protection against shorts between primary and secondary, which could be dangerous. It should be noted that, surrounding the usual laminated core, there are significant alternating magnetic fields that may directly affect some components or induce signals in neighbouring conductors. Large induced currents in low resistance ground loops can produce considerable interference. Transformers, therefore, should be kept away from low level circuits. A change of orientation may also be helpful as is the use of high permeability toroidal transformers, which have much reduced stray fields [G1, H1].

For large output currents, say above a few tens of amperes, it is worth while to consider three-phase rectifiers, as these have greater efficiency and a factor of ten improvement in ripple voltage compared with single-phase circuits. The main drawback is that three-phase supplies are generally less easily accessible than single-phase. These circuits, together with those previously considered, are discussed in greater detail in numerous references, for example [a1, b1, c1, g1, h1, i1, p1, q1].

7.1(b) *Rectifier diodes*

Rectifier diodes are selected for a particular application on the basis of three main parameters: peak inverse voltage, average current, and peak current. Relationships between the various parameters are given in Table 7.1.1 for a capacitor input filter [a1, b1, c1, d1].

Table 7.1.1 Capacitor input filter parameters

	Half-wave	Centre-tap	Bridge	Doubler
$\dfrac{\text{d.c. output voltage } E_C}{\text{r.m.s. input voltage } E_T}$	1·2	1·2	1·2	2
$\dfrac{\text{peak inverse voltage}}{\text{r.m.s. input voltage } E_T}$	2·8	2·8	1·4	2·8
$\dfrac{\text{average d.c. load current } I_L}{\text{average d.c. current/rectifier, } I_o}$	1	2	2	1

In most cases, all these requirements may be generously met for a nominal increase in the cost of the rectifiers, which makes design easier and provides a safety factor.

In the half-wave and centre-tap circuits, the rectifiers have a maximum inverse voltage of twice the transformer peak voltage (or 2·8 E_T). In the bridge circuit two rectifiers in series share this voltage. The peak inverse rating of the rectifier should exceed the actual value by a fair margin (say 20 per cent) to allow for mains fluctuations and transients. This rating is of particular importance, as exceedingly short transients can result in breakdown and destruction of the rectifier junction. Rectifiers must not be connected in series to obtain a higher peak inverse voltage (PIV) rating, as there is no guarantee that the voltage will be equally shared. With special precautions to ensure that the voltage is equally shared, the rectifiers can be connected in series, but it is usually better to use specially manufactured units, for example the International Rectifier 1AV/1BV series with ratings of 2–13 kV at 10 mA and frequencies up to 100 kHz, the largest being only 40 mm long by 8 mm in diameter [s1, u1, E1]. Where transient voltages or fault conditions may result in exceeding the

PIV rating, reverse avalanche rectifiers, which have a characteristic similar to a high voltage zener, will give good protection. Instead of the junction undergoing destructive breakdown, a non-localized avalanche breakdown occurs, which can dissipate a considerable power for short periods [I1, J1].

Peak current must be considered under two headings, initial and repetitive. At *switch-on*, the filter capacitor is uncharged and presents an effective short. The initial surge current will be limited only by the source resistance of the transformer, which includes the transformed primary resistance. This non-repetitive surge current must be less than the limiting value fixed by the manufacturer, or the life of the device may be shortened. The limiting value is usually quite large compared with the average current rating, say a factor of 10 to 50, depending on type and form of encapsulation.

Since the capacitor voltage does not fall to zero between cycles, the rectifiers will conduct for only that part of the cycle when the input voltage exceeds the capacitor voltage (Fig. 7.1.1). Thus, current is supplied in a series of pulses where the peak value is much greater than the average output current. This repetitive peak current also has a limiting value, varying from about 5 to 10 times the average current rating [r1]. The power dissipated in the rectifier may readily be found since the forward voltage, V_F, is effectively constant at about 1 to 1·5 V, irrespective of current flowing or rating. The power is then just V_F times the average current, and it makes little difference that the current flows in pulses. (If the rectifiers were equivalent to a linear resistance, twice the current for half the time would give the same average current, but twice the power dissipation I^2R.)

Standard rectifiers are useful only up to about 10 kHz, because of hole storage effects, leading to long reverse recovery times. Above 10 kHz special fast recovery types must be used [e1, k1, m1, v1] (Sec. 7.8). For very low voltage supplies, say ⩽6 V, reduced rectifier loss due to very much lower forward voltage, may be obtained using Schottky-barrier (hot-carrier) rectifiers; see for example [f1, o1, w1, x1]. These have about 1/3 the forward drop of a silicon rectifier and excellent high frequency performance, but have increased reverse leakage current.

7.1(c) *Filter capacitors*

The value of the filter capacitor is chosen to give the desired ripple voltage. If the voltage decay between cycles is assumed linear, then the ripple is given by:

$$\Delta E_C = \frac{E_C T}{R_L C} \qquad (7.1.1)$$

where T is the period of the rectified wave, and R_L the load resistance. Values of $\Delta E_C/E_C$ of 5 to 10 per cent may be obtained.

It is important to note that, for feeding a regulator, it is the minimum value of E_C that must be considered. E_C must be chosen such that the minimum value that may occur will still leave enough voltage across the series element of the regulator for it to operate satisfactorily. This minimum value must allow for mains changes from nominal (say 10 per cent), decrease with load due to transformer and rectifier resistance, and the minimum of the ripple. A d.c. test meter will ignore the ripple.

Electrolytic capacitors, generally, are used for all but high voltage applications.

They are rated for steady d.c. voltage, transient surge voltage, and ripple current, all ratings being temperature dependent. If excessive voltages or ripple currents are applied, the capacitor will break down and overheat, leading to large internal pressures that may be released in a spectacular and messy explosion. They should be selected to withstand the peak a.c. transformer voltage, as the load may be removed.

If an electrolytic capacitor stands idle for a long period, the dielectric film deteriorates and excess leakage current will flow for some time until the film is reformed [B1]. There is also an irreversible deterioration with time due to the drying out of the electrolyte, but good quality units may be expected to have a life exceeding ten years. This is dependent on temperature and ripple current: halving the ripple current can double the life, while reducing the temperature from 50°C to 25°C may quadruple it. Since rectifier smoothing capacitors often carry large ripple currents, special types are made for this service for use in the more extreme cases [z1, A1, B1, C1].

More detailed analysis of rectifier circuits is usually made on the basis of performance curves derived by Schade [g1] and Waidelich [h1]. These are reproduced in several handbooks and application reports [a1, b1, q1, c1, d1, n1, D1], and allow rapid determination of voltages, currents, and ripple for any given conditions. From these curves values of C can be determined for given ripple and load resistance, R_L. For full-wave circuits, some useful design values are shown in Table 7.1.2, together with corresponding current ratings. These are not general relations and do not necessarily apply under different conditions, but they are appropriate for the average application. Note particularly that C is in farads.

Table 7.1.2 Design parameters for full-wave rectifier

Voltage ripple, %	$\omega R_L C$
1	70
5	15
10	7

R_L = load resistance (ohms)
C = smoothing capacity (farads)
$\omega = 2\pi f_{mains} = 314$ (50 Hz) or 377 (60 Hz)

$$\frac{\text{average d.c. current per rectifier}}{\text{d.c. load current}} = 0.5$$

$$\frac{\text{repetitive peak current per rectifier}}{\text{d.c. load current}} = 4$$

$$\frac{\text{r.m.s. current per rectifier}}{\text{d.c. load current}} = 1.3$$

$$\frac{\text{r.m.s. ripple current through capacitor}}{\text{d.c. load current}} = 1.6$$

7.1(d) *Controlled rectifiers*

A normal rectifier will conduct significantly with about half a volt of forward bias. A silicon controlled rectifier (SCR) will not conduct until a rated high voltage is reached, unless a suitable trigger pulse is applied to a third terminal, the gate. Once conducting, the gate has no further influence until the forward current falls below a low value holding current. The device then latches off until a further trigger is applied under forward bias conditions (Sec. 8.3). Controlled rectifiers can be used to provide variable output voltage rectifier circuits from a fixed voltage supply. This may be achieved by replacing the rectifiers in the circuits above, or for example, by the circuit shown in Fig. 7.1.3 [i1, j1, l1].

The full-wave rectified voltage is shown by E_1. By varying the phases of the trigger pulses, any output voltage from zero to the peak value, E_P, is obtained across C. This corresponds to trigger times from a to b. Triggers earlier than b will give a constant output equal to E_P. It is important that there be no capacity across E_1, so that it goes to zero as shown to ensure that the SCR latches off at low output voltages.

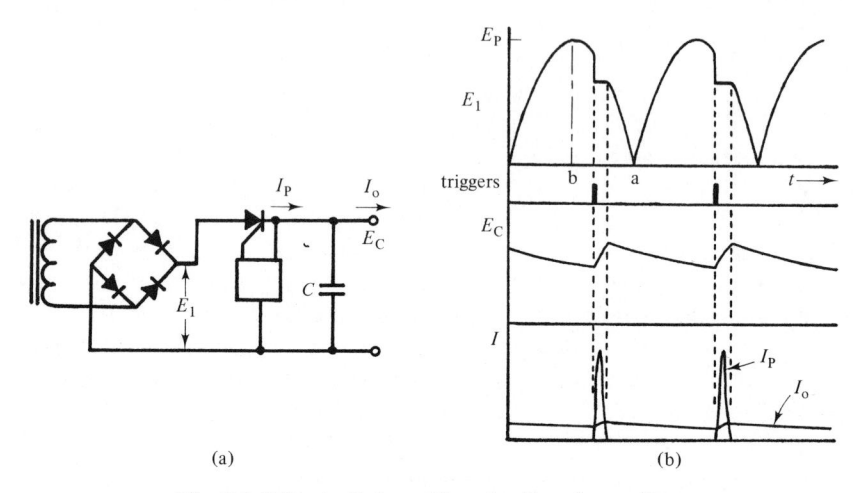

Fig. 7.1.3 Controlled rectifier circuit and waveforms

Since the actual conduction angle or time is quite short, very large peak currents I_P will flow, compared with the average output current I_o. This results in much increased power dissipation (I^2R) in the transformer. The peak as well as average current must be considered in selecting the SCR.

To obtain regulation, feedback from the output can be used to control the trigger phase. This is useful, for example, when a pre-regulator is required for a variable output regulator (Sec. 7.2). To keep the series element dissipation to a minimum the pre-regulator is controlled to keep the voltage across the series element constant. It is common for the triggers to be applied to the SCR via a small pulse transformer, so that isolation between the monitoring circuit and the SCR presents no problem.

There is a serious drawback to this type of circuit. The fast high current pulses result in considerable induced and radiated interference, which is readily picked up by the following regulator amplifier or other nearby circuits. In attempting to minimize the effects, good high frequency capacitors should be used.

7.2 Voltage regulators

The output from a rectifier circuit will have ripple and a variable d.c. level, both being dependent on the load. Fluctuations and transients from the mains supply will also be present. To obtain a stable ripple-free supply with low output impedance, it is necessary to use a regulating servo system. A series element between input and output is controlled by an amplifier, the input of which is the difference between the regulator output and a fixed reference voltage. Any change in output is amplified to control the conductance of the series element in the correct sense to counteract the initial change. Although there are many ways of realizing such a regulating system, only one particular arrangement will be discussed here, since it covers most requirements and has many advantages. The basic circuit, drawn in the conventional configuration for regulators, is shown in Fig. 7.2.1 [a1, b1, D1, E1].

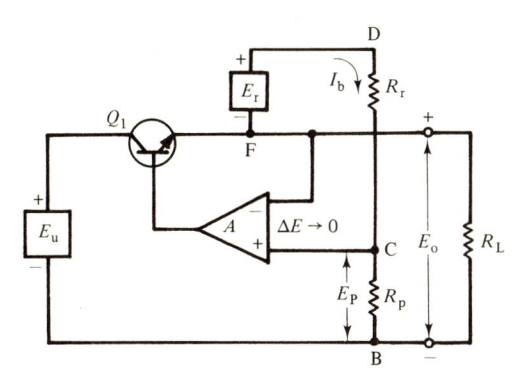

Fig. 7.2.1 Series voltage regulator (Adapted courtesy Hewlett-Packard)

The unregulated d.c. input voltage, E_u, feeds the series element, transistor Q_1, which controls the output E_o. E_r represents a stable reference voltage (e.g., a zener diode) and A is a standard differential input amplifier (Sec. 2.3). The connection of the amplifier is such that it always acts, via Q_1, to reduce the voltage between its inputs to zero, i.e., $\Delta E \to 0$. If this is so, then the voltage at C is equal to the voltage at F, or $E_p = E_o$. Since the voltage across the reference resistor, R_r, is thus kept constant and equal to the reference voltage E_r, then the current I_b through R_r is constant. Insofar as the input resistance of the amplifier is high, the same current flows through R_p. Thus:

$$E_o = E_p = I_b R_p = \frac{E_r R_p}{R_r} \qquad (7.2.1)$$

Since $I_b = E_r/R_r$ is constant, the output voltage E_o is proportional to the programming resistance, R_p. This provides simple control of the output voltage from maximum (E_u—drop required across Q_1), to zero. The output is also proportional to E_r and inversely to R_r, but variation of R_p is the usual choice. For precise voltage setting, this may be a helipot or a series of digital switches. It is usual to choose R_r such that I_b will be some round number (say, 1 mA), so that the programming constant will be a convenient figure (1 kΩ/V).

The form of Eq. (7.2.1) is reminiscent of a previous relation, Eq. (2.2.4), and in fact Fig. 7.2.1 can be redrawn as in Fig. 7.2.2 to show that the circuit is just a high power operational amplifier.

The corresponding points B, C, D, F are marked. The apparent use of the incorrect (+) input of the amplifier is compensated by the extra signal inversion in Q_1. Applying the usual analysis gives the same result as Eq. (7.2.1), $E_o = -E_r R_p/R_r$, the extra negative sign being only a matter of definition of the sense of E_o when deriving Eq. (7.2.1). Recognition of this power supply as an operational amplifier means that all the relations previously derived in chapter 2 can be utilized. There is an important limitation, however, in that a large capacitor C_o is usually connected across the output terminals, which results in a rather limited bandwidth. This capacitor is added to enhance frequency stability, and to give low output impedance at high frequencies where the amplifier gain falls off.

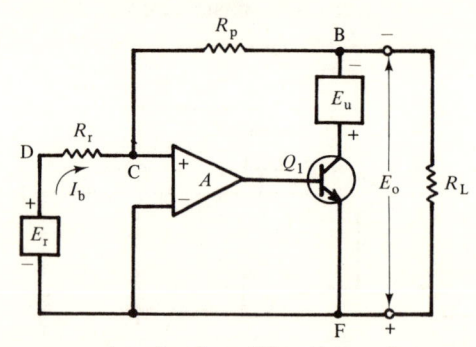

Fig. 7.2.2 Regulator as an operational amplifier (Adapted courtesy Hewlett-Packard)

It is possible to redraw Fig. 7.2.1 in yet another way, which shows that it has the form of a bridge (Fig. 7.2.3).

The amplifier acts to keep the bridge in balance by varying the conduction of arm FB. Then $-E_o/E_r = R_p/R_r$, to give the same result as before. All three views are completely equivalent, and this circuit is commonly referred to as a bridge regulator.

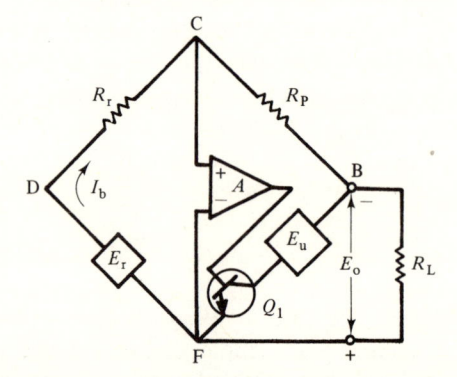

Fig. 7.2.3 Regulator as a bridge (Adapted courtesy Hewlett-Packard)

The regulation achieved may be readily determined by using the results previously obtained for operational amplifiers in Sec. 2.2. From Eq. (2.2.15) the output resistance is given by:

$$\frac{\partial E_o}{\partial I_o} = \frac{R_Q + R_u}{1 + AK\beta} \qquad (7.2.2)$$

where R_Q and R_u are the resistances of Q_1 and E_u, K is the gain of Q_1 and $\beta \doteq R_r/R_p$. This gives the variation of output voltage, ∂E_o, for changes ∂I_o in the load. Although it is not clear what values to use for R_Q and R_u, as these may be dependent on load or on amplitude of variation, in a good regulator the output resistance may be of the order of a milliohm.

The effect of changes in input voltage, E_u, may be determined from Eq. (2.2.10) and Fig. 7.2.2. As far as the output, E_o, is concerned a change in E_u is equivalent to a change of gain A in Eq. (2.2.10) for a fixed reference E_r. Thus, since $E_o = GE_r$:

$$\frac{\partial E_o}{E_o} = \frac{1}{1+AK\beta} \cdot \frac{\partial E_u}{E_u} \qquad (7.2.3)$$

The influence of changes in reference voltage is obtained from Eq. (7.2.1) directly:

$$\frac{\partial E_o}{\partial E_r} = \frac{R_p}{R_r} \qquad (7.2.4)$$

A further consideration, especially with regard to programmed regulators, is the speed of response. An undesired change in E_o can only be corrected, or a programmed change achieved, at a rate dependent on the slewing rate of the amplifier and Q_1. Since this is finite, there will be transient changes in E_o whenever E_u, R_L, R_p, or E_r are changed. If large changes are involved, the response will not be the same for increases and decreases, as it depends on whether Q_1 is on (active) or off. In the latter case, the response depends on the discharge time of C_o through the load, while in the former it depends on the active charging of C_o through the low output impedance of the regulator.

Other configurations of voltage regulator are discussed in [w1, C1, F1].

7.3 Current regulators

In most voltage regulators it is now customary to have some form of protection that limits the current that can be drawn. If this current can be held constant, irrespective of load, a further very useful facility will then be available. For example, in producing

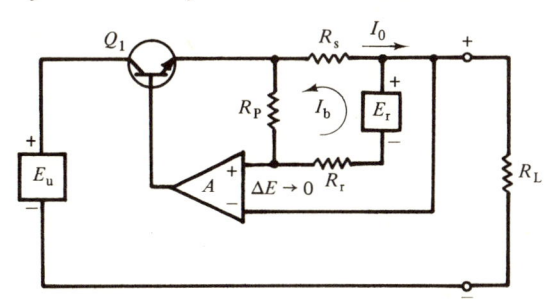

Fig. 7.3.1 Series current regulator (Adapted courtesy Hewlett-Packard)

a stable magnetic field by means of an electromagnet it is necessary to stabilize the current flowing rather than the voltage applied (copper has a temperature coefficient of resistance of ≈ 0.4 per cent/°C). A circuit arrangement for a current regulator, that operates in a similar manner to the voltage regulator, is shown in Fig. 7.3.1.

The output current, I_o, passes through a sensing resistor, R_s, the voltage drop across this being compared with that across R_p. Since I_b flows through R_s as well as R_p, the balance condition is:

$$(I_o - I_b)R_s = I_b R_p, \quad \text{with} \quad I_b = E_r/R_r$$

so

$$I_o = \frac{E_r}{R_r}\left(\frac{R_p}{R_s}+1\right) \qquad (7.3.1)$$

Thus, I_o is not proportional to the programming resistance R_p unless the bridge current $I_b \ll I_o$. Thus, I_b is the lower limit to the output current and, for very low currents, an alternative arrangement must be used.

For low currents the bridge arrangement is altered to remove I_b from the series resistance R_s. Figure 7.3.2 shows how this may be achieved [w1, a1, x1].

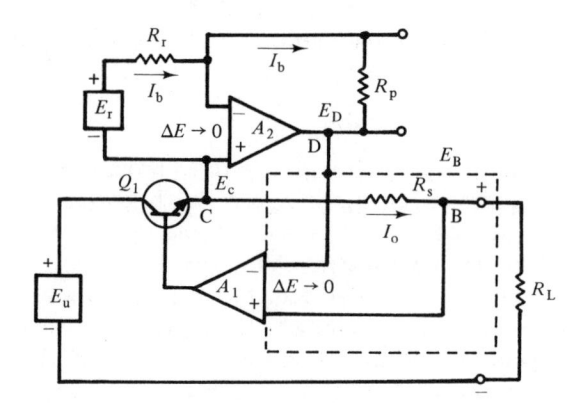

Fig. 7.3.2 Low current regulator (Adapted courtesy Hewlett-Packard)

The amplifier A_2 acts as a standard operational amplifier to give an output voltage $E_C - E_D = E_r R_p / R_r$, which can therefore be programmed by R_p. This voltage is compared with the drop $E_C - E_B = I_o R_s$ across R_s by A_1, which controls Q_1. Thus:

$$I_o R_s = E_r R_p / R_r \quad \text{or} \quad I_o = E_r R_p / R_r R_s \tag{7.3.2}$$

In low current regulators stray leakage to the positive output terminal could degrade performance. To eliminate this a conductive guard is included (shown dotted) which is connected to point D. Since $E_D = E_B$, the guard is always at the same potential as the positive terminal. Therefore, no current flows between them, and any leakage from outside the guard flows only in the guard circuit. A voltmeter connected to the output terminals would also draw undesirable current, but this may be avoided simply by connecting it to the guard instead.

Simple operational amplifier circuits may also be used as current regulators. If the load can be floating, Fig. 7.3.3 is suitable.

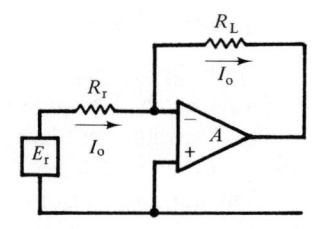

Fig. 7.3.3 Operational amplifier current regulator

If one end of the load must be grounded, then the reference voltage E_r must be floating, but common-mode limits must be considered. An alternative with grounded reference and load is the Howland circuit [y1, z1, o1], (Fig. 7.3.4).

The amplifier acts to keep the voltage between its inputs zero, i.e., $E_- = E_+$ (Sec. 2.5). The following equations can then be written:

$$I_1 a R_1 = E_- - E_o = E_+ - E_o = I_3 a R_2, \quad \text{or} \quad I_1 R_1 = I_3 R_2$$

$$E_2 - E_+ = I_2 R_2, \qquad E_1 - E_- = I_1 R_1 = I_3 R_2$$

$$I_L = I_2 - I_3 = \left(\frac{E_2 - E_+}{R_2}\right) - \left(\frac{E_1 - E_-}{R_2}\right) = \frac{E_2 - E_1}{R_2} \tag{7.3.3}$$

Load currents of either sense may be obtained depending on the relative values of E_1 and E_2. It is not necessary to have both input voltages; one or other input could well be grounded. For single input operation, it is more convenient to ground E_2

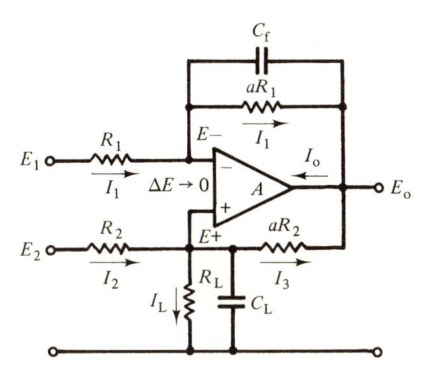

Fig. 7.3.4 Howland current regulator

than E_1, since R_2 is fixed by the load current and may be small, making I_2 large, whereas I_1 can be kept small by making R_1 large since I_L is not dependent on this. For the configuration with $E_2 = 0$:

$$I_L = -E_1/R_2 \tag{7.3.4}$$

$$\frac{I_1}{I_L} = \frac{-R_2}{R_1} \cdot \left(1 + \frac{R_L}{R_2}\right) \tag{7.3.5}$$

$$I_o = \frac{E_1}{R_1}\left(1 + \frac{R_L}{R_2}\right)\left(1 + \frac{R_1}{R_2}\right) \tag{7.3.6}$$

$$E_o = -aE_1\left[1 + \frac{R_L}{R_2}\left(1 + \frac{1}{a}\right)\right] \tag{7.3.7}$$

Thus, if $R_2/R_1 < 1$ then $I_1 < I_3 = I_2 + I_L$ and the circuit has current gain, although the effective gain I_L/I_1 may be greater or less than unity depending on the relative values of R_2 and R_L, Eq. (7.3.5). The equations for I_o and E_o fix the output requirements for the amplifier while, $E_+ = I_L R_L$ determines the common-mode capability. Note that if $R_L = 0$, Eqs. (7.3.6) and (7.3.7) reduce to the equations for a simple feedback amplifier Eq. (2.2.4), with load resistance aR_2, as they should.

A two-terminal current regulator is often of use. An effective circuit is shown in Fig. 7.3.5.

$V_{z1} - V_{BE2}$ sets a fixed current i_2 in R_2 which also flows in Z_2, assuming base currents to be negligible. $V_{z2} - V_{BE1}$ sets a fixed current i_1 in R_1, which flows in Z_1. Thus, each side provides a constant current which leads to more stable zener voltages, see Sec. 7.10(b), and gives a total constant current $i = i_1 + i_2$. Other types of two-terminal device are discussed in Sec. 7.10(c).

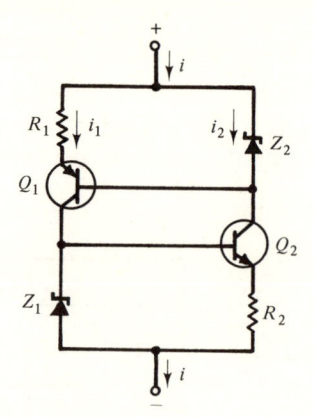

Fig. 7.3.5 Two-terminal current regulator

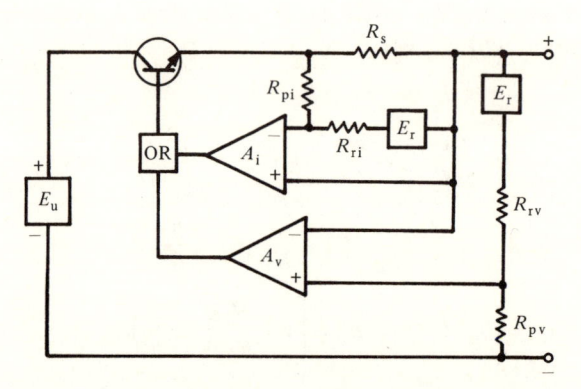

7.4 Constant voltage, constant current regulators

A combination of the constant voltage and the constant current regulators provides protection for the regulator and the load in case of faults or accident. The circuit of the combined regulator is shown in Fig. 7.4.1, and is a combination of Figs. 7.2.1 and 7.3.1 [b1, c1, d1].

Fig. 7.4.1 Constant voltage, constant current regulator

The two regulating circuits operate simultaneously except that an exclusive -OR gate allows one or the other to control the series element, depending on which has the dominant control voltage. The state of the gate can be used to indicate which mode is operational, if required [c1]. The particular mode of operation depends on the load resistance for given settings of the voltage and current programming resistances (Fig. 7.4.2).

308

For high resistance loads, R_L, the current will be small and the regulator will operate in the constant voltage mode. As R_L is decreased the current increases, the voltage remaining constant, until a critical value $R_L = R_C$ is reached, where the

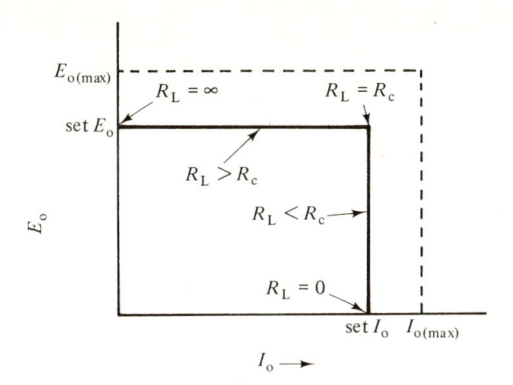

Fig. 7.4.2 Constant voltage, constant current regulator operating characteristics

current is that programmed by R_{pi}. At this point the current regulator takes over and the current is held constant as R_L decreases to zero. The corner is not sharp as there will be a small region where both regulators are active. Thus, in whichever mode it is desired to operate, there is a protection limit which can be set to suit the characteristics of the load. If the regulator is intended for constant voltage operation only, a simpler current limiting system can be used (Sec. 7.6).

7.5 Series and parallel operation

To obtain higher voltages or currents, it is sometimes convenient if several smaller supplies can be connected together to obtain the required output. With other forms of regulator, series and parallel connection present some problems, but the types discussed above overcome these very effectively [c1, d1, e1, k1].

For series connection to give higher voltages, the reference circuits of the *slave* supplies are disconnected, and the output of the *master* is used to provide the reference current I_{bs} through R_{rs} (Fig. 7.5.1).

The two slave regulators operate to keep the voltage across R_{rs} equal to E_o. Thus:

$$E_o = \frac{E_{rm} \cdot R_{pm}}{R_{rm}}, \quad I_{bs} = \frac{E_o}{R_{rs}} = \frac{E_{rm} \cdot R_{pm}}{R_{rm} \cdot R_{rs}},$$

$$E_{o1,2} = I_{bs} R_{p1,2} = \frac{E_{rm} \cdot R_{pm} \cdot R_{p1,2}}{R_{rm} \cdot R_{rs}} \tag{7.5.1}$$

All the outputs are proportional to R_{pm}, and variation of this single control will cause all the supplies to vary in proportion set by $R_{p1,2}$. The arrangement can be extended to any number of slave supplies. The diodes D across the individual outputs protect them from possible reverse voltage which could occur, for example, at switch-on where one regulator may come on before another. The maximum output current in this series connection is that of the lowest rated supply.

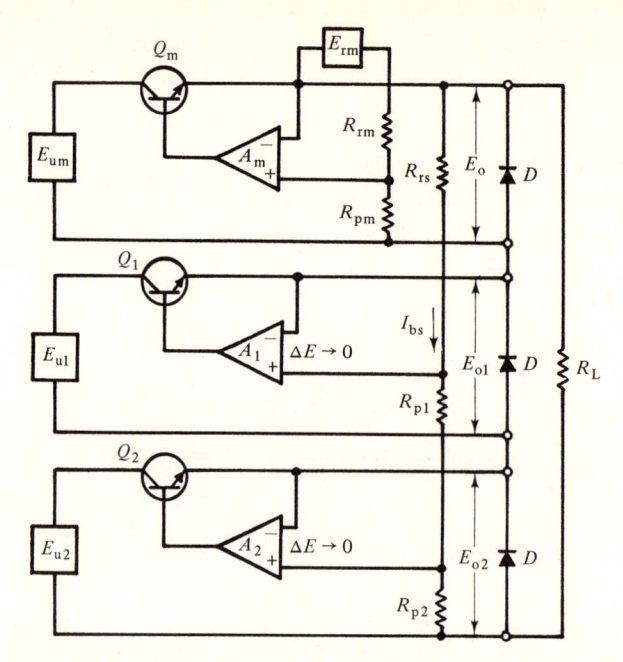

Fig. 7.5.1 Series-connected regulators (Adapted courtesy Hewlett-Packard)

For parallel connection (Fig. 7.5.2) the master supply functions normally, while the slaves operate to keep the voltage drop across their current monitoring resistors, $R_{s1,2}$, equal to that across the master's, R_{sm}.

All the current resistors have a common output terminal, the other ends of R_{s1} and

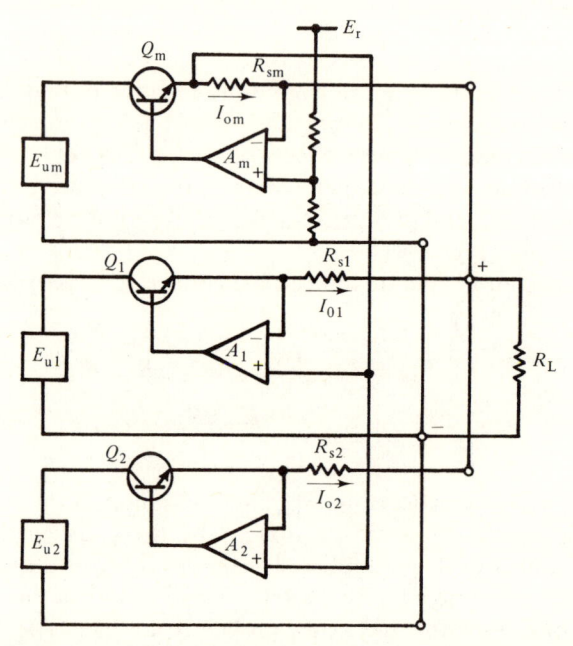

Fig. 7.5.2 Parallel connection of regulators (Adapted courtesy Hewlett-Packard)

R_{s2} being kept at the same potential as the inner end of R_{sm}. Thus, the individual output currents are inversely proportional to the monitoring resistors:

$$I_{om}R_{sm} = I_{o1}R_{s1} = I_{o2}R_{s2} \qquad (7.5.2)$$

This overcomes the most serious difficulty in connecting ordinary supplies in parallel. A good voltage regulator will have low output resistance, so that even a small difference in output voltages will result in a large current being forced through the lower supply by the higher [j1].

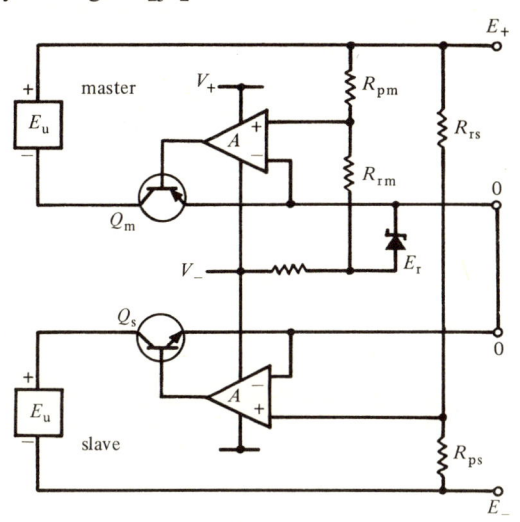

Fig. 7.5.3 Dual voltage regulator (Adapted courtesy Hewlett-Packard)

Balanced positive and negative supplies are often required, and two units in series, as discussed above, would be suitable. However, if a unit is required for permanent operation in this configuration, it is more economical to use complementary series transistors in the two supplies, so that both control amplifiers can operate from the same auxiliary supplies $\pm V$ (Fig. 7.5.3), which also provide for the reference voltage, E_r. The negative supply is referenced to the positive output so that R_{pm} varies both outputs E_+, E_- simultaneously.

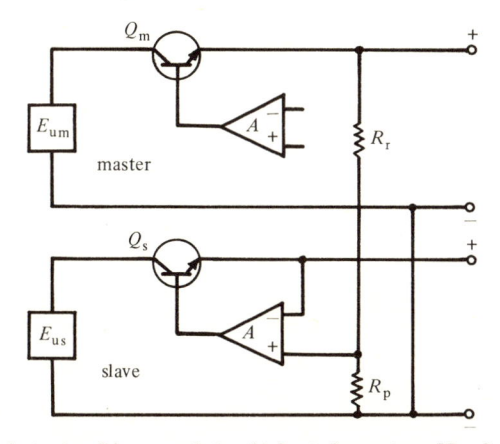

Fig. 7.5.4 Auto-tracking regulator (Adapted courtesy Hewlett-Packard)

311

All the control elements are near ground potential, which is of particular convenience for high voltage supplies. If the two supplies are of the same polarity, then the higher voltage unit must be the master: if both voltages are the same $R_r = 0$ (Fig. 7.5.4).

A further variation leads to the power supply/amplifier configuration. It has already been shown (Fig. 7.2.2) how the regulator can be drawn in the operational amplifier form, but this circuit is only capable of providing a unipolar output. To obtain an output that can be varied from plus to minus through zero, the circuit of Fig. 7.5.5 may be used [f1, b1].

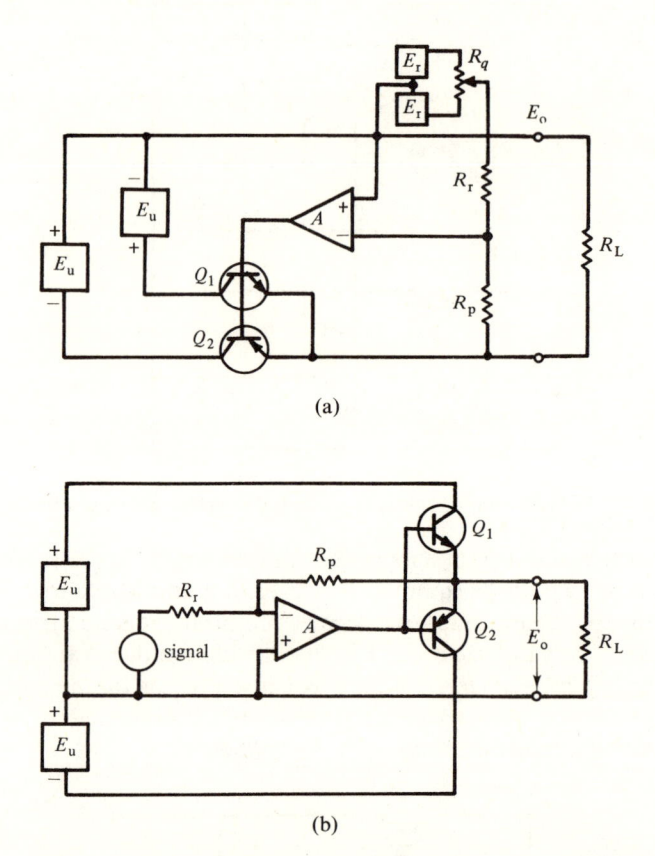

Fig. 7.5.5 Power supply amplifier configuration, (a) power supply, (b) amplifier (Adapted courtesy Hewlett-Packard)

In the power supply mode, Fig. 7.5.5(a), the bipolar reference voltage, E_r, gives a bipolar output, E_o, by turning on the complementary transistors Q_1 or Q_2, either through variation of R_q, or by switching the appropriate reference voltage and variation of R_p. The former, however, does not give a linear output variation, since the effective R_r is varying also. In the amplifier mode, Fig. 7.5.5(b), the reference voltage is replaced by an external signal, to give a bipolar power operational amplifier of gain $-R_p/R_r$. To obtain a useful frequency response the usual capacitors across the output must be eliminated, and other means of ensuring the frequency stability and low output impedance employed.

A low voltage regulator can be adapted to regulate a much higher voltage by using the *piggy-back* technique (Fig. 7.5.6) [d1]. The programming resistor R_p is connected across both supplies so that the regulator corrects for variations of both. The output, E_o, is set to be E_{u1} plus, say, half the available voltage $E_{o2(max)}$, so that control will be exercised for variations of about $\frac{1}{2}E_{o2(max)}$. The diode D ensures that reverse voltage will not damage the regulator.

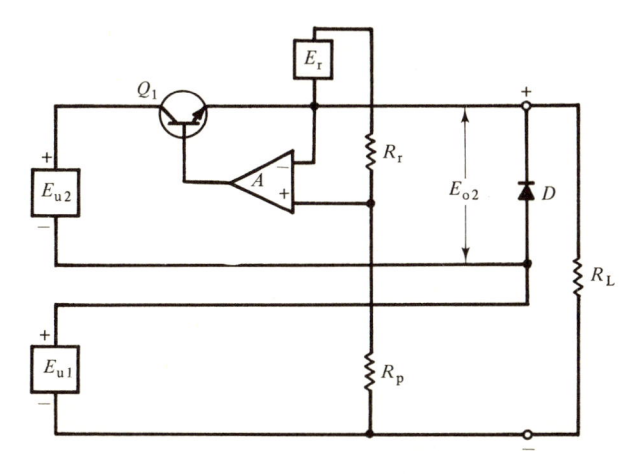

Fig. 7.5.6 Piggy-back regulator (Adapted courtesy Hewlett-Packard)

7.6 Protection and ancillary circuits

Some protective measures have been discussed above, but there are a number of others that are desirable or useful. Several of these are illustrated in Fig. 7.6.1.

Diodes, $D_{1,2}$, protect the amplifier input. Since the voltage between the inputs is normally zero the diodes are non-conducting and, hence, have no effect unless there is some fault condition.

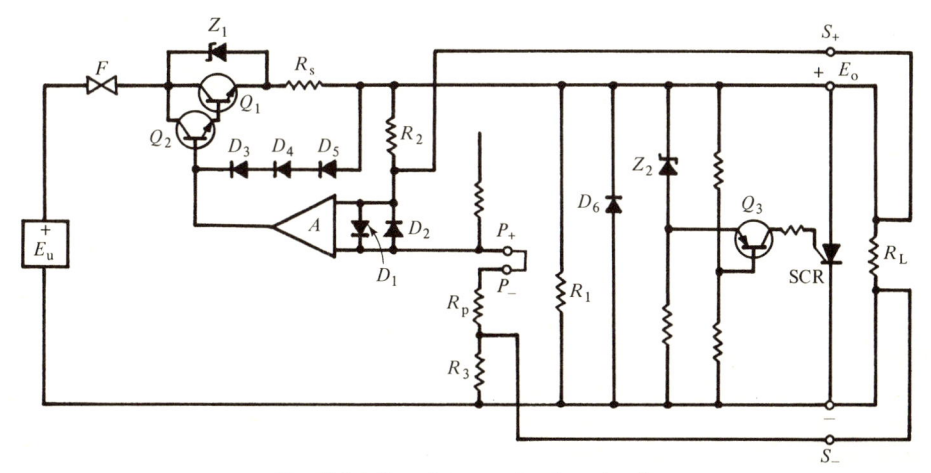

Fig. 7.6.1 Regulator protection circuits

313

If the output is shorted, the full input voltage appears across Q_1. If this could exceed the breakdown voltage of Q_1, a suitable zener diode Z_1 should be included, which must be capable of carrying the maximum fault current for long enough to allow the fuse F to blow. The selection of suitable series transistors is discussed in [j1, m1] (Sec. 1.9).

When the full constant current performance is not required, a simpler current limiting circuit may be used (R_s, D_{3-5}). The output current, I_o, produces a voltage across R_s. When this exceeds the forward voltage of one of the diodes (the other two compensate for the voltage across the two emitter–base junctions of Q_1 and Q_2), the diodes conduct and bypass further drive from Q_2. The output will vary as shown in Fig. 7.6.2(b) [e1, r1, n1].

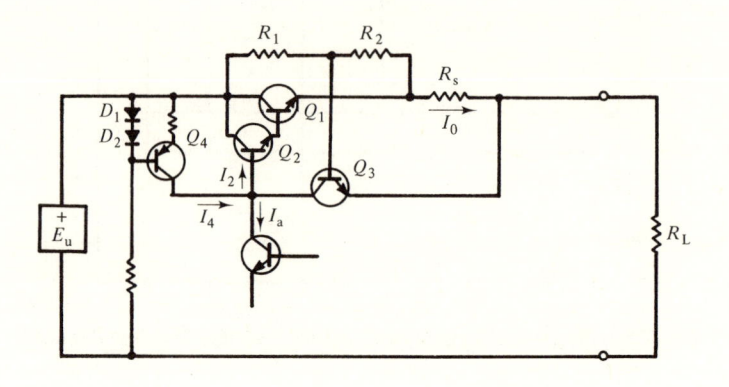

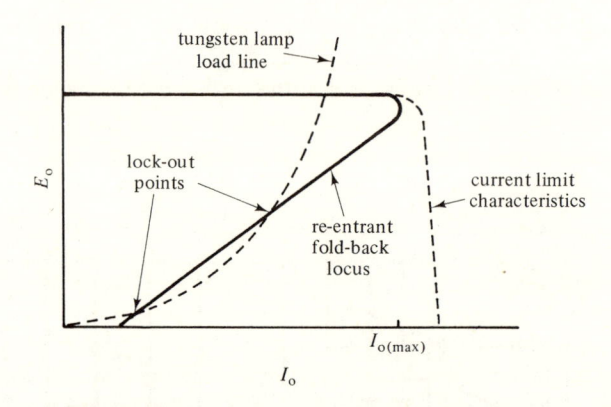

Fig. 7.6.2 (a) Foldback overload protection, (b) overload characteristics

Diode D_6, Fig. 7.6.1, protects the output against externally applied reverse voltages, and should be capable of carrying substantial current.

With no load connected, the leakage current through $Q_{1,2}$ has nowhere to go, so E_o will rise, and this A will try, in vain, to correct. A suitable bleeder resistor R_1 should be included, which also ensures discharge of the output capacitor.

In some situations it would be disastrous if the output voltage, E_o, rose above its set value. This is particularly serious when devices are operated near to their absolute maximum supply voltage as, for example, in logic IC's. The overvoltage *crowbar* circuit (SCR, Q_3, Z_2) operates to short circuit the output, in case E_o rises above some preset value. The base of Q_3 is set equal to the zener voltage. A small increase of E_o above its nominal value causes Q_3 to conduct and switch on the silicon controlled rectifier (SCR), which stays on and shorts the output. It will remain in this state until the input power is removed [f1, g1].

The various current control systems described, so far, result in large power dissipation in the series control element for small or zero load resistance, since there will be a large voltage across it while it is passing maximum current. To avoid this, the regulator can be given a foldback or re-entrant characteristic using the circuit shown in Fig. 7.6.2(a) [a1, b1, c1].

Q_4 and $D_{1,2}$ form a constant current source fixing I_4, which is normally equal to $I_a + I_2$. If R_L is decreased, the output current I_o increases and eventually Q_3 starts conducting, stealing current from the base drive to Q_2. The output voltage, E_o, begins to decrease and turns on Q_3 further, as a result of the increased drop across R_2. This positive feedback has a loop-gain <1, so the system is still stable. Further decrease of R_L will reduce E_o and I_o along the foldback locus until, when $R_L = 0$, $E_o = 0$ and $I_o = I_L$. The ratio $I_{o(max)}/I_L$ is a measure of the efficiency of the foldback protection, and may have a value of 10 or 20. The aim is to make the power dissipation in Q_1 ($=E_u I_L$) less than the maximum dissipation in normal operation ($=(E_u - E_o)I_{o(max)}$). If the short circuit is removed, the regulator will return to normal unless the contribution to the base current of Q_3 from R_1, R_2 is greater than that from the drop across R_s due to I_o. In this case, the positive feedback loop-gain has become >1 and the regulator will remain shut down. A reset control is then required to restore normal operation. The positive feedback can be controlled by variation of R_2 [t1].

Regulators with re-entrant characteristics are not suitable for use with some types of non-linear load, e.g., tungsten lamps. As shown in Fig. 7.6.2(b), the lamp load line may cross the regulator characteristic at three places, and could well lock-out at one of the two on the re-entrant section. Some regulators delay the implementation of the re-entrant characteristic, and operate in a current limit mode for a short time (≈ 200 ms) to overcome this difficulty.

The voltage drop, due to the resistance of the leads from the regulator to the load, will degrade the voltage regulation at the load if a substantial current is drawn. For example, a current of 10 A in 16 gauge wire results in a voltage drop of 120 mV/metre. To eliminate this problem, separate sensing terminals (S_+, S_-, Fig. 7.6.1) are provided. For remote sensing these are connected by separate leads directly to the terminals of the load, so that the voltage here, rather than at the ($+$), ($-$) terminals, is regulated. The low value resistors R_2, R_3 are included in case S_+, S_- are accidently left unconnected: in normal use they should be connected directly to ($+$) and ($-$) [u1, v1].

For remote programming, R_p may either be removed to the remote location, or left at zero and an external resistance connected between P_+ and P_-, which are otherwise shorted. This allows, for example, the control of light output using a photoresistor or of temperature using a thermistor [u1]. If voltage programming is used, many other control systems are possible. In this case, the programming resistor may still be required to set some zero level.

7.7 IC regulators

The considerable demand for power supplies has led to the design and production of many different types of IC regulator [p1, x1, a1, t1]. These can be divided into two classes, the flexible general purpose and the completely integrated dedicated types. An example of each of these, types 723 and L036, will be examined in detail.

The 723 is a general purpose type that can be applied as a series positive or negative, floating, shunt, or switching voltage, or a current regulator. To provide this versatility, the device is provided with numerous access connection points, so that external

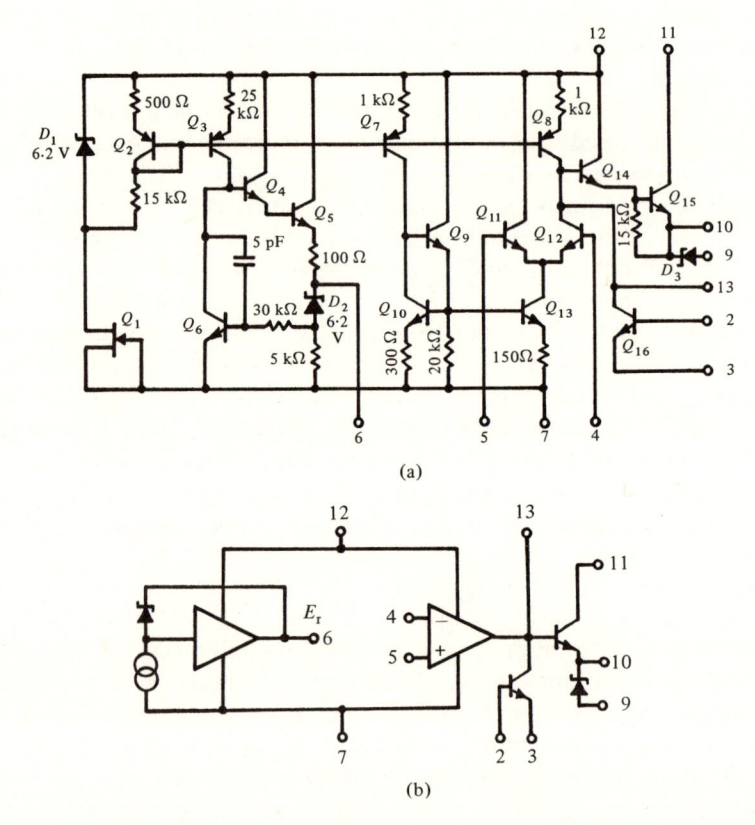

Fig. 7.7.1 Type 723 IC regulator, (a) schematic, (b) equivalent circuit (Courtesy Fairchild Semiconductor)

connections and components may be added to obtain the desired performance. The schematic and equivalent circuits are shown in Fig. 7.7.1 [s1].

Q_1, Q_2, and D_1 provide a stable bias voltage for the three constant current sources Q_3, Q_7, Q_8. The regulator reference voltage is provided by D_2 and the voltage reference amplifier Q_4, Q_5, Q_6. The output regulator amplifier consists of Q_{11}, Q_{12} with constant current tail Q_9, Q_{10}, Q_{13}, and load Q_8. The emitter follower, Q_{14}, drives the series transistor Q_{15}, and Q_{16} allows current limiting or foldback to be applied.

An indication of the performance of the 723, together with that of several other types, is given in Table 7.7.1. The performance is not limited to the maximum values

Table 7.7.1 Comparison of IC regulators

	V_{in} (abs. max)	V_{out}	I_{out} (mA)	Ripple rejection (dB)	Load regulation (%)	Comments
µA723	40	2–37	50	85	0·03	External transistor for increased current
L036	27	12	720	60	0·3	Fixed voltage series. Re-entrant protection
MC1469	35	3–32	600	85	0·005	MC1463 for negative outputs
SG3502	50($\pm$25)	0–23	100	75	0·02	$\pm$ Dual regulator
LM309	35	5	>1000	75	1	Fixed voltage. Current limiting and thermal shutdown
LM320	−30	−5 to −15	>1000	70	30 mV	Fixed voltage series. Current limit and thermal shutdown
LM340	35 (40)	5 to 24	>1000	60	100 mV max	Fixed voltage series. Current limit and thermal shutdown
LM323	20	5	3000	65	0·5	Fixed voltage. Current limiting and thermal shutdown
µA7800	35 (40)	5 to 24	1000	65	0·08	Fixed voltage series. Current foldback and thermal limiting. µA78N00, MC7900 negative equivalents

shown in the table; with external components the ratings may readily be increased to hundreds of volts and tens of amperes. Details of the circuits are given in the data sheet or in [s1] with additional applications in [b1, i1]. To illustrate the use, circuits for a basic and a high current regulator are shown in Fig. 7.7.2.

For the basic regulator, the design equations are:

$$E_o = E_r \left(\frac{R_1 + R_2}{R_2} \right)$$

$$E_r = 7\cdot 15 \text{ V}, \quad \frac{E_o}{R_1 + R_2} \doteq 1 \text{ mA} \tag{7.7.1}$$

$$R_3 = \frac{R_1 R_2}{R_1 + R_2} \quad \text{for minimum temperature drift}$$

$$I_{lim} = \frac{E_s}{R_s}, \quad E_s = 0\cdot 65 \text{ V at } 25°C$$

For larger output currents, an external power transistor is added, as shown in Fig. 7.7.2(b). Because of the extra gain, this requires an increase of C_1 to maintain stability. The maximum output current will now be about 5 A, this being set by the maximum IC output current times the power transistor h_{FE}.

As an example of the preset output IC regulator, the type L036 will be examined [c1]. This is one of a series that have commonly used output voltages of 5, 12, and 15 V. They are supplied in a TO-3 package, which may readily be bolted to a heat sink and which allows a substantial output current (Table 7.7.1). A companion

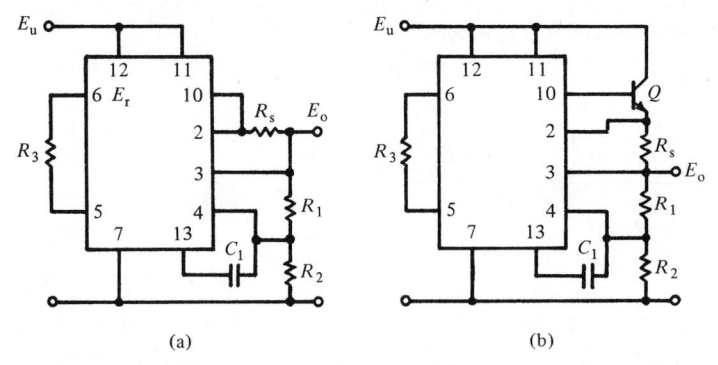

Fig. 7.7.2 Type 723 IC regulator application, (a) basic, (b) high current

series (TBA 625) in the smaller TO-39 can, has a smaller current rating but allows the regulator to be located on the circuit board adjacent to where the power is required. This may eliminate long supply leads or provide isolation from other parts of the circuit.

The circuit of the L036 is shown in Fig. 7.7.3.

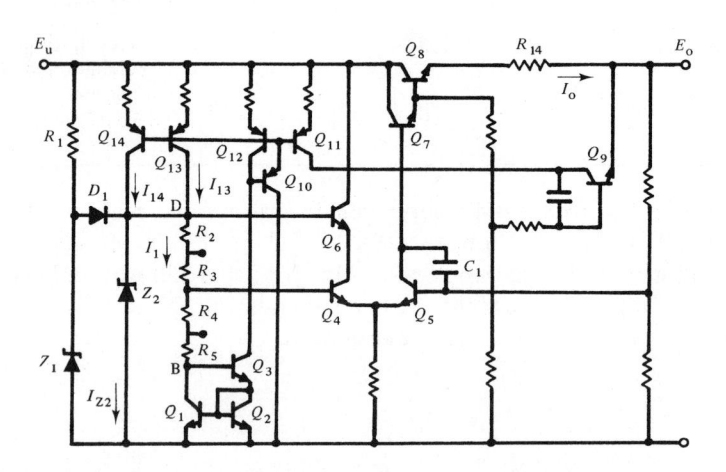

Fig. 7.7.3 Type L036 preset voltage IC regulator (Courtesy SGS-ATES)

Q_7 and Q_8 are the driver and series transistors. The control amplifier, Q_4, Q_5, operates with constant current load Q_{11} and low impedance supply Q_6; C_1 provides frequency stability. Q_{12}, Q_{13}, and Q_{14} are biased by Q_{10} to provide three equal constant currents, $I_{12} = I_{13} = I_{14}$. The current mirror Q_1, Q_2, Q_3 (Sec. 1.10(a)) establishes $I_{12} = I_1$, and since $I_{13} = I_{14}$, then $I_{Z2} = I_1 = (V_{Z2} - V_{BE2} - V_{BE3})/(R_2 + R_3 + R_4 + R_5)$. The temperature coefficients of the V_{BE} ($2 \times (-1.85 \text{ mV/°C})$) overcompensate the coefficient of V_{Z2} ($+2.65$ mV/°C) by nearly the correct amount to cancel the coefficient of $(R_2 + R_3 + R_4 + R_5)$ ($+1.3$ per cent/°C). Thus, I_{Z2} and I_1 are constant, independent of temperature and of input voltage, E_u. The temperature coefficient of the voltage at point B is that of two V_{BE}'s, -3.70 mV/°C, while that at D is $+2.65$ mV/°C. The point of zero coefficient reference voltage, E_r, is thus given by $(R_4 + R_5)/(R_2 + R_3) = 3.70/2.65 = 1.40$. The small resistors R_3, R_4 are included to allow variation of the tapping point for E_r, according to production variations in

Z_2. These ingenious compensation techniques illustrate again the advantages of IC construction.

At switch on, Z_2 is not conducting so that $I_{Z2}=0$. Since I_{14} has nowhere to go, the condition $I_{12}=I_{13}=I_{14}$ can only be met if the currents are zero, and the reference circuits will remain off. To overcome this, a start-up circuit R_1, D_1, Z_1 is included. Current is supplied from E_u, via R_1 and D_1, to Q_1 causing a corresponding current I_{12} due to the current mirror. This turns Q_{10} on, providing base drive to Q_{13}, Q_{14} causing some I_{13}, I_{14} to flow. This adds to the original current from R_1, D_1 so the process is regenerative, the voltage across $(R_2+R_3+R_4+R_5)$ rising until Z_2 turns on. At this point the gain is reduced, as I_{14} flows in Z_2, and the system reaches a stable condition. As $V_{Z1} \leqslant V_{Z2}$, D_1 will then be reverse biased, so disconnecting the starting circuit, and input voltage fluctuations, from the reference circuit.

Foldback current limiting is provided by Q_9. The voltage across R_{14}, due to the output current I_0, is monitored by Q_9. When the drop across R_{14} is great enough to turn Q_9 on, base drive is diverted from Q_7 and foldback is produced in a manner similar to that described in Sec. 7.6. The ratio $I_{\max}/I_{\lim}$ is approximately 7.

The regulator can be used with external components to achieve higher voltage or current, as a current regulator or as a switching regulator [c1]. Two units may also simply be connected in parallel to give higher output current. The higher voltage unit (one will always be marginally higher than the other) will supply the first half of the current, and then go slightly into current overload. The output voltage will drop slightly, until the second regulator comes on and supplies the second half of the output current.

In using IC regulators it should be remembered that they may have gain, up to very high frequencies. Therefore, in common with most IC's, good layout with short leads and effective high frequency by-passing is necessary if oscillations are to be avoided. In particular, a good high frequency capacitor should be connected across input and output, as close as possible to the device.

7.8 Switching regulators

The term *switching regulator* is used, here, to cover two distinct types. The first has a form similar to the standard series regulator (Sec. 7.2), but the series element is switched on and off rather than operating in the linear mode. The advantage of this is the considerably reduced power dissipation and greatly improved efficiency (>90 per cent). The second type is the so-called transformerless power supply which is, in fact, not so, but uses a small high frequency rather than a large low frequency transformer. This results in a considerable reduction in weight, volume, and power dissipation.

7.8(a) *Series switching regulator*

A schematic circuit diagram of a series switching regulator is shown in Fig. 7.8.1 [c1, d1, D1, I1, V1, W1, X1].

Two modes of operation may be used: self-oscillation, in which the frequency is varied to suit the load, or fixed frequency oscillator drive, where the mark–space ratio is varied. Consider, initially, the latter. When Q_1 is conducting it will be hard on, and the voltage across it will be $V_{CE(sat)}$. This is very small (<1 V) so that the power dissipation in Q_1 is low. Since $E_D \doteq E_u$:

$$E_u - E_o = L(dI_L/dt) \tag{7.8.1}$$

The current, I_L, creates the magnetic field of L, recharges C and provides I_o. When Q_1 is switched off, I_L begins to decay, i.e., dI_L/dt changes sign and, since E_o is held substantially constant by C, the voltage E_D reverses sign causing D_1 to conduct with a forward drop E_f. The collapsing magnetic field of L now supplies the necessary

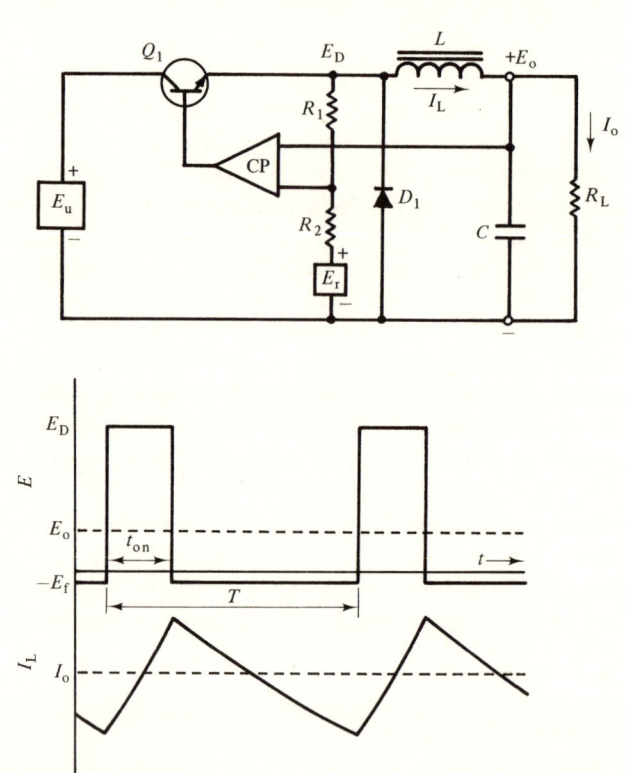

Fig. 7.8.1 Series switching regulator (self-oscillating), (a) schematic, (b) waveforms

current I_o to the load R_L via D_1. As E_o drops, current is also supplied by C. L, therefore, must be large enough to keep I_o flowing for the whole of the time, t_{off}. Higher switching frequencies (smaller T) allow the use of a smaller inductance.

Since the energy stored in an inductor is given by $\frac{1}{2}LI_L^2$, whereas the output power from the regulator is proportional to I_L, the inductance L must be much higher for light loads than for heavy (c.f. the swinging choke sometimes used in rectifier smoothing filters). Thus, for light loads, the current I_L may fall to zero, but C then supplies the output current. The value of C is chosen to restrict the output voltage ripple, ΔE_0 [c1]:

$$\Delta E_o \doteq t_{on}^2 (E_u - E_o)/2LC \tag{7.8.2}$$

t_{on} is not a variable, as this fixes E_o:

$$E_o = \frac{E_u t_{on}}{T} = E_u t_{on} f \tag{7.8.3}$$

To regulate the output, feedback is applied to vary the mark–space ratio [c1].

The system may be made self-oscillating, as shown in Fig. 7.8.1. When E_o is below the reference voltage, E_r, the output of the comparator, CP, will be positive and the series transistor, Q_1, will be hard on. The output rises until $E_o > E_r$, when the comparator switches over and turns Q_1 off. It is important that the changeover be as rapid as possible, so as to limit power dissipation in Q_1. The speed is improved by a small amount of positive feedback via R_1 ($R_1 \gg R_2$) (Sec. 6.1), but it is also important that Q_1 has short switching times. If the load increases, the oscillation frequency increases, because E_o falls more rapidly during the off period.

In practice, frequencies of 10 to 100 kHz are found to be best, as lower frequencies result in bulkier inductors, while higher lead to increased dissipation in Q_1 because of the limited switching speed of power transistors [h1, Y1]. Inductor values of a few microhenries with capacitors of a few tens of microfarads, can give a regulation of a few tenths of a per cent and ripple of tens of millivolts, for output currents of amperes. The efficiency is generally about 85 to 90 per cent. Inductors must be suitable for high frequency operation, and are usually of toroidal form.

Diode D_1 carries large currents, and operates at frequencies above those for which ordinary rectifiers can be used (≈ 10 kHz) since these have poor performance, as a result of hole storage effects. Fast recovery rectifiers are available with reverse recovery times of 200 ns, e.g., 1N3879 series (6 and 12 A) or BYX50 and 55 series (4 and 12 A, up to 600 PIV), or even down to 20 ns [c2]. The more recently introduced hot-carrier rectifiers are very efficient for low voltage applications (PIV = 20 V), since they do not exhibit reverse recovery time and require only about one-third of the forward voltage as the high speed silicon rectifiers for the same current, e.g., 0·5 V at 25 A [d2] (Sec. 1.9).

Discrete control circuits may be desirable, for example, in high voltage systems, but many of the standard IC regulators can be used to give equal performance more compactly [d1, e1, u1]. Note that, as a result of the fast switching waveforms and high operating frequencies, considerable interference can be generated. Switching regulators, therefore, should be well screened and kept away from low-level circuits [N1, o1, a2, b2].

7.8(b) *'Transformerless' regulator*

These regulators eliminate only the bulky mains transformer, but to achieve isolation from the mains some form of transformer is essential. The principle of operation is direct rectification from the mains to drive a high frequency inverter. Feedback from the d.c. output is used to control the mark–space ratio of the inverter and, hence, regulate the output (Fig. 7.8.2) [g1, l1, m1, b1, k1, E1].

The a.c. mains is directly rectified by D_{1-4} and smoothed by C_i. An inverter Q_1, Q_2 is driven at some high frequency, f (10 to 100 kHz), via transformer T_2. The high frequency output from T_1 is rectified by $D_{5,6}$ and smoothed by C_o: the high frequency greatly increases the effectiveness of this capacitor. The output voltage, E_o, is monitored by amplifier A, whose output controls the width of the pulses generated by a pulse-width modulator, PWM. If E_o decreases, because of load or mains changes, the pulse width is increased to compensate. This feedback signal is coupled in with a small high frequency transformer, T_2, so there is no d.c. connection between the input (mains) and output circuits.

There is a difficulty with the circuit shown. At switch-on, the inverter is not being driven so there is no power available to operate the oscillator, i.e., the system is not self-starting. This could be overcome by using a miniature mains transformer to provide an independent supply for the oscillator, or the inverter could be made to self-oscillate until E_o appears and the oscillator takes over. The take-over may be implemented by relay operating from E_o, or by making the self-oscillation frequency less than f, so that it will lock-in to the higher frequency when present.

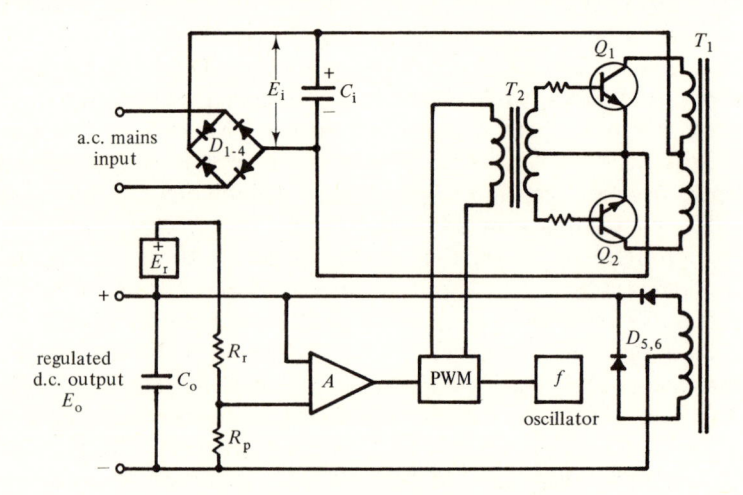

Fig. 7.8.2 Mains-transformerless regulator

7.9 Cells and batteries

For portability or isolation, power must be obtained from electrochemical cells. These can be divided into two groups, the primary or consumable, and the secondary rechargeable. Although there are several types in each group only the most common will be considered here. For the primary there are, in order of increasing cost, the common Lechlanché dry cell, the alkaline manganese, and the mercury cell. The most commonly used secondary type is the nickel–cadmium alkaline cell. A third category, the Weston or standard, while not a power cell, is included here for convenience. Some important characteristics are listed in Table 7.9.1 [c1, d1, r1, o1, n1, k1, s1, t1, u1, f1, y1, A1].

7.9(a) *Primary cells*

All three types, dry, mercury, and alkaline manganese are available in a wide range of sizes and capacities. In general, they are readily interchangeable as far as dimensions are concerned, but there is an extended range of mercury cells down to miniature button types. For higher voltages or capacities, many standard batteries of cells are also available. Discharge characteristics are somewhat dependent on rates, and whether continuous or intermittent. A rough comparison for equal capacity cells is shown in Fig. 7.9.1.

Alkaline manganese cells, which are direct replacements for the dry cell in voltage, last longer by at least three times for light current drain and up to ten times for

Table 7.9.1 Characteristics of some primary and secondary cells

	Voltage	Shelf-life	Capacity		Temperature range °C
			W min/cm³	Ah*	
Primary					
Lechlanché (dry cell)	1·3	50 per cent after 2 year at 20°C	3	2·5	−20 to 70
Alkaline/manganese	1·3	95 per cent after 2 years	13	7	−20 to 70
Mercury	1·25	95 per cent after 2 years at 20°C	19	2	−20 to 70 −60 to 160 store
Metair	1·3	85 per cent after 1 year at 20°C	28	22	−20 to 55
Secondary					
Nickel/cadmium	1·2	80 per cent after 1 month	5·8	3·5	−20 to 45 store 60
Lead/acid	2	2·5 years to minimum charge at 25°C	5·5	2·5	−40 to 65
Standard					
Saturated (K-375-C)	1·01860 ± 100 µV, −40 µV/°C over range 0 to 43°C. Stability ±1 µV/year at constant temperature. Current <10 µA. Size 4·5 cm × 1·3 cm diameter, wire leads at same end.				
Unsaturated (K-391-A)	1·0190 ± 10 µV at 25°C, −3 µV/°C over range 0 to 40°C. Decreases 10 µV/year and 1 µV per 20 mC up to 2·5 C. Current <10 µA, internal resistance 650 ohm. Size 7 cm × 1·1 cm diameter, wire leads opposite ends.				

* *Note:* Ah—ampere-hours for size D cells.

heavy. The mercury cell does not have depolarization limitations (since the polarization barrier formed is mercury, which is a good conductor) and can deliver power intermittently or continuously with equal efficiency.

An important characteristic of mercury and alkaline manganese cells is that they are not liable to corrosion. Standard types of Lechlanché cells are rather prone to this, as the outer case is eaten away by the cell reaction. If the casing is pierced the electrolyte can cause considerable damage to surrounding materials. This would occur naturally only if the cell were left for a fair time after it was discharged, and certain makes are fitted with extra sealed protection to eliminate this.

7.9(b) *Secondary cells*

The considerable increase in the use of portable equipment requiring substantial power, has been possible as a result of the development of several types of sealed rechargeable cell. The most commonly used is the nickel–cadmium type. This is available in a number of standard sizes similar to the primary cells, as well as small button and large capacity packs.

Sealed nickel–cadmium cells can deliver peak currents (in amperes) of up to five times their rated capacity Ah (in ampere-hours) for times of less than a minute. For steady loads the current should not exceed Ah amperes. The internal resistance is low and the discharge characteristic is reasonably flat varying from 1·35 V at full

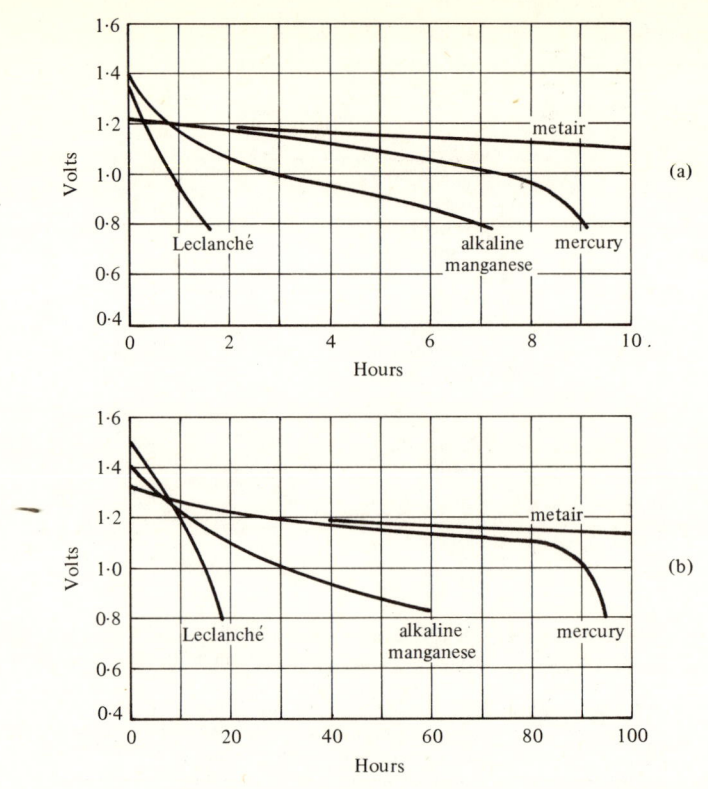

Fig. 7.9.1 Primary cell discharge characteristics (AA size cells), (a) heavy load = 200 mA, (b) light load = 50 mA

charge to 1·1 V at the end point (Fig. 7.9.2). Charge retention with time is reasonable, varying from 80 per cent after one month to 20 per cent after five months.

The main problem encountered in the use of sealed rechargeable cells is recharging. When fully charged further charging results in the evolution of gas. If this were excessive the cell would explode unless some venting provision is made, but this could lead to drying out of the electrolyte. In sealed cells, the gas produced can be eliminated by internal reaction if the production rate is not too high. There is little

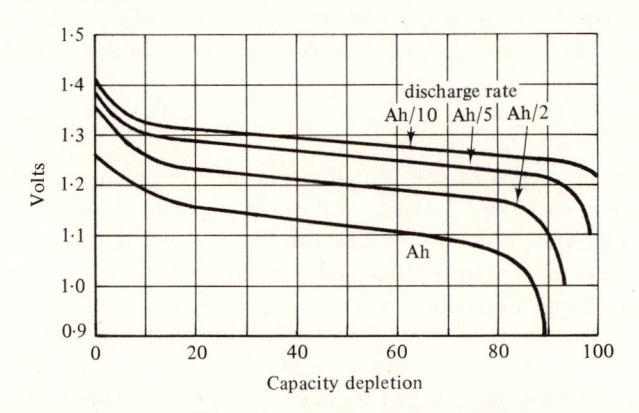

Fig. 7.9.2 Nickel–cadmium cell characteristics

324

change in voltage where the cell becomes fully charged, so it is difficult to monitor this condition. Thus, unless the amount of charge removed is known closely so that just this much can be replaced, some overcharging is necessary to ensure that the unit is charged fully. The small sealed cells considered here can be overcharged safely up to 20 times capacity Ah at a rate Ah/10 or less. It is, therefore, safe to charge a cell at Ah/10 for 15 hours whatever its state of charge. Cylindrical cells can be charged at rates less than Ah/50 indefinitely, while for button cells this should be Ah/100.

As the cell has low resistance, it is highly desirable that the charging supply should be constant current rather than voltage. The latter can cause difficulty as increase in temperature due to charging results in increased current, which could lead to thermal runaway. Recently fast charging methods, at rates up to 20 Ah, involving very short current reversal periods for depolarization have been used to obtain full charging in about 10 minutes! Although steady high charge rates result in reduced life, pulse charging and reversal appears to preserve the ability to be recharged [z1, p1]. This technique is clearly of considerable interest and further development is likely.

In using rechargeable cells in a dual purpose mains/portable unit, it is common to transform the mains and rectify to the battery voltage. This supply then keeps the batteries fully charged and either supplies the unit directly or, for higher voltages, via an inverter; Sec. 7.8(b). Then, if the mains supply is removed, the battery takes over automatically [v1, h1, i1, j1, l1, m1, B1, C1].

7.9(c) *Standard cells*

The Weston type cell is, at present, the basic standard of voltage and is not intended to supply current. There are two types, the so-called standard or saturated, and the reference or unsaturated. The former has an e.m.f. with an accurately known variation with temperature [d1, w1, x1, g1].

$$E_T - E_{20} = -40 \cdot 6(T-20) - 0 \cdot 95(T-20)^2 + 0 \cdot 01(T-20)^3$$

where E_{20} is the value at 20°C, and T the temperature. These also have greater stability with time. The highest precision models will have an e.m.f. $E_{20} = 1 \cdot 018\,58$ to $1 \cdot 018\,64$ volt absolute (accuracy 0·001 per cent). Reference cells have substantially lower temperature coefficients, but lesser stability with time than the standard cell. Recent developments have resulted in small portable units suitable for direct insertion in circuit boards, for example, two representative types being listed in Table 7.9.1. These cells are commonly used in such instruments as high resolution digital voltmeters which can resolve better than 1 µV in 1 V. To achieve this very high performance, temperature stabilized units are available. It is of interest to note that the Weston cell is likely to be displaced as the absolute standard of potential by a more fundamental quantum standard, based on the a.c. Josephson effect [a1].

7.10 Voltage and current regulator diodes

There are a number of two terminal (diode) devices that serve to regulate voltage or current. These include zener, avalanche, and stabistor diodes for voltage regulation, and FET current regulators. The two terminal configuration and the fact that they are powered by the circuit in which they are used, makes them very useful circuit elements.

7.10(a) *Voltage regulator diodes*

Voltage regulator diodes are essentially ordinary diodes operated at high enough reverse bias so that voltage breakdown occurs. The diodes can be prepared so as to give breakdown voltages from a few to several hundred volts, and so that the breakdown occurs over the whole of the junction rather than at a localized point. Typical voltage–current characteristics are illustrated in Fig. 7.10.1 [a1, j1, k1, J1].

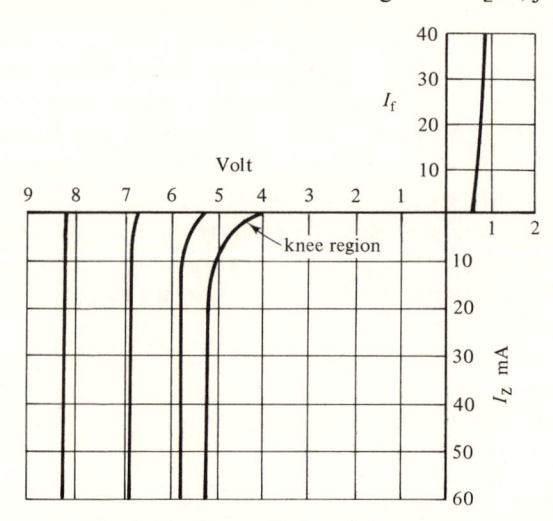

Fig. 7.10.1 Zener diode characteristics

Although these diodes are commonly referred to as zener diodes (after the proposer of a particular electrical breakdown mechanism) the term is strictly applicable only to low voltage devices below about 5 V. For voltages above about 7 V, the breakdown mechanism is different, being an avalanche effect. However, the term zener is well established and commonly used, and will be used here. The main point of interest as far as the user is concerned is that the two breakdown mechanisms have opposite temperature coefficients (zener negative), so that there will be some voltage, between 5 and 7 V, where the temperature coefficient is zero. This will be further considered in Sec. 7.10(b).

The important parameters of a zener diode are listed in Table 7.10.1, together with the approximate range of each.

In view of the low dynamic resistance in the breakdown region, the zener diode should always be used with a suitable series resistance. A separate resistor is not necessary if there is suitable inherent resistance in the circuit.

Table 7.10.1 Zener diode characteristics

Breakdown voltage, V_Z	3 to 200 V, specified at a given current, I_Z
Dynamic slope resistance $R_Z = \dfrac{\partial V}{\partial I}$	1 to 2500 Ω. Depends on V_Z and I_Z with a minimum at $V_Z = 6$ V. Decreases as I_Z increases
Maximum power dissipation	0.2 to 100 W. Above a few watts, requires a heat sink
Temperature coefficient of V_Z	−0.1 to +0.1 per cent/°C. Specified for a particular I_Z, and depends on V_Z. Approximately zero for $V_Z = 5$ to 6 V
Current range	few μA to 15 A

A simple voltage regulator is shown in Fig. 7.10.2, where R_Z represents the inherent dynamic resistance of the zener [H1, I1, a1].

The usual requirement is for a stable voltage, E_o, independent of input voltage, E_i, or load resistance, R_L. This is only possible within certain limits of E_i and R_L, the regulation depending on R_S and R_Z. The limits are readily derived. The controlling factor is the allowable power dissipation of the zener. For a given E_Z this fixes the

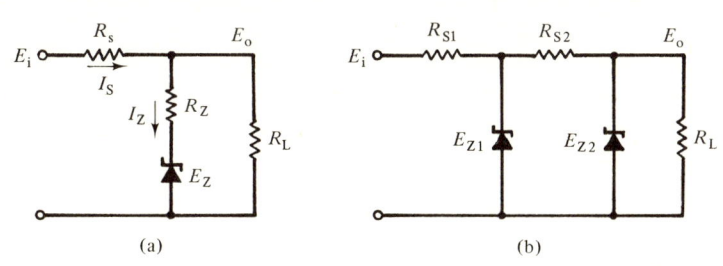

Fig. 7.10.2 Zener voltage regulator, (a) single stage, (b) two stage

maximum current $I_{Z(max)}$. With $R_L = \infty$, $I_L = 0$ and $I_{S(max)}$ must be $< I_{Z(max)}$, so that for a given $E_{i(max)}$:

$$R_{S(min)} = \frac{E_{i(max)} - E_{Z(min)}}{I_{Z(max)}} \qquad (7.10.1)$$

For a given value of I_S, $I_{L(max)}$ must be such that the minimum zener current, $I_{Z(min)}$ (determined by the required maximum dynamic resistance $R_{Z(max)}$), is not reached.

$$I_{L(max)} = \left(\frac{E_{i(min)} - E_Z}{R_S}\right) - I_{Z(min)}, \qquad R_{L(min)} = \frac{E_Z}{I_{L(max)}} \qquad (7.10.2)$$

The stabilization factor, S, is simply derived if it is assumed that $R_Z \ll R_S$ or R_L, which is the main intention of the circuit. Then, for fixed I_L and temperature:

$$S = \frac{\partial E_o}{\partial E_i} = \frac{R_Z}{R_S + R_Z} \doteq \frac{R_Z}{R_S} \qquad (7.10.3)$$

since the circuit is effectively a simple potential divider. For good regulation, S must be as small as possible. The limiting factors are power dissipation in the zener and R_S, and the available input voltage E_i. The regulation against changes in load is just the output resistance for constant input E_i:

$$R_o = \frac{\partial E_o}{\partial I_L} = \frac{R_Z R_S}{R_Z + R_S} \qquad (7.10.4)$$

If greater stability against input voltage variations is required, a two stage regulator may be used. Two circuits, as shown in Fig. 7.10.2(b), are connected in series, the first providing a stabilized input voltage for the second. The overall regulation factor, SE_i/E_o, is then the product of the individual regulation factors. This technique will not improve the output resistance, but it is often used with zener reference diodes, Sec. 7.10(b), which generally work into constant loads [K1]. Further applications of zener regulators are discussed in [a1, J1, j1].

The breakdown mechanism in zener diodes produces a certain amount of noise, depending on the current and bandwidth of measurement. For bandwidths of tens of kilohertz, the noise voltage can vary between tens and hundreds of microvolts. Connection of a 0·1 µF capacitor, in parallel with the zener, will reduce the noise by a factor of about 10. The noise voltage increases rapidly in the region of and below the knee of the characteristic; see Fig. 7.10.1.

Diode junction capacity decreases as the reverse voltage is increased, levelling off as breakdown is approached. Higher zener voltage units will have lower capacity, and high power units greater capacity. The actual capacity can be quite large, varying from tens to thousands of picofarad. This can be of importance, for example, where zeners are used for protection purposes at points where high frequency signals may be present. For protection purposes, the speed of response is an important factor. Although the junction capacity affects this, the actual breakdown mechanism is very rapid, and takes place in a few nanoseconds or less [J1, C1]. In fact, for low capacity units biased near their breakdown voltage, zeners make good high frequency rectifiers, because of the sharp knee, and absence of the usual diode reverse recovery phenomena [k1].

Low voltage zeners generally have a soft knee region as shown in Fig. 7.10.1. If this is not suitable special low voltage avalanche zeners are available with much sharper knee [e1]. Alternatively, an active integrated zener (LM103) gives a sharp knee for voltages from 2·4 to 5·6 V [b1]. For even lower voltages, forward conducting diodes may be used. Standard diodes do not have a very sharp rise in conduction, and special types have been produced for this purpose. These are referred to as stabistors (e.g., EVR1 and SG series, 0·26 and 0·64 V at 1 mA) or forward reference diodes (MR2361, 1·35 V at 10 mA). Some light-emitting diodes (LED's) also have a sharp rise, e.g., hp5082–4484 at 1·6 V. This can be seen to be working!

7.10(b) *Voltage reference diodes*

These devices are basically the same as the voltage regulator diodes, but are specially selected or compensated to provide as stable a reference voltage as possible. The simplest reference zeners can be obtained by selection from devices with voltages in the range 4·5 to 5·5 V, where the temperature coefficient passes through zero. However, this requires a stable zener current and it is difficult to produce diodes with zero coefficient at the same current [a1, d1, m1, o1, r1].

Improved performance as well as various voltages, may be obtained by using one or more compensation diodes in series with the zener. Forward biased silicon diodes have a temperature coefficient of about -2 mV/°C, while zeners have coefficients ranging from $+2$ mV/°C at 5·5 V to $+6$ mV/°C at 10 V. The appropriate combinations of forward and reverse biased junctions can give a very low temperature coefficient, but only at a specified current (± 1 per cent). Various coefficients down to 0·0005 per cent/°C over the voltage range 6·2 to 200 V are available. The specified current is usually 7·5 mA for the lower voltages, reducing to 2·5 mA at 200 V. To reduce the power dissipation, low current (100 µA) devices have also been produced [P1].

To obtain a reference zener, less sensitive to current variation, an active circuit can be used. An example is shown in Fig. 7.10.3 (BZX47 series). Since the circuit is two terminal it can be produced as a diode if made up in IC form [c1].

If the overall applied voltage is high enough, zener Z_1 breaks down, and current flows in R. When the voltage across R is large enough, Q conducts. The overall zener voltage, E_Z, is thus E_{Z1} plus the forward conducting base–emitter diode V_{be} of Q, i.e., just the compensated arrangement discussed above. Any increase in zener current, I_Z, will flow mainly through Q. Since V_{be} provides only about 10 per cent of E_Z, the increase with increase of I_Q makes only a very small change in E_Z. The change in I_{Z1} with I_Z is, thus, very much reduced compared with the series compensated zener, and Z_1 operates at essentially constant current and, hence, constant temperature

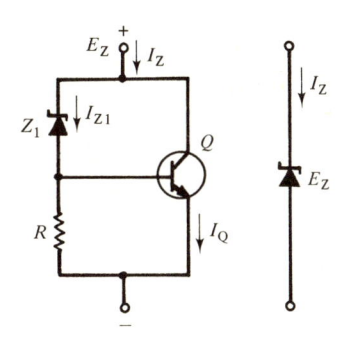

Fig. 7.10.3 Active zener voltage reference

coefficient. The BZX47 has a temperature coefficient of 0·0005 per cent/°C (5 p.p.m./°C) at 2 mA, which is equal to that of a Weston reference cell, Sec. 7.9(c). It changes to 0·001 per cent/°C for current between 1 and 3 mA, but this stability is only achieved after a stabilization period of about 100 hours. The diodes are supplied already stabilized for operation at 2 mA. Time stability is within 1 mV/1000 hours after stabilization.

To improve the stability further, a constant current supply may be used instead of the usual series resistor. This could be of the type shown in Fig. 7.3.5, or one of the FET constant current diodes described in Sec. 7.10(c).

The techniques described above are not applicable for very low voltages. A circuit has been described that will operate from a supply of 1·5 V and provide reference voltages from 0·1 to about 1 V [O1]. The lowest temperature coefficient is obtained in the region of 430 mV. The use of reference zeners, together with an operational amplifier, to provide a variable voltage at low impedance is discussed in [11]. When in need a reverse biased base–emitter junction of a transistor may be used as a zener. These usually have a breakdown voltage between 6 and 8 V, with a positive temperature coefficient. If the collector–base junction is also included, as a forward biased series diode, then good temperature compensation may be obtained. Todd [j1, p. 227] gives values lower than 0·001 per cent/°C. It should be noted that the current gain of the device (as a transistor) may be seriously degraded by operation in this mode.

7.10(c) *FET constant current diodes*

A two terminal constant current device is of considerable use in many applications, such as a supply for zener diodes, a differential amplifier tail, unity-gain emitter follower load, or linear ramp generator. Although a two terminal circuit can be made using transistors and zeners (Fig. 7.3.5), the most convenient device is formed from a field-effect transistor [f1, g1, i1]. Figure 7.10.4 shows an *N*-channel FET together with typical characteristics.

For a given value of V_{GS}, the current I_D is practically constant over a wide range of V_{DS}, from about twice the pinch-off voltage, V_P, to nearly the breakdown voltage, BV_{DS}. For a required I_D, see Eq. (8.1.2):

$$V_{GS} = V_P[1-(I_D/I_{DSS})^{1/2}], \qquad R_S = V_{GS}/I_D \qquad (7.10.4)$$

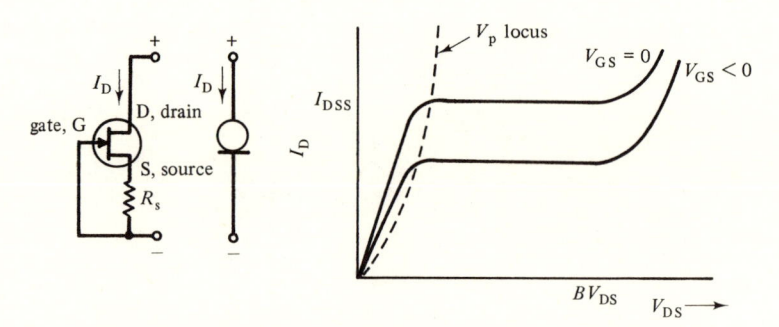

Fig. 7.10.4 FET constant current source and characteristics

The important parameter of the circuit is the output conductance, g_o, which should be as low as possible for best current regulation:

$$g_o \doteq \frac{g_{os}}{1+R_S g_{fs}}, \qquad g_{os} = \frac{\Delta I_D}{\Delta V_{DS}}, \qquad g_{fs} = \frac{\Delta I_D}{\Delta V_{GS}} \qquad (7.10.5)$$

where g_o is given in terms of the device conductance, g_{os}, and transconductance, g_{fs}. If $R_s=0$ then $I_D=I_{DSS}$. For a good FET, g_{os} may be 1 μmho, giving a dynamic resistance $1/g_{os}=1$ MΩ. Inclusion of R_S improves this, and replacement of R_S by another FET improves this even more so, so that very high dynamic resistances may be obtained [h1, f1, t1] (Fig. 7.10.5).

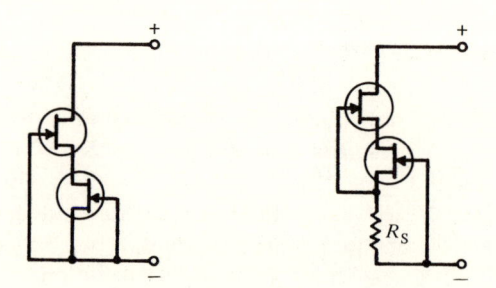

Fig. 7.10.5 Cascade FET current regulators

These circuits may readily be produced in integrated form and supplied as a two terminal diode. Examples of constant current diodes are the 1N5283–5314 and the CL2210–4710 series [Q1, S1]. These cover a current range from 0·2 to 5 mA, with a minimum voltage of 1 V, and a maximum of 100 V. The dynamic resistance varies from 25 MΩ at low currents, to 200 kΩ for 5 mA devices.

References section 7.1: Rectifiers

a1 Dayal M: Power Rectification with Silicon Diodes: Mullard Tech. Comm. 7, 230–262, 1964, and 9, 46–47, 1966, and Mullard Tech. Publication 1310, 1972.
b1 Unvala B A: DC Power Supply Circuits Using Silicon Rectifiers; Texas Instruments Application Report D4 1968.
c1 Dale R: Silicon Rectifier Handbook; Motorola 1966.
d1 Motorola: Silicon Zener Diode and Rectifier Handbook; Motorola 1961.
e1 Perkins D: Applications of Fast-Recovery Rectifiers; Motorola Application Note AN-512, 1970.
f1 Shiner B C: Improve the Efficiency of Low-Voltage, High Current Rectification; Semiconductors (Motorola) 2, 78–81, 1971, and Motorola Application Note AN517, 1970.
g1 Schade O H: Analysis of Rectifier Operation; Proc IRE 31, 341–361, 1943.
h1 Waidelich D L: Analysis of Full-Wave Rectifier and Capacitive Input Circuits; Electronics 20, No.9, 121–123, 1947.
i1 Gutzwiller F W: SCR Manual (4th Edn); General Electric 1967.
j1 Bugg R E F; Thyristor Power Supplies for Television Receivers. Design Considerations; Mullard Tech. Comm. 12, 129–144, 1972.
k1 Dayal M: Rectifier Diode Operation at Kilocycle Frequencies; Mullard Tech. Comm. 8, 66–67, 1964.
l1 Bugg R E F: Full-Wave Thyristor Power Supply for Television Receivers; Mullard Tech. Comm. 13, 198–209, 1975.
m1 Mullard: Fast Soft-Recovery Rectifier Diodes BYW19 Series; Mullard Data Sheet Sep. 1975.
n1 RCA: Power Circuits, DC to Microwave; RCA Handbook 1969.
o1 Mullard: Schottky Barrier Rectifier Diodes BYW13; Mullard Data Sheet Nov. 1975.
p1 Millman J, Halkias C C: Electronic Devices and Circuits. Chapter 20 Rectifiers and Power Supplies; McGraw-Hill 1967.
q1 RCA: Solid-State Power Circuits Designer's Handbook; RCA Technical Series SP-52, 1971.
r1 Delaney C F G: Electronics for the Physicist; Penguin Books 1969.
s1 International Rectifier: Fast Recovery Miniature High Voltage Cartridge Rectifiers 1AV/BV Series; International Rectifier Bulletin E2408.
t1 Wales S: The Suprataxial Junction; Electron 25 Sep. 1975.
u1 Semtech: Metoxilite Sub-Miniature High Voltage Silicon Rectifiers SM20/25/30; Semtech Data Sheet.
v1 TRW: Ultra-Fast Recovery Double Slug Rectifiers series DSR; TRW Semiconductors Data Sheet 1970.
w1 Motorola: Lead Mounted Hot Carrier Power Rectifier MBD5300; Motorola Data Sheet Nov. 1970.
x1 Moore D W: Analyzing the Principles of Schottky Diodes; Electronic Equipment News Dec. 1973, 61–64.
y1 Merrett J: Summary of Factors Affecting Power Supply Choice and Design; Mullard Tech. Comm. 13, Oct. 1974, 153–156.
z1 Habermel P D: High-Grade Long-Life Aluminium Electrolytic Capacitors; Mullard Tech. Publication TP1452, 1974.
A1 Mason D: High Capacitance Electrolytics; Mullard Tech. Publication TP1094, 1969.
B1 Forssander P H: Aluminium Electrolytics are Hard to Beat for Large Capacitance in a Small Package and at Low Cost; Electronic Design 11 Oct. 1974, 78–82.
C1 Eimar R: Stretch Electrolytic Life by Avoiding Six Deadly No-No's; Electronic Design 1 Apr. 1975, 124–127.
D1 Sevastopolous N et al: Voltage Regulator Handbook; National Semiconductor 1975.
E1 Semtech: Ministic High Voltage Silicon Rectifiers Series SFMS; Semtech Data Sheet Oct. 1972.
F1 Gutzwiller F W: Overcurrent Protection of Semiconductor Rectifiers; General Electric Application Note 200.10, 1961.
G1 Avel-Lindberg: Toroidal Power Transformers; Avel-Lindberg Data Sheets.

H1 Daniels K W: Toroidal Transformers Pack Performance into Small Size; Electronic Components 18 June 1974, 10–11.
I1 Ferranti: Silicon Controlled Avalanche Rectifiers ZAR710; Ferranti Data Sheet 1965.
J1 General Electric: Transient Voltage Protected Rectifiers A14 Series; General Electric Data Sheet 1967.
K1 Norton J J: Quick Calculation Gives Filter-Capacitor Value; Electronics 22 July 1976, 121–122.

References section 7.2: Voltage regulators

a1 Birman P: Power Supply Handbook; Kepco 1965.
b1 Hewlett-Packard: DC Power Supply Handbook: Hewlett-Packard Application Note 90, 1968.
c1 Bhola S K: Design of Regulated Power Supplies with Monolithic Operational Amplifiers; Transitron Application Report MD/AP3-68.
d1 Hewlett-Packard: The Present Attainments of Adjustable Power Supplies; Hewlett-Packard J 13, NO.11, July 1962.
e1 Hewlett-Packard: Power Supply/Amplifier. Concepts and Modes of Operation; Hewlett-Packard Application Note 82, Sep. 1966.
f1 Williams P: Very Low Voltage DC Reference: Electronic Eng. 40, 348–349, 1968.
g1 Verster T C: Temperature Compensated Low Voltage Reference; Electronic Eng. 41, 65, 1969.
h1 Perkins D: True RMS Voltage Regulator; Motorola Application Note AN-90, 1969.
i1 Kesner D: Regulators Using Operational Amplifiers; Motorola Application Note AN-480, 1969.
j1 Hollingsworth P: Stabilized DC Power Supplies; Industrial Electronics Sep. 1967, 406–409.
k1 Mammano R A: Dual Polarity IC Regulators Aid Design and Packaging; Electronics 15 Feb. 1973, 108–111.
l1 Raytheon: 4194 Dual Tracking Voltage Regulator; Raytheon Application Note Oct. 1972.
m1 Dobkin R C: Build High-Stability Regulators; Electronic Design 3 Feb. 1972, 62–63.
n1 Zakarevicius R A: Analysis of Series Regulators as Active Two-Port Networks; Radio Electronic Engr. 27, 237–243, 1964.
o1 Lappalainen P: Precision Reference Voltage Supply; Electronic Eng. 42, Oct. 1970, 95–96.
p1 Kalanit G: Voltage Regulator for Battery-Powered Instruments; Electronic Eng. 46, Nov. 1974, 21, 23.
q1 Austin D: Precision Ring-of-Two Circuit with Op Amps; Electronic Eng. 46, Dec. 1974, 23–24.
r1 Fairchild: High-Voltage Supply Uses IC Operational Ampliffer; Electronic Eng. 44, Feb. 1972, 47–48.
s1 Falkner A H: The Simplest Voltage-Halving Circuit May Be the Most Useful; Electronic Eng. 44, Sep. 1972, 68–69.
t1 Markus J (Ed): Electronic Circuits Manual. Chapter 71 Regulator Circuits; McGraw-Hill 1971.
u1 Blandford D, Bishop A: Power Supplies for COS/MOS; RCA Application Note SUN-1107, 1974.
v1 Aldridge D, Wellenstein N: Designing Digitally Controlled Power Supplies; Motorola Application Note AN-703, 1973.
w1 RCA: Power Circuits, DC to Microwave; RCA Handbook 1969.
x1 Thomson–CSF: Les Regulateurs de Tension; Thomson–CSF Manuel d'Application CIL, Tome 2, 1974.
y1 RCA: High-Speed, High-Voltage, High-Current Power Transistors; RCA Technical Series PM-80, 1970.
z1 Merrett J: Summary of Factors Affecting Power Supply Choice and Design; Mullard Tech. Comm. 13, Oct. 1974, 153–156.

A1 Sevastopolous N et al: Voltage Regulator Handbook; National Semiconductor 1975.
B1 Lo C C, Fan B: Constant Pulse Energy Power Supply for a High Repetition Rate Laser System; Rev. Sci. Instrum. 47, 63–65, 1976.
C1 RCA: Solid-State Power Circuits Designer's Handbook; RCA Technical Series SP-52, 1971.
D1 Hamilton T D S: Stabilised Power Supplies; Electronic Equipment News Feb. 1968, 38–44.
E1 Hewlett-Packard: DC Power Supply Handbook; Hewlett-Packard 1970.
F1 RCA: Transistorized Voltage Regulators; RCA Application Guide ICE-254, 1961.
G1 Hadley M: Power-Supply Regulator Simplified with Norton Op Amps; Electronic Design 15 Mar. 1976, 106.

References section 7.3: Current regulators

a1 Perkinson J C, Pierce W C: Precision DC Current Sources; Hewlett-Packard J 21, 15–20, 1969.
b1 Keene J P, Hayden D W: The Uncommon Versatility of the Common Current Generator; Electronics 1 Feb. 1971, 40–43.
c1 Wilbur-Ham J, Jackson K S: 22mA DC Supply Stable to 1 Part in 10(6) per Day; J Sci. Instrum. 36, 86, 1962.
d1 Haisty, R W: Constant Current Supply for Very High Resistance Loads; Rev. Sci. Instrum. 31, 1297–1298, 1960.
e1 Brookshier W K: Accurate Low Level Current Source; Rev. Sci. Instrum. 32, 359–360, 1961.
f1 Libbey R: Chopper Amplifier's PPM Stability Enables Electron Microscope to Scrutinize Individual Molecules; Analog Dialogue 2, No.1, 1–5, Mar. 1968.
g1 Retsky M W, Wall J: One Ampere Current Supply Stable to One Part per Million per Hour; Rev. Sci. Instrum. 43, 384–385, 1972.
h1 Kyser D F, Horne D E: High Voltage Sweep and Controlled Magnetic Lens Current Supplies for the Electron Microscope; Rev. Sci. Instrum. 43, 1334–1338, 1972.
i1 Eklund K: Use of Operational Amplifiers in Precision Current Regulators; Rev. Sci. Instrum. 30, 328–331, 1959.
j1 Garwin R L: Efficient Precision Current Regulator for Low-Voltage Magnets; Rev. Sci. Instrum. 29, 223–224, 1958.
k1 Garwin R L, Penman S, Shapiro G: Efficient Precision Current Regulator for High Power Magnets; Rev. Sci. Instrum. 30, 105–107, 1959.
l1 Rothwarf F, Bateman C O, Ford D, Milke P: Silicon-Controlled Rectifier Circuitry for Producing Pulsed Magnetic Fields; Rev. Sci. Instrum. 38, 1241–1244, 1967.
m1 Babbs R S: Precise Constant Current Source for BZV10, 1N821 and BZX90 Series Voltage Reference Diodes; Mullard Tech. Comm. 12, Apr. 1973, 234–239.
n1 Holder B E, Maddux A S: Solid State Power Supply for High Impedance NMR Magnets; Rev. Sci. Instrum. 45, 1228–1231, 1974.
o1 Henry T: Analysis and Design of the Op Amp Current Source; Motorola Application Note AN-587, 1972.
p1 Peerboom R: Digitally-Controlled Current Sources for New Ways of Making Automatic Measurements; Hewlett-Packard J 24, Aug. 1973, 14–20.
q1 Sullivan N S, Vaissiere J, Mauc C: A Simple Reliable Current-Voltage Power Supply for Superconductive Solenoids; Rev. Sci. Instrum. 46, 198–200, 1975.
r1 Carter R L: High Stability Operational Amplifier Current Sources; Rev. Sci. Instrum. 46, 495–496, 1975.
s1 Bloyet D, Gonord P, Varoquaux E J-A, Vibet C: High Precision Current Supply; J Phys. E Sci. Instrum. 8, 636–638, 1975.
t1 Maxson D, Seiler D G, Tipton L: Current Regulated, High Voltage Power Supply for CW Gas Lasers; Rev. Sci. Instrum. 46, 1110–1112, 1975.
u1 Chapman R: Versatile Wide Range Electron Current Regulator; Rev. Sci. Instrum. 43, 1536–1538, 1972.

v1 Debe M K, Johnson D C: Simple DC Technique for Precise Electron Beam Current Regulation; Rev. Sci. Instrum. 47, 37–38, 1976.
w1 Hewlett-Packard: DC Power Supply Handbook; Hewlett-Packard Application Note 90, 1968.
x1 Hewlett-Packard: DC Power Supply Handbook; Hewlett-Packard 1970.
y1 Philbrick/Nexus: Applications Manual for Operational Amplifiers; Philbrick/Nexus Research, 2nd. Edn. 1968.
z1 Smith J I: Modern Operational Circuit Design; Wiley-Interscience 1971.
A1 Botos B: FET Current Regulators—Circuits and Diodes; Motorola Application Note AN-462, 1969.
B1 Hewlett-Packard: Applications of a DC Constant Current Source; Hewlett-Packard Application Note 128, Sep. 1970.
C1 Hewlett-Packard: Increased Output Resistance for DC Regulated Power Supplies; Hewlett-Packard Application Note 83, Sep. 1966.
D1 Defreese J D, Woodruff T A, Malmstadt H V: New Type of Programmable Current-Regulated Power Supply for Operation of Hollow Cathode Lamps in a High Intensity Programmed Mode; Analytical Chemistry 46, 1471–1476, 1974.
E1 Motorola: A Constant-Current Battery Charger with Voltage Limiting; New Electronics 15 Feb. 1972, 28.
F1 Rosenthal L A: Constant Current Ballast; Rev. Sci. Instrum. 47, 630–631, 1976.

References section 7.4: Constant voltage/constant current regulators

a1 Hewlett-Packard: The Present Attainments of Adjustable Power Supplies; Hewlett-Packard J 13, July 1962.
b1 Hewlett-Packard: DC Power Supply Handbook; Hewlett-Packard Application Note 90, 1968.
c1 Birman P: Power Supply Handbook; Kepco 1965.
d1 Hewlett-Packard: DC Power Supply Handbook; Hewlett-Packard 1970.

References section 7.5: Series and parallel operation

a1 Gowthorpe A: Economical Dual-Polarity Regulated Power Supplies; Electronic Eng. 42, Mar. 1970, 33–35.
b1 Pecchio S: A Versatile Bipolar Power Supply/Amplifier for Lab and Systems Use; Hewlett-Packard J 25, July 1974, 15–19.
c1 Hewlett-Packard: DC Power Supply Handbook; Hewlett-Packard Application Note 90, 1968.
d1 Hewlett-Packard: The Present Attainments of Adjustable Power Supplies; Hewlett-Packard J 13, July 1962.
e1 Birman P: Power Supply Handbook; Kepco 1965.
f1 Hewlett-Packard: Power Supply/Amplifier. Concepts and Modes of Operation; Hewlett-Packard Application Note 82, Sep. 1966.
g1 Fairchild: Tracking Voltage Regulator uA78T00; Fairchild Data Sheet 1973.
h1 Mammano R A: Using a Dual-Polarity Tracking Voltage Regulator (SG3501); Silicon General Applications Bulletin No.1, 1971.
i1 Microsystems International: A Simple Tracking Regulator; Microsystems International Application Note 1974.
j1 Darbie A M: Avoid the Pitfalls of Power-Supply Connections; Electronic Design 15 Feb. 1970.
k1 Hewlett-Packard: DC Power Supply Handbook; Hewlett-Packard 1970.
l1 Silicon General: Adjustable Dual Voltage Regulator SG3502; Silicon General Data Sheet May 1971.
m1 Silicon General: Dual Voltage Tracking Regulator SG3501; Silicon General Data Sheet Oct. 1970.
n1 Raytheon: Dual Tracking Voltage Regulator 4194 (Variable); Raytheon Application Note Oct. 1972.

o1   Raytheon: Dual Tracking Voltage Regulator 4195 (Fixed); Raytheon Data Sheet.

p1   Smathers T, Sevastopoulos N: LM125/126/127 Precision Dual Tracking Regulators; National Semiconductor Application Note AN-82, May 1974.

q1   Motorola: Dual +/− 15Volt Tracking Regulator MC1468; Motorola Data Sheet Dec. 1972.

References section 7.6: Protection and ancillary circuits

a1   Eimbinder J (Ed): Application Considerations for Linear Integrated Circuits, Chapter 14 Sullivan D R, Mamie H W: Voltage Regulator ICs with Foldback Current Limiting; Wiley-Interscience 1970.

b1   Hill R H: Greater Regulator Efficiency with Foldback Current Limiting; Electronic Eng. 43, Mar. 1971, 67–69.

c1   Riley W J: Adding Foldback Resistor Provides Overload Safety; Electronics 15 Mar. 1973, 1908.

d1   Dobkin R C: General Purpose Power Supply; National Semiconductor Linear Brief LB-28, June 1974.

e1   Wright M: Protect Series-Pass Transistors from Thermal Overload by Adding Current-Limiting Circuitry to the Power Supply Regulator; Electronic Design 6 Dec. 1973, 82–86.

f1   Hewlett-Packard: Power Supply Overvoltage 'Crowbars'; Hewlett-Packard Application Note 109, Apr. 1969.

g1   Pierce W C: Is a Crowbar Alone Enough?; Electronic Design 27 Sep. 1974, 106–111.

h1   Phillips R: Transistor and Zener Protect Series Regulator; Electronics 41, 8 July 1968, 92–93.

i1   Merrkken L N: Fuses or Circuit Breakers; Electronic Design 20 Dec. 1974, 66–70.

j1   RCA: High-Speed, High-Voltage, High-Current Power Transistors; RCA Technical Series PM-80, 1970.

k1   General Electric: Transient Voltage Suppression Manual; General Electric Handbook 1975.

l1   Hampson L: Fuse Protection of Semiconductor Diodes, Thyristors, and Triacs; Mullard Tech. Comm. 13, 203–319, Oct. 1975.

m1   RCA: Solid-State Power Circuits Designer's Handbook; RCA Technical Series SP-52, 1971.

n1   Texas Instruments: Silicon Transistor Voltage Regulator Overload Protection; Texas Instruments Application Note.

o1   Babbs R S, Howarth N F, Cunningham B: Transient Voltage Suppression Using Transient Suppressor Diodes; Mullard Tech. Comm. 12, 94–112, 1972.

p1   Walters W: Transient Suppression with a Power Zener Diode; Motorola Application Note AN-461, 1969.

q1   Sahm W H: A Highly Reliable, Fail Safe, Precision Undervoltage Protection Circuit; General Electric Application Note 90.83, 1970.

r1   Breece H T: Current Limiting for Transistor Series Voltage Regulators; RCA Application Note SMA-18, 1963.

s1   Gutzwiller F W: Rectifier Voltage Transients: Their Generation, Detection and Reduction; General Electric Application Note 200.11, 1961.

t1   Fairchild: More Voltage Regulator Applications Using the uA723; Fairchild Application Brief APP-133, 1969.

u1   Birman P: Power Supply Handbook; Kepco 1965.

v1   Hewlett-Packard: DC Power Supply Handbook; Hewlett-Packard 1970.

References section 7.7: IC regulators

a1   Eimbinder J (Ed): Application Considerations for Linear Integrated Circuits, Chapter 15 Renschler E L: Integrated Voltage Regulators (MC1460/1461), Chapter 16 Widlar R J: Positive Voltage Regulators (LM100/105), Chapter 17 Widlar R J: Negative Voltage Regulators (LM104); Wiley-Interscience 1970.

b1 Fairchild: More Voltage Regulator Applications Using the uA723; Fairchild Application Brief APP-133, 1969.
c1 Cini C: L005-L036-L037 Power Voltage Regulators; SGC Product Profile 102, Feb. 1971.
d1 Renschler E, Schrock D: Development, Analysis, and Basic Operation of the MC1560-61 Monolithic Voltage Regulators; Motorola Application Note AN-500, 1969.
e1 Geinger M, Kesner D: Voltage and Current Boost Techniques Using the MC1460–61; Motorola Application Note AN-498, 1969.
f1 Renschler E, Schrock D: Shutdown Techniques for the MC1460/61/69 Monolithic Voltage Regulators; Motorola Application Note AN-499, 1969.
g1 Kesner D, Grubbs E: A Floating Voltage and Current Regulator—the MC1466; Motorola Application Note AN-497, 1969.
h1 Kesner D: Using a General Purpose, High Current Monolithic Voltage Regulator—the MC1469; Motorola Application Note AN-515, 1970.
i1 Ricks R: Voltage Regulator Applications Using μA723—Number 2; Fairchild Application Brief 146, 1970.
j1 Frederiksen T M: A Monolithic High-Power Series Voltage Regulator; Motorola Application Note AN-473, 1969.
k1 National Semiconductor: IC On-Card Regulation for Logic Circuits (LM309); New Electronics 5 Sep. 1972, 53–54.
l1 National Semiconductor: New Uses for the LM100 Regulator; National Semiconductor Application Note AN8-1, 1969.
m1 Sevastopolous N, Cleveland G, Sherwin J: LM330 Series Three Terminal Positive Regulators; National Semiconductor Application Note AN-103, Mar. 1974.
n1 Smathers T, Sevastopolous N: LM125/126/127 Precision Dual Tracking Regulators; National Semiconductor Application Note AN-82, May 1974.
o1 Microsystems International: A Low Cost Regulated Supply Using the ML723; Microsystems International Application Note 1974.
p1 Thomson–CSF: Les Regulateurs de Tension; Thomson–CSF Manuel d'Applications CIL, Tome 2, 1974.
q1 Fairchild: 4-Terminal Positive and Negative Adjustable Voltage Regulators μA78G, μA79G; Fairchild Data Sheet July 1975.
r1 Sevastopolous N et al: Voltage Regulator Handbook; National Semiconductor 1975.
s1 Keen M J (Ed): The Application of Linear Microcircuits Volume 2; SGS Handbook May 1969.
t1 National Semiconductor: Linear Applications; National Semiconductor Handbook Feb. 1973.
u1 Petersen W R: Application Considerations for Hybrid Series Voltage Regulators; RCA Application Note AN-6026, 1972.
v1 Widlar R J: A Monolithic Voltage Regulator SFC2100/2200/2300. Design and Applications; Sescosem (Thomson–CSF) Application Note 87A, Nov. 1970.
w1 Widlar R J: Designs for Negative Voltage Regulators (LM104); Design Electronics Nov. 1970, 45, 46, 49, 50, 53.
x1 National Semiconductor: 3 Amp–5 Volt Positive Regulator LM323; National Semiconductor Data Sheet May 1973.
y1 National Semiconductor: 3-Terminal Adjustable Regulator LM317; National Semiconductor Data Sheet Feb. 1976.
z1 National Semiconductor: LM340 Series 3-Terminal Positive Regulators; National Semiconductor Data Sheet Aug. 1973.
A1 National Semiconductor: LM320 Series 3-Terminal Negative Regulators; National Semiconductor Data Sheet.
B1 Fairchild Semiconductor: 3-Terminal Positive Voltage Regulators μA7800 Series; Fairchild Semiconductor Data Sheet 1976.
C1 Fairchild Semiconductor: 3-Terminal Negative Voltage Regulators μA7900 Series; Fairchild Semiconductor Data Sheet 1976.
D1 Fairchild Semiconductor: 4-Terminal Positive and Negative Adjustable Voltage Regulators μA78G, μA79G; Fairchild Semiconductor Data Sheet 1976.

E1 Fairchild Semiconductor: Precision Voltage Regulator µA723; Fairchild Semiconductor Data Sheet Sep. 1968.
F1 Motorola: High Power NPN Silicon Power Voltage Regulator MPC 1000; Motorola Data Sheet 1973.
G1 Jung W G: Application of the AD580: The Monolithic Voltage Regulator as a Flexible 3-Terminal Circuit Building Block; Analog Dialogue 9, No.2, 1975, 20–21.

References section 7.8: Switching regulators

a1 Widlar R J: Switching Regulators. Chapter 16 Eimbinder J (Ed): Designing with Linear Integrated Circuits; Wiley 1969.
b1 Maytum M: Inverters; Texas Instruments Application Report B83, Jan. 1971.
c1 Rupra K: Switching Mode Regulators; Texas Instruments Application Report B76, and Electronic Components 8 Jan. 1971, 42–47.
d1 Widlar R J: Designing Switching Regulators; National Semiconductor Application Note AN-2, 1967.
e1 Shiner B: Switching Voltage Regulator Uses Discrete and IC Approaches; Motorola Application Note AN-457, 1969.
f1 Maytum M: Chopper Power Supplies Using BUY69/70 High Voltage Power Transistor; Texas Instruments Application Report B116, 1971.
g1 Hnatek E R: Design of Solid-State Power Supplies; Van Nostrand Reinhold 1971.
h1 Soares R, Tuley J H, Hounam E: Planar Power Switching Transistors (BDY60 Series); Mullard Users Guide TP1178, 1970.
i1 Bothner P A: Off-Line 1-Kilowatt Driven Converter; RCA Application Note AN-6045, 1972.
j1 Myers R S: Compact 5-Volt Power Supplies Using High Voltage Power Transistors; RCA Application Note AN-4509, 1971.
k1 Burchall M: A Guide to the Specification and Use of Miniature Switching Power Supplies; Advance Electronics 1972.
l1 Norris B (Ed): Semiconductor Circuit Design Section 2 Power Transistor Applications (Switching Mode, Chopper and Inverter Supplies); Texas Instruments 1972.
m1 Jansson L E: A Survey of Converter Circuits for Switched-Mode Power Supplies; Mullard Tech. Comm. 12, July 1973, 271–278.
n1 George B: Variable 35V 10A Switched-Mode Voltage Regulator; Mullard Tech. Comm. 12, July 1973, 279–292.
o1 Jansson L E: Radio Frequency Interference Suppression in Switched-Mode Power Supplies; Mullard Tech. Comm. 12, 294–298, 1973.
p1 Dudley B W, Peck R D: High Efficiency Modular Power Supplies Using Switching Regulators; Hewlett-Packard J 25, Dec. 1973, 15–19.
q1 Haver R J: Regulated Line Operated Inverter Uses High Voltage Power Transistors and Hot Carrier Rectifiers; Motorola Application Note AN-529, 1970.
r1 Houldsworth J A, Hampson L: Fast Cycle Switching and Power-Control System for use with Transformer Load Controlled by Three-Phase Fully-Controlled AC controller; Mullard Tech. Comm. 13, 90–104, 1974.
s1 George B: 6V 100A Switched-Mode Power Supply Operating Directly from the Mains; Mullard Tech. Comm. 13, 105–124, 1974.
t1 Burgum F J: Electrolytic Capacitors for Output Filters of Switched-Mode Power Supplies; Mullard Tech. Comm. 13, 125–140, 1974.
u1 Widlar R J: Switching Regulator Designs Using Negative-Voltage Regulators; Design Electronics Dec. 1970, 72, 75, 76.
v1 Barrow C: Cores for Switched-Mode Power Supply Transformers; Mullard Tech. Comm. 13, 170–181, 1974.
w1 Newton T: Switching Mode Power Supply for Monochrome TV; Semiconductors (Motorola) 1974/2, 19–21.
x1 Hetterscheid W: Base Circuit Design for High-Voltage Switching Transistors in Power Converters; Mullard Tech. Comm. 13, 157–169, 1974.

y1 Mortensen H H: +5 to −15 Volts DC Converter; National Semiconductor Linear Brief LB-18, July 1972.

z1 Microsystems International: Description and Application of the ML4270, ML4270-15 DC-DC Converter; Microsystems International Application Note 1974.

A1 O'Sullivan G A: Which DC/AC Inverter? Electronic Design 6 Dec. 1974, 54–59.

B1 Norris B: Industrial Switching Mode Power Supplies; Texas Instruments Application Note B159, 1974.

C1 Mullard: FX3700 Series Transformer Cores and Coil Formers for SMPS; Mullard Tech. Comm. 13, 225–228, 1975.

D1 Hnatek E R: Choose Switching Regulators for Your Computer Power Supply Design; Electronic Design 1 Apr. 1975, 54–59.

E1 Wood P N: Switch Your High-Power Supply Design to an Off-Line Regulation Technique; Electronic Design 1 Apr. 1975, 116–122.

F1 Johnson K R: High Voltage Power Supply from 5-V Source Regulated by Timer Feedback Circuit; Electronic Design 1 Apr. 1975, 132.

G1 DiFrancesco M: A High Current Power Supply for Systems that Use 5-Volt IC Logic Extensively; Hewlett-Packard J 26, Apr. 1975, 14–19.

H1 Haver R J: A 20kHz, 1kW Line Operated Inverter; Motorola Application Note AN-588, 1972.

I1 Haver R J: A New Approach to Switching Regulators; Motorola Application Note AN-719, 1974.

J1 Plessey: Switch Mode Power Supply Control Circuit SL442; Plessey Data Sheet PS1431, Dec. 1974.

K1 Plessey: Switch Mode Power Supply Applications; Plessey Publication PS1452, July 1975.

L1 Palouda H: A Switching Regulator Using an RCA PNP Power Darlington Transistor; RCA Application Note AN-6195E, 1975.

M1 RCA: A Safe-Area Rating System for Power Inverters Handling Capacitive and Inductive Loads; RCA Application Note AN-6330, 1975.

N1 Turnbull J: Squelch FRI in Switching Supplies; Electronic Design 27 Sep. 1975, 96–98.

O1 Hnatek E R: Build DC/DC Converters that Work; Electronic Design 24 May 1975, 82–86. Circuits; Wiley 1969

P1 Wood P. N: Design of a 5 Volt, 1000 Watt Power Supply; TRW Application Note 122, 1975.

Q1 TRW: High Frequency Power Switching; TRW Semiconductors Application Note.

R1 Jansson L E: Semiconductors for Switch-Mode Power Supplies; New Electronics 24 Feb. 1976, 24, 26.

S1 Jansson L E: Power-Handling Capability for Ferrite Transformers and Chokes for Switched-Mode Power Supplies; Mullard Tech. Comm. 13, 321–352, Oct. 1975.

T1 Basell M C: 50W Multiple Output Switched-Mode Power Supply; Mullard Tech. Comm. 13, 379–387, Jan. 1976.

U1 Burgum F J: Switched-Mode Power Supply Transformer Design Nomograms; Mullard Tech. Comm. 13, 302–319, Jan. 1976.

V1 RCA: Power Circuits, DC to Microwave; RCA Electronic Components 1969.

W1 RCA: Solid-State Power Circuits Designer's Handbook; RCA Technical Series SP-52, 1971.

X1 Thomson–CSF: Les Regulateurs de Tension; Thomson–CSF Manuel d'Applications CIL, Tome 2, 1974.

Y1 RCA: High-Speed, High-Voltage, High-Current Power Transistors; RCA Technical series PM-80, 1970.

Z1 Perkins D: Applications of Fast-Recovery Rectifiers; Motorola Application Note AN-512, 1970.

a2 Hnatek E R: Switching Regulator-Noise Suppression Techniques; Computer Design Jan. 1975, 94–96.

b2 Hnatek E R: Cut Noise in Switching Regulators by Using Simple Filters; Electronic Design 28 Oct. 1971, 49–54.

c2 TRW: Ultra-Fast Recovery Double Slug Rectifiers Series DSR; TRW Semiconductors Data Sheet 1970.
d2 Motorola: Lead Mounted Hot Carrier Power Rectifier MBD5300; Motorola Data Sheet Nov. 1970.
e2 Delco: 28Volt Darlington Switching Regulator; Delco Electronics Application Note 49, Dec. 1971.
f2 White L M: Television Switched-Mode Power Supply Using the TDA2640; Mullard Tech. Comm. 13, 258–279, 1975.
g2 Palouda H, Marmann A: Switching Regulation with Power Darlingtons; Electronic Eng. Mar. 1976, 39–41.
h2 Snelling E C: Design of Power Transformers Having Ferrite Cores; Mullard Tech. Comm. 12, 2–26, 1971.
i2 Mullard: 5V 20A and 5V 40A Switched-Mode Power Supplies; Mullard Technical Note 32 (TP1519) 1975.
j2 Mullard: Switched-mode Power Supply Control Circuit TDA2640; Mullard Data Sheet Feb. 1976.
k2 Gallace L J, Peterson W R: Taking the Heat Out of Switching Power Supplies; Electronic Eng. Apr. 1976, 49–51.
l2 Levy A: Keep Your Power Flowing with an Uninterruptible Supply; Electronic Design 1 Mar. 1976, 62–64.
m2 Basell M C: 30V 8A Switched-Mode Power Supply Operating from −50V Post Office Exchange Supplies; Mullard Technical Note 20 (TP1491) 1975.

References section 7.9: Cells and batteries

a1 Petley B W: Towards a Quantum Voltage Standard; Contemporary Physics 12, 453–470, 1971.
b1 — —: Parameters of Electrochemical Cells: Electronic Products May 1963, 62–69.
c1 Morehouse C K, Glicksman R, Lozier G S: Batteries; Proc IRE 46, 1462–1483, 1958.
d1 Tucker E W: Standard Cells; Electronic and Power 12, 421–424, 1966, and Muirhead Technique 21, 19–23, 1967.
e1 Freeman S W: Sealed Cells and Their Charging; Design Electronics July 1970, 37–38.
f1 Batteries, Manufacturers Literature from Mallory, Ever Ready, Alkaline, Deac, Varta, Saft, Gates, Varley, Sonnenschein, Energy Conversion (Metair).
g1 Codi Semiconductor: A Comparison of the Accuracy and Precision of Certa-Cell vs. Unsaturated Cells; Codi Semiconductor 1972.
h1 General Electric: Nickel-Cadium Battery Application Engineering Handbook; General Electric 1971.
i1 General Electric: Nickel-Cadium Battery Application Handbook Supplement; General Electric 1973.
j1 Gates: Battery Application Manual; Gates Rubber 1975.
k1 Naylor D: New Primary Cells Help to Reduce Equipment Size; Electronic Eng. 42, Oct. 1970, 74–77.
l1 Sonnenschein: Dryfit PC-, ST-, Batteries; Sonnenschein Data Sheet 1974.
m1 Varley: Accumulators and Batteries; Varley Dry Accumulators Data Sheet.
n1 Mehl W: How Much Electrical Energy Can Be Generated in a Given Volume of an Electrochemical Battery?; Orbit Oct. 1970, 23, 25–27, 29.
o1 — —: Primary Batteries for Lower Power; Design Electronics Jan. 1971, 55, 57, 58, 61. 62, 65.
p1 Ball J V: There's No Overcharge for Fast-Charged Batteries (NiCd); Electronics 22 Jan. 1968, 97–100.
q1 Cahoon N C, Heise G W: The Primary Battery; Wiley 1976.
r1 — —: Parameters of Electrochemical Cells; Electronic Products May 1963, 62–69.
s1 Smith K: Latest Trends in Portable Power Systems; Electron 11 Jan. 1973, 17, 19, 21, 23, 24.
t1 Williams B H: Primary Battery Systems; Electron 14 Mar. 1974, 25, 27, 29, 30.

u1 Lewis J L: Electrical Power Sources. A Survey of Recent Developments (Part 1); Electrical Equipment June 1967, 24–34.
v1 Zinder D A: Fast Charging Systems for Ni-Cd Batteries; Motorola Application Note AN-447, 1972.
w1 Muirhead: Miniature Standard Cell K-375-C; Muirhead Data Sheet 427, 1967.
x1 Muirhead: Reference Cell K-391-A; Muirhead Data Sheet.
y1 Energy Conversion: Batteries Enter a New Era (Metair Batteries); Energy Conversion Databook.
z1 — —: Recharge Batteries in 15 Minutes Only; Design Electronics Jan. 1970.
A1 Mallory: Leakproof Mercury and Alkaline Batteries; Mallory Batteries Designers File.
B1 Roll I, Shenton M, Lucas D: Improvement to Automatic NiCd Battery Charger; Electronic Eng. Mar. 1976, 17.
C1 Bottomly G: Automatic Charger for Nickel-Cadmium Batteries; Electronic Eng. Dec. 1975, 19.
D1 Smith I M: A Designer's Guide to Portable Power; New Electronics 29 June 1976, 33, 35, 36.
E1 Norton B: The State of Charge; New Electronics 29 June 1976, 41, 42, 45.
F1 Marcham D: System Design with Secondary Batteries; New Electronics 29 June 1976, 48, 50.

References section 7.10: Voltage and current regulator diodes

a1 Evans J P (Ed): Mullard Voltage Regulator (Zener) Diodes; Mullard TP652, 1966.
b1 Eimbinder J (Ed): Designing with Linear Integrated Circuits, Chapter 14 Widlar R J: Integrated Low-Voltage Breakdown Diode; Wiley 1969.
c1 Mullard: High-Stability Reference Diodes (BZX47 Family); Mullard TP968, 1968.
d1 Walters C K, Racino R N: Design Considerations and Performance of Motorola Temperature-Compensated Zener (Reference) Diodes; Motorola Application Note AN-437, 1968.
e1 Queen M: A Treatise on the LVA Diode: TRW Semiconductors 1967, and Electronic Design 21 June 1967, 120.
f1 Botos B: FET Current Regulators—Circuits and Diodes; Motorola Application Note AN-462, 1969.
g1 Mullard: The Junction FET as a Constant Current Source; Mullard TP1183, 1970.
h1 Siliconix: The FET Constant Current Source; Siliconix Application Tip 1967.
i1 Watson J: An Introduction to Field-Effect Transistors; Siliconix 1970.
j1 Todd C D: Zener and Avalanche Diodes; Wiley-Interscience 1970.
k1 Ferranti: Silicon Voltage Regulators and Voltage Reference Diodes; Ferranti Application Report 8, 1963.
l1 Hart B L: Voltage Reference Sources; Electronic Components June 1970, 665–666.
m1 Babbs R S, Matkowski Z, Waterman P: 1N821 and BZX90 Series of High Stability Reference Diodes; Mullard TP1339, 1972.
n1 Katz G: FET Voltage Regulator Eliminates Ripple Feedthrough and Permits Self-Starting; Electronic Eng. 44, Dec. 1972, 57–59.
o1 Babbs R S: Precise Constant Current Source for BZV10, 1N821 and BZX90 Series Voltage Reference Diodes; Mullard Tech. Comm. 12, Apr. 1973, 234–239.
p1 Dobkin R C: 1.2 Volt Reference; National Semiconductor Application Note AN-56, 1971.
q1 Fairchild: Precision Voltage Reference μA728; Fairchild Data Sheet.
r1 Babbs R S, Matkowski Z, Tuley J H: 1N821, BZX90 and BZV10 Series of High Stability Voltage Reference Diodes; Mullard Application Note TP1387, 1973.
s1 Parish R G, Rose J A: Voltage References; Electron 28 Feb. 1974, 31, 33.
t1 Sherwin J S: The Field-Effect Transistor Constant Current Source; Siliconix Design Ideas 24/A14 Jan. 1971.
u1 Austin D: Precision Ring-of-Two Circuit with Op Amps; Electronic Eng. 46, Dec. 1974, 23–24.

v1 Perugini M: Special Report on Voltage References; Electronic Products Feb. 1967, 78–80, 82, 84, 86–90.

w1 Brokaw A P: A Simple Three-Terminal IC Bandgap Reference; IEEE J SC-9, 388–393, 1974.

x1 Microsystems International: Description and Application of the ML113 Low-Voltage Reference Diode; Microsystems International Application Note 1974.

y1 Hart B L, Barker R W J: A Low Current Voltage Reference Source; Electronic Components 23 Apr. 1974, 17, 19, 21.

z1 Analog Devices: IC Low Drift Voltage Reference AD580 (2.5 Volt); Analog Devices Data Sheet 1974.

A1 National Semiconductor: Precision Buffered BCD (LH0079:10,000V) and Binary (LH0071:10.240V) References; National Semiconductor Data Sheet Apr. 1975.

B1 Analog Devices: Precision 10.000 Volt Reference AD2700/1/2; Analog Devices Data Sheet 1975.

C1 Raburn W D, Greene H: Response of Voltage Regulating Diodes to Fast Current Pulses; Microelectronics J 7, No.1, Sep. 1975, 38–39.

D1 National Semiconductor: LM199/LM299/LM399 Precision Reference (6.95V); National Semiconductor Data Sheet Aug. 1975.

E1 Brokaw A P: More About the AD580 Monolithic IC Voltage Regulator; Analog Dialogue 9, No.1, 1975, 6–7.

F1 Jung W G: Applications of the AD580; The Monolithic Voltage Regulator as a Flexible 3-Terminal Building Block; Analog Dialogue 9, No.2, 1975, 20–21.

G1 Ferranti: Precision 1.26 Volt Reference Source; Ferranti Data Sheet Aug. 1975.

H1 Mullard: Simple Stabilised Power Supplies; Mullard Tech. Publication TP1164, 1970.

I1 Texas Instruments: Silicon Voltage Regulator Zener Diodes; Texas Instruments Application Report Vol. 1, No.6, May 1960.

J1 Motorola: Silicon Zener Diode and Rectifier Handbook; Motorola 1961.

K1 Wilbur-Ham J, Jackson J S: 22mA DC Supply Stable to 1 part in 10(6) per Day; J Sci. Instrum. 39, 86, 1962.

L1 Motorola: Forward Reference Diode MR2361; Motorola Data Sheet 1967.

M1 Transitron: Silicon and Germanium Stabistors (EVR Series); Transitron Bulletin TE-1332, 1963.

N1 Mullard: Voltage Regulator Diodes (Stabistors) BZY88-COV7/-C1V3; Mullard Data Sheet Apr. 1974.

O1 Williams P: Very Low Voltage DC Reference; Electronic Eng. 40, 348–349, 1968. See also Verster T C: Temperature Compensated Low Voltage Reference; Electronic Eng. 41, 65, 1969.

P1 SGS–Fairchild: Voltage Reference Diodes BZX43/44/45; SGS–Fairchild Data Sheet Sep. 1967.

Q1 Motorola: Field-Effect Current Regulator Diodes 1N5283–5314; Motorola Data Sheet Apr. 1967.

R1 Motorola: Field-Effect Current Regulator Diodes MCL1300–1304; Motorola Data Sheet Feb. 1968.

S1 Siliconix: N-Channel Silicon Junction FET Current-Limiter Diodes E500–507; Siliconix Data Sheet June 1972.

T1 Siliconix: Current Regulator Diode CR022/470; Siliconix Data Sheet June 1974.

U1 Ferranti: Precision Voltage Reference Source ZN423T (1.26V); Ferranti Data Sheet Apr. 1976.

V1 General Semiconductor: Transzorb Transient Protector MPT Series; General Semiconductor Data Sheets 1976.

W1 Johnson K C: Unfamiliar Forms of Temperature Compensated Voltage Reference; Wireless World July 1976, 43–44.

X1 National Semiconductor: Precision Reference LM399 (6.95V); National Semiconductor Data Sheet 1976.

8 Circuit devices

8.1 Field-effect transistors

Though the initial proposals for field-effect devices predate bipolar transistors by a considerable time [f1], it is only in the past few years that field-effect transistors have become available in a substantial number of types and at economic prices. They can perform most of the functions for which bipolars are now used, but it will be their special properties and applications that will be considered here. There are, now, many good treatments of field-effect devices, and reference should be made to these for a fuller discussion [a1, b1, c1, g1, h1, s1, t1, j2].

A basic structure for a field-effect transistor (FET) is illustrated in Fig. 8.1.1. (The two P regions are directly connected.)

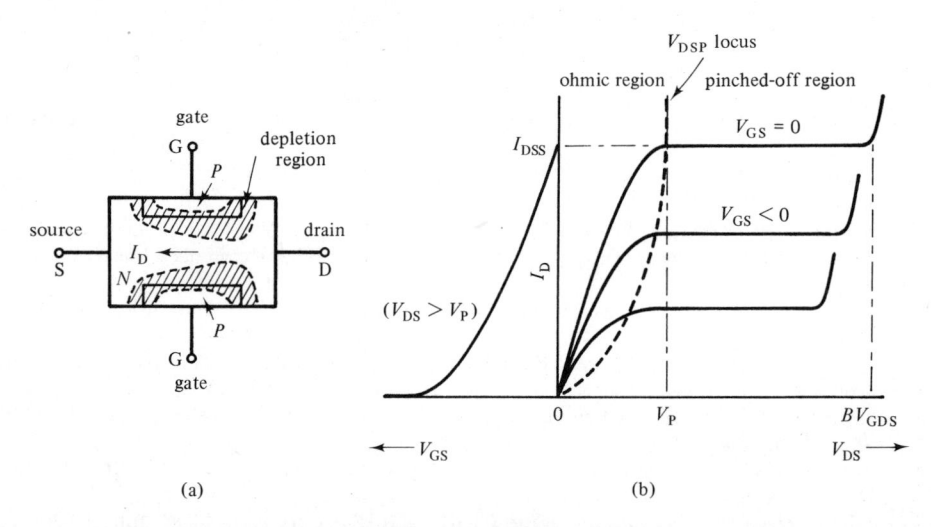

Fig. 8.1.1 *N*-channel junction field-effect transistor, (a) cross-section showing structure, (b) characteristic curves

With no gate–source bias, V_{GS}, the depletion region around the gate will be a minimum, and the maximum conduction channel allows electrons to flow from the source S to drain D. When the gate is biased negatively, the depletion region extends so as to reduce the channel and, hence, drain current I_D. The depletion region is not symmetrical around the gate electrode, since the voltage drop from D to S as I_D flows, produces an additional field distribution. Thus, as either V_{GS} goes more negative or

V_{DS} increases, the channel is eventually closed or pinched-off. The influence of V_{DS} alone cannot completely stop conduction, since the mechanism operating depends upon the flow of I_D, so the current levels off and becomes effectively independent of V_{DS}, as shown to the right of the V_{DSP} locus in Fig. 8.1.1(b). At high V_{DS}, breakdown will occur, as a result of avalanche effects. The value quoted is BV_{GDS}, the gate-to-drain breakdown with source shorted to drain. In normal operation the breakdown voltage is lower for increasing V_{GS}.

With $V_{GS}=0$ the drain current $I_D = I_{DSS}$ for $V_{DS} > V_P$, the pinch-off voltage. As V_{GS} becomes more negative, it assists V_{DS}, and pinch-off occurs at a lower value of V_{DS}, giving the locus of pinch-off voltage $V_{DSP} = V_P - V_{GS}$ as shown. The region to the left of this locus is known as the pre-pinch-off, ohmic, or *triode* region. That to the right is called the pinched-off, saturation, or *pentode* region. Triode and pentode refer to valves, or tubes, and for those of us who date back to this era the FET brings us full circle since many of the techniques, terminology, and usage of FET's are identical to those of valves. Here we will be concerned with operation in the pinched-off region; the ohmic mode will be considered in Sec. 8.2.

Relative to bipolar transistors there are several significant differences which it is important to appreciate [b1, B1].

(i) FET's depend on the flow of majority carriers only, i.e., they are unipolar rather than bipolar. There are thus no effects from the storage of minority carriers as, for example, in switching circuits.
(ii) FET's have very high input resistance. For IGFET's this can be $> 10^{12}$ ohm.
(iii) The channel is an ohmic conductor, i.e., there are no P–N junctions and, thus, no offset voltage at zero current. This is important for low-level switches or choppers (Sec. 8.2).
(iv) Since drain current decreases with increase of temperature, FET's are not prone to thermal runaway.
(v) The performance of FET's can improve with decrease of temperature. Some may be operated at temperatures as low as 4 K [s2, t2, p2, u2, Q2].

There are two families of field-effect transistors, generally referred to as junction (JFET) and insulated gate (IGFET). The latter are also commonly called MOSFET's (metal oxide silicon), but since they can be made in other ways, IGFET is the more satisfactory term. In the JFET the gate is formed from a reverse biased P–N junction, while in the IGFET the gate is completely isolated by an insulating dielectric layer. The JFET is operated with the gate reverse biased, the so-called depletion mode, but the channel can be either P or N to give two polarities as for bipolar transistors. (The gate may be slightly forward biased also, ≈ 200 mV say, since below this, forward conduction in the gate P–N junction is negligible.) In the IGFET the channel can again be P or N but, since the gate is insulated, it may be biased in both polarities relative to source. This gives four types of IGFET. To make this clearer all six types are illustrated in Fig. 8.1.2, showing voltage polarities and transconductance variation.

Note that depletion IGFET's can also operate in the enhancement mode, and that the pinch-off voltage is often referred to as the threshold voltage, V_{th}.

The parameters usually measured for FET's are V_P, I_{DSS}, the mutual- or transconductance, g_{fs}, and the output conductance, g_{os}. The conductances are defined by

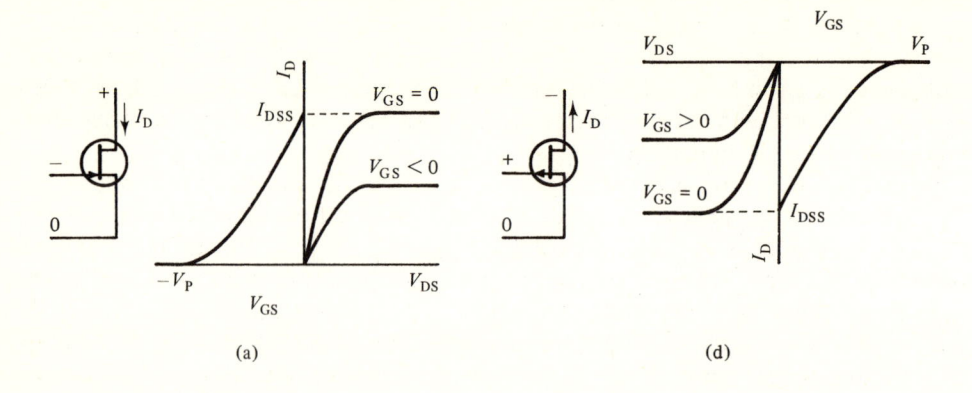

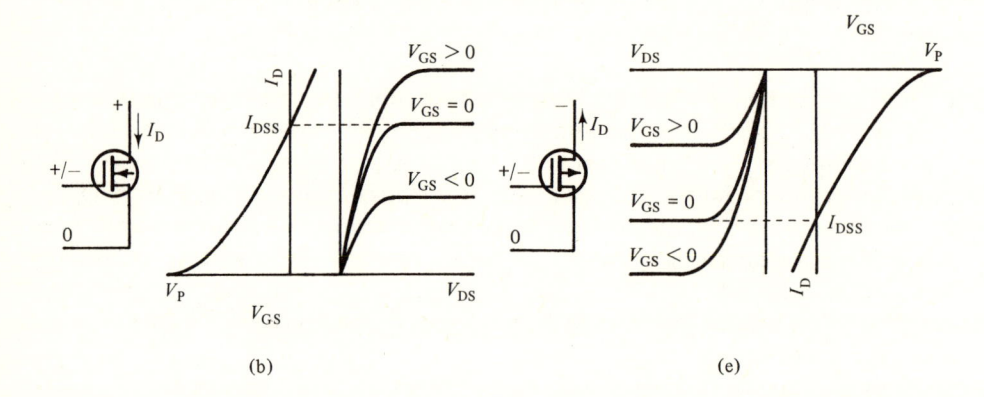

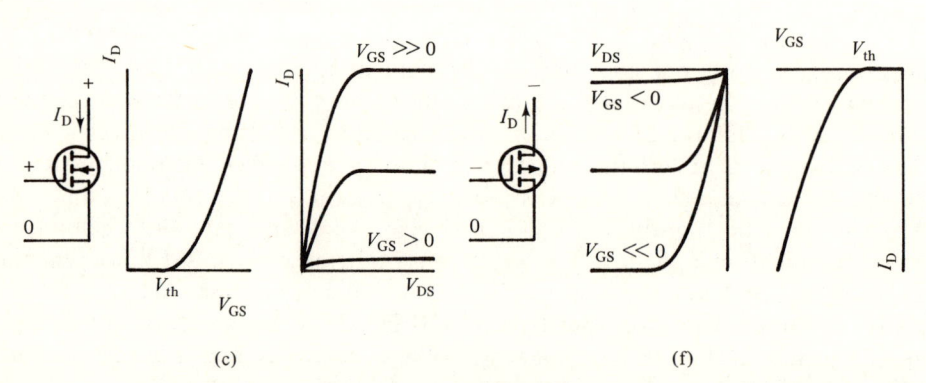

Fig. 8.1.2 Types of field-effect transistor, (a) *N*-channel JFET, (b) *N*-channel depletion IGFET, (c) *N*-channel enhancement IGFET, (d) *P*-channel JFET, (e) *P*-channel depletion IGFET, (f) *P*-channel enhancement IGFET

(y is sometimes used in place of g):

$$g_{fs} = \frac{\partial I_D}{\partial V_{GS}} \quad (V_{DS} = \text{constant})$$

$$\Rightarrow g_{fso} \quad \text{at} \quad V_{GS} = 0, \quad I_D = I_{DSS} \tag{8.1.1}$$

$$g_{os} = \frac{\partial I_D}{\partial V_{DS}} = \frac{1}{r_{ds}} \quad (V_{GS} = \text{constant})$$

where g_{fs} and g_{os} are in mhos.

g_{fs} is the slope of the I_D versus V_{GS} curve at the specified quiescent operating point, and g_{os} is the slope of the I_D versus V_{DS} curve for the particular value of V_{GS}.

There are a number of relationships between various parameters that are useful in determining operating conditions [a1, b1, g1, j1, l1, n1, B1, H1]. These refer to operation in the pinch-off region, $V_{DS} \lesssim V_{DSP}$.

$$I_D = I_{DSS}\left[1 - \frac{V_{GS}}{V_P}\right]^n \quad (\text{in practice, } n = 2)$$

$$g_{fs} = \frac{\partial I_D}{\partial V_{GS}} = \frac{-2I_{DSS}}{V_P}\left[1 - \frac{V_{GS}}{V_P}\right] = \frac{-2}{V_P}(I_{DSS} \cdot I_D)^{1/2}$$

$$g_{fso} = \frac{-2I_{DSS}}{V_P} \quad (\text{for } V_{GS} = 0) \tag{8.1.2}$$

$$g_{fs} = g_{fso}\left[1 - \frac{V_{GS}}{V_P}\right] = g_{fso}\left(\frac{I_D}{I_{DSS}}\right)^{1/2}$$

$$g_{os} = 0, \quad \frac{1}{r_{ds}} = \infty, \quad \text{on this model, but as a guide:}$$

$$g_{os} \approx \frac{g_{fs}}{100} \quad \text{or} \quad g_{fs}\frac{V_P}{V_0}, \quad \text{where} \quad V_0 \approx 500 \text{ V [g1]}$$

If the appropriate curves are not available then, for normally available JFET's, curves can be derived from the characteristic parameters using normalized universal curves [l1]. The curves that are published are typical, and do not show the rather large variability between different units, but limit values are usually given for the main parameters. These parameters are also temperature dependent so that if low drift or wide temperature range is required, allowance must be made [e1, d1, g1, l1, a1, b1, j1, w1, C1, M1].

There are two temperature dependent mechanisms affecting drain current for a fixed value of V_{GS}: charge carrier mobility, and the diffusion potential of the P–N junction, which affects V_P. The affects of these two on drain current are of opposite sign and it is possible to find a value of $V_{GS} = V_{GSZ}$ at which they just cancel. This value is given by:

$$V_{GSZ} \doteq V_P + 0.7 \text{ volt}$$

$$I_{DZ} \doteq I_{DSS}\left(\frac{0.7}{V_P}\right)^2 \tag{8.1.3}$$

$$g_{fsz} \doteq g_{fso}\left(\frac{0.7}{V_P}\right)$$

There is some variation in the *constant* (0·7) so some means of adjustment will still be necessary. If not biased to V_{GSZ}, then the equivalent drift of V_{GS} is given by:

$$\Delta V_{GS} = 2\cdot 2\left[1 - \frac{I_D}{I_{DZ}}\right]^{1/2} \text{ mV/K} \tag{8.1.4}$$

There are, of course, other causes of drift, such as the variation of gate leakage current I_G, but the effect depends on the resistance of the gate circuit. I_G doubles for every 10 K temperature rise, and is proportional to $V_{GS}^{1/2}$ [I1, J1].

In circuit applications, FET's must be carefully biased to obtain optimum performance [k1, x1, v1, r1, j1, a1, b1, B1]. The aim should be to minimize the effect of wide parameter variation or temperature on quiescent operating conditions. As an amplifier the common-source configuration is most often used. A general biasing scheme is shown in Fig. 8.1.3.

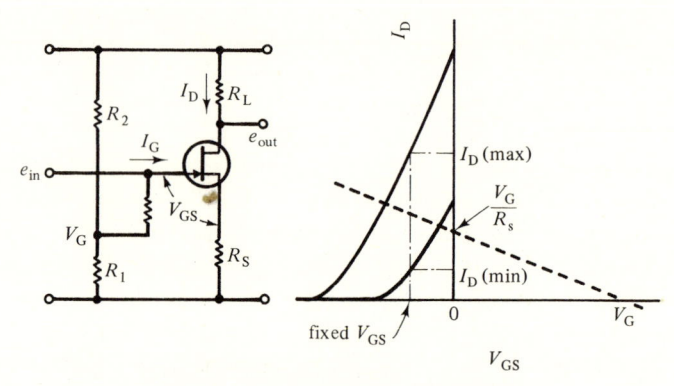

Fig. 8.1.3 Common-source amplifier

If the two curves represent the extreme characteristics for the particular FET type, it is evident that a fixed value of V_{GS} will result in a substantial difference in quiescent drain current from I_D (min) to I_D (max). However, in the circuit shown, there is negative feedback due to R_S, so that we expect less dependence on the characteristic of the active component (Sec. 2.2) but at the expense of gain. For the gate source loop we have (no e_{in} and $I_G = 0$):

$$V_{GS} = I_D R_S - V_G \tag{8.1.5}$$

which gives the self-bias load line shown. It has slope $1/R_S$, and intercepts the V_{GS} axis at V_G and the I_D axis at V_G/R_S. The variation in quiescent drain current is clearly much reduced.

The small-signal equivalent circuit of the FET is quite simple [B1, a1, r1]. Including the load (R_L) and source (R_S) resistors, gives the circuit of Fig. 8.1.4. Ignoring the capacitors, the circuit will be good up to say 100 kHz, and with them up to several MHz.

The voltage gain may readily be found to be:

$$A_v = \frac{e_{out}}{e_{in}} = \frac{-g_{fs}R_L}{1 + g_{fs}R_S + g_{os}(R_L + R_S)} \tag{8.1.6}$$

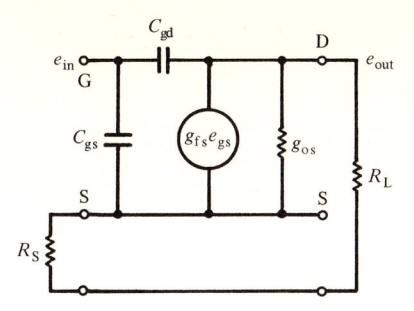

Fig. 8.1.4 FET small-signal equivalent circuit, showing common source connection

and the output resistance:

$$R_{out} = \frac{(1+g_{fs}R_S)R_L}{1+g_{fs}R_S+g_{os}(R_L+R_S)} \tag{8.1.7}$$

The input impedance will be primarily capacitive. If A_s is the gain to the source ($A_s \gtrsim +1$) then:

$$C_{in} = C_{gs}(1-A_s) + C_{gd}(1-A_v) \tag{8.1.8}$$

so the effect of C_{gs} is small compared with C_{gd}. If R_S is bypassed with a capacitor then, at signal frequencies, the above equations hold with R_S and A_s zero.

Junction FET's are particularly appropriate for low-noise amplifiers where source impedances are high, but IGFET's are at present rather noisy. This aspect is covered in Secs. 4.1 and 1.8.

One of the commonest uses of FET's is to obtain high input impedance as, for example, in electrometer applications Secs. 4.6 and 6.5, or to transform from high to low impedance using the source follower configuration. There are a number of variations on the source follower, depending on whether a gain as near unity as possible, zero input–output offset, or large positive and negative voltage swings, are required [a2, a1, v1, B1, E1, K1]. Some of the variations are shown in Fig. 8.1.5.

The simplest arrangement, Fig. 8.1.5(a), has limited gain and output swing if R_S is returned to ground, but both these may be improved by returning it to a large

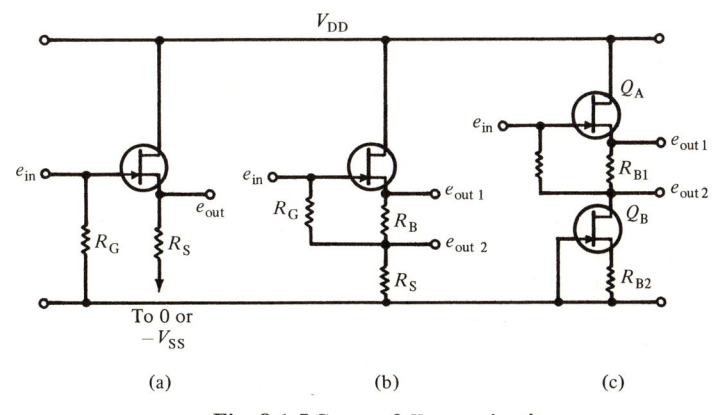

Fig. 8.1.5 Source follower circuits

347

negative voltage $-V_{SS}$. The gain, A_{vs}, input resistance, R_{is}, and output resistance, R_{os}, are given by:

$$A_{vs} = \frac{g_{fs}R_S}{1+R_S(g_{fs}+g_{os})}$$

$$\doteq \frac{g_{fs}R_S}{1+g_{fs}R_S} \quad (g_{os} \ll g_{fs})$$

$$\doteq 1, \quad \text{if } g_{fs}R_S \gg 1$$

$$R_{os} = \frac{R_S(1+g_{os}R_S)}{1+R_S(g_{fs}+g_{os})} \tag{8.1.9}$$

$$\doteq \frac{R_S}{1+g_{fs}R_S} \quad (\text{if } g_{os}R_S \ll 1)$$

$$\doteq \frac{1}{g_{fs}}, \quad \text{if } g_{fs}R_S \gg 1$$

$$R_{is} = R_G$$

The input resistance can be increased by boot-strapping (Sec. 2.5) as shown in Fig. 8.1.5(b). R_B is chosen to provide the necessary bias for the desired drain current, which in turn fixes R_S, knowing V_{SS} and the desired output voltage. The output may be taken from two places. Output 1 will have the impedance given by Eq. (8.1.9) but an offset voltage of V_{GS}. Output 2 has higher output impedance with R_B in series with R_{os}, but the offset voltage can be made zero by choice of R_S or R_B.

The gain may be further improved by replacing R_S with a large dynamic impedance or constant current source (Secs. 1.10 and 7.10(c)) as shown in Fig. 8.1.5(c). R_{B2} sets the current in Q_B, $V_{GSB} = I_D R_{B2}$. If matched transistors are used (e.g., a dual FET) and $R_{B1} = R_{B2}$, then, since the matching makes $V_{GSA} = V_{GSB}$:

$$e_{in} = -V_{GSA} + I_D R_{B1} + e_{out\,2}$$
$$= -I_D R_{B1} + I_D R_{B1} + e_{out\,2}$$
$$= e_{out\,2} \tag{8.1.10}$$

so there is zero offset. Temperature drift will also be low as a result of the matching and thermal tracking.

Very low output impedance is difficult to achieve, because of the limited values of g_{fs} available. Lower R_{os} can be obtained by combining a FET with a bipolar transistor as shown, for example, in Fig. 8.1.6 [v1, N1, h1, R1, b1, S1, q1, B1].

In this arrangement the effective g_{fs} is increased to $h_{FE}g_{fs}$ so that the gain and output resistance are now

$$A_{vs} \doteq \frac{h_{FE}g_{fs}R_S}{1+h_{FE}g_{fs}R_S} \doteq 1$$

$$R_{os} \doteq \frac{R_S}{1+h_{FE}g_{fs}R_S} \doteq \frac{1}{h_{FE}g_{fs}} \tag{8.1.11}$$

The value of the bias resistor R_D (1 kΩ here) is a compromise. $g_{fs} \propto I_D^{1/2}$ so a large drain current is desirable; Eq. (8.1.2). The value of the bias resistor is then fixed, since it must produce the necessary bias V_{BE} for the transistor Q_2. Too low a value of R_D relative to h_{ie} of Q_2 reduces the gain.

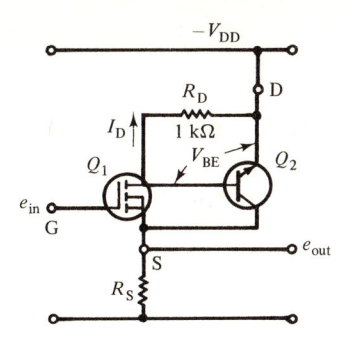

Fig. 8.1.6 FET-bipolar combination follower TAA320 (Courtesy Mullard)

For applications such as low-level d.c. amplifiers, it is desirable to use matched differential pairs to reduce temperature effects, even if only a single-ended input is required [k2, K2, J2, r1]. It is difficult to select devices that will remain matched at different operating conditions or over a range of temperature. Though a number of discrete duals are available, integrated duals are readily available and generally give superior performance [m1, q1, X1, r1, k2, z2]. Addition of a dual FET to a bipolar amplifier can give a high performance operational amplifier [G2, B2, E2, A2, D2, J2]. Monolithic or hybrid amplifiers are also generally available [H2, T1, d2, F2, e2] (Sec. 4.6).

MOSFET transistors are particularly vulnerable to gate-channel breakdown, due to excessive voltage. The gate input resistance is very high and the capacity low, so that even quite small charges, as for example from static or friction effects, can result in exceeding the breakdown voltage. Once the insulating dielectric is punctured, the device is destroyed. Devices, therefore, are usually supplied with a shorting strap or ring on the leads which should be left in position until the device has been connected into the circuit. Even then there is still a danger, and unless the very high input resistance is really required, some form of protection is most desirable. This can be provided by low-leakage diodes or zeners. Though these may reduce the input resistance to say 10^9 ohm, this will often be acceptable. Protection with higher input resistance is possible with feedback techniques [Y1]. MOSFET's with integrated protection devices are also available [w2]. In devices where MOS construction is used, for reasons other than especially high input resistance, protection is usually included [A1, W1, o2].

8.2 Voltage-controlled resistors and switches

Field-effect transistors are just voltage-controlled resistors (VCR). In Sec. 8.1 we considered their operation as active amplifying devices operating in the pinch-off region. Here, we will consider their use as a variable resistance conducting channel, the resistance being determined by V_{GS}. Operation will generally be in the ohmic region, i.e., $V_{DS} < V_{DSP}$. Enlarging the region around the origin of Fig. 8.1.1, we obtain Fig. 8.2.1 [a1, b1, c1, d1, e1, F1, S1, C1, n1, f1].

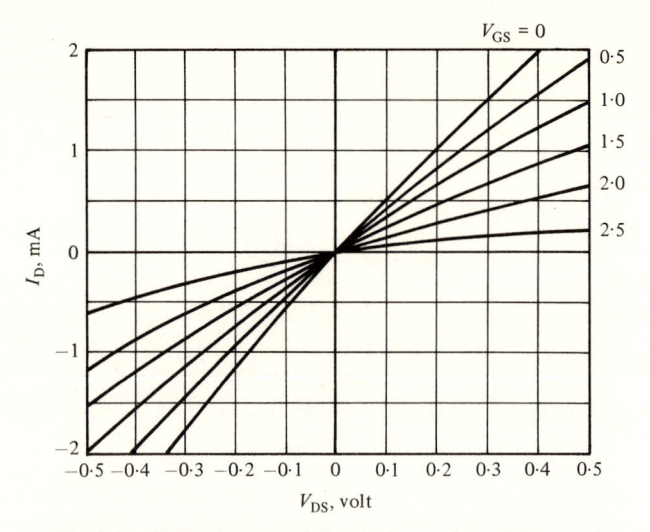

Fig. 8.2.1 FET characteristics in the region of the origin

Three characteristics are evident:

(i) There is zero offset voltage, i.e., $I_D = 0$, for $V_{DS} = 0$. (In practice, there may be a small offset $\approx \mu V$.)
(ii) For small V_{DS} the characteristics are reasonably linear (ohmic), more so for smaller V_{GS} than for larger.
(iii) The resistance of the channel, $R_{DS} = V_{DS}/I_D$, can be controlled by variation of V_{GS}.

The value of R_{DS} for $V_{GS} = 0$, $V_{DS} = 0$ is called $R_{DS(on)}$. Lowest practical values are in the region 1 to 10 ohm, with maximum values of about 10 kΩ. For operation in quadrants I and III devices with symmetrical geometry (interchangeable source and drain) are desirable. Devices made specifically for use as VCR's are available [U1]. For JFET's, maximum V_{DS} in quadrant III is limited by the onset of gate conduction.

In the ohmic region the drain current, I_D, is given by [F1, T1]:

$$I_D = I_{DSS}\left[\left(1 - \frac{V_{GS}}{V_P}\right)^2 - \left(1 - \frac{V_{GS} - V_{DS}}{V_P}\right)^2\right]$$

$$= \frac{2I_{DSS}V_{DS}}{V_P^2}\left[V_{GS} - V_P - \frac{V_{DS}}{2}\right] \quad (8.2.1)$$

Because of the presence of the $V_{DS}/2$ term, the relation between I_D and V_{DS} is not linear unless V_{DS} is small compared with $V_{GS} - V_P = V_{DSP}$. The channel conductance G_{DS} is given by:

$$G_{DS} = \frac{1}{R_{DS}} = \frac{I_D}{V_{DS}} = \frac{2I_{DSS}}{V_P^2}\left[V_{GS} - V_P - \frac{V_{DS}}{2}\right] \quad (8.2.2)$$

and

$$R_{DS(on)} = \frac{-V_P}{2I_{DSS}} \quad (V_{GS} = V_{DS} = 0)$$

This d.c. conductance is not necessarily the same as the small signal or incremental conductance, g_{os}. They are the same only if the characteristic is linear:

$$g_{os} = \frac{1}{r_{ds}} = \frac{\partial I_D}{\partial V_{DS}} = \frac{2I_{DSS}}{V_P^2} \quad (V_{GS} = V_P - V_{DS})$$

(8.2.3)

but
$$r_{ds(on)} = \frac{-V_P}{2I_{DSS}} = R_{DS(on)}$$

R_{DS} can be varied over a very wide range by changing V_{GS}. However, as V_{GS} approaches V_P, the rate of change is very rapid and control is difficult. For reasonable control, a range of 10:1 is satisfactory and 100:1 possible. The variation is near linear with V_{GS}, from $R_{DS(on)}$ to about 4 times this value. If a modified pinch-off voltage, V'_P, is defined as the value of V_{GS} for which $I_D/I_{DSS} = 0.001$, then it is found that a normalized graph of r_{ds} can be drawn as shown in Fig. 8.2.2 [F1].

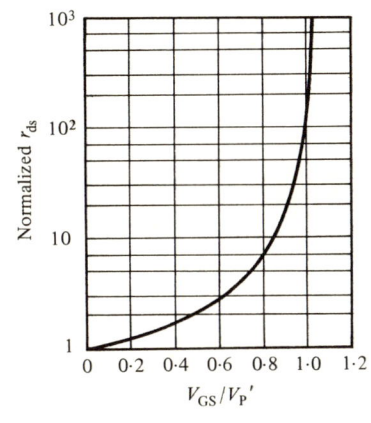

Fig. 8.2.2 Normalized voltage-controlled resistance curve

Variation of R_{DS} with V_{DS} causes distortion of the signal. Reasonable linearity for a large variation of V_{DS} requires a large V_P. For a given device type, large V_P usually means higher I_{DSS} and lower $R_{DS(on)}$ [a1]. Reduction in signal distortion as a result of this nonlinearity is best accomplished by a negative feedback arrangement. From Eq. (8.2.1) or (8.2.2) it can be seen that if a signal of amplitude $V_{DS}/2$ is fed back to the gate then the $V_{DS}/2$ term is cancelled and $I_D \propto V_{DS}$, G_{DS} = constant.

An arrangement for a voltage-controlled attenuator using negative feedback is shown in Fig. 8.2.3(a). R_2 and R_3 are large compared with the other resistors R_1, R_L, or $R_{DS(on)}$. If $R_2 = R_3$, a signal $V_{DS}/2$ is fed back in series with the control voltage,

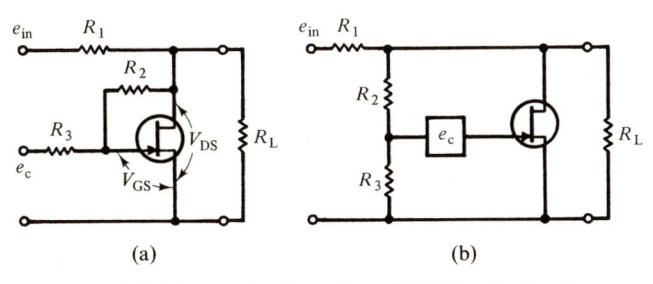

Fig. 8.2.3 Improving linearity of VCR by feedback

e_c, so that $V_{GS} = e_c + V_{DS}/2$. Thus, from Eqs. (8.2.1) and (8.2.2):

$$I_D = \frac{2I_{DSS}V_{DS}}{V_P^2}(e_c - V_P)$$

$$G_{DS} = \frac{2I_{DSS}}{V_P^2}(e_c - V_P)$$

(8.2.4)

With this arrangement the distortion can be reduced by an order of magnitude [F1, V1, b1, f1, d1, T1]; the price is the increased control voltage required. If an isolated control voltage, e_c, is available, then the arrangement of Fig. 8.2.3(b) will have lower distortion than the feedback arrangement, and the same sensitivity as in the unfeedback case.

We have so far considered FET's as continuously variable resistors. If operation is only at the extremes of R_{DS}, i.e., hard-on or off, then we can consider it as a switch. A comparison of the characteristics of an ideal controlled switch, or relay, with practical types is given in Table 8.2.1 [g1, y1, n1, m1].

Table 8.2.1 Switch comparison

	Relay/Reed	FET	Bipolar	Ideal
On resistance	3	2	2	zero
Off resistance	3	3	1	infinite
Speed	0	3	3	very fast
Isolation	3	1	0	complete
Offset	3	3	0	none
Bounce	0	3	3	none
Drive power	0	3	2	nil
Signal capability	3	1	1	high for v and i

Note: Higher number = better performance

For applications where high speed and bounce are not important the miniature reed relay is the nearest to the ideal [c2, z2, A2, R1, B2]. Otherwise the various forms of FET are the best choice [h1, m1, y1, n1, g1, r1, D1, i1, q1, N1, t1, T1].

Two main applications may be distinguished: choppers and analogue gates. Choppers are used to modulate a signal as, for example, in the low-level amplifiers discussed in Sec. 2.3(b). Here a low-level d.c. signal is chopped so that it may be passed through an a.c. amplifier to reduce the effect of drift. Though high efficiency (which requires a high on-off ratio) in the conversion process is desirable, this is not vital. What is important, however, is stability, since the signals to be chopped may be only a few microvolts. It is also important that the chopping drive voltage be excluded from the signal. Feedthrough transients from this source can be quite large depending on frequency, chopper capacities, and load and source resistances [r1, g1, D1, t1, N1, e1, i1, q1].

Choppers may be of the series, shunt, or the combined series-shunt configuration. The latter is generally the most effective and is illustrated in Fig. 8.2.4. The series switch Q_1 and shunt switch Q_2 are fed with antiphase gate signals, so that when R_{DS1} is a minimum, R_{DS2} is a maximum, and the input signal e_{in} passes with minimum attenuation to the load R_L. During the other half of the switching cycle the resistances of Q_1 and Q_2 are reversed, and no signal reaches R_L. The signal, e_{in}, is thus chopped into a square wave at R_L. The efficiency of this configuration is higher than that of either the series or shunt alone, and it has the added attraction that transients fed through the FET capacities are balanced and, hence, substantially reduced in the output signal. The choice of switching frequency and waveshape should be made to reduce transient effects, as far as possible, without adversely affecting the chopper significantly. This means using the lowest chopping frequency consistent with the bandwidth required, and using a somewhat rounded square wave or sine wave form.

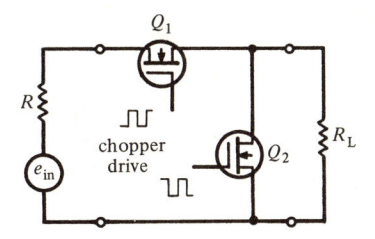

Fig. 8.2.4 Series-shunt chopper

The circuit shown uses depletion IGFET's, but enhancement devices or JFET's are also appropriate. As will be seen below, the driving circuits for analogue gates present a number of problems since large signal voltages are involved. However, since choppers are generally used with very small signals, the signal excursions may be ignored in designing the chopper drive.

When switches are used to connect or disconnect signals, i.e., to allow them to pass or not, they are usually referred to as gates. There is a difficulty with nomenclature in talking about gates and switches. When a switch is closed, i.e., contact is made, then as a gate it is said to be open, and vice versa. It is safer to use make and break for switches to avoid confusion.

An open gate should pass the signal with minimum distortion and when closed it should completely disconnect it. Thus, not only is the on-off resistance ratio of interest, but also the linearity as a function of signal amplitude. In many circumstances transient feedthrough of the control signal is of minor importance, but it should be kept to a minimum.

There are three generally available gate types, each using a different FET and requiring a different drive circuit. The FET's used are N-channel JFET, P-channel MOSFET and Complementary MOSFET [h1, m1, y1, n1, q1, i1, p1, B1, W1, a2, b2, c2, C1, L1, u1, l2, p2]. There are problems in the design of driver circuits for gates since the large signal voltages involved may be comparable with or even reverse the gate bias [H1, k1, s1, m1, c2, C1, j1, n1, B1]. However, the design of drivers will not be considered here since many integrated driver-switch devices are available, in which these problems have been taken care of. Inputs to the drivers are mostly arranged to be compatible with the standard logic systems such as TTL or CMOS.

It is difficult to be general about the types of gate, as new technology is producing rapid changes. A rough comparison of some important parameters is given in Table 8.2.2, where 3 represents the better performance. R_{DS} refers to the undesirable modulation of R_{DS} as a function of signal amplitude, and high-frequency isolation to the feedthrough with the gate closed.

Table 8.2.2 Comparison of gate switches

	$R_{DS(on)}$	R_{DS}	Switching speed	HF isolation
N-JFET	3	3	2	3
CMOS	2	2	2	2
P-MOS	1	1	3	1

Note: Higher number = better performance

It appears, at present, that for general purposes the CMOS type is most suitable, especially if multiple gates are required [o1, v1, p1, W1, z1, X1, Y1, E2, y2]. For analogue signals up to ±10 to 15 V, the gates may be used in any convenient arrangement. For signals greater than this, current-mode operation is used, which makes use of the properties of the operational amplifier virtual ground (Fig. 8.2.5) [c2].

The output of the gate, Q_1, will always be at zero volts. When the gate is open, the voltage across it will be:

$$V_{DS(on)} = i_{in} R_{DS(on)} = \frac{e_{in} R_{DS(on)}}{R_i} \tag{8.2.5}$$

and this can be kept small, even for very large e_{in}, by suitable choice of R_i. The gain is effectively R_f/R_i; the FET Q_2 is matched to Q_1 and serves to compensate for temperature effects. When the gate is closed, the voltage across it would rise to e_{in}, but this is prevented by the clamping diodes $D_{1,2}$. $V_{DS(on)}$ must also be less than the conduction voltage of $D_{1,2}$, but zener diodes in series, or diodes to the supply lines, may be used if this is marginal. R_i must also be chosen so that the maximum gate current is not exceeded. Note also that the current i_{in} must be *supplied* by the amplifier output.

The gates shown in Fig. 8.2.5 are P-channel JFET's, which were not mentioned above. Though those gates can be used, a series of low-cost gates has been specially produced for this application [y1, f2, o2]. The choice of P-channel devices allows them to be driven directly from TTL logic.

When signals to be gated contain high frequency components, problems arise because of the feedthrough capacity of the gate. The capacities involved may only be a few picofarads, but 1 pF has an impedance comparable with the gate off-resistance ($\approx 10^{12}$ ohm) at only 0·1 Hz. It is uncommon, however, that the load resistance be comparable to the gate off-resistance and, at high frequencies, low resistances are usual to obtain short time constants. In practice, the feedthrough problem becomes

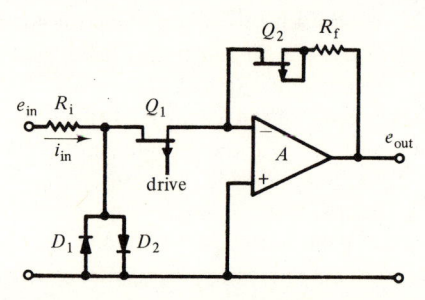

Fig. 8.2.5 Current-mode gate using operational amplifier

significant at frequencies above about 100 kHz or risetimes of about 1 V/μs, but this depends on the degree of isolation required. This is discussed in [E1] which also provides useful design nomographs. Improved isolation can be achieved by using the series-shunt arrangement (Fig. 8.2.4) or three gates in a tee configuration.

In multiplexing applications, where a number of alternative signals are to be connected to a point, it is convenient to use monolithic multiple gates which can include drivers and channel select decoders [v1, w1, z1, E2]. In this application consideration should also be given to coupling (cross talk) between channels [E1, L1]. To avoid interactions between sources the switches should be *break-before-make*, i.e., the on switch should break before another makes. If this is not so, then two sources may be connected via a low resistance with possible damage.

8.3 Thyristors

8.3(a) *PNPN four-layer devices*

Thyristor is a generic name for a family of *PNPN* semiconductor switches [R1, G1, s2, t2] though it is sometimes used to refer to a particular member the silicon controlled rectifier (SCR); see Sec. 8.3(b). Different devices may have two, three, or four accessible electrodes and may conduct uni- or bidirectionally. A comprehensive discussion of these devices is given in [R1, t2]. We will first consider the basic operation of *PNPN* devices, and then the characteristics of the main types of switch. The *PNPN* configuration, Fig. 8.3.1(a), may be viewed as a combination of an *NPN* and a *PNP* transistor; Figs. 8.3.1(b) and (c) (see page 356). The significance of this view is that it shows the current gain of the sections, and the existence of positive feedback. These two factors are necessary to obtain the desired switching and latching operation; see Secs. 3.2, 5.3(a), and 6.1(b).

The operation depends on the polarity and voltage applied between the various electrodes. The simplest case leaves the two gate electrodes G_K, G_A open, and the applied voltage biasing the anode A positive relative to the cathode K. Positive feedback is provided by the interconnection of the collectors and bases, so the current gain around the loop $L = \beta_1 \beta_2$. From Sec. 3.2 it may be expected that if $L \geqslant 1$, then regenerative positive feedback will cause a switching action. If the collector–base leakage current is I_{C0}, then we can write the equations [h3, p. 19]:

$$I_{C1} = \beta_1(I_{C2} + I_{C01}) + I_{C01}$$
$$I_{C2} = \beta_2(I_{C1} + I_{C02}) + I_{C02} \quad (8.3.1)$$
$$I_A = I_{C1} + I_{C2} = I_K$$
$$= \frac{(1+\beta_1)(1+\beta_2)(I_{C01} + I_{C02})}{1 - \beta_1 \beta_2}$$

or, alternatively, in terms of the transistors' α ($= I_C/I_E \leqslant 1$) rather than β:

$$I_A = \frac{I_{C02} - I_{C01}}{1 - (\alpha_1 + \alpha_2)} \quad (8.3.2)$$

With only small leakage currents flowing, the values of β will be very small so that $\beta_1 \beta_2 \ll 1$, and $I_A \doteq I_{C01} + I_{C02}$ is also small. If the loop-gain, $\beta_1 \beta_2$, can be increased

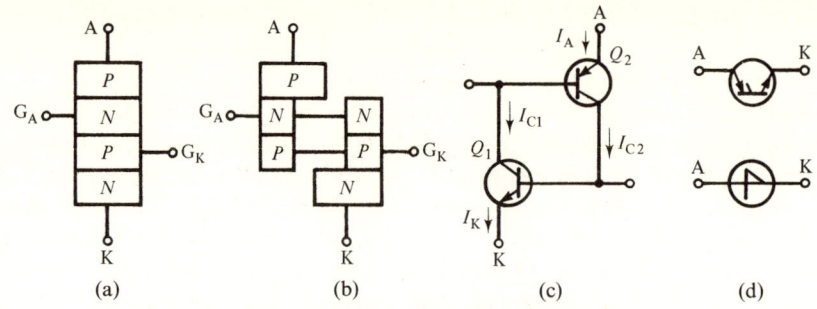

Fig. 8.3.1 *PNPN* **four-layer thyristor**

to ≈ 1 then I_A increases rapidly, becoming nominally infinite for $\beta_1\beta_2 = 1$. The positive feedback drives both transistors into saturation with a fast switching time, the saturation reducing the gain to just maintain $L = 1$ and, hence, the stability of the on state. The net voltage across the device will be the sum of $V_{BE} + V_{sat} \approx 0.7$ V or a little more. The current flowing will be primarily limited by the external circuit, unless the external impedance is particularly small.

The value of β can be changed by several mechanisms [R1, p. 8]:

(i) Overall voltage, which eventually causes avalanche multiplication of the leakage currents and hence an increase of β. This is the mechanism used in the diac.
(ii) Rate of change of overall voltage. If the rate is high, enough current will flow through the junction capacities to raise β and cause switching. This is known as the dv/dt effect, and introduces an important limitation on the use of thyristors.
(iii) Temperature. Leakage current in silicon devices doubles for every 8°C temperature rise, again causing increase of β.
(iv) Direct injection of current, or more properly charge, via a gate electrode to increase the conduction current by transistor action. This is the commonest technique and is applicable in all three-terminal devices.
(v) Photo generation of carriers in a base region to give an effect similar to (iv). This is used in the photo SCR or light-activated SCR (LASCR) [R1, p2].

When the overall voltage is reversed in polarity the two outer *PN* junctions are reverse biased, but in practice the structure is not a simple symmetric one, as illustrated above, and the *anode* junction is primarily responsible for the reverse voltage rating. If this is exceeded, avalanche breakdown may occur as in a simple diode (Sec. 1.9) destroying the device. The characteristics of the four-layer diode, thus, will be as shown in Fig. 8.3.2.

When the current reaches the critical value I_B for $L = 1$ breakdown occurs, the characteristic having a negative resistance region which is traversed rapidly ($\approx \mu$s) to reach a current I_H on the *diode* characteristic. The current continues to rise to the value set by the external circuit. If the current does not reach I_H, then the device switches back to the non-conducting regime when the voltage is reduced. The situation is somewhat more complex than this and, depending on capacity, oscillations may occur [H1]. I_H is known, therefore, as the holding current. In practice, a current I_L somewhat larger than I_H must initially be reached if the device is to latch in the on state. This higher latching current is due to transient effects in the spread of conduction across the junction from the localized gate. After latching is completed the current can drop to I_H, before switch-off occurs.

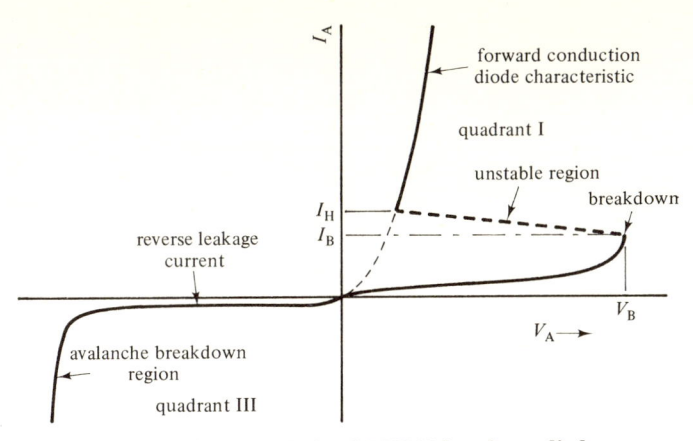

Fig. 8.3.2 Characteristic of *PNPN* four-layer diode

There are a number of devices based on the *PNPN* structure, the two most important being discussed in subsequent sections. The others are summarized in Fig. 8.3.3 [q1, R1, S1]. It should be mentioned that the bilateral trigger diode, or trigger diac, is not a 4-layer but a 3-layer device [J1, R1]. However, since the characteristic and application is the same as the thyristor diac it is convenient to include it here.

8.3(b) *Silicon controlled rectifier*

The most commonly encountered thyristor is the silicon controlled rectifier (SCR), which has the structure discussed above with the gate electrode G_K also available. The characteristic is the same as Fig. 8.3.2, except that the breakdown voltage, V_B, can be reduced by a large factor by injection of charge into the gate region, i.e., mechanism (iv) above; see Fig. 8.3.4. The reverse characteristic remains the same.

The forward characteristic corresponds to that of a current-controlled negative resistance device [i3, p. 477]. It is similar to the UJT, Sec. 5.3(b), and in fact the programmable UJT is just a low power SCR.

The SCR could be operated in two ways. A given gate current I_G is set up and V_A varied, as if, for example, an a.c. voltage is applied. Alternatively, the d.c. or a.c. voltage is applied and the gate current pulsed at the desired triggering time. The latter is generally used, and involves not only injecting enough charge carriers but also allowing time for them to cause conduction across the whole cathode. A pulse current equal to the d.c. triggering current may need to be applied for 100 to 1000 µs. A 1 µs pulse may require 10 times that current. Higher gate currents of a given duration decrease the turn-on time, down to some limiting time [R1, p. 64; G1, p. 227].

An additional requirement for triggering is that the current, I_A, must exceed the holding (or latching) current for $I_G = 0$, i.e., I_{H0}. If this is not achieved the SCR will revert to the blocking state when I_G returns to zero.

For a supply voltage V_1 and load resistance R_1, we obtain a d.c. load line A as shown. With $I_G = 0$, there are three stable states possible, at points X_1, X_2, X_3. Normally the device is at X_1 in the forward blocking condition. If a gate current I_{G1} is applied, the SCR will have a new characteristic, as shown. There is now only one stable state, at X_3, and the system remains there even when I_G returns to zero, i.e.,

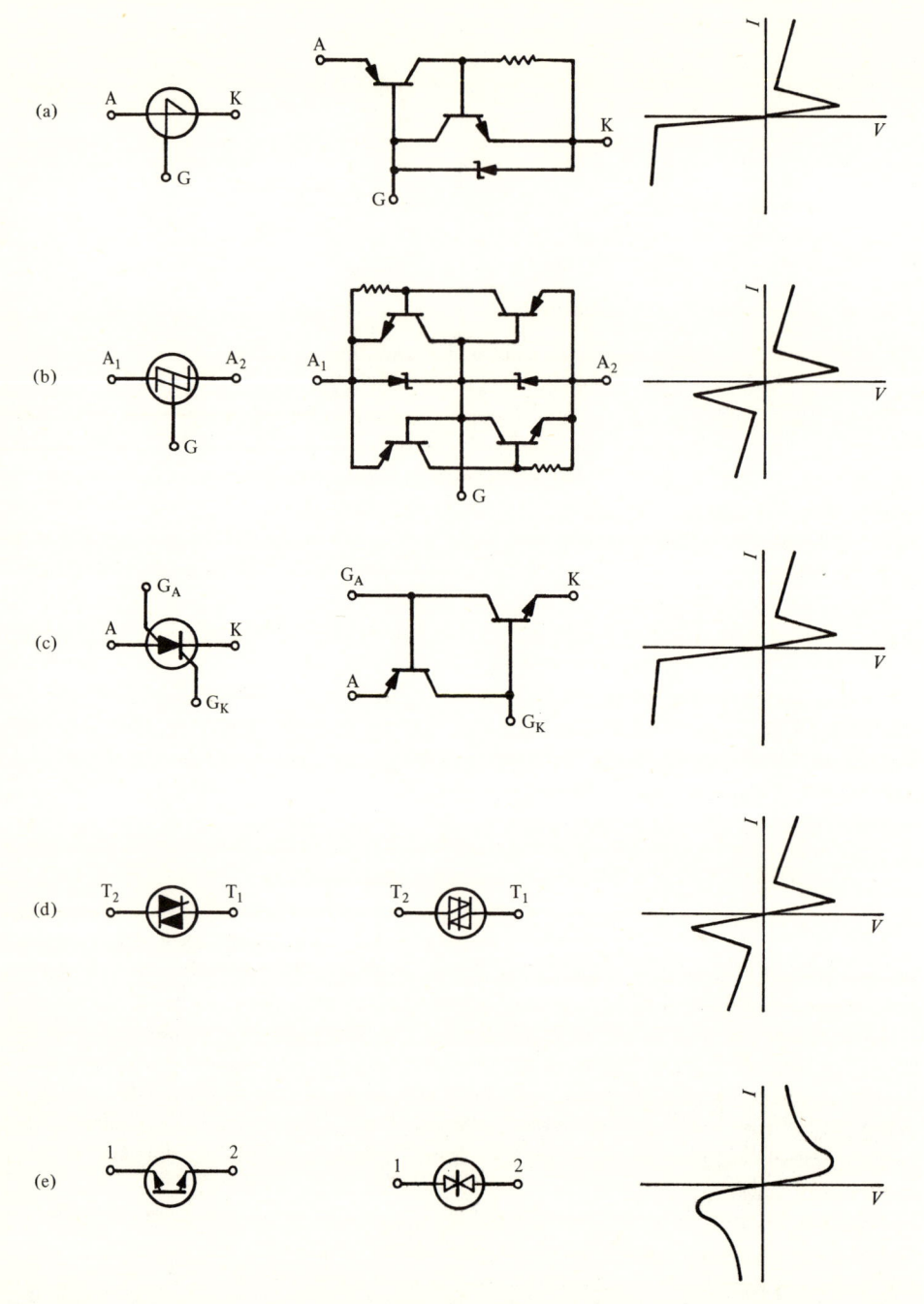

Fig. 8.3.3 *PNPN* devices, (a) silicon unilateral switch, (b) silicon bilateral switch, (c) silicon controlled switch, (d) diac or bidirectional diode thyristor, (e) bilateral trigger diode or trigger diac

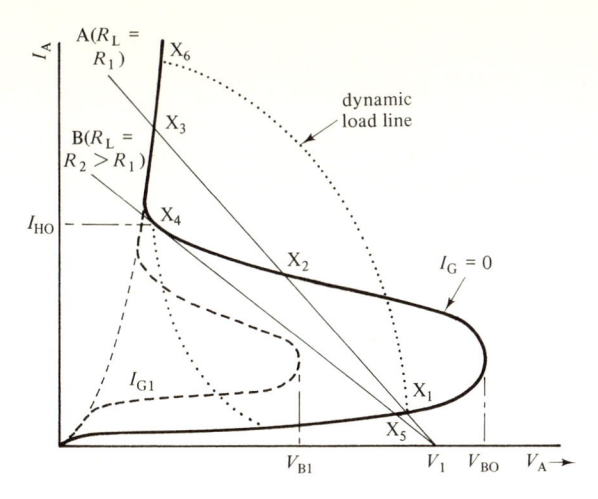

Fig. 8.3.4 Silicon controlled rectifier characteristics with load lines

the SCR is now latched in the on state. If R_L is increased, a limiting value R_2 is reached with load line B, operating point X_4 defining the holding current I_{HO}. Any further increase in R_L, or decrease of V_1, will cause the SCR to return to the forward blocking condition with the operating point near X_5.

The paths followed by the system in going from X_1 to X_3 or X_4 to X_5 do not follow the load lines, since these represent d.c. conditions. When the switching transitions occur, the parasitic elements of the circuit and internal time constants of the SCR cause the system to follow rather different paths, much as discussed in Sec. 5.3(b) and shown in Fig. 5.3.6. Capacities, for example, try to prevent the voltage changing rapidly, so transitions tend to start off more 'vertical', as shown in Fig. 8.3.3, e.g., path X_1, X_6, X_3 when switching on.

The triggering requirements depend on the anode voltage, V_A, and on the load, R_L, so these are specified with the gate requirements I_G and V_G. The input characteristic of the gate varies considerably as V_G is increased and I_A begins to flow, and even more when regeneration starts. Data sheets for SCR's usually specify a maximum d.c. gate current and voltage (I_{GT}, V_{GT}) required to trigger, and these values will hold for pulses down to the order of 100 µs. The output impedance of the gate trigger source is thus also of importance [R1, p. 53].

There are a number of ways of generating suitable pulses to trigger the SCR [t2, i1, k1, n1, r1, s1, R1, m2, r2, s2, w2, y2]. Most commonly, one of the two-terminal devices described in Sec. 8.3(a) is used to discharge a capacitor into the gate. A simple example is illustrated in Fig. 8.3.5. In some applications it is necessary that the control circuit be isolated from the SCR. The coupling may then be achieved by small pulse transformers [n1, G1] optical isolators (Sec. 9.6) [g1, G1] or by direct optical triggering as in the LASCR [R1, p. 21; p2].

For controlling a.c. power as, for example, for heating, lighting, or motor drive, the SCR is triggered to conduct for a greater or lesser part of a cycle. This is called phase control and is illustrated in Fig. 8.3.5.

As the supply voltage increases, C_t begins to charge via the variable resistor R_t. When V_c exceeds the trigger voltage of the silicon unilateral switch, it breaks down and discharges C_t into the SCR gate to fire it. Increasing R_t delays the triggering

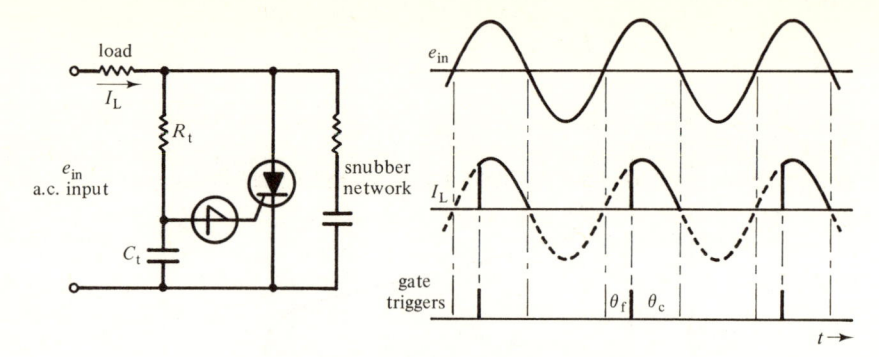

Fig. 8.3.5 Simple SCR phase control

further and, hence, reduces the power delivered to the load. As the supply voltage reverses, the SCR turns off and there is no conduction during the second half of the cycle. Since the triggers are derived from the input they will be synchronized with it. The delay from zero cross-over is called the firing angle, θ_f, and the remainder of the half cycle the conduction angle, θ_c. With this circuit it is not possible to vary θ_c over the whole 180°, a region at each end being inaccessible because of low supply voltage. However, this will have little effect so far as power control is concerned. Though the effective current or power dissipation in both load and SCR can be calculated for any given conduction angle, this is more readily determined from graphs [R1, p. 28] or curves commonly included in device data sheets. These quantities must be known to determine the temperature rise in the device and the heat sinking required to limit this to an allowable value. Design should be conservative as peak temperatures due to, for example, high current short duration pulses, may exceed ratings.

If phase control is used with feedback from a sensor of some type, e.g., thermistor or tachogenerator, then it is convenient to use one of several available IC devices [u2, y1, v1, H2]. These provide timing, triggers, inhibit control and protection circuits, and are powered from the supply voltage.

In the simple circuit described above, half of each cycle is not used, and the power output will fluctuate rather more than in a full-wave circuit [f2]. Two SCR's could be used, one for each half cycle, or a triac, Sec. 8.3(c), but a convenient alternative is to rectify the a.c. first, as shown in Fig. 8.3.6 [R1, p. 173].

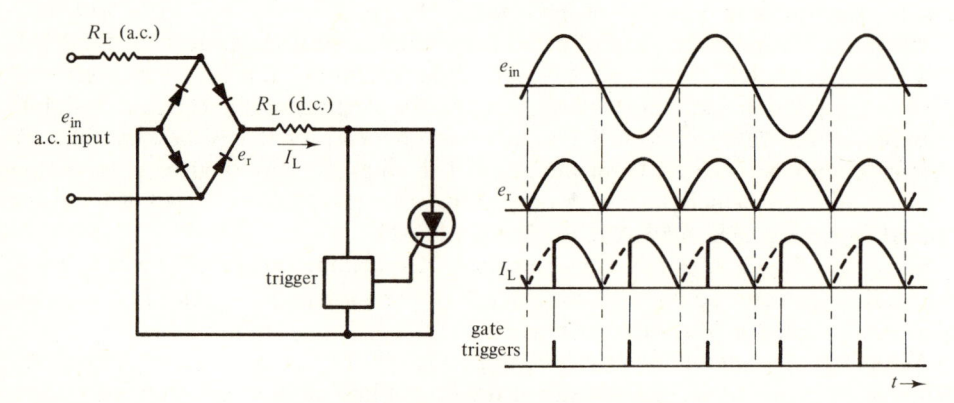

Fig. 8.3.6 Full-wave SCR phase control

360

The operation of the circuit is as before, except that there are two locations for the load, depending on whether uni- or bidirectional currents are required in the load. A further application of a similar circuit is discussed in Sec. 7.1(d).

There is the problem, in this form of circuit with reactive loads, that the SCR voltage may not fall low enough for it to turn off [t2, p. 16]. An alternative circuit is the half-controlled bridge using two SCR's (Fig. 8.3.7) but even here there can be difficulties in commutation unless a flywheel diode is included [t2, pp. 42, 81]. The use of thyristors with reactive rather than resistive loads presents additional problems. Voltage and current are not in phase, inductive loads can cause triggering as a result of dv/dt effects as currents are cut off, and capacitive loads may cause damage as a result of di/dt effects producing localized heating [C1, v2, t2, R1, D2, E2].

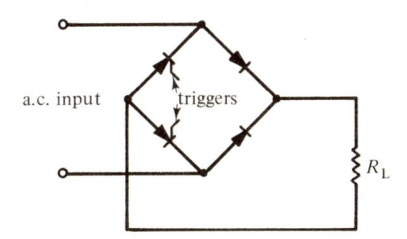

Fig. 8.3.7 Half-controlled SCR bridge

To damp any transients it is usual to connect a series RC snubber circuit, in parallel with the thyristor (Fig. 8.3.5). The values used depend on load current, voltage, and allowable dv/dt, and though they can be calculated they are more easily read from graphs [A1, g2, M1, t2, W1]. For load currents of 1 to 10 A r.m.s., C ranges from 0·1 to 1 µF and R from 1 kΩ to 100 Ω for an allowable dv/dt of 1 V/µs. Note that the capacitor must have a suitable a.c. voltage rating.

8.3(c) *Triac*

A.C. power can be controlled by means of two SCR's, but since this is a very common requirement a device consisting, in effect, of two SCR's connected in inverse parallel, the triac, has been developed [R1, h1, e1, B1, D1, C1, b2, z2]. The characteristic is the same as the SCR in quadrant I, and this is reflected in quadrant III; Fig. 8.3.8.

The main terminals are called T_1 and T_2 (sometimes $MT_{1,2}$), the gate being adjacent to T_1. The triac, in contrast to the SCR, can be triggered by positive or negative gate currents. There are, therefore, four modes given by the two polarities of overall voltage, I and III, and gate currents (+, −). Triggering sensitivity is greatest in modes I+ and III−, less in I− and lowest in III+. The turn-off conditions of a triac are also more severe than those of an SCR or of two SCR's used as a triac equivalent. In the SCR there is a half cycle available for this, while for the triac there is only a very short period about zero volts. This imposes severe frequency limitations on triacs, but they can be used at the standard power frequencies up to 400 Hz [G1, p. 238].

The simplest triggering circuit is similar to that shown in Fig. 8.3.5, except that the unilateral switch is replaced by a bidirectional diac or trigger diode (Fig. 8.3.3) [a1, M1, m2, z2, b2, e1, g1]. For convenience, devices incorporating trigger diode and

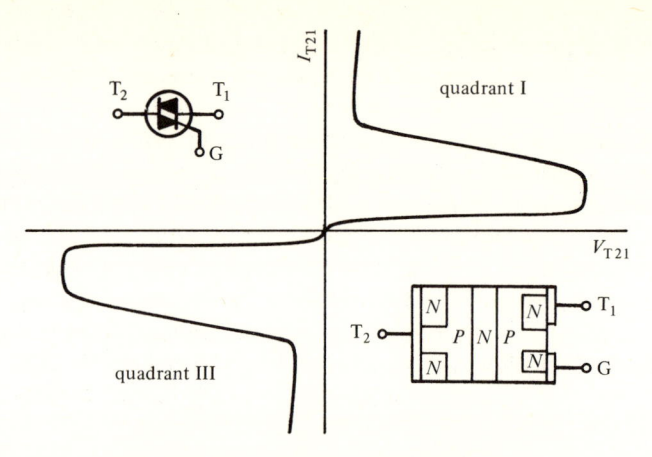

Fig. 8.3.8 Triac device and characteristics

triac may be used [T1]. There is a problem with triac control systems of this type, in that the initial switch on will occur at a different firing angle to subsequent triggers. This arises from the drop in voltage across the timing capacitor, C_t, at the first trigger so that subsequent charging cycles start from a different level, i.e., a much lower value of R_t is required to switch on than to switch off. The hysteresis this introduces may not be of consequence but, in some applications, it can cause difficulties. For example, in a light-dimming application the lamp will initially come on rather brightly and not gradually as desired. If R_t is increased to dim the lamp, then a transient could cause the triac to switch off and it will not automatically restart. This effect can be decreased, and at the same time the range of conduction angle θ_c increased, by using the double time constant circuit of Fig. 8.3.9 [M1, T1, b2, G1].

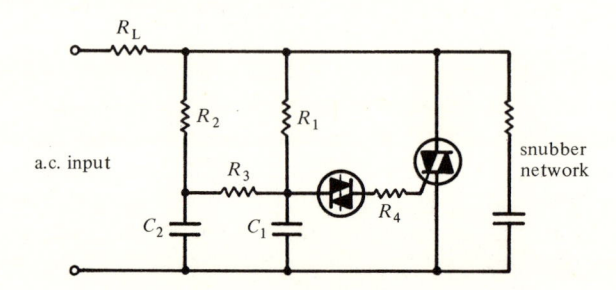

Fig. 8.3.9 Wide-range triac phase control

C_2 serves to compensate partially for the drop in V_{C1} on triggering, and a small resistor R_4 limits the discharge current and hence the drop in V_{C1}. An alternative technique for reducing hysteresis is to use the single time constant circuit of Fig. 8.3.5, but with an asymmetrical trigger diode [F2].

8.3(d) *Zero-voltage switching*

The large and rapid changes of current, encountered in thyristor applications, has a serious drawback in many situations, in that serious electrical interference is produced. This may adversely affect neighbouring equipment, and may be transmitted either radiatively or conductively via the mains. If these are substantial, it may lead to difficulties with communication and power generation authorities. As discussed previously, in many applications it is the average power that is of interest rather than the details of the instantaneous power variations. In these cases, the technique of zero-voltage switching (ZVS) is particularly attractive as it virtually eliminates interference. The technique consists of triggering the thyristor as the a.c. voltage passes through zero, so that there are no sudden changes in current to cause the interference. The average power is controlled by means of the number of half cycles on and off, i.e., controlling the mark-space ratio but only in half (or full) cycle steps. The popularity of this technique has led to the production of a number of IC's to carry out the zero-volt detection, triggering, and control of the mark-space ratio [u1, w1, x1, y1, z1, q2, V1, N2].

The integrated zero-volt switches have built-in rectifiers or regulators which, in conjunction with an external dropper resistor, allow them to operate directly from the mains, if required. They also include a differential amplifier whose output controls the generation of triggering pulses. The input to the amplifier usually derives from an external bridge circuit, that measures the deviation of the controlled quantity from the desired value. For example, if the appropriate arm of the bridge is a thermistor [j3] or a photoconductor (Sec. 9.3), temperature or illumination may be regulated. The more versatile IC's have additional facilities such as an external inhibit input [V1, w1] and a saw-tooth generator for use in proportional control applications [w1]. Proportional rather than on-off control can provide a significant improvement in control differential [R1, b1, w1]. The saw-tooth generator runs with a period greater than the mains period, but less than the time constant of the load. The sensor bridge sets a reference voltage and, while the saw-tooth voltage is less than this, trigger pulses are generated at each zero crossing and power is delivered to the load. If the controlled quantity falls below the desired value the reference level is raised, so that more cycles of power are allowed for each cycle of the saw-tooth. This is illustrated in Fig. 8.3.10.

The system is, in effect, being sampled repeatedly by the saw-tooth to see if it needs more or less power. The CA3059 [V1] includes a fail-safe circuit which inhibits

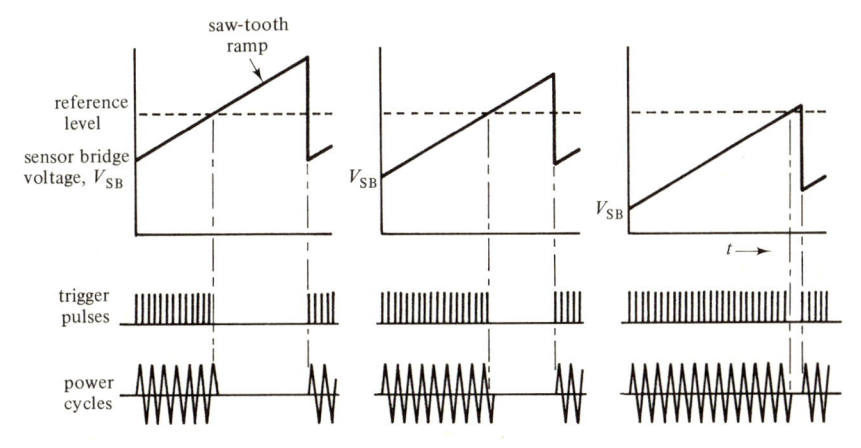

Fig. 8.3.10 Proportional control using zero-voltage switch and ramp (Texas Instruments, with permission)

triggering in the event of the sensor being either short or open circuited, but there are limits on the resistance of the sensor [b1].

It should be noted that the zero-volt switch produces only one polarity of trigger pulse so that, if used to control a triac, it should be arranged to deliver negative pulses.

Though generally referred to as zero-voltage switching, it is actually zero-current switching that is desired. For resistive loads the two are synonymous, but with reactive loads current and voltage are no longer in phase. A technique for detecting zero current, by measuring the voltage across the thyristor, is described in [c1].

References section 8.1: Field-effect transistors

- a1   Watson J: An Introduction to Field Effect Transistors; Siliconix.
- b1   Bijlsma N R, Burwell P, Evans E G (Eds): Field Effect Transistors; Mullard 1972.
- c1   Ghausi M S: Electronic Circuits (Devices, Models, Functions, Analysis, and Design); Van Nostrand Reinhold 1971.
- d1   Sevin L J: The Behaviour of Field-Effect Transistor Characteristics with Temperature; Texas Instruments Application Report C22 1968.
- e1   Mullard: Temperature Dependence of Junction FET Parameters; Mullard Application Note TP1117, 1969.
- f1   Durrant N F: The Insulated Gate Transistor—A Brief History; Electronic Eng. 42, May 1970, 70–73.
- g1   Overgoor B J M: Junction Field Effect Transistors: Their Structure and Operation; Mullard Tech. Comm. 10, 52–56, 1968.
- h1   Miles J F: Metal-Oxide-Semiconductor Transistors and Their Applications; Mullard Tech. Comm. 9, 54–63, 1966.
- i1   Botos B: Low Frequency Applications of Field-Effect Transistors; Motorola Application Note AN-511, 1969.
- j1   Botos B, McRoberts L: Using the FET Designers Data Sheet for Worst Case Amplifier Circuit Design; Motorola Application Note AN-455, 1968.
- k1   Sherwin J: Biasing of FETs Ensures Consistent Circuit Performance; Electronic Eng. 43, Apr. 1971, 52–56.
- l1   Strange N: Universal Normalised JFET Characteristic Curves; Electronic Eng. 42, Feb. 1970, 53–58.
- m1   Analog Devices: Choosing and Using N-Channel Dual J-FETs; Analog Dialogue 4, No.2, Dec. 1970, 4–9.
- n1   Robinson F N H: Understanding the Field Effect Transistor; Electronic Components 26 Nov. 1971, 1231–1232, and 25 Feb. 1972, 160.
- o1   Stevens M, Wood A: The FET as a Chopper; Texas Instruments Application Report B60, 1968.
- p1   Mullard: The Junction FET in Switching Circuits; Mullard Application Note TP1189, 1970.
- q1   Wollensen D L: How to Bias a Duel JFET; Electronic Eng. 44, Mar. 1972, 50–51.
- r1   Teledyne: JFET Applications and Specifications; Teledyne Handbook June 1972.
- s1   Cobbold R S C: Theory and Applications of Field Effect Transistors; Wiley-Interscience 1970.
- t1   Gosling W, Townsend W G, Watson J: Field-Effect Electronics; Butterworths 1970.
- u1   Mullard: Use of Field Effect Transistors with Capacitor Microphones; Mullard Application Note TP1104, 1969.
- v1   Siliconix: High-Input-Impedance Unifet Amplifiers; Siliconix Application Note Feb. 1963.
- w1   Stevens M: The FET in Direct Coupled Amplifier Circuits; Texas Instruments Application Report B51, 1968.

x1   Holcomb S W, Sevin L J: Field-Effect Transistor for Low-Level Circuits; Texas Instruments Application Report C21, 1968.
y1   Kane J F, Wollesen D L: Field-Effect Transistor in Theory and Practice; Motorola Application Note AN-211, 1966.
z1   Texas Instruments: FET Amplifier Circuits; Texas Instruments Application Report EB18/21/22, 1968.
A1   RCA: COS/MOS Integrated Circuits Manual; RCA Technical Series CMS-270, 1970.
B1   Millman J, Halkias C C: Electronic Devices and Circuits; McGraw-Hill 1967.
C1   Barker R W J, Hart B L: IGFETs in Low Drift DC Amplifiers; Electronic Components 15 Oct. 1971, 1061–1062.
D1   Soares R: An Introduction to MOS; Design Electronics Sep. 1970, 61, 62, 65. Want Some MOS Theory?; Nov. 1970, 61–62, 64–65, 112. A Little More MOS Theory; Dec. 1970, 51–52, 57.
E1   Todd C D: Silicon Epitaxial FETs; Part 1; Basic Field Effect Fundamentals; Electronic Components Jan. 1966, 43–52. Part 2: FET Parameters and Their Measurement; Feb. 1966, 135–142. Part 3: FET AC Parameters; Mar. 1966, 249–255. Part 4: FET as a Voltage Variable Resistor; Apr. 1966, 347–350. Part 5: FET DC Amplifiers; June 1966, 571–576. Part 6: FET as a Chopper Switch; July 1966, 663–669. Part 7: FET Active Filters; Aug. 1966, 746–750. Part 8: FET as a Source Follower; Sep. 1966, 831–836. Part 9: Follower Circuits with Bipolar Transistors; Oct. 1966, 943–948. Part 10: Negative Resistance Circuits; Nov. 1966, 1041–1045. Part 11: FET Timing Circuits; Feb. 1967, 153–158.
F1   Greunke R L: FET Small Signal Analysis; EDN Oct. 1966.
G1   Sherwin J S: FET Parameters and Their Applications; Electronic Components Mar. 1968, 281–288.
H1   Siliconix: The Relationship Between V(P), I(DSS) and g(fs); Siliconix Application Tip 1/A17, 1964.
I1   MacDonald C L: Behaviour of FET Gate Current; Siliconix Application Tip 3, Apr. 1969.
J1   Watson J: Testing Gate-Leakage Current in FETs; Electronic Eng. 44, June 1972, 53–55.
K1   Ferranti: Field Effect Transistors and Applications; Ferranti Application Note 22, May 1964.
L1   Freyling N: FET Differential Amplifier; Electronics Industry Oct. 1975, 26–28.
M1   Ferranti: Biasing of Field Effect Transistors for Zero Temperature Coefficient; Ferranti Application Note 33, 1967.
N1   Blaser L, MacDougall J S; Applications of the Silicon Planar Field-Effect Transistor; SGS–Fairchild Application Note AR-138, Dec. 1964.
O1   Ahrons R W, Gardner P D; Complementary MOS Integrated Circuits; RCA Publication ST-3379A, 1967.
P1   General Electric Co.: Electrometer MOST MBH 1 Series; General Electric Co. Semiconductors Data Sheet.
Q1   Crystalonics: Power Field-Effect Transistor—Powerfet; Crystalonics Application Note ANF-9, Sep. 1965.
R1   Mullard: Integrated MOST Level Sensor TAA320A; Mullard Data Sheet July 1973.
S1   Mullard: 95BFY Development Type Metal-Oxide Semiconductor Transistor; Mullard Tech. Pub. TP602, Mar. 1965.
T1   Sullivan D R, Maidique M A: High Performance IC Fet-Input Op Amp; Analog Dialogue 4, No.2, Dec. 1970, 1–3.
U1   Evans L L: Biasing FETs for Zero DC Drift; Electrotechnology 74, Aug. 1964, 93–96.
V1   Compton J B: High-Frequency Junction FET Characterisation and Application; Design Electronics Mar. 1970.
W1   Reynolds T: Motorola Complementary MOS I/Cs; Motorola Application Note AN-538, 1970.
X1   Analog Devices: Trak-FET Monolithic Dual Junction FETs; Theory and Practice; Analog Devices Application Note 1972.
Y1   Barker R W J, Hart B L: Gate-Circuit Protection Safeguards MOSFET Amplifier; Electronic Eng. 44, Jan. 1972, 31–32.

Z1 MacDougall J S: Applications of the Silicon Planar II MOSFET; SGS–Fairchild Application Report AR-136, 1964.
a2 Sherwin J S: Build Better Source Followers 10 Ways; Electronic Design 7 June 1970, 80–84.
b2 Evan-Hart G D: The Replacement of Thermionic Valves by Junction Field Effect Hybrid Circuits; Electronic Components 26 Jan. 1974, 78–81.
c2 Reich S: Using MOSFET Integrated Circuits in Linear Circuit Applications; RCA Application Note AN-4590, (Handbook SSD-202C, 1975).
d2 Underwood R K: New Design Techniques for FET Op Amps (LH0022/42/52); National Semiconductor Application Note AN-63, Mar. 1972.
e2 Harris S: The AD503 vs. . . . ?; Analog Dialogue 4, No.2, Dec. 1970, 11.
f2 Compton J B: Junction FET High Frequency Applications; Siliconix Application Note.
g2 Overgoor B J M: Marched Field Effect Transistors in the Differential Input Stage of an Operational Amplifier; Mullard Tech. Comm. 11, Sep. 1969, 6–16.
h2 Trout B: Small-Signal RF Design with Dual-Gate Mosfets; Motorola Application Note AN-478, 1969.
i2 Reich S: MOS/FET Biasing Techniques; RCA Application Note AN-4125, (Handbook SSD-202C, 1975).
j2 Siliconix: An Introduction to FETs; Siliconix Application Note 53/A29, Dec. 1973.
k2 Witten S: Designing Junction FET Input Op Amps; Siliconix Application Note AN74-3, Aug. 1974.
l2 Watson B: Audio-Frequency Noise Characteristics of Junction FETs; Siliconix Application Note AN74-4.
m2 Fabian M: Selecting FETs for Low Noise Applications; Siliconix Application Note 43, Dec. 1972, Aug. 1974.
n2 Siliconix: 2N3631 High Performance at Low Temperatures; Siliconix Application Tip Nov. 1968.
o2 Painter R R: Gate-Oxide Protection Circuit in RCA COS/MOS Digital Integrated Circuits; RCA Application Note ICAN-6218, 1970.
p2 Miyoshi D S, Cotts R M: Helium Cooled Radio Frequency Preamplifier for Use in NMR; Rev. Sci. Instrum. 39, 1881–1884, 1968.
q2 Strauss L: Wave Generation and Shaping, Chapter 5: Field Effect Transistors; McGraw-Hill 1970.
r2 Gray P E, Searle C L: Electronic Principles. Physics, Models and Circuits; Wiley 1969.
s2 Kingston F E, Lee K: Field Effect Transistors at 4·2 K; Rev. Sci. Instrum. 39, 599–601, 1968.
t2 Rogers C G, Jonscher A K: Operation of Field-Effect Transistors at Liquid-Helium Temperatures; Electr. Lett. 3, 210–211, 1967.
u2 Jonscher A K: Semiconductors at Cryogenic Temperatures; Proc IEEE 52, 1092–1104, 1964.
v2 RCA: Application Notes, Linear Integrated Circuits and MOS Devices; RCA Solid-State Databook Series SSD-202, 1972.
w2 Jacobus L A, Reich S: Design of Gate Protected MOS Field Effect Transistors; RCA Application Note AN-4018.
x2 Mullard: Field-Effect Transistors in a Pre-Amplifier for use with Solid-State Radiation Detectors; Mullard Application Note TP1106, 1969.
y2 DeMassa T A, Goddard G: The Drift Field-Effect Transistor, Semiconductors (Motorola) 1971, 86–89.
z2 Analog Devices: TDN: Temperature-Drift-Nonlinearity—A New Dual-FET Specification; Analog Dialogue 6, No.1, 13–14, 1972.
A2 Thomas R: FETs for Op-Amps; Electron 5 Apr. 1973, 63, 65–67.
B2 Mullard: FET Input Stage for an Integrated Operational Amplifier; Mullard Application Note TP1149, 1970.
C2 Barker R W J, Hart B L: An Ultra-High Input Impedance Amplifier and its Drift Performance; Electronic Components 27 Oct. 1972, 1007–1009.
D2 Harris: FET Input Preamplifier HA-2000/2005; Harris Semiconductor Data Sheet June 1972.

E2   Burwen R S, Sullivan D: IC FET Input Operational Amplifiers AD503/506; Analog Devices Tech. Bull. Aug. 1971.
F2   Burwen R S, Sullivan D: IC FET Input Operational Amplifiers AD513/516; Analog Devices Tech. Bull. Aug. 1971.
G2   Analog Devices: A Low-Noise, Low-Drift FET-Input Amplifier Design (AD840+ AD301A); Analog Dialogue 7, No.1, 14, 1974.
H2   Siegel B: Application for a High Speed FET Input Op Amp (LH0062); National Semiconductor Application Note AN-75, Dec. 1972.
I2   Aria R: Dual FETs for Low Offset Source Followers; Siliconix Application Note AN-17, Aug. 1970.
J2   Aria R: Dual FETs for Differential Amplifiers; Siliconix Application Note AN-16, Nov. 1970.
K2   Matzen N: Improve IC Op-Amp Performance with Inexpensive FET; Siliconix Application Tip AN-5.
L2   Sherwin J: Liberate Your FET Amplifier . . .; Electronic Design 24 May 1970, 78–83.
M2   Unsworth L: Using Junction FETs; Wireless World 78, May 1972, 219–222.
N2   Jenkins J O M: Ten Practical FET Source-Follower Circuits; Wireless World 77, Aug. 1971, 366–367.
O2   Owens A R, Perry M A: Temperature Coefficient of Drift of MOS Transistors; Electr. Lett. 2, 309, 1966.
P2   Black G G A, Smith K C: A JFET Circuit for Instrumentation Applications; IEEE Trans IM-22, 2–8, 1973.
Q2   Alderman D W: Liquid Helium Temperature CW NMR S/N Improvement Using a MOSFET RF Amplifier; Rev. Sci. Instrum. 41, 192–197, 1970.
R2   Mullard: Theory and Applications of DMOS; Electronics Industry Dec. 1975, 34–37, 39.
S2   Beer A F: The Double Diffused M.O.S. Transistor or D.M.O.S.; New Electronics 24 Feb. 1976, 38, 41–42.
T2   Budak J: Power Control Using Touch Switches; New Electronics 20 Apr. 1976, 34, 36.
U2   Siliconix: High Frequency Junction FET Characterisation and Application; Siliconix Technical Article TA-70, 1970.
V2   Oxner E: Junction FETs in Active Double-Balanced Mixers; Siliconix Application Note 73/4, June 1973.
W2   Hawke J: High Specification Amplifier with Unity Gain; Electronic Eng. June 1976, 21–22.
X2   Kirk W J, Carter L S, Waddell M L: Eliminate Static Damage to Circuits by Tracing its Causes and Reducing the Voltage Levels; Electronic Design 29 Mar. 1976, 80–85.

References section 8.2: Voltage-controlled resistors and switches

a1   Capella D, Jenkins M: Voltage Controlled Resistors Using the Junction FET; Electronic Components 29 Jan. 1974, 17–21.
b1   Mullard: The Field-Effect Transistor as a Voltage-Variable Resistor; Mullard Application Note TP1110, 1969.
c1   Union Carbide: A Voltage Variable Impedance Element Utilizing the Field-Effect Transistor; Union Carbide Application Note AN-13, Apr. 1967.
d1   Texas Instruments: New AGC Circuits Using FETs; Texas Instruments Application Report EB8, 1971.
e1   Botos B: Low Frequency Applications of Field-Effect Transistors; Motorola Application Note AN-511, 1969.
f1   Motorola: High Linearity Dynamic Compression with a JFET; Semiconductor (Motorola) 1972, 21–22.
g1   Carlson F M: Chopper Circuits Using RCA MOS Field-Effect Transistors; RCA Application Note AN-3452, 1967.
h1   Givens S: FETs as Analog Switches; Electronic Components 26 Jan. 1973, 70–73, 76, 77 and Siliconix Application Note 42/A18, 1972.
i1   Babbs R: The Junction FET in Switching Circuits; Design Electronics Nov. 1970, 66–68.

j1 Thomas R: Multiplexing with TTL Compatible FETs; Electron 8 Nov. 1973, 38–40.
k1 Jenkins J O M: Interface Circuits Drive High-Level Switches from Low-Level Inputs; Electronic Eng. 43, May 1971, 45–49, and Siliconix Application Note 32, May 1971.
l1 Schaeffer L: CMOS Analog Switches—A Powerful Design Tool; Siliconix Application Note AN-75-1, July 1975.
m1 Fullagar D: Analog Switches Replace Reed Relays for Higher Speed Bounceless Contact and TTL Compatability; Electronic Design 21 June 1973, 98–101.
n1 Gazin J F: The MOS Transistor—an Analogue Switching Device; Electronic Components 13 Aug. 1974, 11, 13, 15, 16, Part 2 Applications; 10 Sep. 1974, 31, 33, 34.
o1 Rosen H, Robrish P, deVries G J: Design of a Simple and Inexpensive Analog Gate; Rev. Sci. Instrum. 46, 1115–1116, 1975.
p1 Van Aken R: CMOS Quad Switches and Multiplexers; Analog Dialogue 7, No.2, 1973, 8–9.
q1 Mullard: The Junction FET in Switching Circuits; Mullard Application Note TP1189, 1970.
r1 Stevens M, Wood A: The FET as a Chopper; Texas Instruments Application Report B60, 1968.
s1 Evans A D: IC's End the 'Driver Gap' in FET Analog Signal Switching; Electronic Design 22 Nov. 1966, and Siliconix Application Note AN20, 1966.
t1 Miles J F: Metal-Oxide-Semiconductor Transistors and Their Applications; Mullard Tech. Comm. 9, 54–63, 1966.
u1 Wollensen D: Analogue-Signal Commutation Using MOS ICs; Electron 20 Apr. 1972, 15–16.
v1 RCA: Uses of Quad Bilateral Switches; Electron 13 July 1972, 29–30.
w1 Jenkins J O M: IC Multiplexer Increases Analogue Switching Speeds; Electronic Eng. 45, Feb. 1973, 73–75, and Siliconix Application Note 44/A27, Feb. 1973.
x1 Siliconix: The MOSFET as a Switch; Electronic Eng. 45, May 1973, 11.
y1 Fullagar D: Understanding and Using the Analogue Switch; New Electronics 10 July 1973, 90–92, 94, and Intersil Application Bulletin A003, Apr. 1973.
z1 Reynolds T: MOS Multiplex Switches; Motorola Application Note AN-523, 1970.
A1 Jenkins M: A Versatile MOSFET Analogue Switch; Electron 25 Oct. 1973, 49–50.
B1 LaBelle G: Designing with Analog Gates; Electronic Components 24 Mar. 1972, 277–279.
C1 Teledyne: JFET Applications and Specifications (JFET Voltage Controlled Resistors p. 146, Switches with Junction FETs p. 123); Teledyne Semiconductor Handbook, June 1972.
D1 Ferranti: The Use of Field-Effect Transistors in Chopper Amplifiers; Ferranti Application Note 30, 1966.
E1 Hage D, Givens S: Switching High-Frequency Signals with FET Integrated Circuits; Siliconix Application Note 47/A25, Mar. 1973.
F1 Capella D: FETs as Voltage Controlled Resistors; Siliconix Application Note 46/A24, Feb. 1973.
G1 Dixon G: Analog Switches in Sample and Hold Circuits; Siliconix Application Note AN74-2, May 1974.
H1 Siliconix: Driver Circuits for the JFET Analog Switch; Siliconix Application Note 49/A28, Aug, 1973.
I1 RCA: Linear Integrated Circuits and MOS Devices: Application Notes; RCA Solid State Databook Series SSD-202, 1972.
J1 Matthews P: Touch-Controlled Switches Using CMOS; New Electronics 14 Oct. 1975, 39, 42, 46.
K1 National Semiconductor: AH5009 Series Low Cost Analog Current Switches; National Semiconductor Data Sheet, Apr. 1974.
L1 Thomas R: Multiplexing with FETs; Electronic Equipment News Dec. 1974, 27–30.
M1 Kane J: The Field-Effect Transistor in Digital Applications; Motorola Application Note AN-219, 1966.
N1 Eaton K: Metal Oxide Silicon Field-Effect Transistors (MOSFETs) as Low Level Choppers; General Microelectronics Application Note 1, No.2.

O1 Siemens: Touch Switching-Integrated Circuits; Siemens Application Note.
P1 Emihus: Tuning by Fingertip Touch; Electron 14 Sep. 1972, 37.
Q1 Emihus: Novel Touch Tuner; Electronic Eng. 44, Nov. 1972, 29.
R1 Klein D: The Speed of Miniature Relays; Electronic Equipment News June 1972, 67–68.
S1 Teledyne: JFET Voltage Controlled Resistors; Electron 30 Aug. 1973, 45.
T1 Bijlsma N R, Burwell P, Evans E G (Eds): Field-Effect Transistors; Mullard 1972.
U1 Siliconix: N- and P-Channel Junction Voltage-Controlled-Resistor FETs VCR2-20; Siliconix Data Sheet 1967.
V1 von Ow H P: Reducing Distortion in Controlled Attenuators Using FETs; Proc IEEE 56, 1718–1719, 1968.
W1 Fullagar D: A New CMOS Analogue Gate Technology; New Electronics 10 Dec. 1974, 72.
X1 Motorola: McMOS Handbook: Products, Characteristics, Applications; Motorola Handbook Oct. 1973.
Y1 Mrazek D: High Speed MOS Commutators; National Semiconductor Application Note AN-28, Jan. 1970.
Z1 National Semiconductor: FET Circuit Applications; National Semiconductor Application Note AN-32, Feb. 1970.
a2 Wollesen D L: Analog-Signal Commutation; National Semiconductor Application Note AN-33, Feb. 1970.
b2 Stump R, Wollesen D: Applications of MOS Analog Switches; National Semiconductor Application Note AN-38, May 1970.
c2 National Semiconductor: High Speed Analog Switches (AM1000 Series); National Semiconductor Application Note AN-53, Sep. 1971.
d2 Battison D J: Analogue Signal Multiplexing Without FETs; Electronic Eng. 46, 17, Dec. 1974.
e2 Krabbe H, Molinari F: AD555 Monolithic 'uDAC' Quad Switches Make 4-Quadrant Multiplying DAC's with 12-Bit Linearity; Analog Dialogue 5, No.2, 3-5, 1971.
f2 Intersil: Low Cost Analog Switches IH5009–IH5024; Intersil Data Sheet Feb. 1972.
g2 Analog Devices: Quad SPST Current Steering Switch AD7519; Analog Devices Data Sheet.
h2 Wollesen D L: Analog Switching—High Speed with JFETs; EDN 15 Jan. 1970.
i2 Cohen J M: Sample and Hold Circuits Using FET Analog Gates; EEE Jan. 1971.
j2 Gordon B: Digital Sampling and Recovery of Analog Signals; EEE May 1970.
k2 Watson J: An Introduction to Field Effect Transistors; Siliconix.
l2 Taylor J: Driving the JFET Switch; Siliconix Application Tip AN21/A16, Nov. 1969.
m2 Hargrave D: Commutating and Interfacing with Junction and MOS FETs; Electronic Eng. 41, 56–59, 1969, and Siliconix Application Note AN-4.
n2 Sherwin J S: Cut Transients in FET Analog Switches; Electronic Design 27 Apr. 1972, 50–54.
o2 Intersil: The IH5009 Series of Low Cost Analog Switches; Intersil Application Bulletin A004, Jan. 1972.
p2 Intersil: Low Cost Analog Switches IH5025–IH5038: Intersil Data Sheet, Apr. 1972.
q2 Gosling W, Townsend W G, Watson J: Field-Effect Electronics, Chapter 11 The FET as a Variable Resistor; Chapter 10 Choppers and Analog Gates; Butterworths 1970.
r2 Trofimenkoff F N, Smallwood R E: JFET Circuit Linearizes Transducer Output; IEEE Trans IM-22, 191–193, 1973.
s2 Macken W J: FETs as Variable Resistances in Op Amps and Gyrators; Electronic Eng. 44, Dec. 1972, 60–61.
t2 Analog Devices: Guide to Analog CMOS Switches and Multiplexers; Analog Devices Handbook 1974.
u2 Millman J, Taub H: Pulse, Digital and Switching Waveforms, Chapter 17 Sampling Gates; McGraw-Hill 1965.
v2 Whitmore J: Keys to Longer Life for CMOS. Here's How CMOS Can be Protected Against Abuses; Analog Dialogue 8, No.2, 20–21, 1974.
w2 Burr-Brown: C-MOS Analog Multiplexers MCP 8D, MPC 16S; Burr-Brown Data Sheet PDS-315, Oct. 1974.

x2 Bellamy N W, West M J: Solid State Switches for Use in Hybrid Computing; Design Electronics June 1970, 54, 57, 58.

y2 Wilenken R: Beware of CMOS-Switch Failure Modes; Electronic Design 15 Mar. 1975, 68–71.

z2 Fletcher J: Developments in Mercury Film Switching; Electronic Components 1 Oct. 1971, 1015, 1018, 1019.

A2 Gledhill S P: Reed Switch Circuit Hazards and Their Mitigation; Electronic Components 25 Feb. 1972, 175–178.

B2 Donaldson J: Design Considerations Using Reed Relays; Electron 26 Sep. 1974, 51, 52, 55.

C2 Clare: Technical Application Reference for Mercury-Wetted Contact, Dry Reed and Mercury-Wetted Reed Relays; C P Clare Manual, Jan. 1975.

D2 Sherwin J: A Linear Multiple Gain-Controlled Amplifier; New Electronics 9 Dec. 1975, 26–28.

E2 Siliconix: Analogue Switches as CMOS Circuit Building Blocks; New Electronics 27 Jan. 1976, 20, 24–25.

F2 Analog Devices: DI CMOS Protected Analog Switches AD7510/11/12; Analog Devices Data Sheet 1976.

G2 Dromgoole W V: Linear Voltage-Controlled Attenuator—DC to 20kHz; Electronic Eng. Mar. 1976, 43–45.

H2 Ben-Yaakov S: Use CMOS in Chopper Designs; Electronic Design 16 Feb. 1976, 164–166.

I2 Torrero E A: Focus on IC Analog Switches and Multiplexers; Electronic Design 1 Sep. 1975, 64–72.

J2 Siliconix: Analogue Switches—and their Applications; Siliconix 1976.

K2 Siliconix: Latchproof Monolithic CMOS Switch with TTL Compatible Driver DG300/3; Siliconix Data Sheet.

References section 8.3: Thyristors

a1 Hall G: Triacs Can Misfire with the Wrong Triggering; Electronic Eng. 45, June 1973, 65–67.

b1 Granieri G J: Application of the RCA-3058 and RCA-3059 Zero-Voltage Switches in Thyristor Control; RCA Application Note ICAN-6158, 1971.

c1 Kleinman H M, Sheng A: Applications and Extended Operating Characteristics for the RCA-3059 IC Zero-Voltage Switch; RCA Application Note ICAN-6268, 1970.

d1 Haver R J, Rees L T: Zero Point Switching Techniques; Motorola Application Note AN-453, 1968.

e1 Budek J: Triacs—Theory and General Applications; Texas Instruments Application Report B61, 1968.

f1 RCA: Zero Voltage Switching; Electron 9 Nov. 1972, 41–42.

g1 Yellin J: Triac Power Controls for Three-Phase Systems; RCA Application Note AN-6054, 1972.

h1 Thompson G H: Triac Operating Modes; Electronic Components 12 Feb. 1974, 22–25.

i1 Jarratt T J: Transistorized SCR Firing Circuits; Mullard Tech. Comm. 7, 141–157, 1963.

j1 Payne R A, Reeves E S: Switch-Off Circuits for SCRs Operating on DC; Mullard Tech. Comm. 7, 158–161, 1963.

k1 Payne R A: Precise Phase Angle Control of SCRs; Mullard Tech. Comm. 7, 162–168, 1963.

l1 Lim J S, Wilson K: Some Aspects of Thyristor Series Operation; Mullard Tech. Comm. 7, 266–270, 1964.

m1 Botos B, Haver B: A Fuse-Thyristor Coordination Primer; Motorola Application Note AN-568, 1972.

n1 Mazda F F: Thyristor Firing Transformers; Electron 28 Sep. 1972, 33–35.

o1 Smith C J: Thyristors—Selection for Power Conversion; Electron 14 Feb. 1974, 23, 25, 27.

p1 Clarke S: Switching Losses in High-Frequency Thyristors; New Electronics 19 Feb. 1974, 16, 17, 20.
q1 Newmire L J: Theory, Characteristics and Applications of Silicon Unilateral and Bilateral Switches; Motorola Application Note AN-526, 1970.
r1 Mazda F F: Using the Thyristor; Electronic Components 17 Sep. 1971, 947–957.
s1 ITT: 25 Circuits Using BRY Series Thyristors; ITT Semiconductors Application Note 6218/441E, 1970.
t1 Texas Instruments: Silicon Controlled Rectifiers. Principles of Operation; Texas Instruments Application Report B3, 1968.
u1 SGS/ATES: Triac/SCR Burst Control L121; SGS/ATES Data Sheet 1973.
v1 SGS/ATES: Triac/SCR Phase Control L120; SGS/ATES Data Sheet 1973.
w1 Texas Instruments: Zero-Voltage Switch SN72440; Texas Instruments Data Sheet.
x1 General Electric Semiconductors: Zero-Voltage Switch MB424; General Electric Semiconductors Data Sheet.
y1 Plessey Semiconductors: Power Control Circuit SL440; Plessey Semiconductors Data Sheet Nov. 1972.
z1 Motorola: Zero Voltage Switch MFC8070; Motorola Data Sheet 1971.
A1 Wojslawowicz J E: Analysis and Design of Snubber Networks for dV/dt Suppression in Thyristor Circuits; RCA Application Note AN-4745, 1971.
B1 Budek J: Power Control with Triacs; Texas Instruments Application Report B130.
C1 Budek J: Triacs with Resistive and Inductive Loads; Norris B (Ed) Semiconductor Circuit Design Vol. 1; Texas Instruments.
D1 Budek J: Solid-State Switching Using Triacs and Thyristors; Norris B (Ed) Semiconductor Circuit Design Vol. 1; Texas Instruments.
E1 Budek J: Burst Firing Techniques Using Triacs; Norris B (Ed) Semiconductor Circuit Design Vol. 1; Texas Instruments.
F1 Budek J: Thyristor Reversible DC Supply; Norris B (Ed) Semiconductor Circuit Design Vol. 1; Texas Instruments.
G1 RCA; Solid-State Power Circuits, Chapter 9 Thyristors, Chapter 13 Thyristor AC Line-Voltage Controls; RCA Solid State Division, Technical Series SP-52, 1971.
H1 Ferranti: Silicon 4 Layer Switching Diodes; Ferranti Application Report No.1, Dec. 1959.
I1 RCA: Silicon Controlled Rectifier Experimenters Manual; RCA Technical Series KM-71, 1967.
J1 RCA: Transistor Thyristor and Diode Manual; RCA Technical Series SC-15, 1969.
K1 Marston R M: 110 Semiconductor Projects for the Home Constructor, Chapter 4, 15 Silicon Controlled-Rectifier Projects; Iliffe 1969.
L1 Zinder D A: Constant-Speed Motor Control Using Tachometer Feedback; Motorola Application Note AN-518, 1970.
M1 Bruder H, Waterman G: The Triac. Examples for Applications of Type Range TW6-TW10; AEG-Telefunken Technical Information 6, E43.14.604E/1272.
N1 Westinghouse: Hyreg Module Zero Switching Controller Type ZC1, and Phase Controller Type AC1; Westinghouse Data Sheet.
O1 Ashman W G, Chumbley R: Power Control Using Hybrid Technology; New Electronics 20 Feb. 1973.
P1 Westinghouse: Modular Power Regulator; Electron 12 Sep. 1974, 63.
Q1 International Rectifier: PH400 Pace Pack Series Power Integrated Circuits; International Rectifier Data Sheet Bulletin E2720.
R1 Gutzwiller F W (Ed): Silicon Controlled Rectifier Manual, Including the Triac; General Electric Co. 4th Edn. 1967.
S1 Clearly J F: Transistor Manual 7th Edn., Chapter 16, Silicon Controlled Switches; General Electric Co. 1964.
T1 Yonushka J V: Triac Power-Control Applications; RCA Application Note AN-3697, 1968.
U1 Mullard: Four Layer Switching; Electron 5 Apr. 1973.
V1 RCA: Zero-Voltage Switches CA3058, CA3059, CA3079; RCA Data Sheet 1970.

W1 Merrett J: Voltage Transient and dV/dt Suppression in Thyristor Bridges; Mullard Tech. Comm. 10, 40–51, 1968.

X1 Janssen D J G: Circuit Logic with Silicon Controlled Switches; Mullard Tech. Comm. 10, 57–64, 1968.

Y1 Merrett J: Current Overload Protection in Thyristor Phase Control Systems; Mullard Tech. Comm. 8, 262–270, 1966.

Z1 Mazda F F: Design of High-Frequency Thyristor-Chopper Circuits; Electronic Eng. 42, Feb. 1970, 34–39.

a2 Rattcliff G: AC Power Control Incorporating Zero-Voltage-Switching; Electronic Components May 1969, 580–583.

b2 Galloway J H: Using the Triac for Control of AC Power; General Electric Application Note 200.35, 1966.

c2 Gutzwiller F W: Universal Motor Speed Controls; General Electric Application Note 200.4, 1961.

d2 Grafham D: PNPN Switches with Gate Turn-Off Control; General Electric Application Note 200.23, 1962.

e2 Yonushka J V: Application of RCA SCRs to Speed Control of Universal Motors; RCA Application Note SMA-38, 1965.

f2 Roman B J, Neilson J M: Circuit Factor Charts for RCA Thyristor Applications (SCRs and Triacs); RCA Application Note AN-3551, 1967.

g2 Buczynski R J: Commutating dV/dt and its Relationship to Bidirectional Triode Thyristor Operation in Full-Wave AC Power-Control Circuits; RCA Application Note ST3492, 1967.

h2 Evangelisti A: Trigger Circuits for Phase-Controlled SCRs Feeding an Inductive Load; SGS–Fairchild Application Report AR167, Aug. 1966.

i2 Romano A: A 300 Watt Domestic Light Dimmer Controller Using SCRs Type BTX60; SGS–Fairchild Application Report AR168, Aug. 1966.

j2 Haver R J, Zinder D A: Conventional and Soft-Start Dimming of Incandescent Lights; Motorola Application Note AN-436, 1968.

k2 Gregson R E: AC Overvoltage and Overcurrent Protective Circuit with Automatic Reset; Motorola Application Note AN-454, 1968.

m2 Zinder D A: Unijunction Trigger Circuits for Gated Thyristors; Motorola Application Note AN-413, 1968.

n2 Zinder D A: Suppressing RFI in Thyristor Circuits; Motorola Application Note AN-295, 1967.

o2 Brookmire J L: Temperature Controls Incorporating Zero Voltage Switching; General Electric Application Note 200.45, 1966.

p2 Eckoldt F: Photo-Thyristor BPY78 and its Applications; AEG–Telefunken Application Note B2/V.7.06/0569E.

q2 General Electric: Integrated Circuit Zero Voltage Switch PA424 (Includes Galloway J H: Applications of the PA424 Monolithic Integrated Zero Voltage Switching Trigger Circuit for Thyristor Control); General Electric Data Sheet.

r2 Ritamaki P: Optocoupler is Zero-Crossing Detector and Isolator in Triac Power Control; Electronic Design 27 Sep. 1975, 104.

s2 Owers L W: Thyristors; Mullard.

t2 Rose M J (Ed): Power Engineering Using Thyristors. Vol. 1 Techniques of Thyristor Power Control; Mullard 1970.

u2 General Electric: Integrated Circuit Phase Control PA436 (Includes Application Note Howell E K: Applications of the PA434 Monolithic Integrated Phase-Control Trigger Circuit); General Electric Data Sheet 85.31, 1968.

v2 Gutzwiller F W, Meng J D: Phase Control of SCRs with Transformer and Other Inductive AC Loads; General Electric Application Note 200.31.

w2 Mazda F F: Thyristor Control; Newnes–Butterworths 1973.

x2 Murphy J M D: Thyristor Control of AC Motors; Pergamon 1973.

y2 Atkinson P: Thyristors and Their Applications; Mills and Boon 1972.

z2 Howell E K: Triac Control for AC Power; General Electric Application Note 200.35, 1964.

A2 RCA: Power Circuits, DC to Microwave. Thyristor AC Line-Voltage Controls; RCA Technical Series SP-51, 1969.

B2 Bosterling W: Concerning the Turn-On and Turn-Off Power Losses in Fast Thyristors; AEG–Telefunken Technical Information 4, E43.14.601/0871.

C2 Bosterling W, Tscharn M: Current Handling Capacity of Fast Thyristors at Medium Operating Frequencies; AEG–Telefunken Technical Information 5, E43.14.602/1071.

D2 Wechsler R: Designing SCR Circuits for High Inrush Loads; Motorola Application Note AN-170.

E2 Wechsler R: Reducing di/dt-Effect Failures in Silicon Controlled Rectifiers; Motorola Application Note AN-173.

F2 General Electric: Silicon Asymmetrical AC Trigger ST4; General Electric Data Sheet 1971.

G2 Sprague: Unicircuit Amplifier-SCR Firing Circuit ULN-2300M; Sprague Electric Eng. Bulletin 27400A.

H2 AEG–Telefunken: High Precision Phase Angle Control UAA145; AEG–Telefunken Data Sheet B2/V.2.256/0672A1.

I2 Wells D: Phase Control of Resistive Loads; Electronic Equipment News Sep. 1974, 83–84.

J2 Zinder D A: Electronic Speed Control for Motors in Domestic Appliances; Semiconductors (Motorola) 1974/2, 28–33.

K2 Kaye D N: ICs and Transistors Provide Brain and Muscle for Motor Control; Electronic Design 11 Oct. 1974, 38, 40, 42, 44.

L2 Salvadori M: ICs for Phase and Burst Control of SCR or Triac (L120, L121); New Electronics 26 Nov. 1974, 33, 35, 36, 39.

M2 Hoyer J: Electronic Ignition Systems for Motor Cars; Semiconductors (Motorola) 1973/3, 11–19.

N2 Fairchild: Zero Crossing AC Trigger-Trigac µA742; Fairchild Data Sheet.

O2 Motto J W: A New Quantity to Describe Power Semiconductor Subcycle Current Ratings; Trans IEEE IGA-7, 510–517, 1971.

P2 Schonholzer E T: Fuse Protection for Power Thyristors; Trans IEEE IA-8, 301–309, 1972.

Q2 RCA: Programmable Comparator with Memory CA3099E; RCA Data Sheet 1973.

R2 Lavallee J M: Thyristor Trigger Circuit for a Reversible DC Motor Drive with Regenerative Braking; Mullard Tech. Comm. 12, 70–79, 1972.

S2 Burri M: Digitally Controlled Ramp Generator; Electron 26 Sep. 1974, 27, 29, 32.

T2 Taylor J R, Sunda J A, Schaffner H: Thyristor RFI Suppression and Mains-Borne Voltage Transient Filters; Waycom Technical Pub. Feb. 1974.

U2 O'Sullivan G A: Which DC/AC Inverter?; Electronic Design 6 Dec. 1974, 54–59.

V2 Mullard: Trigger Integrated Circuit TCA280A; Mullard Data Sheet Oct. 1974.

W2 Moore D W: Todays' Power Semiconductors; New Electronics 18 Feb. 1975, 67–68.

X2 Sheng A C N, Granieri G J, Yellin J: Features and Applications of RCA Integrated Circuit Zero-Voltage Switches (CA3058, CA3059, CA3079); RCA Application Note ICAN-6182, 1975.

Y2 Rydeski J: Test That SCR Turn-Off Time if you would Forstall Burnout; Electronic Design 15 Mar. 1975, 74–76.

Z2 McNulty T C, Digneffe H: Power Switching Using Solid State Relays; New Electronics 16 Oct. 1973, 70, 75, 76, 78.

a3 Kalfus M: Latching, Gate-Trigger Circuits Using Thyristors for Machine-Control Applications; RCA Application Note AN-6286, 1974.

b3 AEG: Monolithic Integrated Triac Control Circuit with Touch Switch U112B; AEG–Telefunken Data Sheet.

c3 Mullard: TCA280A Trigger IC for Thyristors and Triacs; Mullard Technical Note TP1490, 1975.

d3 Kalfus M: Thyristors in CD (Capacitor Discharge) Ignition Systems; RCA Application Note AN-6288E, 1974.

e3 RCA: Gate-Turn-Off (GTO) Silicon Controlled Rectifiers TAG5001/2/3 Series; RCA Data Sheet 1974.

f3 Babcock W E: The ITR for Horizontal Deflection (Integrated Thyristor and Rectifier); RCA Application Note AN-6248, 1974.

g3 Becke H, McKeon E, Neilson J, Wojslawowicz J: Gate-Turn-Off Silicon Controlled Rectifiers—A Users Guide; RCA Application Note AN-6357, 1974.

h3 Gronner A D: Transistor Circuit Analysis; Simon and Schuster 1970, Revised Edition.

i3 Millman J, Taub H: Pulse, Digital and Switching Waveforms; McGraw-Hill 1965.

j3 Hyde F J: Thermistors; Iliffe Books 1971.

k3 Hampson L: Fuse Protection of Semiconductor Diodes, Thyristors, and Triacs; Mullard Tech. Comm. 13, 302–319, Oct. 1975.

l3 Mullard: Zero-Point Trigger Circuit for On/Off Control of Triacs TDA1024; Mullard Data Sheet Feb. 1976.

m3 New T C: Thermal Runaway in High Power Thyristors; Motorola Application Note AN580, 1972.

n3 Gregory V: Power Control Using the Zero Voltage Switch (MFC8070); Motorola Application Note AN-597, 1973.

o3 Mazur T: Four Terminal, Optically Isolated Zero Crossing AC Relay; Motorola Application Note AN-598, 1973.

p3 Motorola: Zero Voltage Switch UAA1004; Motorola Data Sheet Nov. 1975.

q3 RCA: Thyristor and Rectifier Manual; RCA Technical Manual TRM-445, 1976.

r3 Becke H, McKeon E, Nielson J, Wojslawowicz J, Digneffe H: Characteristics and Applications of RCA Gate-Turn-Off Silicon Controlled Rectifiers; RCA Application Note AN-6457, 1976.

s3 Digneffe H: Asymmetrical Silicon Controlled Rectifiers; New Electronics 1 June 1976, 30, 32, 34.

9 Optoelectronics

9.1 Light units and measurement

Optoelectronic devices have been available for a considerable time, but the development of solid-state emitters in particular has led to renewed interest and the construction of many useful devices. The use of photons rather than electrons provides a number of advantages, and the whole field of optoelectronics is developing rapidly. There are, however, several problems related to the measurement and specification of light quantities, and this has resulted in the use of a number of different units of measurement. The absolute measurement of optical intensity, for example, is one of the more difficult measurements, of any of the basic quantities of any sort, to be made.

In the past most measurements have been concerned with visible radiation and, hence, the units used have involved the response of the human eye. This has led to the definition of a standard human eye with a response shown in Fig. 9.1.1.

Units based on the response of the eye are referred to as photometric, as against radiometric for physical units based on mass, length, and time. Radiometric units are preferable unless visual considerations are involved. More specifically, SI units should be used for all new measurements. In the past, it has been usual to measure

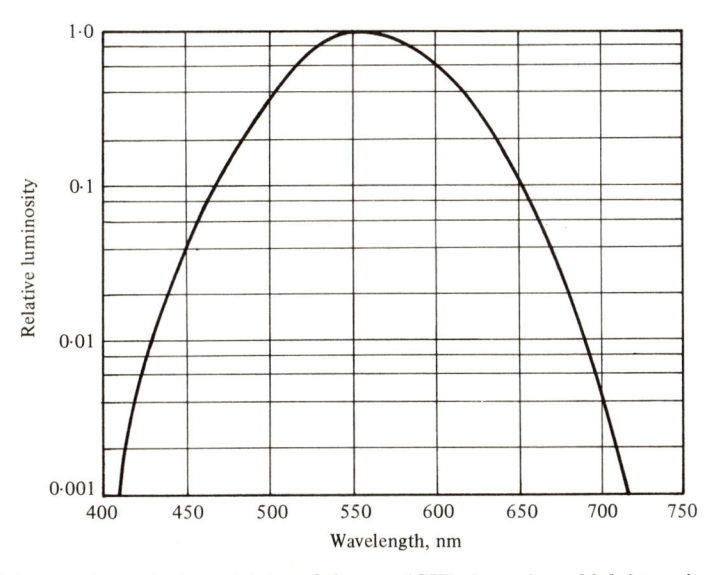

Fig. 9.1.1 Standard spectral sensitivity of the eye (CIE photopic or high intensity response)

spectral variations as a function of wavelength of the radiation, but frequency is, for several reasons, more appropriate and is now generally preferred. It should be made clear that any reference to *light* or to *optical* effects does not here only refer to visible radiation. Photoelectric detectors, with which we will be primarily concerned, at present operate from about 10^{13} Hz (30 μm) at least up to the x-ray region (3×10^{18} Hz or 0·1 nm). In ordinary circumstances only the region up to $1\cdot5 \times 10^{15}$ Hz (200 nm) is of practical interest, since frequencies above this are strongly absorbed by the atmosphere. The visible region is rather small, extending from about 7 to 4×10^{14} Hz (400 to 800 nm). Detectors for operation below the limit for photoelectric detectors are generally based on thermal effects, but these will not be considered here [v1, h1, i1].

The many units for the measurement of radiant energy lead to much confusion and to problems of converting from one to another. With the introduction of SI units this has been rationalized with the following definitions [n1, j1, f1, w1, x1, y1, b1, e1, r1, g1, q1].

Flux Φ: the rate at which energy is passing to, from, or through a surface.
Incidence E: the flux per unit area (S) incident upon the surface of the receptor; $E = \partial\Phi/\partial S$.
Exitance M: the flux per unit area leaving the surface of a source; $M = \partial\Phi/\partial S$.
Intensity I: the flux per unit solid angle (Ω) leaving from a source of finite area; $I = \partial\Phi/\partial\Omega$.
Sterance L: the intensity per unit area of the source; $L = \partial^2\Phi/\partial S\, \partial\Omega$.

Adding the prefixes radiant or luminous to the name and suffixes e (energy) or v (visible) to the symbol, specifies the radiant or photometric system, e.g., radiant flux Φ_e. It is sometimes useful to measure in terms of quanta, when the suffix q is used. The terms defined above differ somewhat from those previously used, the relationships and units being shown in Table 9.1.1.

The relation between radiant and photometric fluxes at the peak of the standard CIE (Commission Internationale de l'Eclairage) eye response at 555 nm, is 680 lumen/watt. At other wavelengths there will be less lumens per watt according to the CIE curve.

In the visible and infrared regions, the optical standard is a black-body [v1, g1, l1,

Table 9.1.1 Radio- and photometric units

Radiometric units		Photometric units	
SI	Old	SI	Old
Radiant flux, Φ_e (watt)	Power	Luminous flux, Φ_v (lumen)	
Radiant incidence, E_e (watt/m^2)	Irradiance	Luminous incidence, E_v (lumen/m^2)	Illuminance (lux)
Radiant exitance, M_e (watt/m^2)	Emittance	Luminous exitance, M_v (lumen/m^2)	
Radiant intensity, I_e (watt/steradian)		Luminous intensity, I_v (lumen/steradian)	(candela)
Radiant sterance, L_e (watt/steradian.m^2)	Radiance	Luminous sterance, L_v (lumen/steradian.m^2)	Luminance (candela/m^2)

Table 9.1.2. Advantages and disadvantages of opto detectors
(Texas Instruments, with permission) [y1]

Advantages	Disadvantages
Photoresistor:	
large light to dark ratio	slow response
zero offset voltage	hysteresis effects
large sensitive area	
Photovoltaic:	
no external bias required	slow response
linear response in short-circuit mode	low level output
large sensitive area	
Photodiode:	
very high speed	low level output
linear response	
low noise	
Phototransistor:	
integral current gain, large output	moderate speed
many configurations and arrays	non-linear response
Photomultiplier:	
very high gain, speed, sensitivity, and bandwidth	large size
low noise	high voltage
large output and good linearity	
wide spectral response	
large sensitive area	

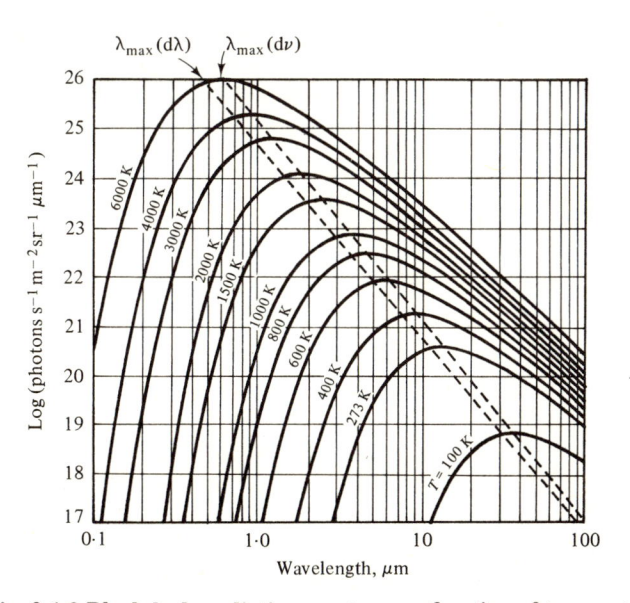

Fig. 9.1.2 Black-body radiation spectra as a function of temperature

s1, k1]. The distribution of emission is given by Planck's law for the radiant exitance at absolute temperature T.

$$M_e(v) = \frac{2\pi h^3}{c^2[\exp(hv/kT)-1]} \qquad M_e(\lambda) = \frac{2\pi hc^2}{\lambda^5[\exp(hc/kT)-1]} \qquad (9.1.1)$$

where h is Planck's constant, k is Boltzmann's constant, and c the velocity of light. The peak of the distribution depends on T only, and varies according to Wien's displacement law. The factor of proportionality depends on whether measurement is made per unit frequency (dv) or per unit wavelength (dλ) interval.

$$\lambda_{max}(dv) = \frac{3670}{T} \mu m\ K^{-1}, \qquad \lambda_{max}(d\lambda) = \frac{2897 \cdot 8}{T} \mu m\ K^{-1} \qquad (9.1.2)$$

These lines are shown dashed in Fig. 9.1.2, together with the distributions for a range of temperatures T. Figure 9.1.3 shows the variation of relative sensitivity for several detectors, compared with the black-body distribution for a temperature equivalent to that of a tungsten lamp.

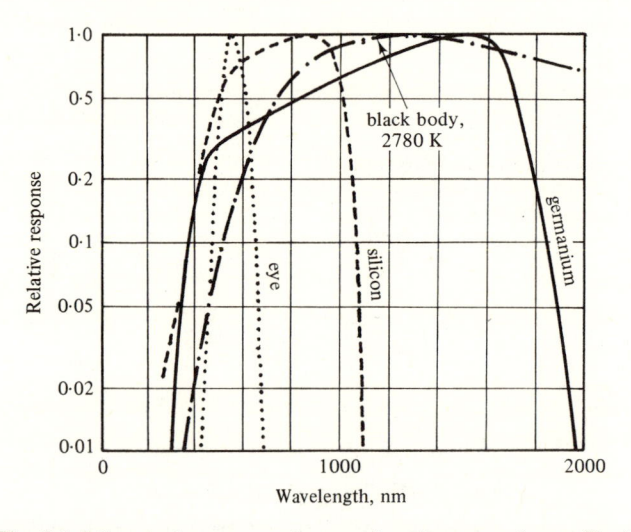

Fig. 9.1.3 Spectral response of some photodetectors (normalized)

9.2 Photodiodes and phototransistors

If a P–N junction is irradiated with photons of high enough energy, an electron can be raised from the valence to the conduction band, producing an electron–hole pair. These will separate under the influence of the junction electric field, generating an open circuit potential. If the external circuit is completed, a current will flow. When an external reverse bias is applied, only the reverse leakage current I_S (Sec. 1.9) will flow, but when irradiated the carriers produced increase the conductivity and an increased current flows. The normal diode characteristic will thus be modified by the irradiation as shown in Fig. 9.2.1.

In quadrant III, the diode is operating in the photoconductive mode. In quadrant IV, it is operating in the photovoltaic mode, generating an open circuit voltage, V_{oc},

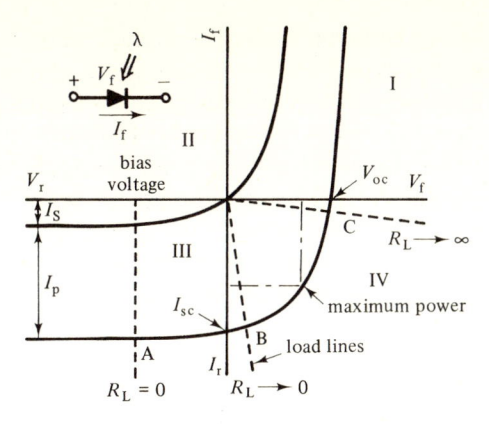

Fig. 9.2.1 Photodiode characteristics

and a short circuit current, I_{sc}. The maximum power output, as would be required for *solar cells*, is somewhere between these two extremes where VI is a maximum. For silicon, V_{oc} is about 0·55 V in sunlight, and the maximum-power voltage about 0·4 V at currents of 30 mA/cm². The practical efficiency is a little over 10 per cent for sunlight, falling with increasing temperature. Power output is of the order of 10 mW/cm², so that many cells of large total area are required to generate significant power. Recently, high temperature gallium arsenide/gallium aluminium arsenide cells have been fabricated to produce over 20 W/cm² with light intensities of 2000 times sunlight, so that small area cells may be used with focused light.

Photodiodes can have high speed response, with rise and fall times ranging from about 10 μs to less than 1 ns [v2, t1, M1, N1, 11]. For the fastest response PIN diodes are commonly used, since high junction electric fields can be produced so that the charge carriers are collected in a shorter time [m1, q1, W1, w2, X1]. The very low dark current also enables this type of diode to be used to detect low intensities.

The characteristic curves for a photodiode operating in the photoconductive mode (Fig. 9.2.1) show that above a small bias voltage the photocurrent is essentially independent of voltage. This indicates that the device acts as a current generator with an equivalent circuit shown in Fig. 9.2.2(a).

The value of $R_p = \partial V_r / \partial I_r$ is very high, say tens of megohms, while the ohmic resistance of the diode $R_s \lesssim 100$ ohm. The capacity, C_p, depends on the junction area, bias voltage, and package, being about 10 pF for small diodes. The current generator means that the same output current will flow irrespective of load, so the simplest way to use it is to connect it in series with a load resistor across a voltage supply; Fig. 9.2.2(b). Then $e_{out} = I_p R_L$ will be proportional to the incident radiant intensity.

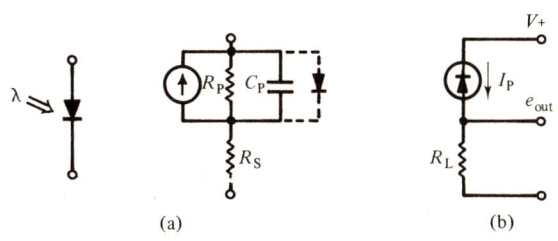

Fig. 9.2.2 Photodiode equivalent circuit

The equivalent circuit in the photovoltaic mode is similar to that for the photoconductive, but with the addition of an ideal diode as shown by the dotted line in Fig. 9.2.2(a) [s1]. The forward voltage generated by irradiation tends to turn this diode on and cause non-linearity in the response. The values of R_p and R_s are similar to the photoconductive values, but C_p will be considerably greater. The prime difference between photovoltaic detectors and power devices (solar cells) lies in the value of R_p. For maximum power transfer, the source and load resistances must be matched (Sec. 1.5) so solar cells have low values of R_p, typically 10 kΩ. Since the photovoltaic diode is hardly turned on at low forward voltages, Eq. (1.9.1), operation into low resistance loads can give good linearity. The diode is operating, in effect, in an unbiased photoconductive mode.

In a normal photodiode there is no current gain to increase the sensitivity. Addition of a second junction gives a transistor, the photodiode forming the base–collector junction. Since the light must reach the latter junction, the geometry of the phototransistor will be somewhat different from a normal transistor. The photocurrent is now the base current, which is amplified by normal transistor action to give a collector current h_{fe} times as great. For maximum sensitivity the phototransistor is operated with base open circuit, as any base connection would divert some photocurrent. However, normal collector–base leakage current must be small (hence silicon planar construction) and the system will be more susceptible to thermal drift. This is particularly true for germanium devices. A phototransistor can be used as a photodiode, by leaving the emitter open circuit.

The light detector and amplifier are integrated into one device in the phototransistor. This, however, has some disadvantages [x2]. Efficient photodiodes and transistors require different resistivity semiconductors, and the amplified photocurrent causes non-linearity. Also, the large base area produces a large collector–base capacity, and this has detrimental effects on the bandwidth as a result of the Miller effect (Sec. 1.6). Typical rise and fall times are a few microseconds. By separating the photodiode and amplifying transistor, though still if required integrating these on the same chip, these disadvantages can be overcome. Response times can be improved by one or two orders of magnitude.

The photoduodiode has a symmetrical *NPN* structure (like a transistor but with interchangeable collector and emitter) which can be used like an ordinary photodiode but with a.c. bias [n1, y2, d2]. Since it has a transistor structure there will also be current gain, which can be substantial.

PhotoFET's are also available and have advantages over ordinary phototransistors of greater gain and bandwidth and easily adjusted sensitivity [o1, p1, y1, z2]. Normally, in a JFET the gate is reverse biased and no base current flows. When illuminated, a photocurrent flows in the reverse biased gate-channel diode, producing a voltage across a gate resistor. Variation of the gate resistor controls the sensitivity over a range of about 10^6. The gate current is delivered by a current generator, so the gate voltage will be proportional to the gate resistor. By using the photoFET as a source follower the output will be a linear function of light intensity. The current gain can be several hundred times that of a phototransistor.

When detecting very low intensities, noise will set the lower limit. The noise performance of the various devices have generally been compared on the basis of the noise equivalent power (NEP) or the directly related detectivity (D or D^*) [A2, B2, Y1]. The NEP is defined as the power of an input signal that produces an output signal equal to the noise output with no input signal applied. The units will be watts/Hz$^{1/2}$ as the basis is unit bandwidth. In practice, other factors will need to be considered, such as the bandwidth required and where this is located, since effects such as $1/f$ noise may be important; Sec. 1.8(c). However, for many detectors NEP is not a satisfactory basis for comparison and, in general, the performance of the whole system must be investigated rather than the detector alone [T1].

The noise performance of the devices mentioned above is not particularly good so they will not be considered in detail [I1]. For this see: photodiodes [f1, c1, l1, j1, g2], PIN diodes [q1, m1], phototransitors [j1, H1], and photoFET [p1]. In solid-state diode devices the primary source of noise is the shot noise of the leakage (dark) and photocurrents. The series resistance, R_s, is usually small and is neglected (Fig. 9.2.2). As far as R_p is concerned some take the view that this is only an *effective* resistance contributing no noise [k1, u1]. Others consider it to be real [f1] and thus to add noise. However, the shot noise of quite small currents will dominate, so, unless the device is operating at low light levels in the photovoltaic mode, the noise from R_p may be neglected. Nevertheless at the lowest light levels and with very low leakage currents, the device will be thermal noise limited because of R_p. At these low levels the output signal from the photodevice will generally require further amplification to obtain a useful signal. This means degradation of the SNR due to the noise contribution of the amplifier, which generally has a worse SNR than the photodevice. Thus, the photodevice signal current must be increased (without increasing the thermal noise) until the amplifier noise contribution is negligible in comparison.

The increase in signal current can be achieved by operating a photodiode with high enough reverse bias to cause avalanche multiplication of the photogenerated carriers. These avalanche photodiodes (APD) have specially constructed *P–N* or *PIN* junctions, and incorporate a guard ring to reduce edge effects [d1, u1, w1, x1, J1, O1, P1, S1, T1]. Because of the statistical nature of the multiplication process there will be an increase in noise. If M is the multiplication factor, then the noise current $i_N^2 \propto M^d$, where d is 2·3 for silicon and 3 for germanium [k1, u1, T1]. This means that the noise current increases faster than the signal current, $i_s^2 \propto M^2$, but this can still give an improvement of system SNR, since the amplifier noise sources $i_{NA}^2 R_f^2$ and $4kTR_f$ (Fig. 9.2.4) dominate at low M. Gains of several hundred can be achieved and an optimum value of M can be derived [k1].

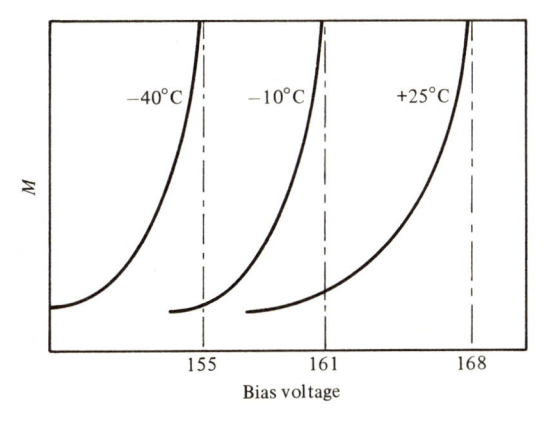

Fig. 9.2.3 Avalanche photodiode characteristics (Adapted courtesy EMI Electronics, Electron Tube division)

Near the breakdown voltage, M varies very rapidly with bias voltage and depends significantly on temperature (Fig. 9.2.3).

For stable operation, therefore, it is vital to regulate the bias voltage and compensate for temperature variations [g1, k1, C2, B1, J1]. This is most readily and effectively done by using dual APD's with matched characteristics and intimate thermal contact (single chip devices). One diode is masked and operated at constant current near breakdown. The change in voltage with temperature, across this reference diode, can then be used to control the voltage applied to the active diode. The supply to the active diode should be current limited so that maximum power dissipation can not be exceeded. Combined APD/stabilizer/amplifier systems are available [C2, Z1], or separate bias controller [a2] and amplifier [b2]. Very high speed operation is possible with APD's [v1, X1].

It is evident that, in considering the performance of photodetectors, the whole system must be considered. The detector must be matched to the amplifier and the system to the application. The close connection between the various parts of the system has led to the production of IC or modular units combining the various functions [s1, r1, c1, z1, A1, D2, i1, E2, C2, E1, c2, F2, o2, p2].

Photoconductive and avalanche photodiodes operate as current sources, the resistance R_p being large, say, 1–50 MΩ. Hence a most convenient and effective way to connect them to an amplifier is to use the current-to-voltage (Fig. 2.5.8) or transimpedance operational amplifier configuration (Fig. 9.2.4).

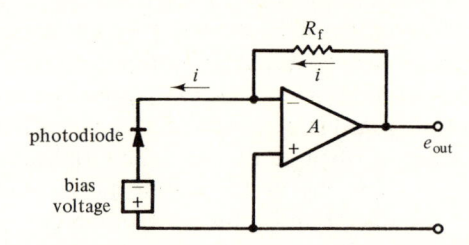

Fig. 9.2.4 Photodiode with transimpedance amplifier

The output voltage $e_{out} = iR_f$, where i is the total current in R_f due to signal, dark current, amplifier noise current, and noise voltage (Sec. 2.9). For high values of R_f the amplifier noise voltage can be neglected, so it is important to choose an amplifier with low noise current and high input impedance, i.e., a FET input amplifier; Sec. 4.1(b) [f1, k1, s1].

An advantage of the above configuration is that the effect of the diode capacity, C_p, is minimized (Sec. 2.8). This is particularly important for large area diodes where the capacity may be as high as 1000 pF and depends on the bias voltage. Note that C_p also affects the noise spectrum as discussed in Sec. 4.6. The voltage across the diode remains fixed at the bias voltage irrespective of diode photocurrent, so the load line is parallel to the current axis as shown in Fig. 9.2.1, load line A. The characteristic curves are equally spaced for equal increments of incident radiant intensity, so the response has good linearity.

In the photovoltaic mode, the diode is forward biased by the incident radiation. The effective source resistance (slope of the characteristic curve) will now depend on the load resistance [s1, f1, x2]. For a high load resistance, the load line will be close to the voltage axis (Fig. 9.2.1, load line B) and the response will be logarithmic. For low load resistance, e.g., the transimpedance configuration Fig. 9.2.4, the load line will be close to the current axis (load line C) and the response can be closely linear. There is no applied bias, so no leakage current and, hence, in the dark the noise will be Johnson due to R_p. To keep the resulting noise current low, R_p must be high, which incidentally also improves the linearity. Dark values of R_p greater than 100 MΩ can be achieved [s1], though lower values are more common. The capacity, C_p, of the junction will be higher than in the photoconductive mode (≈ 3000 pF/cm^2 active area) and hence the frequency response will be restricted. Below about 100 kHz, and particularly below 1 kHz, the photovoltaic mode provides a better SNR [s1].

9.3 Photoresistors

Photoresistors are homogeneous semiconductors whose conductivity varies with the intensity of the incident radiation [o1, p1, v1, w1, f1, g1, z1]. There are no junctions, as for example in photodiodes, and they conduct ohmically and equally in both directions. In the visible region, the most commonly used materials are cadmium sulphide (CdS) and cadmium selenide (CdSe) which have a spectral response as shown in Fig. 9.3.1. These are only approximate responses, since there is some variation with the type of impurity activation.

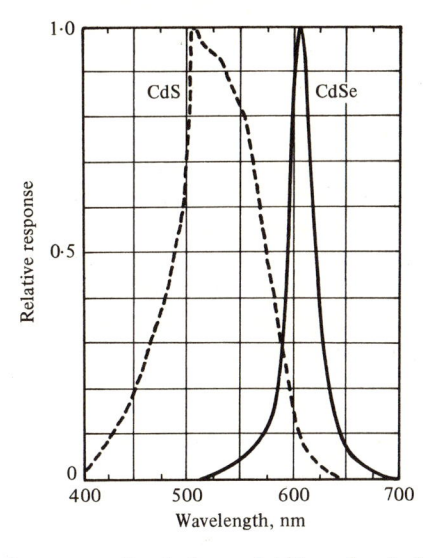

Fig. 9.3.1 Typical spectral response of cadmium sulphide and cadmium selenide photoresistors

Photons of sufficient energy produce free electron–hole pairs, which are separated by the applied electric field and, hence, a current flows. As a result of impurities and crystal imperfections, there are a number of traps and recombination centres. The photo produced holes are rapidly captured by traps where the probability of recombination with an electron is small, while the electrons remain free for a considerably longer time. Thus, electrons extracted at the positive electrode are replaced by electrons emitted at the negative electrode, because of the trapped positive holes. As the recombination time of a hole with an electron is considerably longer than the transit time of electrons between electrodes, a single hole produced by a single photon can promote the passage of a very large number of electrons. In a photoemissive cell, one electron flows per photon, whereas the ratio in a photoconductor may be 10^6, i.e., similar to a photomultiplier [b1]. The dark to illuminated resistance ratio may be as high as 10^5, a typical response being shown in Fig. 9.3.2. Differing materials or impurity activation affect the linearity of the response, but some materials, e.g., monograin CdS [n1] have good linearity.

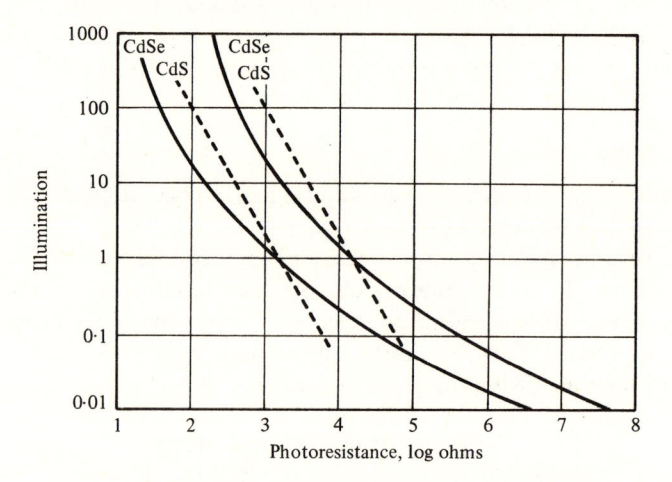

Fig. 9.3.2 Variation of photoresistance with illumination

The time response to changes in illumination intensity is somewhat complex [v1] and depends on material, past illumination history, direction of change, and intensity of illumination. Higher levels of illumination decrease response times and CdSe (and CdS.Se) types are generally faster than CdS. Fastest times are of the order of 1 ms at the highest usable intensity. This increases to seconds for very low light levels. The effect of these time delays is to make the effective a.c. resistance greater than the corresponding d.c. resistance [x1]. Typical time responses as a function of illumination are shown in Fig. 9.3.3.

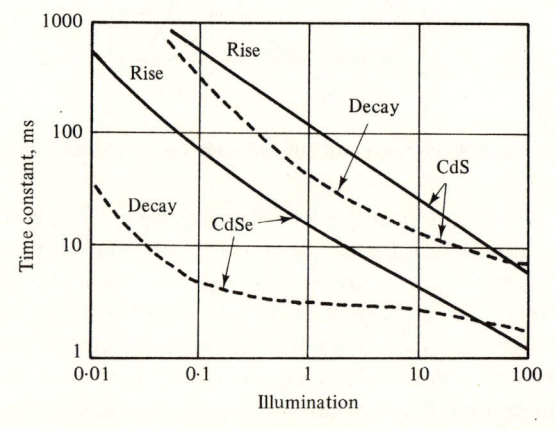

Fig. 9.3.3 Time response of photoresistors with illumination

9.4 Photomultipliers

Photoemissive cells utilize the external photoelectric effect. Electrons are emitted from a cathode when a suitable quantum of light, or photon, is absorbed. An anode, maintained at a positive potential relative to the cathode, collects the electrons so that a photoelectric current flows in the circuit. The two electrodes are usually in a good vacuum so that the electrons are not captured or returned to the cathode. Some photocells have a low pressure gas filling and operate at high enough voltages, so that avalanche ionization multiplication can occur so increasing the current [a1]. However, both these cells have few general attractions compared with other photo-detectors. One particular use for vacuum photodiodes is for ultra-high speed detection of high intensity radiation.

The photomultiplier is a very useful and commonly used device. This consists of a photocell combined with a number of stages of secondary electron multiplication; Fig. 9.4.1 [A1, c1, a1, J2].

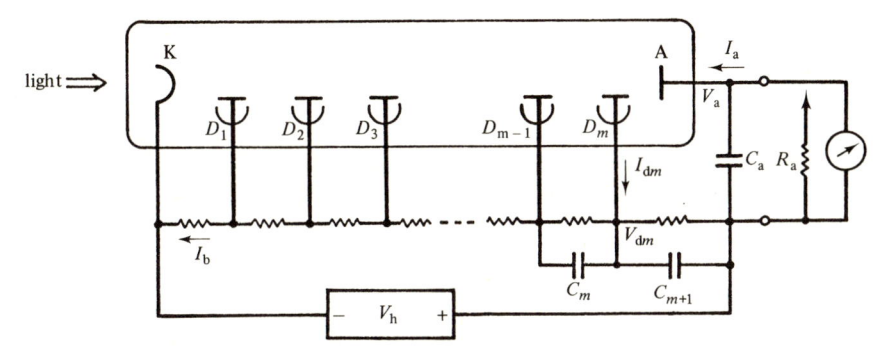

Fig. 9.4.1 Photomultiplier circuit

There are two classes of dynode structure, focused and unfocused. In the focused, the electron-optics is carefully controlled by means of specially shaped dynodes, focusing electrodes, and voltage distribution so that the electrons follow well-defined paths with minimum variation in path length. This has particular effect on the time response and the maximum signal output. The unfocused types generally are a *venetian-blind* structure for each dynode and, less commonly, a box and grid arrangement. These do not have as good a time response nor as large an output signal as the focused types, but generally have lower dark current and noise.

In most high performance tubes the photocathodes are of the semitransparent type deposited on the inside surface of the envelope, while compact lower cost types often use a solid photocathode separated from the envelope. Both types represent a compromise between several competing factors, such as efficiency and depth of light absorption, probability of photoelectron emission, coupling to the light source, and ease of fabrication [A1].

The operating circuit is shown in Fig. 9.4.1. A high voltage is applied to a resistive bleeder chain to provide the appropriate dynode voltages. The anode is usually near ground potential so that the output signal is more readily accessible. If the signal can be a.c. coupled, the cathode may be kept at ground potential which may have some advantage in use. Voltages between dynodes are of the order of 100 V. Photoelectrons emitted from the photocathode, K, are accelerated to the first dynode, D_1. Their energy is now high enough to liberate several secondary electrons, the multiplication factor δ usually being about 3 or 4. These pass to D_2 where they are similarly multiplied, and so on until they are collected at the anode A. If there are m stages of multiplication, i.e., m dynodes, then the overall gain G is:

$$G = f\,\delta^m \qquad (9.4.1)$$

where f is a collection efficiency [w1, m2]. The secondary electron coefficient, δ, is dependent on the energy of the incident electrons and hence on the accelerating voltage, V_s. Since the gain is proportional to a high power of δ it will be particularly sensitive to changes in voltage. An empirical relation for commonly used dynodes is given by [w1]:

$$\delta = 0\cdot 2(V_s)^{0\cdot 7} \qquad (9.4.2)$$

from which the sensitivity of G to variations in overall voltage, V_h, may be found. Since $V_h \propto V_s$, then taking logs of Eq. (9.4.1) and (9.4.2) and differentiating:

$$\begin{aligned}\frac{d\delta}{\delta} &= 0\cdot 7\,\frac{dV_s}{V_s} = 0\cdot 7\,\frac{dV_h}{V_h}\\[4pt]\frac{dG}{G} &= m\,\frac{d\delta}{\delta} = 0\cdot 7\,m\,\frac{dV_h}{V_h}\end{aligned} \qquad (9.4.3)$$

Thus, for a typical photomultiplier with $m=10$ to 14 stages, the fractional change in gain dG/G will be about 10 times the fractional change in overall voltage dV_h/V_h. A well-stabilized power supply is therefore most desirable (chapter 7).

If the anode output current, I_a, is very small then the current in the bleeder chain, I_b, will be the same in all the chain resistors. However, since more electrons leave a dynode than arrive, there must be a current flowing between dynode and chain, as shown. If I_a is comparable with I_b then the chain current, and hence the inter-dynode voltages, will be affected. The overall voltage, V_h, is constant, the voltage merely being redistributed between the dynodes. These changes affect the gain G causing non-linearity in the response [e1, d1]. For linearity within 1 per cent, I_b should be >100 times I_a. A lower ratio may be used for focused tubes. For pulsed or modulated light some compensation is possible by connecting suitable capacitors between dynodes where the changes are greatest, i.e., at the last few dynodes. Since $\delta \doteq 3$, say, the capacitors may be scaled so that $C_{m+1} \doteq 3C_m$ [w1]. With this configuration it should be noted that sudden application of V_h could result in exceeding the maximum inter-dynode voltage rating, since the capacitors will initially appear as short circuits, so V_h will be spread over fewer dynodes.

To obtain good collection of electrons from the cathode, the $K-D_1$ voltage is often made larger than between other dynodes, and sometimes kept constant when the overall voltage V_h is varied to control the gain. This may be achieved by means of zener diodes which replace the resistor R_1. The zeners should be chosen to operate satisfactorily at the lowest chain current (zener impedance increases rapidly at low currents), and be shunted with a capacitor to reduce zener noise (Sec. 7.10).

There is a maximum allowable cathode current ($\approx 10^{-9}$ A) usually set by the significant resistivity of semitransparent cathodes. If the photocathode is cooled, allowance should be made for the substantial increase of resistivity as the temperature is lowered. Solid photocathodes are not limited in this way [A1]. A maximum anode current is set by the allowable anode dissipation $(V_{dm} - V_a)I_a$. At large I_a there will also be effects due to space charge around the anode, leading to non-linearity. The correspondingly large chain current I_b means larger power dissipation in the resistors with consequent instability in their value, and possibly heating of the tube if they are adjacent to it. Space-charge effects can be counteracted by a progressive increase of inter-dynode voltage towards the anode. For general applications the maximum I_a will be quite small, say of the order of 10 µA or less. This may appear rather low, but it may be compared with the weakest detectable signals of say 1 photoelectron/s, for which $I_a \approx 10^{-13}$ A. Even weaker signals may be detected using photon counting as described later.

Since free electrons are moving between dynodes, they are susceptible to the effects of external magnetic fields. The direction of the field relative to the electron paths is important, and focused tubes are significantly more affected than unfocused types. In some applications, an external magnetic field is used to control the effective area of the photocathode [E1, R1, B1]. The effect of magnetic fields can be largely eliminated by means of cylindrical mu-metal shields surrounding the tube. It is important that these shields, and any other conducting material close to or touching the envelope, be at or near cathode potential. They may be connected to the cathode via a high resistance (e.g., 10 MΩ) to minimize the hazard if accidentally touched. Even insulating supports should be of the highest quality, to limit leakage currents to the lowest possible value at the high voltages involved. High voltages between electrodes inside and an earthed screen can cause field emission internally, with consequent increase of dark current and noise. An additional subtle effect is the leakage of current through the glass envelope, which can have a deleterious effect on the glass (ion migration) and can damage the tube [A1].

As far as the output is concerned, the photomultiplier acts as a current source, i.e., the output current is independent of the anode voltage, so long as $V_a - V_{dm}$ is greater than a certain value—usually a few tens of volts. If used in a current output mode, e.g., with a low impedance galvanometer, or a current-to-voltage transimpedance amplifier (Figs. 2.5.8 and 9.2.4), there is no difficulty. If the output current is passed through a resistor and the resulting voltage measured, then the output voltage will reduce $V_a - V_{dm}$, so there is a limit to V_a before linearity is affected.

The wavelength response of the photomultiplier depends on the material and type of photocathode. Many different materials are available, the response of some of the most important being shown in Fig. 9.4.2.

The long wavelength (low frequency v or low photon energy) response is fixed by the work function of the photocathode, while the short wavelength response is controlled primarily by the transmission of the window materials. The sensitivity of the response may be given in radiant terms $E(\lambda)$ in A/W at a particular wavelength λ, or as a quantum efficiency $\eta(\lambda)$. The latter is the ratio of the number of emitted photoelectrons to the number of incident photons, and is generally given as a percentage. The energy of a photon is given by $hv = hc/\lambda$, where h is Planck's constant and c the velocity of light. The relationship between E and λ is then given by (q = electronic charge):

$$E = \frac{\eta \lambda q}{hc} = \frac{\eta \lambda \cdot 10^6}{1 \cdot 24} \text{ A/W} \qquad (9.4.4)$$

Peak quantum efficiencies are about 30 per cent, i.e., only 1 in 3 photons is effective, at best. This corresponds to a radiant sensitivity $E=96$ mA/W at 400 nm. Photometric sensitivity is of little use, and the practice of some manufacturers of only giving this is to be deprecated. Most of the longer established photocathodes contain caesium, and if the temperature exceeds about 60°C this will be evaporated, with serious effects on operation. For higher temperature operation up to about 150°C the bialkali Na–K–Sb type may be used.

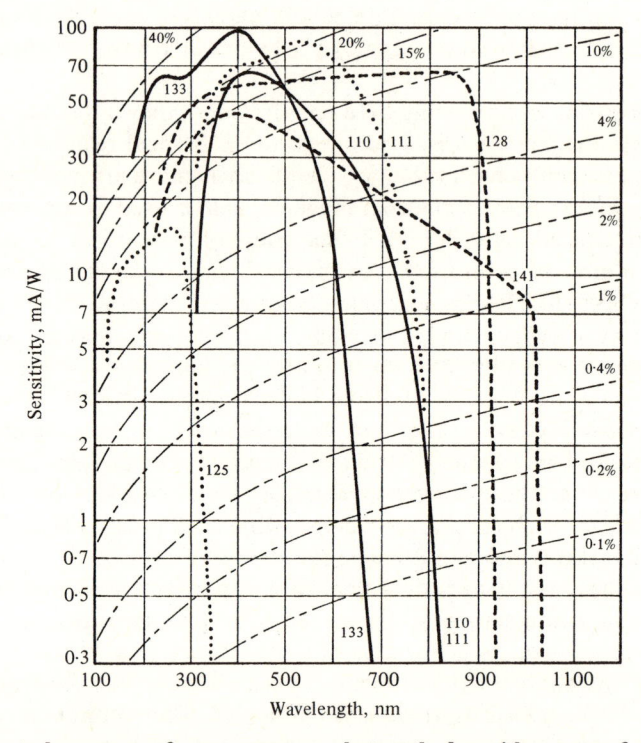

Fig. 9.4.2 **Spectral response of some common photocathodes with curves of constant quantum efficiency (125 = CsTe, 133 = bialkali, 110 = S20, 111 = multialkali, 128 = GaAs, 141 = GaInAs) (Adapted with permission of RCA Solid State Division)**

When the photomultiplier is in complete darkness there will still be some anode current. This is called dark current and arises from several sources: radioactivity in the glass envelope, field emission from sharp points on electrodes, cosmic rays [u1] and, most importantly, thermionic emission from the photocathode [g1, w1, A1]. The latter follows Richardson's law approximately, giving an exponential dependence of emission on temperature. Thus, by cooling the photocathode, the dark current may be reduced substantially. It is generally found that cooling below about $-20°C$ produces little further improvement [s1, m1, w1, A1, D1].

After exposure to light (even when no voltage is applied) there is, in some cases, a long delay of hours or days before the dark current settles to its minimum value. The time delay depends on the particular tube and is sometimes quite short [o1]. There are several considerations in cooling photomultipliers. The resistivity of the photocathode increases so that lower photocurrents can be drawn without voltage drops across the cathode. Cooling should be gradual so as not to stress the envelope thermally, and possibly cause fracture. The condensation of water on the tube and pins must be avoided as this can cause electrical leakage, and stop light from reaching the photocathode. In the pulse counting technique, described later, the effects of leakage are much reduced [O1].

Dark current in itself is not necessarily a limitation on measuring small signals since it can, in principle, be compensated for. What is vital is the fluctuations in it, and other sources of noise, that cannot be compensated for. Though there are several sources of noise, we will concern ourselves, here, only with the fundamental rather than the technical, e.g., poor vacuum. In practice, there will be an optimum overall voltage, V_h, for best signal-to-noise ratio above which the noise will increase faster than the signal [n2]. This is not necessarily the best operating voltage, however, since the performance of any subsequent circuits must be considered, as was done for the avalanche photodiode (Sec. 9.2). As we shall see below, the photomultiplier is a very good low noise wide band amplifier indeed, and its gain should be used if possible rather than adding an external amplifier.

There are two fundamental sources of noise:

(i) The statistical probability of emission of a photoelectron for a constant incident photon flux.
(ii) The statistical fluctuation of secondary emission averaged over the number of dynodes.

We can consider the noise with the photomultiplier operating in two regimes. Firstly, with low intensity light when the output pulses, due to individual photoelectrons from the photocathode, may be measured. Secondly, at higher intensity when the pulses cannot be resolved and the output, effectively, is a continuous current. The two viewpoints should lead to the same result, since the physics of the device is not altered, but they do indicate ways in which noise may be reduced or discriminated against and hence the signal-to-noise ratio improved. The incident light consists of individual photons arriving at random. There is a small correlation effect in thermal light which we can neglect, though it is important in some special applications [W1, X1, Y1, Z1, a2]. The statistical properties of light fields is an area of considerable interest, but cannot be further considered here [D2, E2, F2, A2, Z1, b2, c2, d2].

The randomness of the photons arriving constitutes noise, which may be called noise-in-signal. In considering other situations or devices, the noisiness of the signal was excluded since it was not a fundamental part of the signal. However, there is inherent noise in light that cannot be avoided—the best stabilized light source will still exhibit it. It is especially significant at low light levels, where the photomultiplier has its particular advantage over other optical detectors. The noise-in-signal is not significant at lower frequencies because of the relative energy of the photons or quanta. For example, 1 photon/s in the visible ($\lambda=400$ nm) is equivalent to 5×10^{-19} W. The same power, minute as it is, at a radio frequency of 750 kHz ($\lambda=400$ m) represents 10^9 photons/s!

As the photons arrive randomly they will obey Poisson statistics, so that, if the average number of photons arriving in a time interval τ is $\langle n_p \rangle$, then the variance is given by:

$$\sigma_p^2 = \langle n_p \rangle = I_p \tau \qquad (9.4.5)$$

where I_p is the average photon arrival rate. The signal-to-noise ratio for the photon beam is thus:

$$\text{SNR}_p = \frac{\langle n_p \rangle}{\sigma_p} = \langle n_p \rangle^{1/2} = (I_p \tau)^{1/2} \qquad (9.4.6)$$

so that the SNR increases as the square root of the intensity and the observation time. These photons now interact with the photocathode to produce photoelectrons. The probability that a photon will produce a photoelectron is the quantum efficiency, η, and is less than unity. The probability that no electron is emitted is then $(1-\eta)$. These probabilities also include the effects of reflection at the various interfaces. To determine the effect of these probabilities and those of the subsequent dynode multiplication process, it is most convenient to use the properties of probability generating functions. However, this would take us too far out of our way and reference should be made elsewhere [13]. Here we will only quote some of the results [A1, S1].

First consider a regular stream of incident photons (i.e., no noise so SNR $= \infty$), then the number N of photons reaching the photocathode in any interval τ does not fluctuate. Because of the statistical property of η the resulting number of photoelectrons N_e will fluctuate, and the variance is found to be:

$$\sigma_e^2 = N\eta(1-\eta) \qquad (9.4.7)$$

Since $\langle N_e \rangle = \langle N\eta \rangle$ then:

$$\text{SNR}_e = \frac{\langle N_e \rangle}{\sigma_e} = \frac{N\eta}{[N\eta(1-\eta)]^{1/2}} = \left[\frac{N\eta}{(1-\eta)}\right]^{1/2} \qquad (9.4.8)$$

i.e., for quantum efficiencies $\eta < 1$ the SNR of any incident signal, assumed to be infinite here, will be reduced by photoelectric detection. Now consider the combination of noisy photon signal and photoemission probability, where in a similar manner it can be shown that:

$$\sigma_{pe}^2 = \eta \langle n_p \rangle \qquad (9.4.9)$$

$$\text{SNR}_{pe} = [\eta \langle n_p \rangle]^{1/2} \qquad (9.4.10)$$

Thus, even the best quantum efficiency $\eta \doteq 0.3$ reduces the input SNR to about 55 per cent.

The statistical nature of the dynode multiplication process causes further deterioration in the SNR. The noise contribution can be kept quite small if the secondary electron multiplication factor is large enough. For the output signal at the anode it is found that for m stages of multiplication:

$$\sigma_a^2 = \eta \langle n_p \rangle \delta^{2m} \left[\frac{\delta}{\delta-1}\right] \doteq \eta \langle n_p \rangle \delta^{2m} \quad (\text{for } \delta \gg 1) \qquad (9.4.11)$$

$$\text{SNR}_a = \left[\eta \langle n_p \rangle \frac{\delta-1}{\delta}\right] \qquad (9.4.12)$$

Comparing Eq. (9.4.12) with Eq. (9.4.10) it is seen that if $\delta \gg 1$ then $\text{SNR}_a = \text{SNR}_{pe}$, and the multiplication process is effectively noiseless. The performance of the first dynode is most important, subsequent dynode noise contributions being progressively less important. For standard antimony–caesium dynodes, $\delta \doteq 4$ for voltages around 100 V, which would degrade SNR_a to about 75 per cent of SNR_{pe}. Recently introduced semiconductor dynodes [A1, g2] have $\delta \doteq 40$ at rather higher voltages around 600 V, in which case the multiplication noise contribution would be insignificant.

These results can be considered from the completely analagous view of shot noise in the various currents. The equivalent bandwidth for an observing time, τ, is $1/(2\,\Delta f)$, (Sec. 1.8(b)) so that Eqs. (9.4.6) and (9.4.10) become:

$$SNR_p = \left[\frac{I_p}{2\,\Delta f}\right]^{1/2} \quad (9.4.13)$$

$$SNR_{pe} = \left[\frac{\eta I_p}{2\,\Delta f}\right]^{1/2} = \left[\frac{I_{pe}}{2q\,\Delta f}\right]^{1/2} \quad (9.4.14)$$

where I_{pe} is the current from the photocathode, and q the electronic charge. If we consider I_{pe} the *signal* so that $SNR_{pe} = I_{pe}/I_{Npe}$ then Eq. (9.4.14) gives, for the shot noise I_{Npe}; Sec. 1.8(b):

$$I_{Npe}^2 = 2qI_{pe}\,\Delta f = 2q^2\eta I_p\,\Delta f \quad (9.4.15)$$

The anode noise current, I_{Na}, in the approximate case $\delta \gg 1$ is:

$$I_{Na}^2 = 2qI_{pe}\,\Delta f\,\delta^{2m} = 2q^2\eta I_p \quad (9.4.16)$$

and
$$I_a = I_{pe}\,\delta^m = q\eta I_p\,\delta^m \quad (9.4.17)$$

At the anode there will be a load resistor, R_a, which will contribute Johnson noise I_{NRa} (Sec. 1.8(a)) and possibly an amplifier producing additional noise (Secs. 1.8(d) and 4.1). Considering the simpler case of no amplifier, then from Eqs. (9.4.16), (9.4.17) and (1.8.1):

$$SNR_a = \frac{I_a}{I_{Na} + I_{NRa}} = \frac{q\eta I_p\,\delta^m}{[2q^2\eta I_p\,\delta^{2m}\,\Delta f + (4kT\Delta f)/R_a]^{1/2}} \quad (9.4.18)$$

To maintain the best SNR, the photomultiplier noise should be substantially larger than the noise of the following circuits. From Eq. (9.4.18) this requires:

$$2q^2\eta I_p\,\delta^{2m}\,\Delta f \gg 4kT\Delta f/R_a$$

so
$$\delta^{2m} \gg \frac{0\cdot 1}{2q\eta I_p R_a}, \quad \text{or} \quad \delta^m \gg \frac{0\cdot 1}{2I_a R_a}\left(\frac{4kT}{q} = 0\cdot 1 \text{ at } 300\text{ K}\right) \quad (9.4.19)$$

Including dynode multiplication and other extra noise sources may increase the gain requirement significantly. If condition (9.4.19) is fulfilled, then $SNR_a \doteq SNR_{pe}$, and since the bandwidth will be given by $\Delta f = 1/4R_a C_a$, where C_a is the shunt capacity at the anode, then:

$$SNR_a(\text{max}) = (2\eta I_p R_a C_a)^{1/2} \quad (9.4.20)$$

The gain of a photomultiplier can be high enough (10^6 to 10^8) so that single photoelectrons can produce an easily detectable signal at the anode. This makes possible an alternative method of measurement—the individual output pulses can be counted rather than measuring the averaged output. This pulse counting technique has become very popular and is capable of better SNR than other techniques [O1,

Q1, I1, z1, E1, F1, G1, H1, J1, n1, T1, h1]. There has been some controversy over this claim but it is now well established. There are two basic reasons for the advantage, one practical and one fundamental. The pulses at the anode can be divided into four groups according to their origin:

(i) Photoelectrons from the photocathode.
(ii) Thermionic electrons from the photocathode.
(iii) Pulses from other sources in the photomultiplier that are not amplified by the full gain.
(iv) Large pulses due to high energy sources such as cosmic rays or radioactive nuclei.

By setting two discriminator levels it is possible to eliminate both very small and very large pulses, i.e., primarily (iii) and (iv), and count only those in between, i.e., mainly (i) and (ii). This gives an improvement in the practical SNR rather than the inherent SNR discussed above. In some cases it has been found that, essentially, all the noise comes from the photocathode so that no improvement can be realized by using discriminators [O1]. However, by counting pulses the effect of pulse amplitude variation (i.e., multiplication noise) is eliminated so that the inherent SNR is improved.

Though a somewhat more complex technique than simple d.c. detection (but not than lock-in detection, Sec. 10.2), pulse counting has other attractions. It largely removes the effects of overall gain instability of the system, and it provides information immediately in digital form which can be stored indefinitely or be used directly for digital data processing. A number of variations have been used, e.g., synchronous single photon counting [F1], improved light collection and photocathode area limiting [E1], and measurement of the pulse height distribution [p1]. An alternative technique for very low intensities is to measure the noise itself [j2], but this is not as good as photon counting [H1].

In photon counting, consideration should be given to the optimum times of signal and noise measurement [O1, F1, e3, m3, t3, u3] and to the maximum allowable count rate. If the SNR$=r_S/r_N$, where r is the count rate, then for minimum relative variance the signal should be counted for a fraction α of the time, where:

$$\alpha = 1 + \frac{r_N}{r_S} - \frac{r_N}{r_S}\left(1 + \frac{r_S}{r_N}\right)^{1/2} \qquad (9.4.21)$$

the noise only being counted for the fraction $(1-\alpha)$. Note that r_S is the count rate due to the signal alone—when light is incident the count rate will be $r_S + r_N$. Values for α for various SNR are given in Table 9.4.1.

As a result of the random nature of the pulses they will sometimes occur so close together that, because of the finite resolution time of the system, they cannot be differentiated. Then one count will be registered instead of two. This resolution limit may be due to the dead time of a discriminator, the maximum counting rate of a scaler, or the width of the photomultiplier output pulse. If the resolution time is τ_d, and the true count rate r_t, then the observed count rate r_{ob} is given by [K2, e3, M3]:

$$r_{ob} = r_t/(1 + \tau_d r_t) \qquad (9.4.22)$$

For example, with $\tau_d = 1$ μs and $r_{ob} = 10^5$ counts/s, $r_t = 1.11 \times 10^5$ counts/s, an error of 11 per cent. On the other hand if $\tau_d = 10$ ns, $r_t = 1.001 \times 10^5$, an error of only

0·1 per cent. The limiting factor will be the performance of the photomultiplier itself. In this respect the focused types are superior, in that the transit-time spread is less than for unfocused types. The performance will depend on the details of particular tubes and overall voltages, but rough values are given in Table 9.4.2.

Table 9.4.1 Signal-to-noise counting time ratio for required signal-to-noise ratio

SNR = r_S/r_N	α
0	0·50
0·1	0·51
0·2	0·53
1	0·59
2	0·63
5	0·71
10	0·77
50	0·88
100	0·91
1000	0·97

Table 9.4.2 Photomultiplier time characteristics

	Focused	Venetian blind	Small focused	Channeltron
Transit time, ns	30	50	5	
Transit time spread (FWHM), ns	3	20	4	10
Risetime 10 to 90 per cent, ns	1	10	2	7

FWHM—full-width at half maximum

For fast time applications the design of the dynode chain will generally be different from that for d.c. operation, and the output circuit must be appropriate. This means minimum shunt capacity C_p, low load resistance R_L, and matching of output cables if used (Sec. 1.5). The low impedance of the load requires large output currents to obtain useful signals, which in turn determines the dynode chain and bypass capacitors [r2, s2, t2, v2, G2, w2, u2, S2].

Mention should also be made of continuous strip photomultipliers which have distributed rather than discrete dynodes [M2, N2, P2, Q2, R2]. These are generally open rather than enclosed in a vacuum envelope, since they are primarily used in the vacuum ultraviolet region below about 150 nm, and for particle detection. The commonest type is the channeltron, which consists of a thin glass tube of small diameter with the inside wall coated with a resistive conducting material. It is usually curled up to avoid ion feedback. Applying a high voltage between the ends produces a continuous voltage gradient along the tube. Photons or particles, entering the negative end, produce photoelectrons that then zig-zag down the tube, producing secondary electron multiplication each time they strike the wall. The number of multiplications is unpredictable but, by operating in the *pulse saturated mode* [O2, t1], good performance is obtained. Enclosing the channeltron within a vacuum envelope with a conventional photocathode, produces a small and convenient photomultiplier [t1, L2]. Because of the small *dynode chain* current, the average output current is considerably less than usually used for discrete dynode tubes. However, they are useful for photon counting, though the maximum counting rate will be lower.

9.5 Lamps and light-emitting diodes

The development of optoelectronics has been controlled largely by the types of light source available. Before the discovery of light emitting diodes (LED) the only conveniently available light sources were tungsten and gas discharge lamps. Each source has its particular advantages. These together with some basic operating considerations, will be outlined here.

9.5(a) *Tungsten lamps*

Tungsten lamps are easy to use, are available in a very wide range of physical sizes and power ratings, and produce a broad continuum spectral output. The disadvantages are a limited frequency response due to the long thermal time constant of the filament, a limited lifetime and, often, a rather fragile filament. They also cause large current surges when switched on, since the filament has substantially lower resistance when cold than under normal operating conditions.

A number of useful operating relationships have been found for tungsten lamps. If V_N and I_N are the nominal operating voltage and current, then the current I_B at some other voltage V_B is given by:

$$I_B = \left(\frac{V_B}{V_N}\right)^{0.55} I_N \tag{9.5.1}$$

Similarly, the luminous light output L_B is given by:

$$L_B = \left(\frac{V_B}{V_N}\right)^{3.5} L_N \tag{9.5.2}$$

and the lifetime of a lamp by:

$$T_B = \left(\frac{V_N}{V_B}\right)^{12} T_N \tag{9.5.3}$$

Other effects, such as repeated switching and vibration, will also reduce lifetime. These relationships are illustrated in Fig. 9.5.1.

Tungsten lamps radiate, to a good approximation, like a black-body (Sec. 9.1), but at a temperature slightly lower than their actual temperature. The equivalent black-body temperature is called the colour temperature. This refers, primarily, to the visible region of the spectrum, the spectral fit deteriorating in the ultraviolet and infrared regions. Black-body distributions are shown in Fig. 9.1.2. The small proportion of the emission that is visually effective and the advantage of silicon and germanium detectors is evident from Fig. 9.1.3.

The on to off resistance ratio for a tungsten filament is about 12. Thus, when the voltage is initially applied there will be a large current surge lasting for about 10 ms (Fig. 9.5.2).

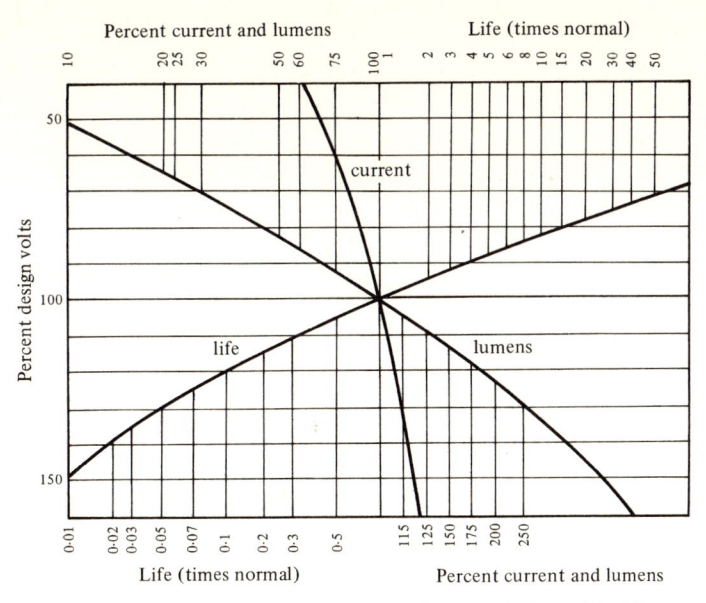

Fig. 9.5.1 Variation of tungsten lamp characteristics with voltage

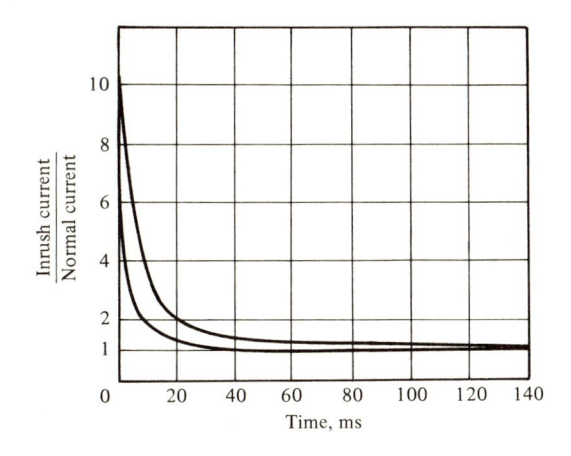

Fig. 9.5.2 Inrush current for cold tungsten lamps

This surge must be borne in mind when designing power supplies, and in some cases will preclude the use of certain types of regulated supply (Sec. 7.6). In some applications it is possible to reduce this surge by running a fraction of the normal operating current through the lamp continuously, so as to give increased resistance but with negligible light output. The great sensitivity of the light output to applied voltage, Eq. (9.5.2), suggests that it would be more effective to monitor the light output directly for the stabilization feedback loop rather than regulate the voltage supply.

9.5(b) *Light-emitting diodes*

Light-emitting diodes, in contrast to tungsten lamps, have narrow band spectral emission, very fast response, are robust mechanically, and have very long lifetime [g1, A1, f1, t1, B1]. They are generally low power devices though some types can operate at substantial peak pulsed power. Laser diodes, emitting coherent radiation are also available [d1, C1, E1, r1, s1].

The electrical characteristics of LED's are similar to normal semiconductor diodes but the forward cut-in voltages will depend on the type of material used. Typical characteristics are shown in Fig. 9.5.3. The curves are only approximate as there are many variations in material composition and doping, with consequent change in the characteristics.

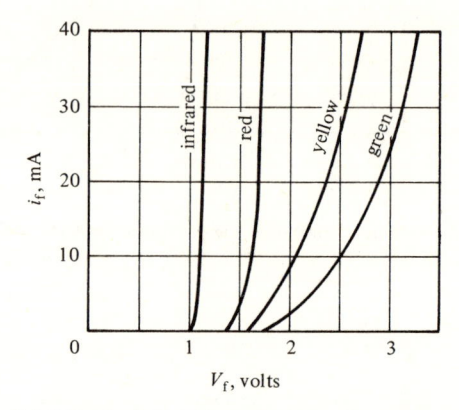

Fig. 9.5.3 Typical *V–I* characteristics for various LED's

Forward current is limited by power dissipation, but high peak currents may be used with an appropriate duty cycle. Up to some limiting current the light output increases slightly faster than linearly, an approximate relationship being, see Eq. (9.5.2):

$$\frac{L_B}{L_N} = \left(\frac{I_B}{I_N}\right)^n \quad \text{where } n \approx 1\cdot3 \tag{9.5.4}$$

This allows higher intensities to be obtained for the same average power dissipation by pulsing the current [A1]. The absolute efficiency (ratio of power in, to light power out) of LED's is low—one per cent or less for visible emitters, but increasing to about 10 per cent for infrared emitters. The spectral distributions for several types of LED are shown in Fig. 9.5.4. This shows also the good matching of the emissions to the photoresponse of silicon (compare Fig. 9.1.3). It is good for the infrared emitter which, with its higher efficiency, makes it the choice for many optocoupler applications (Sec. 9.6), where actual visibility is of no consequence. Where visibility is important the response of the eye is particularly significant, as may be seen from Figs. 9.1.1 and 9.5.4. Even though the absolute efficiency of a green LED is very much less than a red, the response of the eye makes the luminous efficiency quite comparable.

The dynamic resistance, r_e (Sec. 1.9(a)), of LED's is low and similar to silicon diodes. (Note that m in Eq. (1.9.3) depends on the diode material.) Over the normal

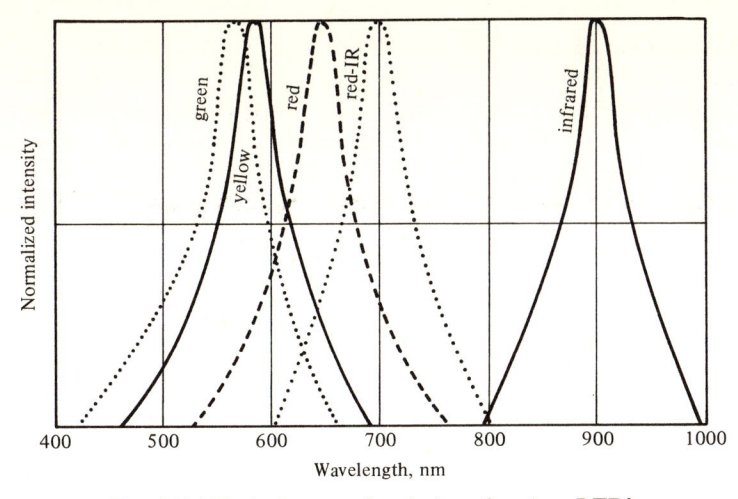

Fig. 9.5.4 Typical spectral emission of various LED's

operating range, r_e falls in the range 0·1 to 10 ohm. These low values together with the variation in cut-in voltage, make them useful as low voltage zeners; Sec. 7.10(a). Response times for LED's vary from about 10 ns rise and fall times to several hundred nanoseconds, with junction capacities of about 100 pF. Fast subnanosecond devices are also available [11]. The reverse breakdown voltage is rather low, usually between 3 and 6 volt, so care must be taken not to exceed this. If there is any possibility of this occurring, a reverse connected silicon diode should be connected in parallel. This would apply, for example, when driving the LED from an a.c. source. Polarity is commonly indicated by a small flat on the side of the LED adjacent to the cathode, by different shaped leads, or by making one lead longer than the other. The latter practice appears undesirable as the leads are often cut, when the identification is lost.

LED's can be driven in many ways, but in general a current rather than a voltage source is preferable. Light output is approximately proportional to current, whereas for a voltage source variations in diodes or temperature changes can result in very large changes in current. The temperature coefficient of LED's is about -2 mV/°C, rather similar to silicon diodes. For small indicator LED's the current required may be estimated from the following subjective values [b1]. At 0·4 mA the light is definitely seen, while at 1 mA it is easily seen. The attention of a casual observer will be attracted at 5 mA, and at 10 mA it is easily seen from a distance of 6 m.

For on–off applications logic gates make convenient LED drivers. The LED with series resistor may be connected either to V_+ or to ground. For the former the gate output voltage in the low state is $\leqslant 0\cdot4$ volts, so $(V_+ - 0\cdot4)$ volts is available. Basic transistor–transistor logic (TTL) gates can sink 16 mA, which is more than enough for LED indicators. With the LED connected to ground, the output voltage in the high state is a minimum of 2·7 V only, so less voltage will be available. Thus, a lower series resistor must be used with the consequent increase in sensitivity to temperature or device variations. Connection to V_+ is to be preferred.

9.5(c) *Gas discharge lamps*

Small gas discharge lamps, commonly called neons, are cold-cathode devices in which the gas is ionized at high voltage. Recombination of the neon ion produces a red glow around the negative electrode. In the case of an a.c. voltage, both electrodes will glow as they will be alternately negative. The initial breakdown voltage is substantially higher than the operating voltage, depending on type of gas, pressure, and electrode spacing. In the operating region a gas discharge has a constant voltage characteristic as shown in Fig. 9.5.5.

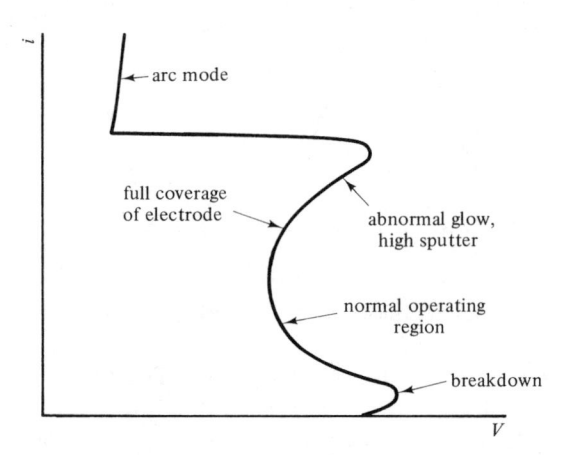

Fig. 9.5.5 Characteristics of a gas discharge

For ordinary indicator types, voltages are somewhat variable as a result of manufacturing tolerances, but ignition voltages are around 80 V and running about 60 V d.c. For a.c. supplies they are usually a little lower. To accommodate the change in voltage after ignition and between devices, it is imperative that a series resistor be used. Normal running currents are ≈ 0.5 mA, which gives a lifetime in excess of 50 kilohours. High brightness types run at ≈ 2 mA, have higher voltages, and a much reduced lifetime. Failure is not catastrophic (unless the series resistor is omitted), light output reducing due to electrode sputtering on the walls, gas absorption, and increase of voltage. If the current is too low the discharge becomes unstable and the lamp flickers. Ionization time depends on applied voltage. If this substantially exceeds the nominal breakdown voltage, the time will be of the order of 10 µs. When switched off there will be a deionization time of the same order. These times will largely control the range of modulation frequency possible. One application for modulated neons is in photochoppers, used for the modulation of low-level signals [C1, D1, E1] (Fig. 4.7.7).

The visible output from neons is between 520 nm and 750 nm, with some emission in the infrared around 850 nm. Green *neons* are also available, the green emission being obtained from a coating of fluorescent material excited by the gas discharge. The gas filling in these is different, and results in increased breakdown and running voltages.

It should be noted that if a neon is operated on a.c. with very long leads, the capacity between leads, or a lead and earth, can allow enough current to flow to light the neon. This may be overcome by connecting a suitable resistor, in parallel with the neon, to bypass this leakage current. The two resistors, now in series, must be proportioned so that, in normal operation, the striking voltage can be reached.

Glow diodes are similar to the ordinary neon, but are made to close electrical tolerances, and to operate at a range of voltages from 50 to 180 V. At the design current, the voltages are specified to ± 1 V. These may be used as voltage regulators or references, and have temperature coefficients of -2 to -10 mV/°C.

For high intensity sources, arc lamps are generally used. The common types are mercury and xenon arcs, which are available with power ratings up to about 10 kW. They are usually enclosed in quartz envelopes, because of the high operating temperatures, which allows the emission of considerable ultraviolet light. This can affect eyes, cause serious *sunburn*, and produce ozone, which is unhealthy except in very low concentrations. The quartz should be cleaned with solvent and not handled, as this can result in deterioration of the quartz. The high power dissipation causes a rise in the internal gas pressure to many atmospheres, so that mechanical protection against possible explosion is essential.

Low pressure lamps have primarily line emission spectra characteristic of the gas filling. As the pressure is raised, the lines are broadened and the continuum emission increases. In high or super-high pressure lamps, the emission is primarily a continuum though the prominent lines are still much in evidence. Thus, it is not possible to give a typical spectrum. The manufacturer's literature should be consulted [y1].

The electrical characteristics of arc lamps present a number of problems with regard to starting and running conditions. To produce the initial breakdown of the electrode gap, very high voltages of the order of 10 to 40 kV are required. This is usually provided by a pulse transformer connected in series with the lamp, and necessitates very careful consideration of the protection of other power supply components. The running voltage, on the other hand, will be a few tens of volts with an approximately constant voltage characteristic in the region of the operating current (Fig. 9.5.5). The operating voltage depends on pressure, and hence on temperature of the gas, and power input, so that operating conditions will change as the lamp warms up. Also, at low currents, the discharge has a negative resistance characteristic, so this region is unstable. Provision, therefore, must be made to pass through this region to reach stable operation. This is commonly achieved by using a current supply, for example a high voltage with a suitable series resistance. As currents are large, in the range 10 to 100 A, this means considerable power dissipation in power supply and lamp. Direct blowing for cooling is undesirable, and operating temperature ranges should be observed. Orientation of the lamp, usually vertical, is also important for arc stability and lamp lifetime. Useful application information is given in [w1, s1, t1, e1] and some power supply designs in [g1, h1, i1, v1, j1, a1]. It is sometimes necessary to pulse or modulate arc lamps for kinetic investigations, or to obtain substantially increased intensities. Techniques are described in [l1, n1, c1, d1, o1] and some limitations in [f1].

9.6 Optoelectronic couplers

One of the most useful developments in the optoelectronic field is the photon coupled isolator [R1, S1, a1, T1, j1, p1, U1]. This consists basically of a LED emitter and a photodetector, usually a phototransistor, with close optical coupling but electrical isolation; Fig. 9.6.1.

Photon coupling has two outstanding properties: electrical isolation up to very high voltages, and the unilateral nature of the signal transfer. In the former property it is like a transformer, but it has the advantage of operating down to zero frequency.

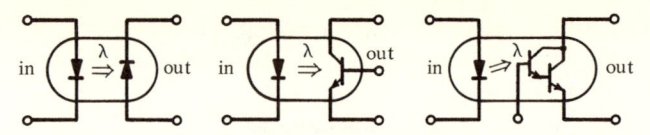

Fig. 9.6.1 Basic photocouplers

The unilateral signal transfer arises since the photodetector does not emit, so there can be no return signal. There will be a small capacity between emitter and receiver (usually <1 pF in practical devices) which does provide a return path, but in critical applications this can be eliminated by a grounded screen. Reduction by physical separation reduces the transfer efficiency, unless an efficient light-pipe or guide is used. The current transfer efficiency is the ratio of the photocurrent in the detector to the input current supplied to the light emitter. This ratio depends on the type of detector, being about 10^{-3} for a photodiode, 0·2 to 1 for a phototransistor, and 5 or more for a photodarlington. The values vary over quite a range for different devices of nominally the same class. The improvement of efficiency through the three classes is paralleled by a decrease in speed of operation.

There is a wide range of applications for optocouplers, e.g.:

(i) Transfer of signals between circuits at widely differing potentials.
(ii) Elimination of common ground bus between circuits, to remove ground loops and common-mode effects.
(iii) Unilateral transfer of signals to avoid reaction, as in coupling an oscillator to a variable load.
(iv) Driving multiple circuits from one source with no interaction between them.
(v) Provision of isolated current source using reverse biased receiver.

Examples of many of these applications are given in [c1, j1, e1, d1, f1, b1, k1, l1, n1, R1, V1]. The attractions of optical coupling has led to the development of many variations on the basic coupler. These include types with SCR and triac receivers [F1, V1], designs for mechanical interruption [S1, C1, D1] and reflective coupling [G1, S1, J1], and those with Schmitt trigger [t1, E1], or logic gate outputs [W1, H1, Q1, r1].

Two simple applications will be illustrated. Figure 9.6.2 shows a photo-SCR coupler used to trigger a higher rating SCR.

C_1 is charged from the a.c. input via R_1 and D_2, to provide a d.c. supply for SCR_1. When SCR_1 is triggered via the photon coupling, C_1 discharges into the gate of SCR_2 to fire it (Sec. 8.3). R_2 limits the current through SCR_1, and C_1 limits the dv/dt on SCR_1. Data and many other configurations for power control are given in [V1].

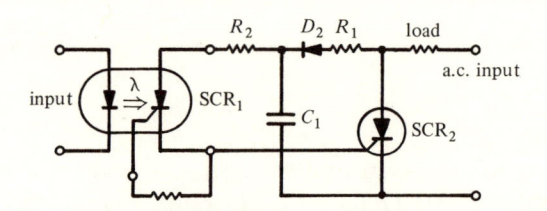

Fig. 9.6.2 Photo-SCR trigger circuit

In a coupler using a phototransistor receiver, the transistor may be used just as any ordinary transistor. For example, Fig. 9.6.3 shows a pick-off for a chopper disc used to modulate a light beam.

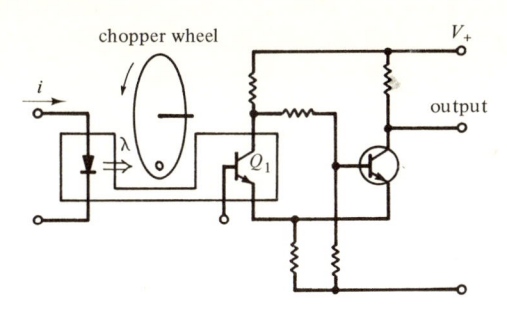

Fig. 9.6.3 Photocoupler timing pick-off

The phototransistor, Q_1, is connected as part of a Schmitt trigger circuit, Sec. 5.3(a), so that a square wave with fast edges is obtained for timing purposes, irrespective of the speed of rotation of the chopper wheel. This application is useful in certain fluorescence measurements, where it has the additional advantage that the infrared radiation from the LED will not contaminate the fluorescence emission at visible wavelengths [X1].

Couplers are normally capable of operation only up to about 100 kHz, being limited primarily by the large collector–base capacity of the phototransistor. This arises because of the base configuration necessary for good light collection. This capacity, together with the use of an open base for increased sensitivity, results in a large Miller effect (Sec. 1.6). Use of a base–emitter resistor increases speed but at the expense of reduced current transfer ratio [Y1]. A more effective technique is the separation of the photodiode and the transistor, as discussed in Sec. 9.2 [R1, d1]. Such a device [q1] can be used in two configurations, as shown in Fig. 9.6.4.

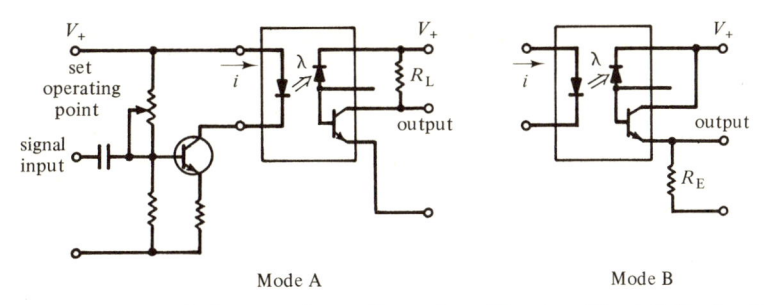

Fig. 9.6.4 High-speed photocoupler configurations (Courtesy Hewlett-Packard)

The driver circuit allows the d.c. quiescent operating point to be set so that linear operation for an a.c. signal is possible. For low load resistance ($R_L = R_E = 100$ ohm) mode A gives a bandwidth of about 3·5 MHz, and mode B about 1 MHz. Pulse rise and fall times in A are about 200 ns, with a delay time of 120 ns. The better performance of A relative to B is at first sight contrary to what one may expect, taking account of Miller feedback. The situation here differs from more usual configurations, in that the base is driven from a high impedance or current source, i.e., the reverse biased diode. This condition is analysed in detail in [A1, Secs. 4.12 and 4.13], where it is shown that the ratio of the 3 dB bandwidths is given by (using the nomenclature of [q1]):

$$\frac{\omega(A)}{\omega(B)} = \frac{1 + R_E \omega_T C_{BE}}{1 + R_L \omega_T C_{CB}} \qquad (9.6.1)$$

Thus, for equal load resistors, the ratio is dependent on the device capacities: $C_{BE} = 8$ pF, $C_{CB} = 0.6$ pF. C_{BE} includes the diode capacity $C_D = 7$ pF, so its position in the circuit is the controlling factor. In A, since the diode is a current source and is a.c. connected between base and emitter, there is negligible voltage change across C_D and, hence, it can be ignored, leaving only C_{CB}. In B there is a voltage change across C_D due to the voltage across R_E, so C_D has a substantial effect. Guessing a value of $\omega_T = 500$ MHz, gives a frequency ratio of about 3 which agrees with the measured characteristics [q1]. An alternative approach, for couplers using phototransistors, is to use an operational current-to-voltage converter (Fig. 2.5.8) which minimizes voltage changes and hence capacitive effects [B1, p. 63; Z1; a2]. Couplers using photodiodes can give even faster response but with transfer ratios of only about 10^{-3}, and so would generally require a suitable following amplifier [u1, s1, K1]. For cases where logic signals are to be transmitted, suitable amplifiers have been integrated into the coupler together with logic compatible output stages [r1, W1, t1, H1]. The fastest types can achieve data rates up to 20 M bits/s, with a delay of 60 ns, and so will cope with most applications.

Where linear operation is required it is usually necessary to use two matched couplers, one in the forward path and the other in a feedback loop to cancel the nonlinearities [B1, p. 65; k1; L1; M1]. If matching controls are included, matched couplers may not be necessary [I1].

In designing circuits to drive the emitters in optocouplers, the characteristics of the LED must be considered (Sec. 9.5). As in ordinary diodes the current increases very rapidly after the cut-in voltage is reached, so that they should be driven from a current rather than a voltage source. It should also be noted that the cut-in voltage is significantly greater than for silicon diodes, and varies with the LED *colour*. This is particularly important when low-voltage rails are being used as, for example, in logic systems.

9.7 Miscellaneous opto devices

There are a number of other optoelectronic devices which perform useful functions. Some of these are described briefly here.

9.7(a) *Voltage sensing LED*

These combine a voltage sensing circuit with a LED. When the applied voltage reaches the design value, the LED is switched on. There are only two terminals, so the switching point cannot be varied. Some hysteresis is included, so the on and off voltages will differ [v1, w1].

9.7(b) *Optically controlled oscillator*

One type produces an output frequency dependent on the incident light intensity [i1]. Another is a relaxation oscillator which can be inhibited by external illumination [h1].

9.7(c) *Light activated switch*

These devices give a switched output when the light input reaches a reference value [j1, k1, l1]. Where changes of light level rather than an absolute value are significant, a dynamic switch may be used [m1, o1]. In another type of switch a repetitive sampling technique is used, to allow operation over a very wide range of light threshold values [n1, o1, z1]. A relaxation oscillator provides a charging pulse to the capacity of a reverse biased photodiode. This charge decays at a rate dependent on the incident light intensity, and the voltage is examined by a comparator when the next oscillator pulse starts. The decision of the comparator as to whether the capacitor voltage has decayed below a reference level, is fed to a bistable output circuit. By altering the oscillator frequency, i.e., sampling earlier or later, a very wide range of input sensitivity can be covered.

9.7(d) *Integrating light detector*

Two reverse biased photodiodes are charged by an input pulse. One diode is screened from the light, and the charge on the other decays at a rate determined by the incident light. The voltage difference on the two diodes is monitored by a differential MOSFET amplifier. The overall differential arrangement gives good compensation for diode dark current and temperature effects [A1, z1]. This type of detector can be extended to arrays of diodes [p1]. With addition of line and bit scanning, these can be used for character or picture detection.

9.7(e) *Light activated thyristors*

These devices are the same as ordinary thyristors (Sec. 8.3) except that optically generated carriers are used to trigger them [d1, B1, x1, q1, r1, s1].

9.7(f) *Photodetector–power amplifier*

This comprises two separate sections, a high sensitivity darlington phototransistor detector and a complementary output power amplifier. Though primarily intended for on–off operation, it can be used for linear outputs with limited power ratings [t1, u1].

References section 9.1: Light measurements and units

a1 Palmer J M: Photocell Inputs Watts or Foof-candles; Design Electronics June 1970, 30, 33–34.
b1 Daughters G T: Characterization of Photoresponsive Junction Devices. The Determination of Luminous Efficiency of Black Bodies; Fairchild Application Note APP-47, 1962.

d1 Havens W H: Improve Optical Measurement Accuracy; Electronic Design 20 Dec. 1973, 92–94.
e1 Vann M A: Opto Conversion and Units; Electronic Components 7 Apr. 1972, 331–334.
f1 Sowan F A: Light Units in SI (Systeme International d'Unites); Mullard Tech. Comm. 10, Sep. 1968, 182–184.
g1 Barnes F A (Ed): Electro-Optics Handbook; RCA Technical Manual EOH-10, 1968.
h1 Betts D B: The Spectral Response of Radiation Thermopiles; J Phys. E Sci. Instrum. 42, 243–247, 1965.
i1 Stair R, Schneider W E, Waters W R, Jackson J K: Some Factors Affecting the Sensitivity and Spectral Response of Thermolectric (Radiometric) Detectors; Applied Optics 4, 703–710, 1965.
j1 Klein M V: Optics, Section 4.1 Radiometry and Photometry; Wiley 1970.
k1 Walsh J W T, Barnett W, Berry R G, Preston J S: Units and Standards of Light Maintained at the National Physical Laboratory, 1915–1960; Proc IEE 108A, 173–181, 1961.
l1 Merritt T P, Hall F F: Blackbody Radiation; Proc. IRE 47, 1435–1441, 1959.
m1 Bell E E: Radiometric Quantities, Symbols, and Units; Proc IRE 47, 1432–1434, 1959.
n1 — —: Nomenclature and Symbols for Radiometry and Photometry; J Opt. Soc. Amer. 57, 854, 1967.
o1 Sensors: Thermopile Detector C1; Sensors Inc. Technical Bulletin 10.
p1 — —: Will Clocks and Rulers Become Interchangeable?; Optical Spectra Apr. 1972, 17–18.
q1 Wunderman I: A Clarification of Spectral Characterization Units for Quantum Detectors and Emitters; Applied Optics 7, 25–28, 1968.
r1 Hewlett-Packard: Photometry of Red LEDs; Hewlett-Packard Application Note 945, Oct. 1973.
s1 Pivovonsky M, Nagel M: Tables of Blackbody Radiation Functions; Macmillan 1961.
t1 Nicodemus F E (Ed): Radiometry: Selected Reprints; American Institute of Physics, New York.
u1 Marette G: Vacuum Ultraviolet Absolute Radiometry Utilizing Total Blackbody Radiation; Applied Optics 15, 440–444, 1976.
v1 Smith R A, Jones F E, Chasmar R P: Detection and Measurement of Infrared Radiation; Oxford Univ. Press 1957.
w1 Hewlett-Packard: Optoelectronic Applications Seminar Handbook; Hewlett-Packard May 1974.
x1 Bliss J: Application of Phototransistors in Electro-Optic Systems; Motorola Application Note AN-508, 1969.
y1 Norris B (Ed): Semiconductor Circuit Design Vol. II, Section 3 Optoelectronics; Texas Instruments 1973.
z1 Deboo G J, Burrous C N: Integrated Circuits and Semiconductor Devices; Theory and Application; McGraw-Hill 1971.
A1 Phelan R J, Cook A R: Electrically Calibrated Pyroelectric Optical-Radiation Detector; Applied Optics 1, 2494–2500, 1973.
B1 Zaha M A: Shedding Some Needed Light on Optical Measurements; Electronics 6 Nov. 1972, 91–96.
C1 Nemhauser R I, Alexander G, Duda R: Radiometry and Photometry: Once over Lightly; Optical Spectra Apr. 1976, 30–34.

References section 9.2: Photodiodes and phototransistors

a1 Bliss J: Application of Phototransistors in Electro-Optic Systems; Motorola Application Note AN-508, 1969.
b1 McCartney M L: Feedback Amplifier Speeds Phototransistor's Response; Electronics 15 Mar. 1971, 77.
c1 Wendland P H: Solid State Combo Senses Light Well Enough to Vie with Tubes; Electronics 24 May 1971, 50–54.
d1 Biard J R, Shaufield W N: A Model of the Avalanche Photodiode; Texas Instruments Application Report M40, 1968.

e1 Bliss J: Theory and Characteristics of Phototransistors; Motorola Application Note AN-440, 1972.
f1 Hamstra R H, Wendland P: Noise and Frequency Response of Silicon Photodiode Operational Amplifier Combination; Applied Optics 11, 1539–1547, 1972.
g1 Nishida K, Nakajima M: Temperature Dependence and Stabilization of Avalanche Photodiodes; Rev. Sci. Instrum. 43, 1345–1350, 1972.
h1 Ameurlaine J, Coester J, Hofheimer H: Breakthrough in Detectors: Photovoltaic HgCdTe; Optical Spectra Oct. 1973, 27–32.
i1 Wendland P H: Silicon Photodiodes Come Into their Own; Optical Spectra Oct. 1973, 33–36.
j1 Daughters G T: Noise Behaviour of the 1N3734 Photodiode, and 2N986 and 2N2452 Phototransistors; Fairchild Application Note APP-46, 1962.
k1 Barelli A E: Improve Avalanche-Photodiode Design; Electronic Design 19 July 1973, 68–74.
l1 EG&G: SGD-100 and SGD-444 Photodiodes; EG&G Application Note 1967.
m1 Fisher R: PIN Diode Detectors for Astronomical Photometry; Applied Optics 7, 1079–1083, 1968.
n1 Texas Instruments: The Photo-Duo-Diode. Theory, Measurement of Parameters, and Operation; Texas Instruments Application Note.
o1 Smith B R: Introduction to the Fotofet and its Applications; Crystalonics Application Note ANF-8, Nov. 1965.
p1 Shipley M: Photofet Characteristics and Applications; Solid State Design Apr. 1964, and Siliconix.
q1 Hewlett-Packard: Threshold Detection of Visible and Infrared Radiation with PIN Photodiodes; Hewlett-Packard Application Note 915, 1967.
r1 EG&G: Silicon Photodiode Application Notes; EG&G Application Note D300B-1, 1973.
s1 EG&G: Silicon Photovoltaic Detectors and Detector/Amplifier Combinations; EG&G Data Sheet D3002A-1.
t1 Lucovsky G, Emmons R B: High Frequency Photodiodes; Applied Optics 4, 697–702, 1965.
u1 Johnson K M: High-Speed Photodiode Signal Enhancement at Avalanche Breakdown Voltage; IEEE Trans ED-12, 55–63, 1965.
v1 Kulczyk W K, Davis Q V: The Avalanche Photodiode as an Electronic Mixer in an Optical Receiver; IEEE Trans ED-19, 1181–1190, 1972.
w1 McIntyre R J: The Distribution of Gains in Uniformly Multiplying Avalanche Photodiodes: Theory; IEEE Trans ED-19, 703–713, 1972.
x1 Conradi J: The Distribution of Gains in Uniformly Multiplying Avalanche Photodiodes: Experimental; IEEE Trans ED-19, 713–718, 1972.
y1 Lehovec K, Seeley W G: Photoeffects in Junction Field Effect Transistors Under Strong Illumination; Solid-State Electronics 15, 1253–1259, 1972.
z1 EG&G: HA-100 Hybrid Operational Amplifier, HAD-130 Op Amp/Photodiode; EG&G Data Sheet HA-100, HA-130, 1968.
A1 Plessey: Integrating Light Detectors OPT1A/1B; Plessey Publication P.S. 1808.
B1 EG&G: Constant Current Operation of Avalanche Photodiodes; EG&G Application Note AV-102, 1968.
C1 EMI: Silicon Avalanche Photodiode Type S30500; EMI Data Sheet.
D1 EMI: Silicon Avalanche Photodiode Type S30501 (Double Ship S30500); EMI Data Sheet.
E1 Centronic: Silicon Photodiode with Integrated Amplifier, OSI-5; Twentieth Century Electronics Information Sheet.
F1 RCA: Photocells: Solid State Photosensitive Devices; RCA Manual CSS-800, 1964.
G1 Plessey: The Use and Applications of OPT1; Plessey Application Note, 1970.
H1 De La Moneda F H, Chenette E R, Van der Ziel A: Noise in Phototransistors; IEEE Trans ED-18, 340–346, 1971.
I1 Van Vliet K M: Noise Limitations in Solid State Photodetectors; Applied Optics 6, 1145–1169, 1967.

J1 EMI: Silicon Avalanche Photodiodes; EMI Application Note.
K1 Mathur D P, McIntyre R J, Webb P P: A New Germanium Photodiode with Extended Long-Wavelength Response; Applied Optics 9, 1842–1847, 1970.
L1 Tsacoyeares C, Levine M A: Electronic Enhancement of Photodetector Performance; Applied Optics 9, 2597–2598, 1970.
M1 Sharpless W M: Evaluation of a Specially Designed GaAs Schottky-Barrier Photodiode Using 6328A Radiation Modulated at 4GHz; Applied Optics 9, 489–494, 1970.
N1 McCall G H: High Speed Inexpensive Photodiode Assembly; Rev. Sci. Instrum. 43, 865–866, 1972.
O1 Ruegg H W: An Optimized Avalanche Photodiode; IEEE Trans ED-14, 239–251, 1967.
P1 Melchior H, Lynch W T: Signal and Noise Response of High Speed Germanium Avalanche Photodiodes; IEEE Trans ED-13, 829–838, 1966.
Q1 Rokos G H S: Optical Detection Using Photodiodes; Opto-Electronics 5, 351–366, 1973.
R1 Bracale M, Zarone G: Noise Considerations in Opto-Electronic Wideband Amplifiers; Opto-Electronics 2, 103–106, 1970.
S1 Lucas A D: Epitaxial Silicon Avalanche Photodiode; Opto-Electronics 6, 153–160, 1974.
T1 Raines J A: The Measurement of Multiplied Noise in Low Noise Silicon Avalanche Photodiodes, and its Effect on Achievable NEP; Services Elec. Res. Lab. Tech. J 21, No.1, Feb. 1971.
U1 Weckler G P: Operation of P-N Junction Photodetectors in a Photon Flux Integrating Mode; IEEE SC-2, 65–73, 1967.
V1 Instrument Technology: Ultra High Speed Photodiodes FD125, HSD50, HSD1850; Instrument Technology Data Sheet.
W1 Hewlett-Packard: HP PIN Photodiode; Hewlett-Packard Application Note 917, Oct. 1970.
X1 Chang J J: Frequency Response of PIN Avalanching Photodiodes; IEEE Trans ED-14, 139–145, 1967.
Y1 Jones R C: Phenomenological Description of the Response and Detecting Ability of Radiation Detectors; Proc IRE 47, 1495–1502, 1959.
Z1 EMI: Photodetector Unit (APD) Types C531–4; EMI Data Sheet.
a2 EMI: Bias Controller (APD) Type C511; EMI Data Sheet.
b2 EMI: Pre Amplifier/Amplifier Types C501, C502; EMI Data Sheet.
c2 Bell and Howell: Type 509 Self-Contained Optical Detectors; Bell and Howell Data Sheet, 1974.
d2 Mullard: Silicon Duo-Photo Diode BPY68/69; Mullard Data Sheet 1967.
e2 Diebold G, Santoro R: Differential Photodiode Detector for a Shock Tube Laser Schlieren System; Rev. Sci. Instrum. 45, 773–775, 1974.
f2 Dobratz B E, Farnsworth R P: Constant False Alarm Rate Bias Control for an Avalanche Photodiode Laser Receiver; Rev. Sci. Instrum. 41, 1191–1195, 1970.
g2 Havens W H: Measurement of Low Level Photodiode Noise Currents; Applied Optics 13, 2209–2211, 1974.
h2 Gosling W, Townsend W G, Watson J: Field-Effect Electronics, Chapter 15 The Photo-FET; Butterworths 1970.
i2 Fairchild: Photoamplifier; Electronic Eng. 44, Feb. 1972, 52–53.
j2 Graeme J G: Op Amp Boosts Phototransistor Speed; Electronic Design 2 Mar. 1972, 62.
k2 Texas Instruments: Silicon Avalanche Photodiode Module TIXL452; Texas Instruments Data Sheet Sep. 1974.
l2 Nordstrom R A, Meindl J D: The Field-Effect Modified Transistor: A High-Responsivity Photosensor; IEEE J SC-7, 411–417, 1972.
m2 Hall D N B, Aikers R S, Joyce R, McCurrin T W: Johnson Noise Limited Operation of Photovoltaic InSb Detectors; Applied Optics 14, 450–453, 1975.
n2 Fry P W: Silicon Photodiode Arrays; J Phys. E Sci. Instrum 8, 337–349, 1975.
o2 EG&G: Photodiode/Operational Amplifier HAD-1000A; EG&G Data Sheet D3007B-1, 1974.
p2 EG&G: PV-100A Photovoltaic Silicon Photodiode and HAV-1000PV Photodiode/Op-Amp; EG&G Data Sheet, 1972.

q2 Conradi J: Planar Germanium Photodiodes; Applied Optics 14, 1948–1952, 1975.
r2 Lynch W T: Elimination of the Guard Ring in Uniform Avalanche Photodiodes; IEEE Trans ED-15, 735–741, 1968.
s2 Connors W P: Lateral Photodetector Operating in the Fully Reverse-Biased Mode; IEEE Trans ED-18, 591–596, 1971.
t2 Hovel H J: Solar Cells. Willardson R K, Beer A C (Eds): Semiconductors and Semimetals Volume 11; Academic Press 1975.
u2 Slifkin M A, McGeary R: A Solid State Detector for a Modulation Excitation Spectrometer; J Phys. E Sci. Instrum. 9, 90–92, 1976.
v2 DeDomenico M, Sharpless W M, McNicol J J: High Speed Photodetection in Germanium and Silicon Cartridge Type Point-Contact Photodiodes; Applied Optics 4, 677–682, 1965.
w2 Anderson L K, McMurty B J: High Speed Photodetectors; Applied Optics 5, 1573–1587, 1966.
x2 Hewlett-Packard: Optoelectronic Applications Seminar Handbook; Hewlett-Packard May 1974.
y2 Millman J, Halkias C C: Electronic Devices and Circuits; McGraw-Hill 1967.
z2 Norris B (Ed): Semiconductor Circuit Design Vol. 11, Section 3 Optoelectronics; Texas Instruments 1973.
A2 Smith R A, Jones F E, Chasmar R P: Detection and Measurement of Infrared Radiation; Oxford Univ. Press 1957.
B2 Kneubuhl F: Diffraction Spectroscopy; Applied Optics 8, 505–519, 1969.
C2 Texas Instruments: The Optoelectronics Data Book; Texas Instruments 1972.
D2 Integrated Photomatrix: Analogue Detector Family IPL16; Integrated Photomatrix Data Sheet PX129, Aug. 1971.
E2 Wilson B L H: Incorporating Photocells in Integrated Circuits; Electronic Eng. 41, Nov. 1969, 32–34.
F2 Texas Instruments: Low-Noise High-Speed Transimpedance Amplifier TIXL151/2; Texas Instruments Data Sheet.
G2 Seib D H, Aukerman L W: Photodetectors for the 0.1 to 1.0μm Spectral Region; Adv. Electronics and Electron Physics (Marton L (Ed)), 34, 95–221, 1973.
H2 Deboo G J, Burrous C N: Integrated Circuits and Semiconductor Devices: Theory and Applications; McGraw-Hill 1971.
I2 Kessler J: Focus on Photodetectors; Electronic Design 15 Mar. 1976, 24–26, 28, 30, 32.
J2 Sahm W H (Ed): Optoelectronics Manual; General Electric 1976.
K2 Melchior H, Fisher M B, Arams F R: Photodetectors for Optical Communication Systems; Proc IEEE 58, 1466–1486, 1970.
L2 Beck G: Photodiode and Holder with 60ps Response Time; Rev. Sci. Instrum. 47, 849–853, 1976.

References section 9.3: Photoresistors

a1 Jeynes G F, Thomas G J: Street Lighting Controller Using a Photoconductive Cell; Mullard Tech. Comm. 7, 271–275, 1964.
b1 Clairex: Photoconductive Cell Application Design Handbook; Clairex Electronics 1970.
c1 Putley E H: Indium Antimonide Submillimeter Photoconductor Detectors; Applied Optics 4, 649–657, 1965.
d1 Morten F D, King R E J: Photoconductor Indium Antimonide Detectors; Applied Optics 4, 659–663, 1965.
e1 Humphrey J N: Optimum Utilization of Lead Sulphide Infrared Detectors under Diverse Operating Conditions; Applied Optics 4, 665–676, 1965.
f1 Larach S (Ed): Photoelectronic Materials and Devices; Van Nostrand 1965.
g1 RCA: Photocells: Solid State Photosensitive Devices; RCA Manual CSS-800, 1964.
h1 Mullard: Cadmium Sulphide Photoconductive Cells: Their Properties and Applications; Mullard 1965.
i1 Hewlett-Packard: The Dual Photocell (4610); Hewlett-Packard Application Note 924.

j1 Hewlett-Packard: Cadmium Sulfo-Selenide Photocells (4600 Series); Hewlett-Packard Data Sheet 1967.
k1 Hewlett-Packard: Low Level DC Operation Using HPA Photochoppers; Hewlett-Packard Application Note 911.
l1 Gray J O: Linear Control of a Photoconductor; J Phys. E Sci. Instrum. 7, 458–460, 1974.
m1 Hewlett-Packard: Photochopper 4501-7; Hewlett-Packard Data Sheets.
n1 Mullard: Photoconductive Device RPY71; Mullard Data Sheet Nov. 1970.
o1 Rose A: Performance of Photoconductors; Proc IRE 43, 1850–1869, 1955.
p1 Moss T S: Lead Salt Photoconductors; Proc IRE 43, 1869–1881, 1955.
q1 Ben-Yaakov S: A Photoconductive Self-Balancing Circuit; Rev. Sci. Instrum. 41, 1718–1724, 1970.
r1 Talbot G S: Neons in Photoconductive Choppers; Signalite Application News 6, No.2, 277–282.
s1 Andrade I, Stevens W H: Pulse Broadening and Harmonic Generation in Photoconductors; J Phys. E Sci. Instrum. 7, 604–605, 1974.
t1 Gore W G, Smith G W: An Ultralow Noise Preamplifier and Bias Supply for Photoconductive Infrared Detectors; J Phys. E Sci. Instrum. 7, 644–646, 1974.
u1 Jervis M H, Morten F D: Mercury Cadmium Telluride Infrared Detectors at 5μm and Normal Ambient Temperature; Mullard Tech. Comm. 11, 182–184, 1970.
v1 Dance J B: Photoelectronic Devices; Iliffe Books 1969.
w1 Beeforth T H, Goldsmith H J: Physics of Solid State Devices; Pion 1970.
x1 Mullard: Cadmium Sulphide Photoconductive Cells: General Explanatory Notes; Mullard Handbook Mar. 1966.
y1 Kimmitt M F: Far-Infrared Techniques; Pion 1970.
z1 Sowan F A (Ed): Applications of Infrared Detectors; Mullard 1971.
A1 Deboo G J, Burrous C N: Integrated Circuits and Semiconductor Devices: Theory and Applications; McGraw-Hill 1971.

References section 9.4: Photomultipliers

a1 Engstrom R W: Phototubes and Photocells; RCA Technical Manual PT-60, 1963.
b1 Eberhardt E H: Threshold Sensitivity and Noise Rating of Multiplier Phototubes; Applied Optics 6, 251–255, 1967.
c1 EMI: An Introduction to the Photomultiplier; EMI Electronics Photomultiplier Tubes Catalogue.
d1 Land P L: A Discussion of the Region of Linear Operation of Photomultipliers; Rev. Sci. Instrum. 42, 420–425, 1971, and 43, 356–357, 1972.
e1 Lush H J: Photomultiplier Linearity; J Phys. E Sci. Instrum. 42, 597–602, 1965.
f1 Keene J P: Fatigue and Saturation in Photomultipliers; Rev. Sci. Instrum. 34, 1220–1222, 1963.
g1 Sharpe J: Dark Current in Photomultiplier Tubes; EMI Electronics Document R/P021 Y70, 1970.
h1 Foord R, Jones R, Oliver C J, Pike E R: The Use of Photomultiplier Tubes for Photon Counting; Applied Optics 8, 1975–1989, 1969, and 10, 1683, 1971.
i1 Sommer A H: Photomissive Materials; Wiley 1968.
j1 Sommer A H, Spicer W E: Photoelectric Emission, Chapter 4 of Larach S (Ed): Photoelectronic Materials and Devices; Van Nostrand 1965.
k1 Pruett H D: Photon-Counting System for Rapidly Scanning Low-Level Optical Spectra; Applied Optics 11, 2529–2533, 1972.
l1 Shardanand: Compact Photomultiplier Housing with Controlled Cooling; Rev. Sci. Instrum. 43, 641–643, 1972.
m1 Davies W E R: Reduction of Dark Current in Photomultiplier Tubes; Rev. Sci. Instrum. 43, 556–557, 1972.
n1 James J F: On the Use of a Photomultiplier as a Photon Counter; Mon. Not. Roy. Astrom. Soc. 137, 15–23, 1967.
o1 Zatzick M R: Photomultiplier Tube Selection and Housing Design for Wideband Photon Counting; SSR Instrument Application Note 71021.

p1 Betzler K, Weller T, Conradt R: Improvement of Photon Counting by Means of a Pulse Height Analyzer; Rev. Sci. Instrum. 42, 1594–1596, 1971.

q1 Rolfe J, Moore S E: The Efficient Use of Photomultiplier Tubes for Recording Spectra; Applied Optics 9, 63–71, 1970.

r1 Bachrach R Z: A Photon Counting Apparatus for Kinetic and Spectral Measurements; Rev. Sci. Instrum. 43, 734–737, 1972.

s1 Broadfoot A L: Refrigeration for Photomultipliers; Applied Optics 5, 1259–1263, 1966.

t1 Wolber W G: The Channeltron Photomultiplier Tube as a Photon Counting Light Detector; Galileo Electro-Optics Application Note 6803, 1968.

u1 Young A T: Cosmic Ray Induced Dark Current in Photomultipliers; Rev. Sci. Instrum. 37, 1472–1481, 1966.

v1 Fain D L: Photomultiplier Sensitivity Limitations; J Opt. Soc Amer. 55, 206–207, 1965.

w1 EMI: Photomultiplier Tubes; EMI Electronics Catalogue 1970.

x1 Eberhardt E H: Noise in Multiplier Phototubes; ITT Laboratories Application Note E8.

y1 Eberhardt E H: Noise Factor Measurements in Multiplier Phototubes; ITT Laboratories 1966.

z1 Zatzick M R: Applying Digital Techniques to Photon Counting; Research/Development 21, Nov. 1970, 16–20, 22.

A1 RCA: Photomultiplier Manual; RCA Technical Series PT-61, 1970.

B1 EMI: Magnetic Focusing Assemblies Types C121, 122; EMI Electronics Data Sheet.

C1 Helvy F A: ERMA: A Guide to the Selection of RCA Photomultipliers Using Multi-Alkali Photocathodes with Extended Red Response; RCA Application Note AN-4637, 1971.

D1 Gadsden M: Some Statistical Properties of Pulses from Photomultipliers; Applied Optics 4, 1446–1452, 1965, and EMI Electronics Document R/P032.

E1 Topp J A, Schrotter H W, Hacker H, Brandmuller J: Improvement of the Signal-to-Noise Ratio of Photomultipliers for Very Weak Signals; Rev. Sci. Instrum. 40, 1164–1169, 1969.

F1 Arecchi F T, Gatti E, Sona A: Measurement of Low Light Intensities by Synchronous Single Photon Counting; Rev. Sci. Instrum. 37, 942–948, 1966.

G1 Zatzick M R: How to Make Every Photon Count; Electro-Optical Systems Design June 1972, 20–23, 26–27.

H1 Jones R, Oliver C J, Pike E R: Experimental and Theoretical Comparison of Photon Counting and Current Measurements of Light Intensity; Applied Optics 10, 1673–1680, 1971.

I1 Nakamura J K, Schwarz S E: Synchronous Detection versus Pulse Counting for Sensitive Photomultiplier Detection Systems; Applied Optics 7, 1073–1078, 1968.

J1 Ortec: The Single-Photon Technique for Measuring Light Intensity and Decay Characteristics; Ortec Application Note AN-35, 1971.

K1 Michels D J, Hunter W R: Detectors for the Extreme Ultraviolet. I Photomultipliers Used in the DC Output Current Mode; Applied Optics 6, 385–390, 1967.

L1 Yguerabide J: Fast and Accurate Method for Measuring Photon Flux in the Range 2500–6000A; Rev. Sci. Instrum. 39, 1048–1052, 1968.

M1 Grodski J J, Schumacher B W: New Wide Band Windowless Photon Detector; Rev. Sci. Instrum. 39, 702–709, 1968.

N1 Mayer U, Mozer M, Reinhardt M: Open Multipliers in the Soft X-Ray Region; Applied Optics 8, 617–625, 1969.

O1 Oliver C J, Pike E R: Measurement of Low Light Flux by Photon Counting; Brit. J App. Phys. (J Phys. D) 1, 1459–1468, 1968.

P1 Franklin M L, Horlick G, Malmstadt H V: Basic and Practical Considerations in Utilizing Photon Counting for Quantitative Spectrochemical Methods; Anal. Chem. 41, 2–10, 1969.

Q1 Alfano R R, Ockman N: Methods for Detecting Weak Light Signals; J Opt. Soc. Amer. 58, 90–95, 1968.

R1 Knight W, Kohanzadeh Y, Lengyel G: Evaluation of Magnetic Defocusing for a Photomultiplier Tube with Large Area Semitransparent Photocathode; Applied Optics 7, 1115–1120, 1968.

S1 Prescott J R: A Statistical Model for Photomultiplier Single-Electron Statistics; Nuc. Instr. Meth. 39, 173–179, 1966.
T1 Young A T: Use of Photomultiplier Tubes for Photon Counting; Applied Optics 10, 1681–1683, 1971.
U1 St. John P A, McCarthy W J, Winefordner J D: Applications of Signal-to-Noise Theory in Molecular Luminescence Spectrometry; Anal. Chem. 38, 1828–1835, 1966.
V1 Murphy M K, Clyburn S A, Veillon C: Comparison of Lock-In Amplification and Photon Counting with Low Background Flames and Graphite Atomizers in Atomic Fluorescence Spectrometry; Anal. Chem. 45, 1468–1473, 1973.
W1 Hanbury Brown R, Twiss R Q: Interferometry of the Intensity Fluctuations in Light. I Basic Theory: The Correlation Between Photons in Coherent Beams of Radiation; Proc. Roy. Soc. A242, 300–324, 1957, Part II A243, 291–319, 1958.
X1 Hanbury Brown R, Twiss R Q: The Question of Correlation Between Photons in Coherent Light Rays; Nature 178, 1447–1448, 1956.
Y1 Purcell E M: The Question of Correlation Between Photons in Coherent Light Rays; Nature 178, 1449–1450, 1956.
Z1 Scully M O, Jacobs S F: Coherence—A Sticky Subject; Applied Optics 9, 2414–2422, 1970.
a2 Bolgiano L: Quantum Fluctuations in Microwave Radiometry; IRE Trans MTT-9, 315–321, 1961.
b2 Bloom A L: Noise in Lasers and Laser Detectors; Spectra Physics Laser Technical Bulletin No.4, 1965.
c2 Yariv A: Quantum Electronics; Wiley 1968.
d2 Maitland A, Dunn H M: Laser Physics; North Holland 1969.
e2 Yariv A, Gordon J P: The Laser; Proc IEEE 51, 4–29, 1963.
f2 Fairchild: DuMont Multiplier Phototubes; Fairchild Camera and Instrument Handbook 1965.
g2 Morton G A, Smith H M, Krall H R: The Performance of High-Gain First-Dynode Photomultipliers; IEEE Trans NS-16, 92–95, 1969.
h2 Eberhardt E H: Multiplier Phototubes for Single-Electron Counting; Electrical Communication 40, 124–133, 1965.
i2 Pao Y-H, Zitter R N, Griffiths J E: New Method of Detecting Weak Light Signals; J Opt. Soc. Amer. 56, 1133–1135, 1966.
j2 Mickey D L, Zucchino P, Born J, Smith W H: Inexpensive Photon Counting System with Internal Gate Generator; Rev. Sci. Instrum. 41, 276–277, 1970.
k2 Keene J P, Black E D, Hayon E: A Photomultiplier and Amplifier Circuit for Kinetic Spectrophotometry; Rev. Sci. Instrum. 40, 1199–1201, 1969.
l2 Tothill H A W: Measurement of Very Low Spectral Intensities; EMI Electronics Document R/P029Z70.
m2 Young A T, Schild R E: Photoelectron Collection Efficiency in Photomultipliers; Applied Optics 10, 1668–1672, 1971.
n2 Jonas M, Alon Y: Dependence of Signal-to-Noise Ratio on Operating Voltage in Photomultipliers; Applied Optics 10, 2436–2438, 1971.
o2 Shaw S A, Grant G R, Gunter W D: Optical Enhancement of Photomultipliers at Ultraviolet Wavelengths; Applied Optics 10, 2559, 1971.
p2 Budde W, Kelly P: Variation of the Spectral Sensitivity of RCA6217 and 5819 Photomultipliers at Low Temperature; Applied Optics 10, 2612–2616, 1971.
q2 Mandel L: Fluctuations of Photon Beams and Their Correlations; Proc. Phys. Soc. 72, 1037–1048, 1958.
r2 Gibson W A: Design of Photomultiplier Socket Assembly with High Gain and Clean Output Signals for Tubes Viewing Organic Scintillator Light Pulses; Rev. Sci. Instrum. 37, 631–635, 1966.
s2 Hyman L G, Schwartz R M, Schluter R A: Study of High Speed Photomultiplier Systems; Rev. Sci. Instrum. 35, 393–406, 1964.
t2 Cernigoi C, Gabrielli I, Iernetti G: Behaviour of Photomultipliers Against Short Light Pulses; Nuc. Instr. Meth. 9, 303–314, 1960.

u2 Rees J D, Givens M P: Variation of Time-of-Flight of Electrons Through a Photomultiplier; J Opt. Soc. Amer. 56, 93–95, 1966.

v2 Belletini G, Bemporad C, Cerri C, Foa L: Determination of the Optimum Working Conditions of Photomultipliers; Nuc. Instr. Meth. 21, 106–112, 1963.

w2 Pietri G: Present State of Research and New Developments at the Laboratories D'Electronique et de Physique Appliquees (LEP) in the Field of Photomultiplier Tubes; IEEE Trans NS-10, 76–92, 1964.

x2 Rosenthal J A, Fiehner M: Automatic Gain Control for Photomultiplier Tubes; Rev. Sci. Instrum. 35, 1560–1563, 1964.

y2 Ageno M, Felici C: Photomultiplier Gain Stabilization Circuit; Rev. Sci. Instrum. 34, 997–1001, 1963.

z2 Bonitz M, Meiling W, Stary F: Prepulses in Photomultipliers; Nuc. Instr. Meth. 29, 314–318, 1964.

A2 Golay M J E: Note on Coherence vs Narrow-Bandedness in Regenerative Oscillators, Masers, Lasers etc; Proc IRE 49, 958–959, 1961.

B2 Tull R G: A Comparison of Photon Counting and Current Measuring Techniques in Spectrophotometry of Faint Sources; Applied Optics 7, 2023–2029, 1968.

C2 Tull R G: A Single Photon Counting Astronomical Spectrophotometer; Applied Optics 7, 2019–2022, 1968.

D2 Johnson F A, Jones R, McLean T P, Pike E R: The Measurement and Analysis of Photon Counting Distributions; Optica Acta 14, 35–40, 1967.

E2 Johnson F A, Jones R, McLean T P, Pike E R: Dead-Time Corrections to Photon Counting Distributions; Phys. Rev. Lett. 16, 589–592, 1966.

F2 Arecchi F T, Rodari G S, Sona A: Statistics of the Laser Radiation at Threshold; Phys. Lett. 25, 59–60, 1967.

G2 Present G, Scarl D B: Single-Photon Time Resolution of Photomultipliers with Gallium Phosphide First Dynodes; Rev. Sci. Instrum. 41, 771–772, 1970.

H2 Kelley P L, Lax B, Tannenwald P E (Eds): Proceedings International Conference on the Physics of Quantum Electronics; McGraw-Hill 1965.

I2 Benci S, Benedetti P A, Manfredi M: Simple Device for Photomultiplier Cooling; Applied Optics 13, 1554–1555, 1974.

J2 Sharpe J: Photoelectric Cells and Photomultipliers; Electronic Technology 38, 196–201 and 248–256, 1961.

K2 Elmore W C: Statistics of Counting; Nucleonics 6, Jan. 1950, 26–34.

L2 Galileo Electro-Optics: Photon Counter Tube Model 7500; Galileo Electro-Optics Data Sheet.

M2 Wiley W C, Hendee C F: Electron Multipliers Utilizing Continuous Strip Surfaces; IRE Trans NS-9, 103–106, 1962.

N2 Goodrich G W, Wiley W C: Continuous Channel Electron Multiplier; Rev. Sci. Instrum. 33, 761–762, 1962.

O2 Schmidt K C, Hendee C F: Continuous Channel Electron Multiplier Operated in the Pulse Saturated Mode: IEEE Trans NS-13, 100–111, 1966.

P2 Adams J, Manley B W: The Mechanism of Channel Electron Multiplication; IEEE Trans NS-13, 88–89, 1966.

Q2 Guest A, Holmshaw R T, Manley B W: Channel Multiplier Plates for Imaging Applications; Mullard Tech. Comm. 10, 210–216, 1969.

R2 Adams J, Manley B W: The Channel Electron Multiplier; Electronic Eng. 37, 180–181, 1965.

S2 Corti M, Vendramini A: Correlation Measurements of the Response of Fast Photomultipliers in the Subnanosecond Region; Rev. Sci. Instrum. 42, 1300–1306, 1971.

T2 Jerde R L, Peterson L E, Stein W: Effects of High Energy Radiations on Noise Pulses from Photomultiplier Tubes; Rev. Sci. Instrum. 38, 1387–1394, 1967.

U2 Paschman G, Shelley E G, Chappell C R, Sharp R D, Smith L F: Absolute Efficiency Measurements for Channel Electron Multipliers Utilizing a Unique Electron Source; Rev. Sci. Instrum. 41, 1707–1711, 1970.

V2 Green M I, Kenealy P F, Beard B G: Fast-Timing Characteristics of Some Channel Electron Multipliers; Nuc. Instr. Meth. 99, 445–451, 1972.

W2 Blattner D, Johnson H, Ruedy J. Sterzer F: Microwave Photomultipliers Using Transmission Dynodes; RCA Review 26, 22–41, 1965.

X2 Krall H R, Helvy F A, Persyk D E: Recent Developments in GaP(Cs)-Dynode Photomultipliers; IEEE Trans NS-17 (12th Scintillation Counter Symposium), 71–74, 1970.

Y2 Rosetto M, Mauzerall D: A Simple Nanosecond Gate for Side Window Photomultipliers and Echoes in Such Photomultipliers; Rev. Sci. Instrum. 43, 1244–1246, 1972.

Z2 Albach G G, Meyer J: A Linear Gate for Photomultiplier Signals; Rev. Sci. Instrum. 44, 615–616, 1973.

a3 Wieme W: A Versatile Circuit for Light Intensity Measurements with a Gated Photomultiplier; J Phys. E Sci. Instrum. 6, 203–205, 1973.

b3 Hamilton T D S: Variable Duration Photomultiplier Gating Circuit; J Phys. E Sci. Instrum. 4, 326–327, 1971.

c3 Hamilton T D S, Razi Naqvi K: Instrument for Time-Resolved Phosphorimetry Using an Electronically Gated Photomultiplier; Anal. Chem. 45, 1581–1584, 1973.

d3 Reisse R, Creecy R, Poultney S K: Single Photon Detection and Sub-Nanosecond Timing Resolution with the RCA C31034 Photomultiplier; Rev. Sci. Instrum. 44, 1666–1668, 1973.

e3 Ingle J D, Crouch S R: Pulse Overlap Effects on Linearity and Signal-to-Noise Ratio in Photon Counting Systems; Anal. Chem. 44, 777–784, 1972.

f3 Ingle J D, Crouch S R: Critical Comparison of Photon Counting and Direct Current Measurement Techniques for Qualitative Spectrometric Methods; Anal. Chem. 44, 785–794, 1972.

g3 Poultney S K: Single Photon Detection and Timing: Experiments and Techniques; Advances in Electronics and Electron Physics (Ed. Marton L), Academic Press 1972.

h3 Jones D P, Kent G S: Measurement of an Overload Effect in a Photomultiplier; J Phys. E Sci. Instrum. 7, 744–746, 1974.

i3 Yamashita M: Photomultiplier Gate with Gating Times Larger than a Few Microseconds; Rev. Sci. Instrum. 45, 956–957, 1974.

j3 Davis P, Gingle A R, Knasel T M: Windowless Seal for Photomultiplier Tubes; Rev. Sci. Instrum. 45, 960, 1974.

k3 Bader H, Gordon H R, Brown O B: Theory of Coincidence Counts and Simple Practical Methods of Coincidence Count Correction for Optical and Resistive Pulse Particle Counters; Rev. Sci. Instrum. 43, 1407–1412, 1972.

l3 van der Does de Bye J A W, van den Bosch A C P, Hart C M, Saitoh M, Slob A, Verhoog P: Multichannel Photon Counter for Luminescence Decay Measurements; Rev. Sci. Instrum. 43, 1468–1474, 1972.

m3 Coates P B: Pile-Up Corrections in Lifetime Experiments; Rev. Sci. Instrum. 43, 1855–1856, 1972.

n3 Pettifer R E W, Healey P G: Signal Induced Noise in a 56TUVP Photomultiplier; J Phys. E Sci. Instrum. 7, 617–620, 1974.

o3 Holzapfel Chr: On Statistics of Time-to-Amplitude Converter Systems in Photon Counting Devices; Rev. Sci. Instrum. 45, 894–896, 1974.

p3 Rager J P, Renaud J F: The Use of a Microchannel Electron Multiplier in Spectroscopic Instrumentation, Involving Frequent Vacuum Breaking; Rev. Sci. Instrum. 45, 922–926, 1974.

q3 Rager J P, Renaud J F, Tezenas du Montcel V: Reversibility of Parameter Changes of Microchannel Electron Multipliers Due to Outgassing; Rev. Sci. Instrum. 45, 927–928, 1974.

r3 Paske W C: He + Afterpulses in Photomultipliers: Their Effect on Atomic and Molecular Lifetime Determinations; Rev. Sci. Instrum. 45, 1001–1003, 1974.

s3 Klobuchar R L, Ahumada J J, Michael J V, Karol P J: An Accurate Method of Photomultiplier Gain Determination; Rev. Sci. Instrum. 45, 1071–1072, 1974.

t3 Davis C C, King T A: Correction Methods for Photon Pile-Up in Lifetime Determination by Single-Photon Counting; Rev. Sci. Instrum. 41, 407–408, 1970.

u3 Davis C C, King T A: Photon Pile-Up Corrections in the Study of Time-Varying Light Sources; J Phys. E Sci. Instrum. 5, 1072–1074, 1972.

v3   Klobuchar R L, Ahumada J J, Michael J V, Karol P J: Details of Dead Time Losses in Scaling and Multiscaling; Rev. Sci. Instrum. 45, 1073–1076, 1974.

w3   Schevey G J, Kerns D V: Output Noise Characteristics of Vacuum Photodiode Circuits; IEEE Trans IM-22, 174–175, 1973.

x3   Bosshard R, Rausch R, Sauce M, Zajde C: Wavelength Dependence of Photomultiplier Single Electron Response Amplitude Spectra; IEEE Trans NS-19, 107–111, 1972.

y3   Pace P W, Atkinson J B: Sensitized Fluorescence Measurements Using a Pulsed Dye Laser; J Phys. E Sci. Instrum. 7, 556–560, 1974.

z3   Coates P B: Fatigue and its Correction in Photon Counting Experiments; J Phys. E Sci. Instrum. 8, 189–193, 1975.

A3   Jameson D G, Martin J J: A Nanosecond Gating Circuit for Use with a Photomultiplier with a Focus Electrode; J Phys. E Sci. Instrum. 8, 635–636, 1975.

B3   Soini E: Stabilization of Photomultipliers in Liquid Scintillation Counters; Rev. Sci. Instrum. 46, 980–984, 1975.

C3   Princeton Applied Research: Photon Counting; Princeton Applied Research 1975.

D3   Amsel G, Bosshard R, Zajde C: Shortening of Detector Signals with Passive Filters for Pile-Up Reduction: Nuc. Instr. Meth. 71, 1–12, 1969.

E3   Cormack A M: Dead-Time Losses with Pulsed Beams; Nuc. Instr. Meth. 15, 268–272, 1962.

F3   Melchior H, Fisher M B, Arams F R: Photodetectors for Optical Communication Systems; Proc. IEEE 58, 1466–1486, 1970.

G3   Aoshima R, Sugita T: A Photomultiplier Cooler with a High Stability of $+/-$ 0.005C; J Phys. E Sci. Instrum. 7, 48–50, 1974.

H3   Smith-Saville R J, Ness S: Photomultiplier Cooling Apparatus; J Sci. Instrum. 44, 631–632, 1967.

I3   Aitken A C: Statistical Mathematics; Oliver and Boyd 1949.

J3   Mack J E, Paresce F, Bowyer S: Channel Electron Multiplier: Its Quantum Efficiency at Soft X-Ray and Vacuum Ultraviolet Wavelengths; Applied Optics 15, 861–62, 1976.

K3   Jones D P: Photomultiplier Sensitivity Variation with Angle of Incidence on the Photocathode; Applied Optics 15, 910–914, 1976.

L3   Beck G: Operation of a 1P28 Photomultiplier with Subnanosecond Response Time; Rev. Sci. Instrum. 47, 537–541, 1976.

M3   Lucke R L: Counting Statistics for Nonnegligible Dead Time Corrections; Rev. Sci. Instrum. 47, 766–767, 1976.

References section 9.5a: Tungsten lamps

a1   Osram: Special Lamps for Technical and Scientific Purposes; Osram Databook June 1967.

b1   Vitality: Filament Lamps; Vitality (General Instrument) Catalogue.

c1   Menzel and Brandau: Micro Gluhlampen Gessellschaft Katalog; Menzel and Brandau Catalogue 70/71.

References section 9.5b: Light-emitting diodes

a1   Major L D, Grotti R D: Efficient High Power GaAs Emitters; Texas Instruments Application Report CA131, 1972.

b1   Windecker R: Optoelectronic Fault Indicator for Logic Circuits; Texas Instruments Application Report CA153, 1972.

c1   Veazey W: Optoelectronic Read Head for Punched Cards and Tape; Texas Instruments Application Report CA154, 1972.

d1   Carroll R: Injection Laser Diode Fundamentals; Texas Instruments Application Report CA155, 1972.

e1   Grotti R D, Major L D: Measuring Light-Emitting Diode Output; Texas Instruments Application Report CA157, 1972.

f1   Hertz L M (Ed): Solid State Lamps—Part I Theory and Characteristics, Part II Applications Manual; General Electric Manuals 3-8270R, 3-0121, 1970.

g1 Bergh A A, Dean P J: Light Emitting Diodes; Proc IEEE 60, 156–223, 1972.
h1 Smith G: LED's and Photometry; Litronix Application Note 1, Mar. 1971.
i1 Holden W S, Hubbard W M, Personick S D: Chromatic Delay in Light Emitting Diodes; Applied Optics 13, 1050–1052, 1974.
j1 Hewlett-Packard: HPA GaAs Sources; Hewlett-Packard Application Note 916, Mar. 1967.
k1 Hall R: 'New Lamps for Old' with Electroluminescent P-N Junctions; Electronic Equipment News Nov. 1973.
l1 Ferranti: Fast Light Sources XP21, XP22; Ferranti Data Sheet Sep. 1967.
m1 Korn S R: How to Evaluate Light Emitters and Optical Systems for Light Sensitive Silicon Detectors; General Electric Application Note 200.59, 1971.
n1 Eckolt F: Die Anwendung von GaAsP-Leuchtdioden; AEG-Telefunken Applikationsberichte B2/V.7.33/0473.
o1 Litronix: Battery Status Indicator RLC400; Litronix Data Sheet June 1974.
p1 Bexon R, Cooke K E: A Light Emitting Diode Device for Use in Fault Finding in Pulsed Laser Holography; J Phys. E Sci. Instrum. 7, 511–512, 1974.
q1 Hewlett-Packard: Contrast Enhancement Techniques; Hewlett-Packard Application Note 964, 1975.
r1 RCA: Solid State Infrared Emitters, Isolators, Laser Diodes; RCA Catalogue OPT-113A, 1974.
s1 RCA: Gallium-Arsenide Lasers and Emitters; RCA Publication OPT-100, 1970.
t1 Wilson B L H: Designing Solid State Lamps; Electronic Eng. 42, Apr. 1970, 65–68.
u1 Hewlett-Packard: Voltage Sensing LED 5082-4732; Hewlett-Packard Data Sheet Dec. 1974.
v1 ITT: 10-Bar Line Array DD10G; ITT Components Data Sheet July 1975.
w1 National Semiconductor: NSL4944 Current Regulated, Universal Diffused-Lens Red LED Lamp; National Semiconductor Data Sheet Apr. 1975.
x1 Deboo G J, Burrous C N: Integrated Circuits and Semiconductor Devices: Theory and Applications; McGraw-Hill 1971.
y1 Graham I: Solid State Displays. The Third Generation; Electronics Industry May 1976, 27–29.
z1 Lefferts P: Constant Current LED NSL4944; National Semiconductor Application Note AN-153, Oct. 1975.
A1 Sahm W H (Ed): Optoelectronics Manual; General Electric 1976.
B1 Norris B (Ed): Semiconductor Circuit Design Vol. II, Section 3 Optoelectronics; Texas Instruments 1973.
C1 Kolody O A: Optoelectronics—A New Dimension in Circuit Design; General Electric Application Note 90.65, 1967.
D1 Hewlett-Packard: Optoelectronic Applications Seminar Handbook; Hewlett-Packard May 1974.
E1 Texas Instruments: The Optoelectronics Data Book; Texas Instruments 1972.

References section 9.5c: Gas discharge lamps

a1 Hodgson B W, Keene J P: Some Characteristics of a Pulsed Xenon Lamp for Use as a Light Source in Kinetic Spectrophotometry; Rev. Sci. Instrum. 43, 493–496, 1972.
b1 Vitality: Notes for Neon Lamp Users and Notes for Glow Diode Users; Vitality Bulbs, Catalogue.
c1 De Sa R J, Gibson Q H: Dual Beam Stopped Flow Spectrophotometer Utilizing Modulated Xenon Arcs; Rev. Sci. Instrum. 37, 900–906, 1966.
d1 Buckley J K, Gerue D R: Modulation of Xenon Arc Lamps; PEK Application Note.
e1 PEK: Application Notes for Design and Testing of Power Supplies and Housing for the PEK200 High Pressure Mercury Arc Lamp; PEK Laboratories Application Note.
f1 Gallo C F, Courtney J E: Acoustical Resonances in Modulated Xenon and Krypton Compact Arc Lamps; Applied Optics 6, 939–941, 1967.
g1 Scouler W J, Mills E D: Current Regulator for Ultraviolet Light Source; Rev. Sci. Instrum. 35, 489–492, 1964.

h1   Schurer K, Stoelhorst J: A Simple Device for Stabilizing the Output of a High Pressure Xenon Arc; J Sci. Instrum. 44, 952–953, 1967.
i1   Redfield D: Arc Lamp Intensity Stabilizer; Rev. Sci. Instrum. 32, 557–558, 1961.
j1   Langelaar J, de Vries G A, Bebelaar D: Sensitivity Improvements in Spectro-Phospho-Fluorimetry; J Phys. E Sci. Instrum. 2, 149–152, 1969.
k1   McKendry F: Glow Lamps. Design, Operation and Application; Signalite (Hivac/General Instrument).
l1   Taylor W B, LeBlanc J C, Whillans D W, Herbert M A, Johns H E: Intensified Ultraviolet Analyzing Lamp for Flash Photolysis; Rev. Sci. Instrum. 43, 1797–1799, 1972.
m1   Hivac: Time Delays in Cold Cathode Tubes; Hivac Application Bulletin 1, 26–27.
n1   Hviid T, Nielsen S O: 35Volt, 180Ampere Pulse Generator with Droop Control for Pulsing Xenon Arcs; Rev. Sci. Instrum. 43, 1198–1199, 1972.
o1   Breeze R H, Ke B: Some Comments on Xenon Arc Lamp Stability; Rev. Sci. Instrum. 43, 821–823, 1972.
p1   Fünfschilling J, Zschokke-Gränacher I: Generation of a Square Wave Xenon Flash; Rev. Sci. Instrum. 45, 598–599, 1974.
q1   Defreese J D, Woodruff T A, Malmstadt H V: New Type of Programmable Current Regulated Power Supply for Operation of Hollow Cathode Lamps in a High Intensity Programmed Mode; Anal. Chem. 46, 1471–1476, 1974.
r1   Schiff P: Ballasting a Mercury Arc Lamp with a Solid State Circuit; Electronics 41, 5 Aug. 1968, 130–135.
s1   Osram: Wotan Super Pressure Mercury Lamps; Osram Databook Apr. 1967.
t1   Osram: Wotan High Pressure Xenon Lamps; Osram Catalogue XBO.
u1   Paresce F, Kumar S, Bowyer C S: Continuous Discharge Line Source for the Extreme Ultraviolet; Applied Optics 10, 1904–1908, 1971.
v1   Stearn J W, Colliver D J: A Demountable High Power Xenon Arc Lamp; J Sci. Instrum. 43, 52–54, 1966.
w1   Osram: Guide to the Design of Equipment for High Pressure Lamps XBO; Osram Databook XBO, 1965.
x1   D'Alessio J T, Ludwig P K, Burton M: Ultraviolet Lamp for the Generation of Intense, Constant Shape Pulses in the Subnanosecond Region; Rev. Sci. Instrum. 35, 1015–1017, 1964.
y1   Thorn Lighting (Mazda), PEK, Engelhard Hanovia, Osram (Wotan).
z1   Pailthorpe M T: The Construction of an Electronically Compensated Spectrofluorophosphorimeter; J Phys. E Sci. Instrum. 8, 194–196, 1975.
A1   Neely W C, West A D, Hall T D: Ozone Removal from Arc Lamp Cooling Air; J Phys. E Sci. Instrum. 8, 543, 1975.
B1   Thorn Lighting: Mazda Hytek Lamps; Thorn Lighting Catalogue 1971
C1   Hewlett-Packard: Optoelectronic Applications Seminar Handbook; Hewlett-Packard May 1974.
D1   Hewlett-Packard: Photochopper 4501-7; Hewlett-Packard Data Sheets.
E1   Talbot G S: Neons in Photoconductive Choppers; Signalite Application News 6, No.2, 277–282.

References section 9.6: Optolectronic couplers

a1   Texas Instruments: Optically Coupled Isolators; Texas Instruments Application Report CB-116.
b1   Reed C: Optical Coupling of Analogue and Digital Signals; Design Electronics June 1970, 36, 39, 40.
c1   Russell H T: Optically Coupled Isolators in Circuits; Texas Instruments Application Report CA156.
d1   Hewlett-Packard: High Speed Optically Coupled Isolators; Hewlett-Packard Application Note 939.
e1   Smith G: Applications of Opto-Isolators; Litronix Application Note 2, Apr. 1971, Electron 27 July 1972, 29–30.

f1 Barton D M: Driving High-Level Loads with Iso-Lit Opto-Isolators; Litronix Application Note 4, May 1972.
g1 Barton D M: Operating LEDs on AC Power; Litronix Application Note 6, Nov. 1972.
h1 Hewlett-Packard: HPA GaAs Sources; Hewlett-Packard Application Note 916, Mar. 1967.
i1 Symons L R P: Small-Signal Opto-Electronic Transformer; Electronic Eng. 41, Nov. 1969, 35–39.
j1 Wunderman I: HPA Photon Coupled Devices; Hewlett-Packard Associates Application Note 5, 1964.
k1 Hewlett-Packard: Electrical Isolation Using the HPA4310; Hewlett-Packard Application Note 909, Aug. 1966.
l1 Hewlett-Packard: Optoelectronic Coupling for Coding, Multiplexing, and Channel Switching; Hewlett-Packard Application Note 910, Aug. 1966.
m1 Ralston J M: An Apparatus for Measuring Quantum Efficiency in Electroluminescent Devices over a Wide Current Range; Rev. Sci. Instrum. 43, 876–878, 1972.
n1 Turner P: Faster Optically-Coupled Isolator is Compatible with TTL Interfaces; Electronic Eng. 46, June 1974, 46–48.
o1 Johnson D B: Test Circuit Checks Optical Isolators; Electronics 27 June 1974, 124.
p1 Wunderman I: Applications for Optical Couplers; Electronics 37, 27 July 1964, 62–67.
q1 Hewlett-Packard: High Speed Optically Coupled Isolators 5082–4350/1/2; Hewlett-Packard Data Sheet May 1972.
r1 Hewlett-Packard: IC Compatible Optically Isolated Gate 5082–4360 and 4364; Hewlett-Packard Data Sheet July 1972.
s1 Monsanto: GaAs Opto-Isolator MCD4; Monsanto Data Sheet 1970.
t1 Akers Electronics: Optical Coupler with TTL/DTL Compatible Schmitt Trigger Output (AE510); Akers Electronics Data Sheet.
u1 Hewlett-Packard: Photon Coupled Isolator 4320; Hewlett-Packard Data Sheet 1967.
v1 Hewlett-Packard: Performance of the 5082-4350/51/60 Series of Isolators in Short to Moderate Length Digital Data Transmission Systems; Hewlett-Packard Application Note 948, 1974.
w1 Jackson T A: Optical Isolation of Data Bus Simplifies Logic Design and Eliminates Noise; Electronic Design 6 Dec. 1973, 138.
x1 Tebra W, van Randeraat B: A Light Coupled Stage in the CAMAC Highway System; Nuc. Instr. Meth. 113, 201–205, 1973.
y1 Christian F: Isolation Techniques Using Optical Couplers; Motorola Application Note AN-571A, 1974.
z1 Box J R: Some Fresh Thoughts on Optically-Coupled Devices; Electronic Components 11 Feb. 1975, 14–15.
A1 Ghausi M S: Electronic Circuits; Van Nostrand Reinhold 1971.
B1 Graeme J G: Applications of Operational Amplifiers: Third Generation Techniques; McGraw-Hill 1973.
C1 Texas Instruments: Optically Coupled Modules Series SDA20; Texas Instruments Data Sheet 1972.
D1 General Electric: Photon Coupled Interrupter Module H13; General Electric Data Sheet 1973.
E1 Hafo: Opto-Coupler with Schmitt-Trigger Output 6EX77; ASEA Hafo Data Sheet Jan. 1974.
F1 General Electric: Photon Coupled Isolator with SCR H11; General Electric Data Sheet 1973.
G1 Hafo: Reflex-Detector 6DX72; ASEA Hafo Data Sheet Dec. 1973.
H1 Litronix: Very High Speed Three State Optical Isolator IL100; Litronix Data Sheet Feb. 1975.
I1 Hewlett-Packard: Simple Photon Coupled Amplifier; Electronic Eng. 45, Feb. 1973, 23.
J1 Fairchild: Light Reflection Emitter/Sensor Array FPA103/4/5; Fairchild Data Sheet Feb. 1973.
K1 Mullard: Solid State Photo Relay 116CPY; Mullard Data Sheet 1968.
L1 Manley A P: Trends in Optoelectronics; Electron 25 Oct. 1973, 28, 29, 33.

M1 Monsanto: Linear Opto-Isolator MCD2-M; Monsanto Data Sheet 1972.
N1 Langford A K: Optically Coupled VFO: Wireless World 80, Nov. 1974, 455–457.
O1 Starr B G: An Opto-Isolated Oscilloscope Trigger Circuit; Mullard Tech. Comm. 13, 289–290, 1975.
P1 Burr-Brown: Optically Coupled Isolation Amplifier Models 3650, 3652; Burr-Brown Data Sheet 1976.
Q1 Litronix: High Speed Three State Optical Isolator IL-101; Litronix: Data Sheet June 1975.
R1 Hewlett-Packard: Optoelectronic Applications Seminar Handbook; Hewlett-Packard May 1974.
S1 Texas Instruments: The Optoelectronics Handbook; Texas Instruments 1972.
T1 Wunderman I: Optoelectronics at Work; Electronics 27 July 1964, 58–62.
U1 Fairchild: Optoelectronics Handbook; Fairchild Semiconductor Feb. 1973.
V1 Korn S R, Locher R E, Sahm W H: Photon Couplers; General Electric Application Note 200.62, 1972.
W1 Monsanto: GaAs Opto-Isolator MCD4; Monsanto Data Sheet 1970.
X1 Hamilton T D S, Razi Naqvi K: Instrument for Time-Resolved Phosphorimetry Using an Electronically Gated Photomultiplier; Anal. Chem. 45, 1581–1584, 1973.
Y1 Barton D M: More Speed from Iso-Lit Optical Isolators; Litronix Application Note 5, June 1972.
Z1 Graeme J G: Op Amp Boosts Phototransistor Speed; Electronic Design 2 Mar. 1972, 62.
a2 McCartney M L: Feedback Amplifier Speeds Phototransistors Response; Electronics Mar. 15, 1971, 77.
b2 Mazur T: Four Terminal, Optically Isolated Zero Crossing AC Relay; Motorola Application Note AN-598, 1973.
c2 Barton D: Increase Optical Isolator Speed by Modifying the Phototransistor's Operating Mode. Frequencies Over 10MHz are Possible, but there are Tradeoffs; Electronic Design 14 Sep. 1972, 128–131.
d2 Sahm W H (Ed): Optoelectronic Manual; General Electric 1976.

References section 9.7: Miscellaneous opto devices

a1 Wilson B L H: Incorporating Photocells in Integrated Circuits; Electronic Eng. 41, Nov. 1969, 32–34.
b1 Murphy H E, Kabell L J: An Integrating Digital Light Meter; IEEE J SC-1, 4–7, Sep. 1966.
c1 Integrated Photomatrix: Analogue Detector Family IPL16; Integrated Photomatrix Information Sheet PX129, Aug. 1971.
d1 Howell E K: The Light Activated SCR; General Electric Application Note 200.34, 1965.
e1 Texas Instruments: Low-Noise High-Speed Transimpedance Amplifier TIXL151/2; Texas Instruments Data Sheet.
f1 Eckoldt F: Photo-Thyristor BPY78 and its Applications; AEG-Telefunken Application Report B2/V.7.06/ 0569E.
g1 Fry P W: Silicon Photodiode Arrays; J Phy. E Sci. Instrum. 8, 337–349, 1975.
h1 Mullard: Optically Controlled Relaxation Oscillator or Time Delay Circuit OM805; Mullard Data Sheet Mar. 1975.
i1 Integrated Photomatrix: Light to Frequency Converter IPL13; Integrated Photomatrix Data Sheet PX102.
j1 Akers: Photoschmitt from Light to DTL/TTL, UH3013/4; Akers Electronics Data Sheets.
k1 Akers: Light Sensitive Schmitt-Trigger UH3011/5; Akers Electronics Data Sheets.
l1 Siemens: Schwellwertschalter fur Fotodioden TPV63 (Threshold Switch for Photodiodes); Siemens Data Sheet 1974.
m1 Integrated Photomatrix: Dynamic Light Activated Switches (IPL1700); Electron 4 May 1972, 53–54.
n1 Ferranti: Bipolar Photoswitch IC ZNP100; Ferranti Data Sheet Mar. 1972.

o1   Integrated Photomatrix: Light Activated Switch Family IPL15/17; Integrated Photomatrix Data Sheet PX131, Feb. 1972.

p1   Plessey: Integrating Light Detectors, OPT5 10 × 10 Array; Plessey Data Sheet Nov. 1970.

q1   General Electric: Light Activated SCR L8, L9 Series: General Electric Data Sheet 1964.

r1   General Electric: Light Activated Silicon Controlled Switch LASCS; General Electric Data Sheet 1966.

s1   Gutzwiller F W (Ed): SCR Manual Chapter 13; General Electric 4th Edn. 1967.

t1   RCA: Photodetector and Power Amplifier CA3062; RCA Data Sheet 1970.

u1   Mazgy J D: Applications of the RCA-CA3062 IC Photo-Detector and Power Amplifier in Switching Circuits; RCA Application Note ICAN-6538.

v1   Optron: Optoelectronic Limit Switches OPS200 Series (Microswitches); Optron Data Sheet 1976.

w1   Sahm W H (Ed): Optoelectronics Manual; General Electric 1976.

x1   General Electric: Planar Silicon Photo-Switch L14T Series; General Eelectric Data Sheet 1971.

y1   Wilson B L H: Incorporating Photocells in Integrated Circuits; Electronic Eng. 41, Nov. 1969, 32–34.

z1   Plessey: Integrating Light Detectors OPT1A/1B; Plessey Microelectronics Publication P.S.1808.

A1   Plessey: The Use and Applications of OPT1; Plessey Microelectronics Application Note 1970.

B1   Korn S R: How to Evaluate Light Emitters and Optical Systems for Light Sensitive Silicon Devices; General Electric Application Note 200.59, 1971.

10 Signal detection

10.1 Signals and noise

The experimenter has two main uses for electronics: control or regulation of the various parameters, and extraction of the signals or information required. Control and regulation have been covered in other chapters, and if the signals we are looking for are large there is no difficulty in detecting and measuring them. What we will be concerned with, here, are those situations where the signal is comparable with or less than the noise, so that special techniques must be devised. There are a number of these in common use such as correlation, signal averaging, and lock-in or phase-sensitive detection.

Correlation is a technique for examining the similarity between waveforms. This may involve the comparison of two waveforms from different sources as a function of time displacement (crosscorrelation), or between a waveform and a time-shifted replica of itself as a function of the time shift (autocorrelation). These techniques imply no *a priori* knowledge of the signals, and would, for example, be particularly useful in cases such as outer space or seismographic signals where the source is inaccessible. If we do know that the signal we are seeking is at a particular frequency, then we may perform the crosscorrelation of the signal with a reference sinusoid at that frequency. In experimental situations it is usual to drive the system at the reference frequency to ensure the coincidence of the frequencies. This is commonly referred to as coherent or lock-in detection.

If the signal sought is not sinusoidal, i.e., it has some more complex waveshape, it is necessary to extract all the harmonics and add them together with the correct phases. This can be done by multiple lock-in system, Fourier comb filters [i1] or, if the signal can be repeated, by signal averaging. Signal averaging is a repetitive cross-correlation of the signal with a synchronous pulse, with averaging of the corresponding results [g1, h1]. This process turns out to be equivalent to a comb filter. One may think of the pulse train as containing all the harmonics of the repetition frequency, so that the corresponding signal harmonics are extracted.

Correlation is usually carried out using digital techniques for processing and storage, which allow complex manipulations of the data and indefinitely long analysis times to be used. Analogue techniques are, however, inherently faster and have particular application to high speed events. The boxcar detector (Sec. 6.5) is an example of this, and may be used in the sub-nanosecond domain.

To appreciate the use of these techniques, it is necessary to understand the characteristics of noise, the properties of all the elements of the detection system, and the requirements of the experiment itself. Some of the properties of noise are discussed in Sec. 1.8, low noise amplifiers in Sec. 4.1, and noise in optical detectors in Secs. 9.4 and 9.2.

The characteristics of noise, which allow us to discriminate against it, are its random nature and its frequency spectrum. A truly random noise voltage, for example, will be as often of one polarity as the opposite so that over a period its average value will tend to zero. The frequency spectrum of noise is effectively white (Sec. 1.8) for Johnson and shot noise, though in practice there are sources of excess noise that have an approximately 1/frequency spectrum. For white noise there is obviously no benefit to be derived from working at any particular frequency, since the noise is the same at all frequencies. $1/f$ noise, however, can be discriminated against by operating at high enough frequency. As a guide the $1/f$ spectrum is generally insignificant relative to the white noise spectrum above 0·1 to 1 kHz. Once this has been done, the noise can be further reduced by restricting the bandwidth of the detecting system, as may be seen from Eqs. (1.8.1) and (1.8.4), as long as the signal will allow this (Sec. 1.4). This can be achieved by a narrow-band filter, either active (Sec. 4.4) or passive, but there are two limitations. First, as the filter bandwidth becomes narrower, the requirements on the frequency stability of the signal are correspondingly increased. Secondly, the time it takes a filter to respond to an input increases as the bandwidth decreases (Sec. 1.4) [c1, d1]. Thus, the narrower the filter, the slower the signal may be allowed to change if it is not to be distorted, i.e., you buy an improvement in signal-to-noise ratio with time.

10.2 Lock-in or coherent detection

The problem of escaping from $1/f$ noise, and of the relative frequency drift with very narrow bandwidth filters, is overcome with lock-in or coherent detection. This is also known as phase-sensitive detection, and is a long established technique [a1, b1, c1]. The approach here is to use a reference (or carrier) oscillator at frequency ω_c, to modulate the system under investigation, so that the signal of interest, e_s, is at this frequency. This allows us to shift amplification and detection to a convenient frequency, where $1/f$ noise is negligible. The signal, e_s, is then multiplied by a fixed amplitude carrier wave, e_c, obtained directly from the reference oscillator (Secs. 6.2 and 6.3). Thus, signal and reference waveform will always be at identical frequencies and any drift in this frequency is immaterial, i.e., the detector is locked-in to the signal. The output of the multiplier is then smoothed by a low-pass filter, whose pass-band determines the overall bandwidth, and hence signal-to-noise improvement, of the detection system (Fig. 10.2.1).

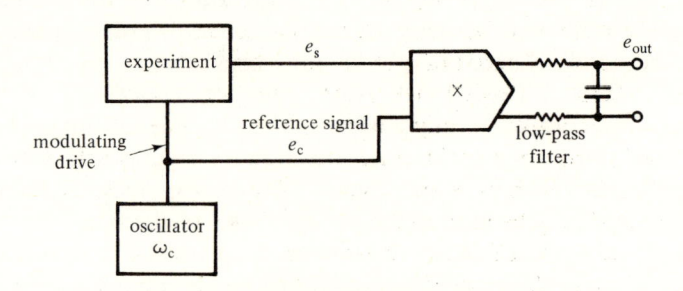

Fig. 10.2.1 Basic lock-in detection system

Disregarding noise, for the moment, the signal and reference inputs to the multiplier may be written:

$$e_s = E_s \cos(\omega_c t), \qquad e_c = E_c \cos(\omega_c t + \phi) \qquad (10.2.1)$$

The output from the multiplier is then, from Eq. (6.3.6):

$$e_m = \tfrac{1}{2} K E_s E_c [\cos(2\omega_c t + \phi) + \cos \phi] \qquad (10.2.2)$$

The cut-off frequency of the subsequent low-pass filter is set to be much lower than the carrier frequency, ω_c (see below). The filter, therefore, removes the component at $2\omega_c$ giving a final output:

$$e_{out} = \tfrac{1}{2} K E_s E_c \cos \phi \qquad (10.2.3)$$

Thus, we obtain a steady output proportional to the signal E_s (E_c is maintained constant) and dependent on the phase difference ϕ—hence the alternative name of phase-sensitive detector. Cos ϕ varies between ± 1, as ϕ varies from 0° to 180°, so e_{out} can vary between $\pm \tfrac{1}{2} K E_s E_c$, including zero. Thus, a phase-shift circuit is often included, usually in the reference channel, to allow compensation for incidental phase shifts in the system. To ensure the constancy of E_c, it is usually limited or clipped either separately or in the multiplier itself (Sec. 6.3), so that it will no longer be sinusoidal. In the extreme case this will be a square wave which can be represented by:

$$e_{c(sq)} = \frac{4 E_c}{\pi} [\cos(\omega_c t) - \tfrac{1}{3} \cos(3\omega_c t) + \tfrac{1}{5} \cos(5\omega_c t) - \cdots] \qquad (10.2.4)$$

Treating each term of this as previously, it is easily seen that there will be an output at all even harmonics, 0, $2\omega_c$, $4\omega_c$, etc., but zero for odd. If the signal, e_s, is distorted, as it often is, then any even harmonics of this ($2\omega_c$, $4\omega_c$, etc.) will mix with the reference to give odd harmonics in e_m, but no d.c. term. However, any odd harmonics of the signal ($3\omega_c$, $5\omega_c$, etc.) will each produce a d.c. output. The contributions of these higher harmonics are often substantially reduced by passing e_s through a band-pass filter before the multiplier. This filter should not be sharply tuned, since the lowest harmonic of e_s it has to discriminate against is the third. It is also necessary to have the minimum of phase-shift variation as a function of frequency so that small drifts of ω_c do not give changes in e_{out} via the cos ϕ term. As discussed below, this filter also serves to reduce the probability of overload.

So far we have not mentioned noise. Again it is simplest to take one component of it, say at frequency ω_n. Then if (see Eq. (6.3.5)):

$$e_n = E_n \cos(\omega_n t) \qquad (10.2.5)$$
$$e_{out} = \tfrac{1}{2} K E_n E_c [\cos(\omega_n + \omega_c)t + \cos(\omega_n - \omega_c)t]$$

Then, unless the difference frequency ($\omega_n - \omega_c$) lies within the pass-band of the smoothing filter, there will be no output. The commonly used *RC* low-pass filter is often said to be performing an integrating function [d1, r1]. Though the *RC* and integrator transfer functions are similar, they are not the same [c2], and the difference has led to misunderstandings [u2]. The effect on in-band signals is minor, but the integrator has a sharper cut-off and hence passes less noise.

The main point of interest is the improvement in signal-to-noise ratio that may be achieved. In principle, this can be as great as you wish, if you are prepared to wait long enough. In practice, of course there are always limiting factors, such as drifts in the system. The equivalent noise bandwidth of a low-pass filter of time constant T is $\delta f = 1/4T$; Eq. (1.8.13). If we are extracting a signal from white noise of bandwidth Δf, then the ratio of input to output noise powers is $\Delta f/\delta f$, and hence the ratio of noise voltages is $(\Delta f/\delta f)^{1/2}$. For example, if $\Delta f = 10$ kHz and $T = 1$ s, then the improvement will be by a factor of about 200. If the actual operating frequency was $f_c = 1$ kHz, then this represents an effective $Q = f_c/\delta f = 4000$, which is rather difficult to achieve at this frequency by other means (see Sec. 4.4) even if the frequency stability requirements can be met.

It is important that the lock-in amplifier should not be overloaded as this introduces non-linearity and extra intermodulation products. The pre-filter, mentioned earlier, limits the input bandwidth and hence reduces the probability of large noise signals overloading the system. However, it is still desirable that a lock-in amplifier have a large dynamic range to cope with noise, temperature drifts, out-of-phase components, and zero offsets [p2].

In an experiment, the interest is usually in how some quantity depends on another. To use the lock-in amplifier we must modulate the independent variable at the carrier frequency, and detect the resulting variation, e_s, of the dependent quantity. It is important to examine the form of the signal, e_s, as we shall see that the output of the

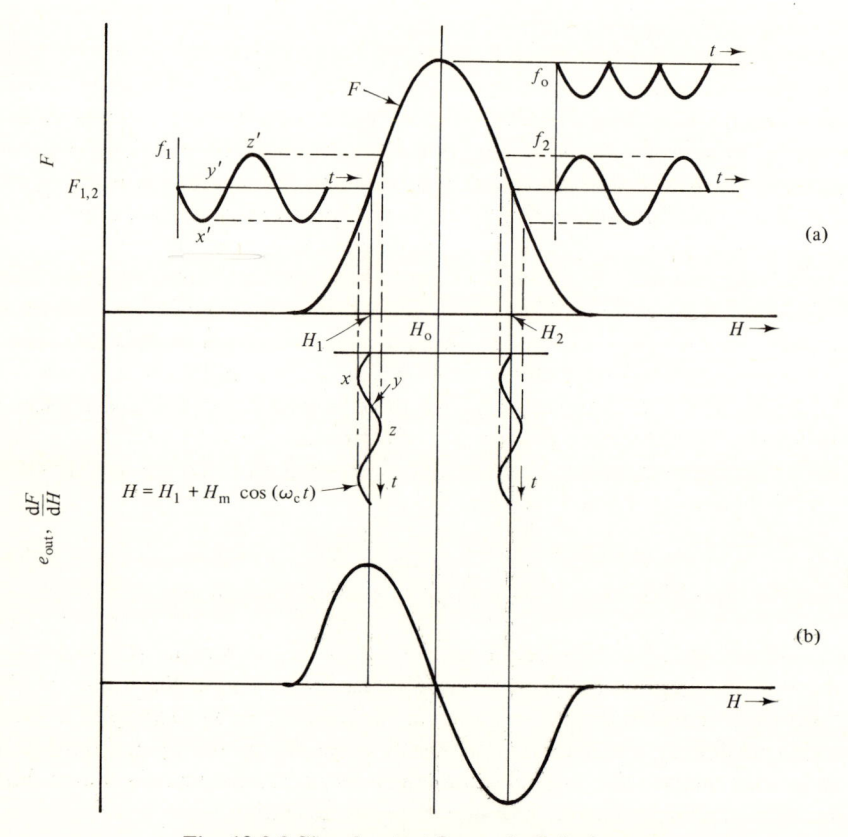

Fig. 10.2.2 Signal output from a lock-in detector

lock-in system is not necessarily a direct representation of the variation of e_s. As an example, consider a spectral line whose intensity F is a function of the variable H (Fig. 10.2.2).

At any particular value of H, say H_1, the intensity F will have a corresponding value F_1. H is modulated at the carrier frequency as indicated on the time axis below H_1. For each instantaneous value of H the resulting output, f_1, can be determined by projecting upwards to the F curve, e.g., points x, y, z give points x', y', z'. The final output of the lock-in is proportional to the amplitude of f_1. It is evident that for small amplitude modulation H_m, f_1 is proportional to the slope of the F curve, i.e., to the derivative or differential dF/dH, and will be a maximum at the region of maximum slope of F. If H_1 is varied across the whole of the F curve, the final output, e_{out}, will have the form shown in Fig. 10.2.2(b). The change of polarity indicates the change of slope between the two sides of F, and hence the 180° phase difference between f_1 and f_2.

To obtain an accurate derivative, H_m must be as small as possible, but then f_1 will also be small. Hence, a compromise is necessary and a value of H_m about five per cent of the line width is usually satisfactory. However, if only the peak position and width are of interest, a substantially larger H_m may be used since, although this will distort the output, it will not shift the cross-over or the peaks of e_{out} significantly [b2]. It may also be noted that for $H = H_0$, i.e., at the centre of the F response, the output f will be at a frequency $2\omega_c$.

To obtain the original response F, e_{out} must be integrated. Usually, however, this is unnecessary as the derivative curve will provide the information required. In some circumstances the second derivative d^2F/dH^2 is of interest [o2, j2, i2, q2, r2, t1], and it would be convenient if this could also be measured directly with the same system. This can readily be done by modulating at frequency ω_c, and using a carrier input to the multiplier of $2\omega_c$. To see how this arises, we express the function F in the vicinity of the operating point, say H_1, in terms of a Taylor series [C1, v2]:

$$F(H) = F(H_1) + (H - H_1)\frac{dF(H_1)}{dH} + \frac{1}{2!}(H - H_1)^2 \frac{d^2f(H_1)}{dH^2} + \cdots \quad (10.2.6)$$

where $F(H_1)$ is the value of F at H_1, $dF(H_1)/dH$ is the value of dF/dH at H_1, etc. Then, if H is modulated and varies as:

$$H = H_1 + H_m \cos(\omega_c t) \quad (10.2.7)$$

the resulting output signal, f_1, will be:

$$e_s = F(H_1) + \frac{dF(H_1)}{dH} H_m \cos(\omega_c t) +$$

$$+ \frac{1}{2!} \frac{d^2F(H_1)}{dH^2} H_m^2 \cos^2(\omega_c t) + \cdots \quad (10.2.8)$$

It is now seen that, to obtain the first derivative, dF/dH, from the lock-in, the reference input must be at frequency ω_c, as we have previously concluded. Similarly, to obtain the second derivative, d^2F/dH^2, the reference frequency must be at $2\omega_c$, i.e., twice the modulating frequency. To obtain $2\omega_c$ from the original ω_c is clearly another application of the basic multiplier circuit (Sec. 6.3) [f1]. Though, in some cases, it may be easier to start with $2\omega_c$ and divide by 2 to get ω_c, e.g., by using a binary flop-flop, Sec. 5.3(a), this may present problems if a sinusoidal modulating waveform is required.

To obtain F directly, using a lock-in, H is switched between a value where $F=0$ and the value H_1 where F is to be measured. The resultant f_1 will be a square wave of amplitude $F(H_1)$, i.e., the first term in Eq. (10.2.8).

Digital lock-in's may also be realized and have some advantages. Two approaches are discussed in [j1, q1] and a useful technique for measuring the response of F to several simultaneous variables is discussed in [H1].

10.3 Signal averaging

If we have a signal obscured by noise then, by examining it many times and averaging the results, we would expect random noise to average to zero while the signal tends to its true value.

The boxcar detector described in Sec. 6.5 does just this, but it is a single channel system that examines only one point during each signal repetition. If we could examine all the points on the signal during each repetition, it would take correspondingly less time to measure the complete signal. This can be achieved using multichannel systems, and many such systems are available. These almost invariably use digital techniques, since these allow long time drift-free storage and the ready application of operations, such as dividing, over a wide dynamic range. Our purpose, here, is not to describe the details of these instruments, since it is uncommon now to construct such systems, but to outline the basis of signal averaging itself. Fundamental considerations are examined in [s1, E1, d1, v1, z1].

Signal averaging may be considered from two equivalent points of view—the time and the frequency domains. We approach it first in the time domain. An essential requirement is that the signal must be repeatable, and that there be some synchronizing trigger to which the signal is accurately related in time. Any jitter in this relationship will result in an additional noise contribution. The sampling theorem (Sec. 6.5) is also applicable. Consider a signal $v(t)$ containing the required signal $e(t)$ and random noise $n(t)$.

$$v(t) = e(t) + n(t) \tag{10.3.1}$$

The kth repetition of $v(t)$ starts at time t_k, and it is sampled at intervals of T (Fig. 10.3.1).

At a particular sample, say the pth, the amplitude will be:

$$\begin{aligned} v(t_k + pT) &= e(t_k + pT) + n(t_k + pT) \\ &= e(pT) + n(t_k + pT) \end{aligned} \tag{10.3.2}$$

since the true signal, e, will be the same at every repetition of v, i.e., e is independent of t_k. However, due to its random nature, n is not independent of t_k and, though it has zero mean value over a large number of samples, it will have an r.m.s. value ρ for a single sample. Thus, for a single sample at pT, the signal-to-noise ratio is:

$$\left(\frac{S}{N}\right)_1 = \frac{e(pT)}{\rho} \tag{10.3.3}$$

After m repetitions of $v(t)$, the amplitude stored in the pth memory will be the sum of m values given by Eq. (10.3.2).

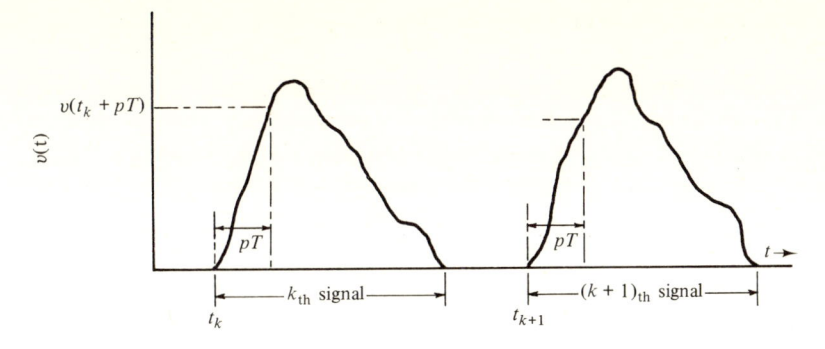

Fig. 10.3.1 Sampling of a repetitive signal

$$\sum_{k=1}^{m} v(t_k + pT) = \sum_{k=1}^{m} e(pT) + \sum_{k=1}^{m} n(t_k + pT)$$
$$= me(pT) + (m\rho^2)^{1/2} \qquad (10.3.4)$$

since all the $e(pT)$ are the same, and for the m random noise signals the nett r.m.s. value will be the square root of the sum of the squares. The signal-to-noise ratio will now be:

$$\left(\frac{S}{N}\right)_m = \frac{me(pT)}{(m\rho^2)^{1/2}} = \frac{m^{1/2}e(pT)}{\rho} = m^{1/2}\left(\frac{S}{N}\right)_1 \qquad (10.3.5)$$

So, if the noise is truly random, the signal-to-noise ratio improves as the square root of the number of repetitions m, e.g., for $m = 100$ the improvement will be by a factor of 10 (20 dB). Here we have just summed the successive samples to build up a total. In practical systems, it is often more convenient to divide after each repetition by the number of repetitions completed, to give the actual shape of $e(t)$, but this makes no difference to the argument above [t1].

When viewed from the frequency domain, signal averaging appears as a comb filter. The process is one of convolution of the signal with a set of impulses spaced T apart. To determine the corresponding frequency response we will use the approach of Lee [z1, p. 315] using the Fourier integral rather than the convolution theorem [G1, I1]. The impulse function of the averager in the time domain is a set of unit impulses δ; Fig. 10.3.2.

$$h(t) = \delta(t) + \delta(t - T) + \delta(t - 2T) + \cdots + \delta(t - (m-1)T) \qquad (10.3.6)$$

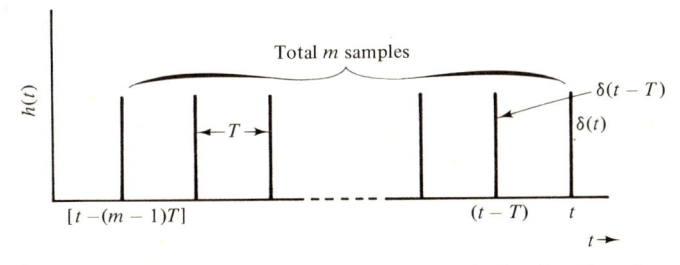

Fig. 10.3.2 Impulse function of an averager in the time domain

The Fourier transform of any function $h(t)$ is:

$$H(\omega) = \int_{-\infty}^{+\infty} h(t)\, e^{-j\omega t}\, dt \qquad (10.3.7)$$

Each term of Eq. (10.3.6) may be treated separately, e.g., for the kth term:

$$\int_{-\infty}^{+\infty} \delta(t-kT)\, e^{-j\omega t}\, dt = e^{-j\omega kT} \qquad (10.3.8)$$

since the operand inside the integral only has a non-zero value where $t = kT$. Thus, the value of Eq. (10.3.7) is

$$H(\omega) = 1 + e^{-j\omega T} + e^{-2j\omega T} + \cdots + e^{-(m-1)j\omega T}$$

$$= \frac{1 - e^{-mj\omega T}}{1 - e^{-j\omega T}} \qquad (10.3.9)$$

using the standard formula for the sum of a geometric series [J1, p. 2]. Since we have a complex exponential, this means that there are amplitude and phase parts to the expression. These may be separated by writing (see appendix):

$$H(\omega) = \frac{1 - e^{-mj\omega T}}{1 - e^{-j\omega T}} = \frac{(e^{mj\omega T/2} - e^{-mj\omega T/2})\, e^{-mj\omega T/2}}{(e^{j\omega T/2} - e^{-j\omega T/2})\, e^{-j\omega T/2}}$$

$$= \frac{\sin(m\omega T/2)}{\sin(\omega T/2)} \cdot \exp[-(m-1)j\omega T/2] \qquad (10.3.10)$$

so
$$|H(\omega)| = \left| \frac{\sin(m\omega T/2)}{\sin(\omega T/2)} \right|$$

$$= m \quad \text{for} \quad \omega = 0,\ 2\pi/T,\ 4\pi/T,\ \text{etc.}$$

The appearance of $|H(\omega)|$ is shown in Fig. 10.3.3 for several values of m. The amplitudes of the peaks, which from Eq. (10.3.10) are proportional to m, have been normalized, for comparison.

The 3 dB bandwidth of one tooth of the comb is given by (for m large):

$$\Delta f = \frac{0.886}{mT} \text{ Hz} \qquad (10.3.11)$$

and the noise equivalent bandwidth associated with one tooth is:

$$\Delta f_n = \frac{1}{mT} \qquad (10.3.12)$$

For a total noise spectrum of f_n, the number of teeth is $f_n T$, so the total noise bandwidth is:

$$\Delta f_n = f_n T \cdot \frac{1}{mT} = \frac{f_n}{m} \qquad (10.3.13)$$

which gives the same $(S/N)_m$ bandwidth as found in Eq. (10.3.5).

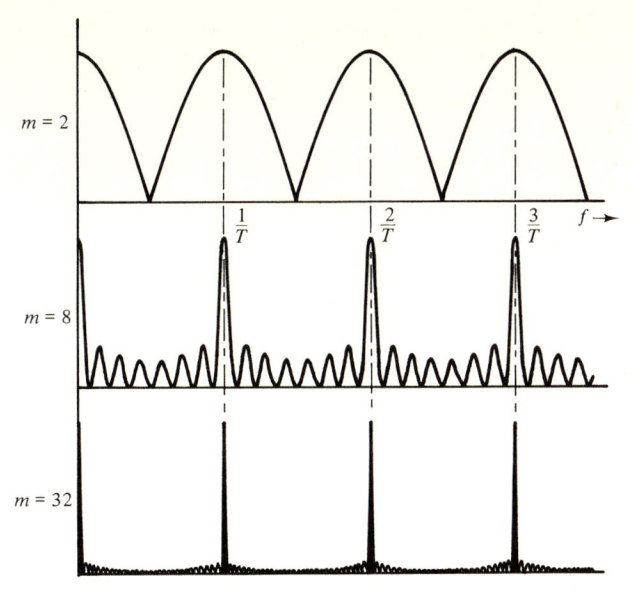

Fig. 10.3.3 Signal averaging comb filter (amplitudes normalized)

10.4 Correlation

In Secs. 10.2 and 10.3 we have described particular cases of correlation. The general expressions for auto, Φ_{11}, and crosscorrelation, Φ_{12}, for two signals v_1 and v_2 may be written [k1]:

$$\Phi_{11}(\tau) = \frac{1}{2T} \int_{-T}^{+T} v_1(t) v_1(t+\tau) \, dt \qquad (10.4.1)$$

$$\Phi_{12}(\tau) = \frac{1}{2T} \int_{-T}^{+T} v_1(t) v_2(t+\tau) \, dt \qquad (10.4.2)$$

What these equations tell us to do is to take one signal $v_1(t)$ and multiply it by the delayed signal $v_{1,2}(t+\tau)$, where τ is a given delay, and sum all the products over the time interval $2T$. This can then be repeated for a range of delays, τ, to give a correlation spectrum. The value to be assigned to T depends on the type of functions involved, i.e., periodic or random; see, for example, [k1, p. 37]. In practice, as usual, a compromise is involved. Signal averaging, or boxcar detection, is just a crosscorrelation between a signal $v_1(t)$ and a synchronous impulse waveform $v_2(t+\tau)$. In the lock-in detector, v_2 is essentially a sinusoidal waveform and τ is kept fixed. However, there is often no knowledge about the waveform, so one cannot use reference signals and, hence, can only use the original signal itself.

Autocorrelation is most appropriate for investigating any periodicities in the signal v_1. Whenever τ is a multiple of a period, the function $\Phi_{11}(\tau)$ will have a peak. Thus, we can determine all the frequencies present in v_1 but, since no phase information is available, v_1 cannot be reconstructed. In other words, a given Φ_{11} does not have a unique relationship with a particular v_1.

Crosscorrelation is suitable for comparing related waveforms, to determine the time delays between the signals. Applications of this technique lie in many fields such as acoustics, vibration, geophysics, oceanography, radar, physiology, and process control. However, to discuss correlation in detail requires further mathematical development that would be inappropriate here [k1, t1, u1]. We will consider only a few simple examples, as illustrations.

Pure random noise of infinite bandwidth will have zero autocorrelation, unless $\tau = 0$. If the noise bandwidth is limited then, depending on the truncating function, the autocorrelation will have finite width, as illustrated in Fig. 10.4.1. The narrower the bandwidth, the wider Φ_{nn} will be. A periodic signal on the other hand will give a periodic Φ_{ee} of the same period, though the form of Φ_{ee} may be quite different from v_1. For the simplest case of a sinusoidal $v_1(t)$, Φ_{ee} is actually of the same form, and a noisy sinusoid will have $\Phi_{vv} = \Phi_{ee} + \Phi_{nn}$ (Fig. 10.4.1). Thus, by varying τ over a sufficient range, an underlying periodicity in a noisy signal may be detected. Notice the symmetry of the autocorrelation function about $\tau = 0$.

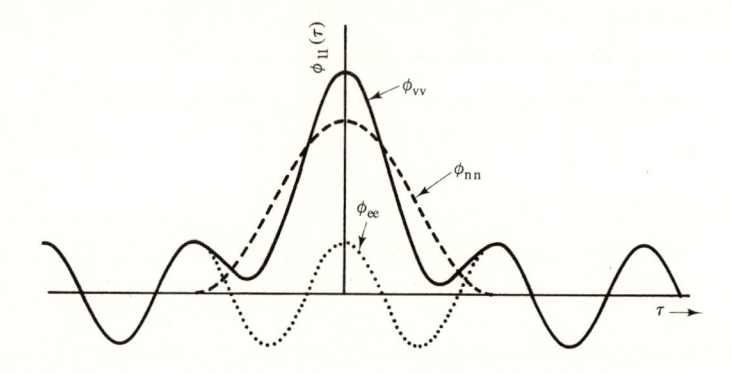

Fig. 10.4.1 Autocorrelation function of a sinusoidal signal plus noise

As an example of crosscorrelation, we may consider the problem of vibration in a machine, or, analogously, seismic reflections from various layers of the earth. One signal $v_1(t)$ is obtained from the apparent source of the vibration, and the other $v_2(t)$ from the location where the vibration is being investigated. On crosscorrelating the two signals, we may obtain a spectrum $\Phi_{12}(\tau)$, as shown in Fig. 10.4.2.

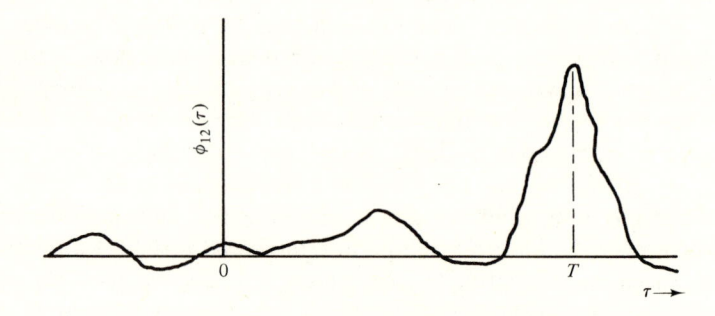

Fig. 10.4.2 Example of a crosscorrelation spectrum

The occurrence of a significant peak in $\Phi_{12}(\tau)$ would indicate that there was a connection between the suspected source and the local vibration, and the delay $\tau = T$, shows how long it has taken for the disturbance to travel between the two locations. If the velocity of propagation is known, the distance may be determined (or vice versa). In crosscorrelation there will be, in general, no noise peak in Φ_{12} at $\tau = 0$, since the noise from the two sources is uncorrelated, and Φ_{12} will not be symmetrical about $\tau = 0$.

A second important example of the use of crosscorrelation is in the determination of the natural or impulse response of a system; Sec. 1.11(a). This is especially useful in testing systems while they are in normal service. The noise at the input (which is there anyway) is crosscorrelated with the output noise, and $\Phi_{12}(\tau)$ is then the impulse response of the system. This may be seen as follows [a1, k1]. If the input is $v_1(t)$, the output $v_2(t)$, and the system impulse response $h(t)$, then using the convolution theorem:

$$v_2(t) = \int_{-\infty}^{+\infty} h(u)v_1(t-u)\,du \qquad (10.4.3)$$

The correlation function is given by:

$$\Phi_{12}(\tau) = \frac{1}{2T}\int_{-T}^{+T} v_1(t-\tau)v_2(t)\,dt$$

$$= \frac{1}{2T}\int_{-T}^{+T} v_1(t-\tau)\int_{-\infty}^{+\infty} h(u)v_1(t-u)\,du.dt \quad \text{using Eq. (10.4.3)}$$

$$= \int_{-\infty}^{+\infty} h(u)\frac{1}{2T}\int_{-T}^{+T} v_1(t-\tau)v_1(t-u)\,dt.du$$

$$= \int_{-\infty}^{+\infty} h(u)\Phi_{11}(\tau-u)\,du \qquad (10.4.4)$$

Allowing the input noise, $v_1(t)$, to have a substantially greater bandwidth than that of the system, then we may assume $h(u)$ to be effectively constant over the range of u for which $\Phi_{11}(\tau-u)$ is significant. For any given value of τ, $\Phi_{11}(\tau-u)$ will be an autocorrelated noise peak, as shown in Fig. 10.4.1, with a width inversely dependent on the noise bandwidth. The constant value of $h(u)$ in this region is, thus, that corresponding to $u = \tau$, i.e., $h(\tau)$. We may now write Eq. (10.4.4) as:

$$\Phi_{12}(\tau) = h(\tau)\int_{-\infty}^{+\infty} \Phi_{11}(\tau-u)\,du$$

$$= h(\tau).\text{constant} \qquad (10.4.5)$$

Since we can use existing noise, or low level injected noise, the measurement of $h(\tau)$ can be made without disturbing the normal operation of the system. In the correlation domain, the δ-like pulse due to the wideband noise, gives an output which is the impulse function of the system just as in the time domain; Sec. 1.11(a).

Useful discussions of recent approaches to correlation are given in [r1, s1, q1, h1].

References section 10.1: Signals and noise

a1 Connor F R: Signals; Edward Arnold 1972.
b1 Sheingold D H: Nonlinear Circuits Handbook; Analog Devices 1974.
c1 Goodyear C C: Signals and Information; Butterworths 1971.
d1 Betts J A: Signal Processing, Modulation and Noise; English Universities Press 1970.
e1 Connor F R: Noise; Edward Arnold 1973.
f1 Connor F R: Modulation; Edward Arnold 1973.
g1 Rex R L, Roberts G T: Correlation, Signal Averaging, and Probability Analysis; Hewlett-Packard J 21, Nov. 1969, 2–8.
h1 Trimble C R: What is Signal Averaging?; Hewlett-Packard J 19, Apr. 1968, 2–7.
i1 May F T, Dandl R A: Active Filter Element and Its Application to a Fourier Comb; Rev. Sci. Instrum. 32, 387–391, 1961.
j1 Rice S O: Mathematical Analysis of Random Noise; Bell System Tech J 23, 282–332, July 1944, and 24, 47–156, Jan. 1945.
k1 Usher M J: Noise and Bandwidth; J Phys. E Sci. Instrum. 7, 957–961, 1974.
j1 Kelly P C, Horlick G: Practical Considerations for Digitizing Analog Signals; Anal. Chem. 45, 518–527, 1973.
m1 Savitzky A, Golay M J E: Smoothing and Differentiation of Data by Simplified Least Squares Procedures; Anal. Chem. 36, 1627–1639, 1964.
n1 Wertheim G K: Novel Smoothing Algorithm; Rev. Sci. Instrum. 46, 1414–1415, 1975.
o1 Schwartz M: Information Transmission, Modulation, and Noise; McGraw-Hill 1970.
p1 Hieftje G M: Signal-to-Noise Enhancement Through Instrumental Techniques; Anal. Chem. 44, May 1972, 81A–88A, and June 1972, 69A–78A.

References section 10.2: Lock-in or coherent detection

a1 Ayrton W E, Perry J: Modes of Measuring the Coefficients of Self and Mutual Inductance; J Soc. Telegr. Engrs. 16, 292–243, 1888.
b1 Dobson G M B, Perfect D S: Physical and Optical Societies Joint Discussion on Photoelectric Cells and their Applications, 79–84, 1930; Physical and Optical Societies, London.
c1 Jones R V: Some Turning Points in Infra-Red History; Radio Electronic Engnr. 42, 117–126, 1972.
d1 Smith K L: The Ubiquitous Phase Sensitive Detector; Wireless World 78, 367–370, 1972.
e1 Brower R: Taking Noise Out of Weak Signals; Electronics 8 July 1968, 80–90.
f1 DeKold D: Frequency Doubler Accepts Any Waveshape; Electronics 17 July 1972, 84–85.
g1 Geist J: Waveform-Independent Lock-In Detection; Rev. Sci. Instrum. 43, 1704–1705, 1972.
h1 Clark W G, Kerlin A L: Solid State Gated Integrator; Rev. Sci. Instrum. 38, 1593–1596, 1967.
i1 Samuelson G L, Ailion D C: Low Cost High Linearity Solid State Digital Double Boxcar; Rev. Sci. Instrum. 40, 676–680, 1969.
j1 Alles H G, Higgins R J: Software Emulated Multichannel Lock-In Detector; Rev. Sci. Instrum. 44, 1646–1650, 1973.
k1 Blume R J: Boxcar Integrator with Long Holding Times; Rev. Sci. Instrum. 32, 1016–1018, 1961.
l1 Collins F G, Katchinoski R: Boxcar Attachment for Oscilloscopes Useful for Low Level Signals; Rev. Sci. Instrum. 44, 1178–1181, 1973.
m1 Williams D R, Lum W T: Lock-In Amplifier Uses Single IC; Analog Dialogue 8, No.1, 18, 1974.
n1 Letzter S G: Explore the Lock-In Amplifier; Electronic Design 11 Oct. 1974, 104–109.
o1 Smith D T: An AC Overload Voltage Indicator; J Phys. E Sci. Instrum. 42, 50, 1965.
p1 Schuster N A: A Phase-Sensitive Detector Having High Balance Stability; Rev. Sci. Instrum. 22, 254–255, 1951.
q1 Morris E D, Johnson H S: Digital Phase Sensitive Detector; Rev. Sci. Instrum. 39, 620–621, 1968.

r1 Faulkner E A, Stannett R H O: A General-Purpose Phase-Sensitive Detector; Electronic Eng. 36, 159–161, 1964.
s1 Faulkner E A, Harding D W: A High-Performance Phase-Sensitive Detector; J Phys. E Sci. Instrum. 43, 97–99, 1966.
t1 Pederson B O: Phase-Sensitive Detection with Multiple Frequencies; Trans IRE 1–9, 349–355, 1960.
u1 Frater R H: A Precision Phase Meter; IEEE Trans IM-15, 9–19, 1966.
v1 Brookdeal: Signal Recovery Improved by Two Orders of Magnitude; Electronic Eng. 42, May 1970, 100.
w1 Ware D, Mansfield P: High Stability Boxcar Integrator for Fast NMR Transients in Solids; Rev. Sci. Instrum. 37, 1167–1171, 1966.
x1 Bletzinger P, Garscadden A, Alexeff I, Jones W D: Sampling Oscilloscope as a Coherent Wide Band Detector; J Sci. Instrum. 42, 358–359, 1965.
y1 Faulkner E A, Grimbleby J B: High Speed Linear Gate; Electronic Eng. 39, 565–567, 1967.
z1 Rainal A J: Zero Crossing Principle for Detecting Narrow-Band Signals; IEEE Trans IM-15, 38–43, 1966.
A1 Tekelec/Airtronic: Lock-In Techniques; Orbit May 1970, 21–26 and 31–34.
B1 Williams P: A Phase-Sensitive Detector with High Noise Immunity; J Phys. E Sci. Instrum. 3, 441–443, 1970.
C1 Russell A M, Torchia D A: Harmonic Analysis in Systems Using Phase Sensitive Detectors; Rev. Sci. Instrum. 33, 442–444, 1962.
D1 Abernethy J D W: The Boxcar Detector; Wireless World 76, 576–579, 1970.
E1 Linsley Hood J L: Wide Bandwidth Phase-Sensitive Detector Uses Junction FETs; Electronic Eng. 42, 62–63, 1970.
F1 Danby P C G: Circuit Configurations for Current-Switching Phase-Sensitive Detectors; Electronic Eng. 40, 668–669, 1968.
G1 Caplan L C, Stern R: An Inexpensive Lock-In Amplifier; Rev. Sci. Instrum. 42, 689–695, 1971.
H1 Harrison G E, Player M A, Sandars P G H: A Multichannel Phase-Sensitive Detection Method Using Orthogonal Square Waveforms; J Phys. E Sci. Instrum. 4, 750–754, 1971.
I1 Grimbleby J B, Harding D W: A New High-Performance Phase-Sensitive Detector; J Phys. E Sci. Instrum. 4, 941–944, 1971.
J1 Gamble G R: Signal Processing Using Synchronous Detectors; Electron 6 June 1974, 29, 31, 33.
K1 Clarke R W G, Russell I P: Spectroscopic Detector Amplifier for 100Hz to 10kHz; Mullard Tech. Comm. 10, 230–233, 1969.
L1 Coles B A: A Fast-Response Phase Detector with Low Output Ripple; J Phys. E Sci. Instrum. 4, 1059–1060, 1971.
M1 Niemela L: A Boxcar Integrator for Pulsed NMR Relaxation Time Measurements; J Phys. E Sci. Instrum. 5, 526–528, 1972.
N1 Danby P C G: Signal Recovery Using a Phase Sensitive Detector; Electronic Eng. 42, 36–41, 1970.
O1 Keithley: A Guide to Selecting and Using Lock-In Amplifiers; Keithley Instrument Product Notes, 1973.
P1 Munroe D: The Logarithmic Lock-In Detector; Ithaco Application Note IAN-22, 1972.
Q1 Murphy M K, Clyburn S A, Veillon C: Comparison of Lock-In Amplification and Photon Counting with Low Background Flames and Graphite Atomizers in Atomic Resonance Spectroscopy; Anal. Chem. 45, 1468–1473, 1973.
R1 Perkins J R, Rogers R N: Diode Switch for Push-Pull Phase Sensitive Detector Applications; Rev. Sci. Instrum. 36, 1883–1885, 1965.
S1 Moore R D: Lock-In Amplifier for Signals Buried in Noise; Electronics 8 June, 1962, 40.
T1 Wooding E R, Pearl P R: A VHF Autocorrelator; J Phys. E Sci. Instrum. 7, 514–516, 1974.
U1 Gangi A: Op Amps Replace Transformer in Phase-Detector Circuit; Electronics 42, 12 May 1969, 108.

V1 Calkins R: Dynamic Tests for Op Amps Use Synchronous Demodulation; Electronics 41, 5 Aug. 1968, 118–123.
W1 Abernethy J D W: Boxcar Detectors; Research Development 22, 24–28, June 1971.
X1 Jones R V, Richards J C S: The Design and Some Applications of Sensitive Capacitance Micrometers; J Phys. E Sci. Instrum. 6, 589–600, 1973.
Y1 George A J, Teany D T: Transistorized Lock-In for Klystron Automatic Frequency Control; Rev. Sci. Instrum. 31, 997–998, 1960.
Z1 Lamers K W: 'Do-it-Yourself' Lock-In Amplifiers—Radio and Audio Frequencies; Nuc. Instr. Meth. 49, 165–169, 1967.
a2 Komachi Y, Tanaka S: Lock-In Amplifier Using a Sampled-Data Synchronous Filter; J Phys. E Sci. Instrum. 8, 967–971, 1975.
b2 Hanisch R J, Hughes G P, Merrill J R: Theoretical Limitations and Extensions of a Modulation Technique for Lineshape Analysis; Rev. Sci. Instrum. 46, 1262–1266, 1975.
c2 Tavares S E: A Comparison of Integration and Low-Pass Filtering; IEEE Trans IM-15, Mar.-June 1966, 33–38.
d2 Blair D P, Sydenham P H: Phase Sensitive Detection as a Means to Recover Signals Buried in Noise; J Phys. E Sci. Instrum. 8, 621–627, 1975.
e2 Leder L B, Simpson J A: Improved Electrical Differentiation of Retarding Potential Measurements; Rev. Sci. Instrum. 29, 571–574, 1958.
f2 Dereppe J M: Phase Sensitive Detector; Rev. Sci. Instrum. 32, 979, 1961.
g2 Adler J G, Jackson J E: System for Observing Small Nonlinearities in Tunnel Junctions; Rev. Sci. Instrum. 37, 1049–1054, 1966.
h2 Swain D W: Boxcar Integrator for Oscilloscopes; Rev. Sci. Instrum. 41, 545–547, 1970.
i2 Williams P, Coon M: An Apparatus for the Observation of Fine Structure in Current-Voltage Characteristics of Tunnel Diodes; J Sci. Instrum. 43, 186–189, 1966.
j2 Evans B L, Thompson K T: A Derivative Attachment for a Prism Spectrometer; J Phys. E Sci. Instrum. 2, 327–330, 1969.
k2 Wade C W: New Signal-Processing Instrument for Dual-Wavelength/Split Beam Spectrophotometers; Rev. Sci. Instrum. 46, 987–994, 1975.
l2 Calo J M, Bailey A D: Phase-Sensitive Pulse Counting in Modulated Beam Mass Spectrometry; Rev. Sci. Instrum. 45, 1325–1330, 1974.
m2 Hidaka T: Time Domain Difference Amplifier; Rev. Sci. Instrum. 46, 152–154, 1975.
n2 Haberland H: Phase Measurements in Chopped Particle Beams; Rev. Sci. Instrum. 46, 183–184, 1975.
o2 Blakemore J S, Borras J A, Kennewell J A: A Comparison of Methods for Measurement of the Magnetophonon Effect; J Phys. E Sci. Instrum. 8, 227–231, 1975.
p2 Brookdeal: Model 401A Lock-In Amplifier; Brookdeal Electronics Handbook.
q2 Hager R N, Anderson R C: Theory of the Derivative Spectrometer; J Opt. Soc. Amer. 60, 1444–1449, 1970.
r2 Bonfiglioli G, Brovetto P: Principles of Self Modulating Derivative Optical Spectroscopy; Applied Optics 3, 1417–1424, 1964.
s2 Abernethy J D W: Signal Recovery Methods; Physics Bulletin 24, 591–593, 1973.
t2 Brookdeal: Your Guide to Lock-In Amplifiers; Brookdeal Electronics 1973.
u2 Rolfe J, Moore S E: The Efficient Use of Photomultiplier Tubes for Recording Spectra; Applied Optics 9, 63–71, 1970.
v2 Boas M L: Mathematical Methods in the Physical Sciences; Wiley 1966, p17.
w2 Thomason W H, Elbers D C: An Inexpensive Method to Stabilize the Frequency of a CO Laser; Rev. Sci. Instrum. 46, 409–412, 1975.
x2 Jung P: Transistorized Frequency Stabilization for Reflex Klystrons Used in Magnetic Resonance; J Sci. Instrum. 37, 372–374, 1960.
y2 Budding R W, Strackee L: A Simple Reference Generator for Lock-In Amplifiers; J Phys. E Sci. Instrum. 5, 744–745, 1972.
z2 Munroe D M: A Lock-In Amplifier Primer; Princeton Applied Research Publication T351, 1975.

References section 10.3: Signal averaging

a1 Porchet J P, Gunthard H H: Optimum Sampling and Smoothing Conditions for Digitally Recorded Spectra; J Phys. E Sci. Instrum. 3, 261–264, 1974.
b1 Cuthrell R E, Schroeder C F: Spectrophotometer Signal Enhancement by Digital Computer; Rev. Sci. Instrum. 36, 1249, 1965.
c1 Soucek B: Minicomputers in Data Processing and Simulation. Chapter 8 Data Sampling and Quantizing; Wiley Interscience 1972.
d1 Rex R L, Roberts G T: Correlation, Signal Averaging, and Probability Analysis; Hewlett-Packard J 21, Nov. 1969, 2–8.
e1 Anderson G C, Perry M A: A Calibrated Real-Time Correlator/Averager/Probability Analyzer; Hewlett-Packard J 21, Nov. 1969, 9–20.
f1 Parks J G, Coulter R L: Simplified Instrumentation for Low Frequency Spectrum Analysis; Rev. Sci. Instrum. 42, 1650–1656, 1971.
g1 Tainal A J: Zero-Crossing Principle for Detecting Narrow-Band Signals; IEEE Trans IM-15, 38–43, 1966.
h1 Bice P K: Get Accurate Fast Fourier Transforms with a Digital Computer; Electronic Design 10 May 1973, 84–87.
i1 Northern Scientific: Noise Reduction by Digital Signal Averaging; Northern Scientific Technical Note 64–1, 1964.
j1 Carlson R, Krakauer S, Magleby K, Monnier R, Van Duzer V, Woodbury R: Sampling Oscillography; Hewlett-Packard Application Note 36, 1959.
k1 Hewlett-Packard: Time Interval Averaging; Hewlett-Packard Application Note 162–1.
l1 Jones B: Circuit Electronics for Scientists; Addison Wesley 1974.
m1 Federal Scientific: Real Time Signal Processing in the Frequency Domain; Nicolet Scientific Corp. Monograph 3, 1973.
n1 Chu D C: Time Interval Averaging: Theory, Problems, and Solutions; Hewlett-Packard J 25, June 1974, 12–15.
o1 Hewlett-Packard: Fourier Analyzer Training Manual; Hewlett-Packard Application Note 140–0.
p1 Hewlett-Packard: Multichannel Analyzer Applications; Hewlett-Packard Application Note 138, June 1971.
q1 Heers A F: Statistical Analysis of Waveforms and Digital Time-Waveform Measurements; Hewlett-Packard Application Note 93, Feb. 1969.
r1 Balmer L, Brooks B: How to Obtain Direct Display of Probability Density Functions; Electronic Eng. 44, Apr. 1972, 37–39.
s1 Trimble C R: What is Signal Averaging?; Hewlett-Packard J 19, Apr. 1968, 2–7.
t1 Deardorff J E, Trimble C R: Calibrated Real-Time Signal Averaging; Hewlett-Packard J 19, Apr. 1968, 8–13.
u1 Roth P R: Digital Fourier Analysis; Hewlett-Packard J 21, June 1970, 2–9.
v1 Amsel G, Bosshard R: Sampling and Averaging Techniques in the Analysis of Fast Random Signals; Rev. Sci. Instrum. 41, 503–514, 1970.
w1 Ernst R R: Sensitivity Enhancement in Magnetic Resonance. I Analysis of the Method of Time Averaging; Rev. Sci. Instrum. 36, 1689–1695, 1965.
x1 Ernst R R, Anderson W A: Sensitivity Enhancement in Magnetic Resonance. II Investigation of Intermediate Passage Conditions; Rev. Sci. Instrum. 36, 1696–1706, 1965. See also Ernst R R: Advances in Magnetic Resonance Vol. II, Waugh J S (Ed), Academic Press, for corrections.
y1 Stejskal E O: Use of an Analog-to-Digital Converter in Pulsed Nuclear Resonance; Rev. Sci. Instrum. 34, 971–975, 1963.
z1 Lee Y W: Statistical Theory of Communication; Wiley 1960.
A1 Linden D A: A Discussion of Sampling Theorems; Proc. IRE 47, 1219–1226, 1959.
B1 Papoulis A: Error Analysis in Sampling Theory; Proc IEEE 54, 947–955, 1966.
C1 Klein M P, Barton G W: Enhancement of Signal-to-Noise Ratio by Continuous Averaging: Application to Magnetic Resonance; Rev. Sci. Instrum. 34, 754–759, 1963.
D1 Whalen A D: Detection of Signals in Noise; Academic Press 1971.

E1 Beauchamp K G: Signal Processing Using Analog and Digital Techniques; George Allen and Unwin 1973.
F1 Bonnet G: Etude Theorique de l'Extraction d'un Signal Periodique dans un Bruit par Accumulation de Donnees; Nuc. Instr. Meth. 37, 217–230, 1965.
G1 Champney D C: Fourier Transforms and Their Physical Applications. Chapter 10 The Retrieval of Information from Noise; Academic Press 1973.
H1 Coor T: Signal Averaging Computers; Industrial Research May 1972.
I1 Holbrook Laplace Transforms for Electronic Engineers; Pergamon Press 2nd Edn. 1966.
J1 Boas M L: Mathematical Methods in the Physical Sciences; Wiley 1966.
K1 Steingraber O J, Berlman I B: Versatile Technique for Measuring Fluorescence Decay Times in the Nanosecond Region; Rev. Sci. Instrum. 34, 524–529, 1963.
L1 Kiss A Z: A Calibrated Computer-Based Fourier Analyzer: Hewlett-Packard J 21, June 1970, 10–20.
N1 PAR: Signal Averagers; Princeton Applied Research 1973.
O1 Bletzinger P, Garscadden A, Alexeff I, Jones W D: Sampling Oscilloscope as a Coherent Wide-Band Detector; J Sci. Instrum. 42, 358–359, 1965.
P1 Wilson W E, Roesch W C: Fast Pulse Signal Averaging; Rev. Sci. Instrum. 37, 1623–1624, 1966.

References section 10.4: Correlation

a1 Rex R L, Roberts G T: Correlation, Signal Averaging, and Probability Analysis; Hewlett-Packard J 21, Nov. 1969, 2–8.
b1 Anderson G C, Perry M A: A Calibrated Real-Time Correlator/Averager/Probability Analyzer; Hewlett-Packard J 21, Nov. 1969, 9–20.
c1 Langenthal I M: Correlation and Probability Analysis; Signal Analysis Industries TB14, 1970.
d1 Levine R I: Correlation—Theory and Practice; Electronic Products Nov. 1963, 21–23, 104–106.
e1 Chamberlain L J: A Simple Discussion of Time-Series Analysis; Time/Data (General Radio) Application Note 1970.
f1 Heers A F: Statistical Analysis of Waveforms and Digital Time-Waveform Measurements; Hewlett-Packard Application Note 93, Feb. 1969.
g1 Cutting R A, Edge G M, Hook R C, Quayle I H, Smith-Saville R J: Extracting and Using Correlation Methods; Electronic Eng. 41, Oct. 1969, 48–52.
h1 Wooding E R, Pearl P R: A VHF Autocorrelator; J Phys. E Sci. Instrum. 7, 514–516, 1974.
i1 Heizman C L: Signal Analysis with Digital Time-Series Analyzers; General Radio Experimenter 44, July/Sep. 1970, 3–7.
j1 Lawton R A: Autocorrelation and Power Measurement with Pyroelectric and Dielectric Bolometers; IEEE Trans IM-22, 299–306, 1973.
k1 Lee Y W: Statistical Theory of Communication; Wiley 1960.
l1 LuBow B: Correlation Entering New Fields with Real Time Signal Analysis; Electronics 39, 31 Oct. 1966, 75–81.
m1 Brophy J J, Epstein M, Webb S L: Correlator Amplifier for Very Low Level Signals; Rev. Sci. Instrum. 36, 1803–1806, 1965.
n1 Bendat J S: Fundamentals of Time Series Analysis; Time/Data (General Radio) Monograph, 1974.
o1 Corti M, De Agostini A, Degiorgio V: Fast Digital Correlator for Weak Optical Signals; Rev. Sci. Instrum. 45, 888–893, 1974.
p1 Ramirez R: Fast Fourier Transform Makes Correlation Easier; Electronics 26 June 1975, 98–103.
q1 Tai I, Hasegawa K, Sekiguchi A: A Real Time Correlator with a Peak Detector; J Phys. E Sci. Instrum. 8, 206–208, 1975.

r1 Ables J G, Cooper B F C, Hunt A J, Moorey G G, Brooks J W: A 1024-Channel Digital Correlator; Rev. Sci. Instrum. 46, 284–295, 1975.
s1 Kam Z, Shore H B, Feher G: Simple Schemes for Measuring Autocorrelation Functions; Rev. Sci. Instrum. 46, 269–277, 1975.
t1 Bendat J S, Piersol A G: Measurement and Analysis of Random Data; Wiley 1966.
u1 Lange F H: Correlation Techniques; Iliffe 1967.

11 Applications

As outlined in the preface it has not been possible to cover both the principles and detailed practical circuits of the wide range of techniques covered in this book. Though each section has a list of references these are primarily of a more specific nature relating to the particular topic or device. In the present chapter are listed a number of references covering a wide range of general applications. They have been selected primarily on the basis of their use of integrated circuits to implement a variety of electronic systems.

As will be seen from the limited number of journals referred to this is not intended to be a comprehensive list. However, it is hoped that these will serve as illustrations of the range of applications of the various types of IC, and as a direct guide to the construction of a particular system.

a1   Karlsson L: Instrumentation for Measuring Bioelectric Signals in Plants; Rev. Sci. Instrum. 43, 458–464, 1972.
b1   Cudney R A, Phelps C T, Barreto E: An ungrounded Electronic Field Meter; Rev. Sci. Instrum. 43, 1372–1373, 1972.
c1   Fay H: Magnetic Hysteresis Loop Tracer Using Operational Amplifiers; Rev. Sci. Instrum. 43, 1274–1279, 1972.
d1   Everett P M: A 1/H Drive for use with Superconducting Solenoids; Rev. Sci. Instrum. 43, 753–755, 1972.
e1   Miller C A: Temperature Control Using Commercially Available DC Amplifiers; J Sci. Instrum. 44, 573–574, 1967.
f1   Kampwirth R T: An Optical Thickness Monitor for Thin Film Vacuum Deposition Control; Rev. Sci. Instrum. 43, 740–743, 1972.
g1   Engel P S: An Inexpensive Electronically Controlled Constant Rate Addition Funnel; Rev. Sci. Instrum. 43, 1707–1708, 1972.
h1   Anderson J R, Sandfort R M, Stone D R: Low Level Tracking Marginal Oscillator for In-Situ Magnetic Field Measurements at Low Temperatures; Rev. Sci. Instrum. 43, 1129–1133, 1972.
i1   Hamstra R H, Wendland P: Noise and Frequency Response of Silicon Photodiode Operational Amplifier Combination; Applied Optics 11, 1539–1547, 1972.
j1   Reed D A, Graham W R: A Simple Liquid Helium Vapour Cooled Field Ion Microscope for the Study of Vapour Deposition; Rev. Sci. Instrum. 43, 1365–1367, 1972.
k1   Marzetta L A: Use of an Operational Amplifier with Helmholtz Coils for Reducing AC Induced Magnetic Fields; Rev. Sci. Instrum. 32, 1192–1195, 1961. See also Rudd M E, Craig J R: Optimum Spacing of Square and Circular Coil Pairs; Rev. Sci. Instrum. 39, 1372–1374, 1968. Cacak R K, Craig J R: Magnetic Field Uniformity Around Near-Helmholtz Coil Configurations; Rev. Sci. Instrum. 40, 1468–1470, 1969. Johnson C B: Tri-Coil Electromagnet; Rev. Sci. Instrum. 46, 1289–1290, 1975.
l1   Samuelson G, Ailion D C: Low-Cost Integrated Circuit Versatile Pulse and Frequency Counter; Rev. Sci. Instrum. 40, 681–683, 1969.
m1   Opal C, Gandrud W B: Feedback-Stabilized Light Chopper with Continuously Variable Frequency; Rev. Sci. Instrum. 38, 838–840, 1967.
n1   Valliant H D: Exact Temperature Control with Operational Amplifiers; Electronics 3 Apr. 1967, 97–98.

o1 Buchalter D N, Hargreaves J H: Angular Displacement Detector; Rev. Sci. Instrum. 43, 1711–1712, 1972.

p1 Lescovec R A, Bevington P R: A Solid State Light Pen and Computer Interface for the Tektronix 611 Storage Oscilloscope; Rev. Sci. Instrum. 42, 602–605, 1971.

q1 Cooke M B D, Eadie R J: Digital Presentation of Sample Concentrations Using an Online Computer; Electronic Eng. 43, Mar. 1971, 59–63.

r1 Burgess A E, Crooks M J: Temperature Controller for Dilution Refrigerators; Rev. Sci. Instrum. 43, 1718–1719, 1972.

s1 Shannon P E V: Variable Frequency Power Source for Synchronous Motors; Rev. Sci. Instrum. 35, 236–237, 1964.

t1 de Sa A, McCartan D G: A Digitally Controlled Scanning Device for a High Resolution Spectrography; J Phys. E Sci. Instrum. 5, 1183–1185, 1972.

u1 Eppeldauer G, Schander J: A Sensitive Filter Fluorometer; J Phys. E Sci. Instrum. 5, 1197–1199, 1972.

v1 Kemper A, Kivits P: A Controlled Apparatus for the Automatic Measurements of Fractional Glow Curves; J Phys. E Sci. Instrum. 5, 1213–1215, 1972.

w1 Nishida K, Nakajima M: Temperature Dependence and Stabilization of Avalanche Photodiodes; Rev. Sci. Instrum. 43, 1345–1350, 1972.

x1 LaForce R C, LaForce G, Hansen C R: A Proton Magnetic Field Controller; Rev. Sci. Instrum. 43, 1695–1698, 1972.

y1 Yamashita M: Light Output Control of a Pulsed Light Source for Use in Stabilizing Scintillation Detectors; Rev. Sci. Instrum. 43, 1719–1721, 1972.

z1 Wobschall D: A Capacitance Meter for Bilayer Membrane Studies; Rev. Sci. Instrum. 43, 1723–1726, 1972.

A1 Babbs R S: Simple Low-Power Temperature Stabilizer; Mullard Tech. Comm. 12, Apr. 1973, 258–260.

B1 Redfield D: Arc Lamp Intensity Stabilizer; Rev. Sci. Instrum. 32, 557–558, 1961.

C1 Schurer K, Stoelhorst J: A Simple Device for Stabilizing the Output of a High-Pressure Xenon Arc; J Sci. Instrum. 44, 952–953, 1967.

D1 Scouler W J, Mills E D: Current Regulator for Ultraviolet Light Source; Rev. Sci. Instrum. 35, 489–492, 1964.

E1 Chopra S, Mandel L: An Electronic Correlator for Photoelectric Correlation; Rev. Sci. Instrum. 43, 1489–1491, 1972.

F1 Hamilton T D S, Razi Naqvi K: Instrument for Time-Resolved Phosphorimetry Using an Electronically Gated Photomultiplier; Anal. Chem. 45, 1581–1584, 1973.

G1 Giffard R P: A Simple Low Power Self-Balancing Resistance Bridge; J Phys. E Sci. Instrum. 6, 719–723, 1973.

H1 Jones R V, Richards J C S: The Design and Some Applications of Sensitive Capacitance Micrometers; J Phys. E Sci. Instrum. 6, 589–600, 1973.

I1 Altwein M, Finkenrath H: The Measurement of Calibrated Current-Voltage Characteristics Up to the Second Derivative; J Phys. E Sci. Instrum. 6, 770–774, 1973.

J1 Altwein M, Finkenrath H, Stockel T: Low Temperature Hall Measurements in a Cryostat with a Built-In Magnet; J Phys. E Sci. Instrum. 6, 623–627, 1973.

K1 Jenkins G J, Lund F P: A Miniature Magnetic Spin Rate Sensor for Sounding Rockets; J Phys. E Sci. Instrum. 6, 637–638, 1973.

L1 Reche J J H, Pulfrey D L: A Reflectance Analog Computer for the Determination of Thin Film Optical Properties; Rev. Sci. Instrum. 44, 914–915, 1973.

M1 Tick P A, Johnson D: A Dynamic Bridge Measurement for Lossy Systems; Rev. Sci. Instrum. 44, 798–799, 1973.

N1 Bloyet D, Piejus P, Varoquaux E: A Sampling Linear Detector for Accurate RF Pulse Amplitude Measurement; Rev. Sci. Instrum. 44, 383–390, 1973.

O1 Yamashita M: A Precision Sampling Circuit; Rev. Sci. Instrum. 44, 638–639, 1973.

P1 Zucker M H: Electronic Circuits for the Behavioural and Biomedical Sciences; W H Freeman 1969.

Q1 Crosswy F L, Hornkohl J O: Signal Conditioning Electronics for a Laser Vector Velocimeter; Rev. Sci. Instrum. 44, 1324–1332, 1973.

R1 Treu J I, Callender A B, Schnatterly S E: Use of a Stable Polarization Modulator in a Scanning Spectrophotometer and Ellipsometer; Rev. Sci. Instrum. 44, 793–797, 1973.
S1 Vanegas C M, Finegold L: Simple, Inexpensive Liquid Helium Temperature Controller, Using Integrated Semiconductor Circuits; Rev. Sci. Instrum. 40, 159–162, 1969.
T1 Bernalte A, LePage J: A New Method for Rapid and Accurate Measurement of Decay Time Constants; Rev. Sci. Instrum. 40, 71–74, 1969.
U1 Kress K A, Lapeyre G J: Operational Amplifier Differentiator for Photoemission Studies: Origin and Control of Errors; Rev. Sci. Instrum. 40, 74–78, 1969.
V1 Emrick R M, McDonald D E: Programmable Temperature Controller for Small Diameter Wires; Rev. Sci. Instrum. 40, 82–84, 1969.
W1 Chase R L: Flyback System for a Constant Velocity Mossbauer Drive; Rev. Sci. Instrum. 40, 85–88, 1969.
X1 Huntress W T, Simms W T: A New Ion and Electron Detector for Ion Cyclotron Resonance Spectroscopy; Rev. Sci. Instrum. 44, 1274–1277, 1973.
Y1 Elliott M T, Blackstead H A: A Magnet Sweep Controller; Rev. Sci. Instrum. 44, 1426–1427, 1973.
Z1 Hicks T R, Reay N K, Scadden R J: A Servo Controlled Fabry-Perot Interferometer Using Capacitance Micrometers for Error Detection; J Phys. E Sci. Instrum. 7, 27–30, 1974.
a2 Praul S H, Hmurcik L V: Instantaneous Temperature Measurement; Rev. Sci. Instrum. 44, 1363–1364, 1973.
b2 Tracy J C, Bohn G K: Auger Electron Spectrometer Preamplifier; Rev. Sci. Instrum. 41, 591–592, 1970.
c2 Smith J B: An Amplifier for Electron Multiplier Pulse Counting Applications; Rev. Sci. Instrum. 43, 488–492, 1972.
d2 Lampton M, Primbsch J H: A Versatile Pulse Amplifier; Rev. Sci. Instrum. 42, 731–732, 1971.
e2 Carra W M, Ehret J E, Locker D R, Meese J M: Beam Scanner for a 1MeV Van der Graaff; Rev. Sci. Instrum. 44, 1407–1408, 1973.
f2 Taylor D G, Booth S, Allen P S: A Flexible, Modular Pulse Programmer Suitable for Diverse Nuclear Resonance Experiments; J Phys. E Sci. Instrum. 7, 105–110, 1974.
g2 Aoshima R, Sugita T: A Photomultiplier Cooler with a High Stability of $+/- 0.005$ C; J Phys. E Sci. Instrum. 7, 48–50, 1974.
h2 Hawk R M, Sharp R R, Tolan J W: A Broadband NMR Spectrometer for Field Stabilization in the Range 4–23kG; Rev. Sci. Instrum. 45, 96–99, 1974.
i2 Paesler M A, Fritsche H: Measurement of Internal Stress in Thin Films; Rev. Sci. Instrum. 45, 114–115, 1974.
j2 Anderson P T, Pipes P B: A Low Noise Amplifier with Application to Noise Thermometry Between 300 and 4K; Rev. Sci. Instrum. 45, 42–44, 1974.
k2 Michaels H B, Basser T E, Taylor W B, Hunt J W: An Automated Facility for Microsecond Kinetic Spectrophotometry; Rev. Sci. Instrum. 44, 1286–1289, 1973.
l2 Pierce R D, Venard W B: Thickness Measurements of Films on Transparent Substrates by Photoelectric Detection of Interference Fringes; Rev. Sci. Instrum. 45, 14–15, 1974.
m2 Auer R E: A Data Acquisition System with Isolated Output Voltage for Acquiring Events-Versus-Voltage Spectra; Rev. Sci. Instrum. 43, 666–669, 1972.
n2 Goodman L A, Arntz F O: Optically Pumped Differential Absorption Apparatus for Study of Slow Traps in Insulators; Rev. Sci. Instrum. 43, 1280–1285, 1972.
o2 Laurendeau N M, Shaw A D: A Preset Timer for Control of Mass Spectrometer Scan Functions; Rev. Sci. Instrum. 43, 1287–1290, 1972.
p2 Micheron F, Godefroy L: Automatic Impedance Measurements Using Thermal Noise Analysis; Rev. Sci. Instrum. 43, 1460–1465, 1972.
q2 Lomnes R K: Data Acquisition System for Residual Gas Analyzer; Rev. Sci. Instrum. 43, 937–938, 1972.
r2 Chance B, Graham N, Sorge J, Legallais V: Rapid Readout from Dual Wavelength Spectrophotometers; Rev. Sci. Instrum. 43, 62–71, 1972.
s2 Elliot J: The Computation of the Best Windward and Running Courses for Sailing Yachts; Radio Electronic Engnr. 43, 715–727, 1973.

t2 Sample H H, Neuringer L J, Rubin L G: Low Temperature Thermometry in High Magnetic Fields. III Carbon Resistors (0.5–4.2K); Thermocouples; Rev. Sci. Instrum. 45, 64–73, 1974.

u2 Carra W M, Ehret J E, Meese J M: Low Cost Beam Current Integrator; Rev. Sci. Instrum. 44, 835–836, 1973.

v2 Beattie A G, Jaramillo R A: The Measurement of Energy in Acoustic Emission; Rev. Sci. Instrum. 45, 352–357, 1974.

w2 Yair R: Charge Sampling Method for Low Current Measurement; Rev. Sci. Instrum. 45, 395–399, 1974.

x2 Jones B E, McNaughton H M: An Investigation of Open and Closed Loop Tilt Monitors Employing Electrolytic Spirit Levels; J Phys. E Sci. Instrum. 7, 582–585, 1974.

y2 Witholt B, Brand L: Versatile Spectrophotofluorometer-Polarization Fluorometer; Rev. Sci. Instrum. 39, 1271–1278, 1968.

z2 Varma M N, Joshi A, Strongin M, Radeka V: Difference Auger Spectroscopy for Studying Small Quantities of Elements on Metallic Surfaces; Rev. Sci. Instrum. 44, 1643–1645, 1973.

A2 Luthjens L H: High Intensity Pulsed Analyzing Light Sources for Nano- and Micro-Second Absorption Spectrophotometry; Rev. Sci. Instrum. 44, 1661–1665, 1973.

B2 Spear W E, Layon H P D, Mort J: Some Applications of Mercury Wetted Contact Relays; J Sci. Instrum. 39, 81–83, 1962.

C2 Baker A R, Firth J G: The Estimation of Firedamp—Applications and Limitations of the Pellistor; Mining Engineer 128, 237–244, 1969.

D2 Chapman R: Versatile Wide Range Electron Current Regulator; Rev. Sci. Instrum. 43, 1536–1538, 1972.

E2 McCarthy S L, Stanko J: Pattern-Generators and Techniques for Electron-Beam Fabrication of Submicron Thin-Film Bridges for Superconductivity Studies; Rev. Sci. Instrum. 45, 335–340, 1974.

F2 Anson M, Bayley P M: Measurement of Circular Dichroism at Millisecond Time Resolution: a Stopped-Flow Circular Dichroism System; J Phys. E Sci. Instrum. 7, 481–486, 1974.

G2 Griffiths B, Stow C D, Syms P H: An Accurate Diode Thermometer for use in Thermal Gradient Chambers; J Phys. E Sci. Instrum. 7, 710–714, 1974.

H2 Warnick A, Anders L R, Sharp T E: A Marginal Oscillator Detector for Ion Cyclotron Resonance Spectrometers; Rev. Sci. Instrum. 45, 929–935, 1974.

I2 Matson G B: A Precision Current Pulse Generator for NMR Self-Diffusion Measurements by the Pulsed Gradient Technique; Rev. Sci. Instrum. 43, 1504–1508, 1972.

J2 Stevens M R, Giffin C E, Shoemaker G R, Simmonds P G: A Portable Self-Contained Gas Chromatograph; Rev. Sci. Instrum. 43, 1530–1534, 1972.

K2 Rubin L G, Golahny Y: An Improved AC Bridge Circuit for Use in Four-Terminal Resistance Thermometry; Rev. Sci. Instrum. 43, 1758–1762, 1972.

L2 Gark A P: Continuous Measurement of Internal Friction and Modulus with a Regenerative Feedback Loop and Composite Oscillator; Rev. Sci. Instrum. 43, 1786–1789, 1972.

M2 Lind A C: A Programmable Digital Pulser for NMR; Rev. Sci. Instrum. 43, 1800–1803, 1972.

N2 Horne D E, Sawatzky E: Modified Magneto-Optic Hysteresigraph; Rev. Sci. Instrum. 43, 1842–1844, 1972.

O2 Benkiki M, Penchina C M: Easy to Build and Low Cost Proportional Temperature Controller Using a Thermocouple Sensor; J Phys. E Sci. Instrum. 9, 95–96, 1976.

P2 Griffing B: A High Voltage Pulse Generator for Acoustoelectric Studies; Rev. Sci. Instrum. 45, 965–6, 1974.

Q2 Sarid D, Cannell D S: A +/− 15 Microdegree Temperature Controller; Rev. Sci. Instrum. 45, 1082–1088, 1974.

R2 Rupert G N: Calibrated Derivative Thermal Analysis Apparatus for Detecting Phase Transitions in High Temperature Materials; Rev. Sci. Instrum. 45, 1127–1133, 1974.

S2 Kibens V, Kovasznay L S G, Oswald J: Turbulent-Nonturbulent Interface Detector; Rev. Sci. Instrum. 45, 1138–1144, 1974.

T2 Paizis S T, Schwarz W H: A Circuit for the Detection of Turbulence; Rev. Sci. Instrum. 45, 348–351, 1974.

U2 Widmer A E, Fellman R: A Millivolt Source for Temperature Programming of Laboratory Furnaces; J Phys. E Sci. Instrum. 7, 610–612, 1974.

V2 Dobkin R C: Versatile IC Preamp (LM321) Makes Thermocouple Amplifier with Cold Junction Compensation; National Semiconductor Linear Brief LB-24, June 1973.

W2 Rogers J S: Conductance Bridge for Electron Tunnelling Measurements; Rev. Sci. Instrum. 41, 1184–1186, 1970.

X2 Wilcox S D, Eide S A, Caldwell D R: Adapting Small DC Motors for Precise Speed Control; Rev. Sci. Instrum. 45, 510–512, 1974.

Y2 Gribble R F, Kristal R: Multifringe Electro-Optic Phase Modulator; Rev. Sci. Instrum. 45, 520–522, 1974.

Z2 Hebard A F, Shumate P W: A New Approach to High Resolution Measurements of Structure in Superconducting Tunnelling Currents; Rev. Sci. Instrum. 45, 529–533, 1974.

a3 Lundsgaard J S, Petersen H A: A Peak Detector for Continuous Mass Spectrometric Measurements; J Phys. E Sci. Instrum. 7, 524–525, 1974.

b3 Wooding E R, Pearl P R: A VHF Autocorrelator; J Phys. E Sci. Instrum. 7, 514–516, 1974.

c3 Parks J G, Coulter R L: Simplified Instrumentation for Low Frequency Spectrum Analysis; Rev. Sci. Instrum. 42, 1650–1656, 1971.

d3 Gutknecht W F, Perone S P: Numerical Deconvolution of Overlapping Stationary Electrode Polarographic Curves with an On-Line Digital Computer; Anal. Chem. 42,

e3 Ellis E J: An Equalizer for an Electro-Magnetic Vibrator System Employing Analogue Computing Techniques; Radio Electronic Engnr. 27, 125–132, 1964.

f3 Zane R: Mossbauer Effect Velocity Drive Linearized by Shape Correction; Nuc. Instr. Meth. 43, 333–337, 1966.

g3 Rowlands R O: Electronic Engineering in Ocean and River Technology; Advances in Electronics and Electron Physics (Marton L (Ed)), 31, 267–300, 1972.

h3 Bunbury D St P: The Design of Apparatus for the Measurement of Mossbauer Spectra; J Sci. Instrum. 43, 783–790, 1966.

i3 Knipe A C, McLean D, Tranter R L: A Fast Response Conductivity Amplifier for Chemical Kinetics; J Phys. E Sci. Instrum. 7, 586–590, 1974.

j3 Beijerinck H C W, Habets A H M, Sessink B W L M, Verster N F: A Flexible Safeguarding System for Experimental Set-Ups; J Phys. E Sci. Instrum. 7, 639–640, 1974.

k3 Rigler R, Rabl C R, Jovin T M: A Temperature Jump Apparatus for Fluorescence Measurements; Rev. Sci. Instrum. 45, 580–588, 1974.

l3 Pelmore J M, Chapman C J S, Walls J M, Summers G G, Southworth H N: A Specimen Temperature Controller for Field Emission and Field-Ion Microscopy; J Phys. E Sci. Instrum. 9, 96–97, 1976.

m3 Balmer M, Brooks B: How to Obtain Direct Display of Probability Density Functions; Electronic Eng. Apr. 1972, 37–39.

n3 Cranshaw T E: Mossbauer Spectroscopy; J Phys. E Sci. Instrum. 7, 497–505. 1974.

o3 Easty A C, Young S; A Small Scale Dewpoint Humidity Measurer; J Phys. E Sci. Instrum. 9, 106–110, 1976.

p3 Heinzerling J: A Magnetic Flux Stabilizer for the Objective Lens of a Corrected Electron Microscope; J Phys. E Sci. Instrum. 9, 131–134, 1976.

q3 Defreese J D, Woodruff T A, Malmstadt H V: New Type of Programmable Current Regulated Power Supply for Operation of Hollow Cathode Lamps in a High Intensity Programmed Mode; Anal. Chem. 46, 1471–1476, 1974.

r3 Clower P: Inexpensive AM Modulator Replaces Clipping Type and Gives Less Distortion; Electronic Design 27 Sep. 1974, 122.

s3 Ewing G W: Current Controller Uses Adjustable Exponent; Analog Dialogue 8, No.1, 19, 1974.

t3 Malanowski G: Automatic Analysis of Human Muscle Signals; Electronic Eng. Nov. 1974, 25, 27.

u3 Weir K G: Analogue Linearized Technique for a Digital Voltmeter; J Phys. E Sci. Instrum. 7, 507–509, 1974.

v3 Tyler I L, Denenstein A, Langenberg D N: Infinite-Hold-Time Electronic Ramp Generator; Rev. Sci. Instrum. 45, 1007–1008, 1974.
w3 Lanz K: Circuit Adds Diagonal Axis to Any Scope; Electronics 19 Sep. 1974, 126–128.
x3 Prossor T F: An Integrated Temperature Sensor-Controller; IEEE J SC1, 8–13, 1966.
y3 Williams P, Coon M: An Apparatus for the Observation of Fine Structure in Current-Voltage Characteristics of Tunnel Diodes; J Sci. Instrum. 43, 186–189, 1966.
z3 Hoyer J: Electronic Ignition Systems for Motor Vehicles; Electronic Eng. 46, Dec. 1974,
A3 Agren C H: Photoelectric Vibration Probe for String Instruments; Electronic Eng. 46, Dec. 1974, 18–19.
B3 Rosenthal L A, Davis D A: Static Electricity Events Detector; Rev. Sci. Instrum. 45, 1239–1241, 1974.
C3 Diebold G, Santoro R: Differential Photodiode Detector for a Shock Tube Laser Schlieren System; Rev. Sci. Instrum. 45, 773–775, 1974.
D3 Olsen S L, Holmes L P, Eyring E M: Pulsed Spectrophotometric Chemical Relaxation Measurements; Rev. Sci. Instrum. 45, 859–861, 1974.
E3 Lundgren G, Lundmark L, Johannson G: Temperature Controlled Heating of the Graphite Tube Atomizer in Flameless Atomic Absorption Spectrophotometry; Anal. Chem. 46, 1028–1031, 1974.
F3 Isett L C, Blakely J M: An Analog Technique for the Measurement of Auger Electron Currents: Application to Sulphur on Ni(110); Rev. Sci. Instrum. 45, 1382–1385, 1974.
G3 Dratler J: A Proportional Thermostat with 10 Microdegree Stability; Rev. Sci. Instrum. 45, 1435–1444, 1974.
H3 Nathan R, Mee C H B: AC Methods for the Determination of Photoelectron Energy Distributions; Rev. Sci. Instrum. 38, 1783–1785, 1967.
I3 Lougheed J H, Zimmerman D: Buried Marking of Point Locations; IEEE Trans IM-22, 399–402, 1973.
J3 Uno M: A Method of Measuring the Peak Value of a Narrow Impulse by the Use of a Voltage-Forced Pulse Lengthener Circuit; IEEE Trans IM-22, 144–147, 1973.
K3 Lamoth I: Automatic Brightness Control and Linearity Correction Circuits for Large Screen Color Oscilloscopes; IEEE Trans IM-22, 138–143, 1973.
L3 Brosseau R, Vanier J: Relaxation Time Measurements by an Electronic Method; IEEE Trans IM-22, 18–22, 1973.
M3 Baty R L, Weiss P B: A Pulsed Hall Device Gaussmeter; IEEE Trans IM-22, 18–22, 1973.
N3 McCartney M L, Highfill J H: An Optically Coupled ECG System; IEEE Trans IM-22, 13–17, 1973.
O3 Barton G W, Tolman L F, Roulette R E: Fast Magnetic Field Sweep; Rev. Sci. Instrum. 31, 995–997, 1960.
P3 Randolph M L: Application of Analog Computers to ESR Spectroscopy; Rev. Sci. Instrum. 31, 949–952, 1960.
Q3 Collins R L: Analog Computer for Magnetic Resonance Data Reduction; Rev. Sci. Instrum. 30, 492, 1959.
R3 Jung P: Transistorized Frequency Stabilization for Reflex Klystrons Used in Magnetic Resonance; J Sci. Instrum. 37, 372–374, 1960.
S3 George A J, Teany D T: Transistorized Lock-In for Klystron Automatic Frequency Control; Rev. Sci. Instrum. 31, 997–998, 1960.
T3 Zipper J J, Perone S P: Theoretical and Experimental Evaluation of Staircase Voltammetry; Anal. Chem. 45, 452–458, 1973.
U3 Rupert G N: Calibrated Derivative Thermal Analysis Apparatus for Determining Phase Transitions in High Temperature Materials; Rev. Sci. Instrum. 45, 1127–1133, 1974.
V3 Hollish C D, Hertel R J: Technique for a Contour Display of Photoemission Uniformity; Rev. Sci. Instrum. 45, 1336–1339, 1974.
W3 Yamashita M: Photomultiplier Gate with Gating Times Larger than a Few Microseconds; Rev. Sci. Instrum. 45, 956–957, 1974.
X3 Yamashita M: Pulse Technique for Measuring Intensity Variations of Continuous Lights in Comparison with Reference Scintillation Pulses; Rev. Sci. Instrum. 957–959, 1974.

Y3 Wiesenfeld J R: Trigger Circuits for use in Flash Photolytic Experiments; Rev. Sci. Instrum. 45, 1465–1567, 1974.

Z3 Zerenner E: Analyze Gaseous Mixtures Without Fuss; Electronic Design 20 Dec. 1974, 82–87.

a4 Ferrone F A, Hopfield J J, Schnatterly S E: The Measurement of Transient Circular Dichroism: A New Kinetic Technique; Rev. Sci. Instrum. 45, 1392–1396, 1974.

b4 Harker K J, Ilic D B: Measurement of Plasma Wave Spectral Density from the Cross-Power Density Spectrum; Rev. Sci. Instrum. 45, 1315–1324, 1974.

c4 Lilley P, Warne D Y, Mordecai B A, Spencer A J: The Use of Electronic Prediction to Achieve Fast Response from a Simple Thermal Mass Flow Meter; J Phys. E Sci. Instrum. 8, 3–5, 1975.

d4 Unsworth J, Rose-Innes A C: Silicon P-N Junctions as Low Temperature Thermometers; Cryogenics 6, 239–240, 1966.

e4 Berberian J G: A Method for Measuring Very Small Conductances; Rev. Sci. Instrum. 46, 107–108, 1975.

f4 Billen J H: Continuously Displayed Emittance Measurements; Rev. Sci. Instrum. 46, 33–40, 1975.

g4 Sample H H, Neuringer L J: Low Temperature Thermometry in High Magnetic Fields. IV Allen-Bradley Carbon Resistors (0.5–4.2K); Rev. Sci. Instrum. 45, 1389–1391, 1974.

h4 Aldridge R V: A Silicon Diode Low Temperature Magnetometer; J Phys. E Sci. Instrum. 8, 9–11, 1975.

i4 Adler J G, Strauss J: Application of Minicomputers in High Resolution Electron Tunnelling; Rev. Sci. Instrum. 46, 158–163, 1975.

j4 Jacobs E P: An Automatic Switching Unit for Polarographic Measurements with Various Electrodes; J Phys. E Sci. Instrum. 8, 7–8, 1975.

k4 Ali S F: Hot Wire Anemometry in Moderately Heated Flow; Rev. Sci. Instrum. 46, 185–191, 1975.

l4 Budding R W, Strackee L: A Dynamic Admittance Meter Based on a Voltage Controlled Oscillator IC (XR-205); Rev. Sci. Instrum. 46, 210–212, 1975.

m4 Budding R W, Strackee L: A Simple Reference Generator for Lock-In Amplifiers; J Phys. E Sci. Instrum. 5, 744–745, 1972.

n4 Domingo G, Holm-Kennedy J W, Daud T: Instrument for Automatic Kilovolt Pulsed Measurement of Electronic Properties; Rev. Sci. Instrum. 46, 147–151, 1975.

o4 Hodgkinson K A: A Versatile Waveform Envelope Generator for the Synthesis of Musical Attack and Decay Transients; J Phys. E Sci. Instrum. 8, 123–126, 1975.

p4 Wampler W R, Matula S, Lengeler B, Durcansky G: Tunable Low-Temperature NMR Oscillator for Magnetic Field Measurements; Rev. Sci. Instrum. 46, 58–61, 1975.

q4 Auer S: Two High Resolution Velocity Vector Analyzers for Cosmic Dust Particles; Rev. Sci. Instrum. 46, 127–135, 1975.

r4 Borchardt I G, Holland L R: Pseudo-Bridge: A Different Way to Compare Resistances; Rev. Sci. Instrum. 46, 67–70, 1975.

s4 Daniels C J: An Integrated Circuit Pile-Up Rejector; Rev. Sci. Instrum. 46, 102–103, 1975.

t4 Bleijerveld R H T, Molenaar J B, Mijlhoff F C: A completely Automatic Pressure Measurement Apparatus; J Phys. E Sci. Instrum. 8, 235–239, 1975.

u4 Blakemore J S, Borras J A, Kennewell J A: A Comparison of Methods for Measurement of the Magnetophonon Effect; J Phys. E Sci. Instrum. 8, 227–231, 1975.

v4 Barletti R, Paterno L: An Instrument for the Measurement of the Mean Square Value of Atmospheric Star Scintillation; Rev. Sci. Instrum. 46, 15–17, 1975.

w4 Griffin J A: An AC Capacitance Bridge Temperature Controller for Use in Strong Magnetic Fields at Low Temperatures; Rev. Sci. Instrum. 46, 5–8, 1975.

x4 Paterson W L: A High Rate T–T Controller for Thermally Stimulated Currents; Rev. Sci. Instrum. 46, 196–197, 1975.

y4 Schwiesow R L, Post M J: Digital Data Acquisition for Laser Scattering Spectroscopy Using the Scatter-to-Incident Light Intensity Ratio; Rev. Sci. Instrum. 46, 413–416, 1975.

z4 Smith D T: An AC Overload Voltage Indicator; J Sci. Instrum. 42, 50, 1965.

A4   Starke T P, Malmberg J H, Vidmar P J: Modified RF Interferometer for Relative Phase Measurements; Rev. Sci. Instrum. 46, 420–424, 1975.

B4   Storm A R: Automatic Bragg Angle Control with Simple, Inexpensive Electronics; Rev. Sci. Instrum. 46, 883–885, 1975.

C4   Hasegawa S, Stokesberry D P: Automatic Digital Microwave Hygrometer; Rev. Sci. Instrum. 46, 867–873, 1975.

D4   Barillet R, Viennet J, Petit P, Audoin C: Circuit pour Régulateur de Température; J Phys E Sci. Instrum. 8, 544–545, 1975.

E4   Weidman P D, Browand F K: Analysis of a Simple Circuit for Constant Temperature Anemometry; J Phys. E Sci. Instrum. 8, 553–560, 1975.

F4   Menzies G, O'Donnell H A, Perry A J, Robinson C J: An Interactive Video-Graphic Display System for Use with Cathode Ray Tube Scanning Devices; J Phys. E Sci. Instrum. 8, 676–681, 1975.

G4   Bockelman H K, Schlect R G, McKay R: High Vacuum Raman Cell for the Study of Finite Particles Effects; Rev. Sci. Instrum. 46, 1008–1009, 1975.

H4   Russ T: Simple and Inexpensive Linear Resistivity Meter for Applications in Pure Water Measurements; Rev. Sci. Instrum. 46, 1118–1119, 1975.

I4   Thomason W H, Elbers D C: An Inexpensive Method to Stabilize the Frequency of a CO_2 Laser; Rev. Sci. Instrum. 46, 409–412, 1975.

J4   Tozer R C, Hobson G S: A High Speed High Stability, Current Pulse Modulator for X-Band IMPATT Diodes; J Phys. E Sci. Instrum. 8, 781–783, 1975.

K4   Osada K, Suehiro J: Digital High-Capacitance Measurements to One Farad; Hewlett-Packard J 26, Feb. 1975, 10–16.

L4   Schrenker H: Flow Control in High-Pressure Liquid Chromatography; Hewlett-Packard J 27, Oct. 1975, 17–24.

M4   Jason A C, Richards J C S: The Development of an Electronic Fish Freshness Meter; J Phys. E Sci. Instrum. 8, 826–830, 1975.

N4   Pettifer R E W, Flavell R G, Robinson G A: A Reliable 60uV Flashlamp Triggering System; J Phys. E Sci. Instrum. 8, 875–877, 1975.

O4   Wunderer B M: Reproducible Control of the Voltage of Langmuir Probes in Steady-State and Afterglow Plasmas; J Phys. E Sci. Instrum. 8, 938–942, 1975.

P4   Langelaar J, de Vries G A, Bebelaar D: Sensitivity Improvements in Spectrophosphofluorimetry; J Phys. E Sci. Instrum. 2, 149–152, 1969.

Q4   Bexon R, Cooke K E: A Light Emitting Diode Device for Use in Fault Finding in Pulsed Laser Holography; J Phys. E Sci. Instrum. 7, 511–512, 1974.

R4   Lefferts P: A New Interfacing Concept; The Monolithic Temperature Transducer; National Semiconductor Application Note AN-132, Dec. 1974.

S4   Egan F (Ed): 400 Ideas for Design Vol.2 (Reprints from Electronic Design 1965–1970); Hayden Book 1971.

T4   Collins A T: Temperature Stabilizer for Nitrogen Flushed Infrared Spectrometers; J. Phys. E Sci. Instrum. 9, 254–255, 1976.

U4   Aldridge R V: An Audiofrequency Spectrum Analyzer; J Phys. E Sci. Instrum. 9, 255–257, 1976.

V4   Lucas B W: A Temperature Controlled Furnace for Neutron Diffraction Studies of Single Crystals; J Phys. E Sci. Instrum. 9, 262–264, 1976.

W4   Patterson P J K, Denne D R, Leckey R C G; A Novel Detection Circuit for Auger Spectroscopy; J Phys. E Sci. Instrum. 9, 304–307, 1976.

X4   Dunn W E, Chao B T, Clausing A M: Simple Optical Detector for Measuring Production Rate and Local Velocity of Drops; Rev. Sci. Instrum. 47, 321–323, 1976.

Y4   Anson M, Bayley P: Versatile Precision Source Ratioing System for Fast Kinetic Spectroscopy; Rev. Sci. Instrum. 47, 370–373, 1976.

Z4   Fichtner W, Hacker W: Time Resolution of Ge Avalanche Photodiodes Operating as Photon Counters in Delayed Coincidence; Rev. Sci. Instrum. 47, 374–377, 1976.

a5   Whyte A: Background Current Subtractor for the Detection of Transient Signals in Kinetic Spectrophotometry; Rev. Sci. Instrum. 47, 379–382, 1976.

b5   Carleton H R: Electronic Stabilization of Scanning Interferometers; Applied Optics 15, 929–933, 1976.

c5 Stokesberry D P, Hasegawa S: Automatic Digital Microwave Hygrometer, Model II; Rev. Sci. Instrum. 47, 556–558, 1976.
d5 Bleys C A: Floating Input, Optically Isolated, High-Voltage Measurement Probe; Rev. Sci. Instrum. 47, 621–623, 1976.
e5 Davies C, Hodgkinson K A: A Sensitive, Yet Inexpensive Relative-Energy Monitor for Pulsed Laser Systems; J Phys. E Sci. Instrum. 5, 544–546, 1976.

Bibliography

Ahmed H, Spreadbury P J: Electronics for Engineers; Cambridge University Press 1973.
Barna A: Operational Amplifiers; Wiley-Interscience 1971.
Bleuler E, Haxby R O (Eds): Methods of Experimental Physics. Vol. 2: Electronic Methods; Academic Press 2nd Edn. Parts A and B 1975.
Brown P B, Maxfield B W, Moraff H: Electronics for Neurobiologists; MIT Press 1973.
Camenzind H R: Circuit Design for Integrated Electronics; Addison-Wesley 1968.
Carter G W, Richardson A: Techniques of Circuit Analysis; Cambridge University Press 1972.
Clayton G B: Operational Amplifiers; Butterworths 1971.
Clearly J F (Ed): Transistor Manual; General Electric 7th Edn. 1964.
Coekin J A: High Speed Pulse Techniques; Pergamon 1975.
Connelley J A (Ed): Analog Integrated Circuits; Wiley-Interscience 1975.
Connor F R: Noise; Edward Arnold.
Connor F R: Modulation; Edward Arnold 1973.
Connor F R: Signals; Edward Arnold 1972.
Dale B (Ed): Silicon Rectifier Handbook; Motorola 1966.
Dale R G (Ed): Semiconductor Power Circuits Handbook; Motorola 1968.
Delaney C F G: Electronics for the Physicist; Penguin Books 1969.
Diefenderfer A J: Principles of Electronic Instrumentation; W B Saunders 1972.
Edwin G, Roddam T: Principles of Feedback Design; Iliffe 1964.
Fairchild: The Complete Linear Book; Fairchild Semidonductor.
Faulkner E A: Principles of Linear Circuits; Chapman and Hall 1966.
Faulkner E A: Introduction to the Theory of Linear Circuits; Chapman and Hall 1969.
Fitchen F C: Electronic Integrated Circuits and Systems; Van Nostrand Reinhold 1970.
Gardner F M: Phaselock Techniques; Wiley 1966.
Ghausi M S: Electronic Circuits. Devices, Models, Functions, Analysis, and Design; Van Nostrand Reinhold 1971.
Gilbert C P: The Design and Use of Electrnic Analogue Computers; Chapman and Hall 1964.
Graeme J G: Applications of Operational Amplifiers. Third Generation Techniques; McGraw-Hill 1973.
Gray P E, Searle C L: Electronic Principles. Physics, Models, and Circuits; Wiley 1969.
Grebene A B: Analog Integrated Circuit Design; Van Nostrand Reinhold 1972.
Gregory B A: An Introduction to Electrical Instrumentation; Macmillan 1973.
Grossner N R: Transformers for Electronic Circuits; McGraw-Hill 1967.
Gutzwiller F W (Ed): SCR Manual; General Electric 4th Edn. 1967.
Hakim S S: Feedback Circuit Analysis; Iliffe 1966.
Hnatek E R: Applications of Linear Integrated Circuits; Wiley 1975.
Howson D P, Smith R B: Parametric Amplifiers; McGraw-Hill 1970.
Huelsman L P: Active Filters, Lumped, Distributed, Integrated, Digital and Parametric; McGraw-Hill 970.
Hunter L P: Handbook of Semiconductor Electronics; McGraw-Hill 3rd Edn. 1970.
Hoenig S A, Payne F L: How to Build and Use Electronic Devices Without Frustration, Panic, Mountains of Money, or an Engineering Degree; Little Brown 1973.
Jolley W P: Cryoelectronics; English Universities Press 1973.
Jones B: Circuit Electronics for Scientists; Addison-Wesley 1974.

Kimmitt M F: Far-Infrared Techniques; Pion Books 1970.
Klein G, Zaalberg van Zelst J J: Precision Electronics; Philips Technical Library 1967.
Korn G A, Korn T M: Electronic Analog Computers; McGraw-Hill 2nd Edn. 1956.
Lynn P A: An Introduction to the Analysis and Processing of Signals; Macmillan 1973.
Malmstadt H V, Enke C G, Crouch S R: Electronic Measurement Systems for Scientists; Addison-Wesley 1974.
Markus J (Ed): Electronic Circuits Manual; McGraw-Hill.
Marston R M: Semiconductor Projects; Iliffe 1968.
Martin A G, Stephenson F W: Linear Microelectronic Systems; Macmillan 1973.
Meiling W, Stary F: Nanosecond Pulse Techniques; Gordon and Breach 1968.
Millman J, Halkias C C: Integrated Electronics: Analog and Digital Circuits and Systems; McGraw-Hill 1972.
Millman J, Taub H: Pulse, Digital and Switching Waveforms; McGraw-Hill 1965.
Morant M J: Introduction to Semiconductor Devices; Harrap 2nd Edn. 1970.
Morrison R: Grounding and Shielding Techniques in Instrumentation; Wiley 1967.
Motchenbacher C D, Fitchen F C: Low-Noise Electronic Design; Wiley 1973.
Motorola: McMOS Handbook. Products, Characteristics, Applications; Motorola 1973.
Motorola: Semiconductor Circuits Manual; Motorola 1964.
Motorola: Power Transistor Handbook; Motorola 1961.
Motorola: Zener Diode and Rectifier Handbook; Motorola 1961.
National Semiconductor: Linear Applications; National Semiconductor 2nd Edn. 1973.
Nicholson P W: Nuclear Electronics; Wiley 1974.
Oberman R M M: Electronic Counters; Macmillan 1973.
Oliver B M, Cage J M: Electronic Measurements and Instrumentation; McGraw-Hill 1971.
RCA: Linear Integrated Circuits and DMOS Devices; RCA Databook SSD-202C, 1975.
RCA: Solid State Power Circuits; RCA Technical Series SP-52, 1971.
RCA: Power Circuits, DC to Microwave; RCA Technical Series SP-51, 1969.
RCA: Linear Integrated Circuits; RCA Technical Series IC-41, 1967.
RCA: Linear Integrated Circuits; RCA Technical Series IC-42, 1970.
RCA: Transistor, Thyristor and Diode Manual; RCA Technical Series SC-14, 1969.
Roberge J K: Operational Amplifiers. Theory and Practice; Wiley 1975.
Robinson F N H: Noise and Fluctuations in Electronic Devices and Circuits; Oxford University Press 1974.
Roehr W D: Switching Transistor Handbook; Motorola 1963.
Scott R E: Elements of Linear Circuits; Addison Wesley 1966.
SGS-Fairchild: The Applications of Linear Microcircuits; SGS-Fairchild 1967.
Shea R F (Ed): Amplifier Handbook; McGraw-Hill 1966.
Smith J I: Modern Operational Circuit Design; Wiley-Interscience 1971.
Strauss L: Wave Generation and Shaping; McGraw-Hill 1970.
Thomason J G: Linear Feedback Analysis; Pergamon 1955.
Tobey G E, Graeme J G, Huelsman L P: Operational Amplifiers; McGraw-Hill 1971.
Todd C D: Zener and Avalanche Diodes; Wiley 1970.
Towers T D: Elements of Linear Microcircuits; Butterworths 1973.
Vassos B H, Ewing G W: Analog and Digital Electronics for Scientists: Wiley-Interscience 1972.
van Randeraat J, Setterington R E: Piezoelectric Ceramics; Mullard.
Wait J V, Heulsman L P, Korn G A: Introduction to Operational Amplifier Theory and Applications; McGraw-Hill 1975.
Weber L J, McLean D L: Electrical Measurement Systems for Biological and Physical Scientists; Addison Wesley 1975.
Williams P, Carruthers J, Evans J H, Kinsler J: Circuit Designs. Collected Circards No. 1; Wireless World 1975.
Young S: Electronics in the Life Sciences; Macmillan 1973.
Zucker M H: Electronic Circuits for the Behavioural and Biomedical Sciences; Freeman 1969.

Appendix: Complex numbers

The use of complex numbers considerably facilitates the mathematical techniques used in this book and in electronics generally. This appendix is a short resumé of those aspects that will be useful in the present context. Complex numbers involve the quantity $\sqrt{-1}$, which is undefined in ordinary algebraic terms. However, it has proved to be so useful that it has its own algebra and a special symbol i or j. Mathematicians use i, but in electrical applications this may be confused with current, so j is used instead.

$$j = (-1)^{1/2} \quad \text{or} \quad j^2 = -1 \tag{A.1}$$

j is called an imaginary number, in contrast to the ordinarily used real numbers. A combination of real and imaginary numbers is a complex number:

Imaginary numbers: $5j$, $26\cdot3j$, $0\cdot43j$, etc.
Real numbers: 5, $26\cdot3$, $0\cdot43$, etc.
Complex numbers: $1+j$, $26\cdot3+5j$, $5-0\cdot43j$, etc.

A complex number Z may most readily be represented geometrically in the Argand diagram. This has a real and an imaginary (j) axis, and the complex number is represented by a point with coordinates given by the real and imaginary parts, i.e., for $Z = x + jy$ we get the point (x, y) (Fig. A.1).

The complex number may also be specified in polar coordinates (R, θ):

$$x = R\cos\theta, \quad y = R\sin\theta$$
$$Z = x + jy = R(\cos\theta + j\sin\theta) \tag{A.2}$$
$$R = (x^2 + y^2)^{1/2}, \quad \theta = \tan^{-1}(y/x)$$

For example, with $Z = 5 + 3j$ (point P in figure):

$$R = (5^2 + 3^2)^{1/2} = (25 + 9)^{1/2} = (34)^{1/2} = 5\cdot831$$
$$\theta = \tan^{-1}(3/5) = \tan^{-1}(0\cdot6) = 30°58' \tag{A.3}$$

The quantity, R, is called the modulus or absolute value of Z and written $|Z|$. θ is called the argument or phase of Z:

$$Z = \text{modulus}\,[\cos(\text{argument}) + j\sin(\text{argument})] \tag{A.4}$$

In the geometrical sense, j may be considered as an operator. If we multiply a real number 5, say, by -1 we get -5, so the effect is to rotate the vector **OQ** through 180° or π radians to the position **OU**. Since $-1 = j^2 = j \times j$, we can interpret the operator j as one that rotates a vector by 90° or $\pi/2$ radians (e.g., $j(\mathbf{OQ}) = \mathbf{OH}$ and $-j(\mathbf{OQ}) = \mathbf{OG}$). A further application of the operator j then completes the rotation to the negative real axis, as it should. This was the original idea, as put forward by the Norwegian surveyor Wessel in 1797 [Holbrook, J. G., *Laplace transforms for Electronic Engineers*, Pergamon, 2nd edn, 1966].

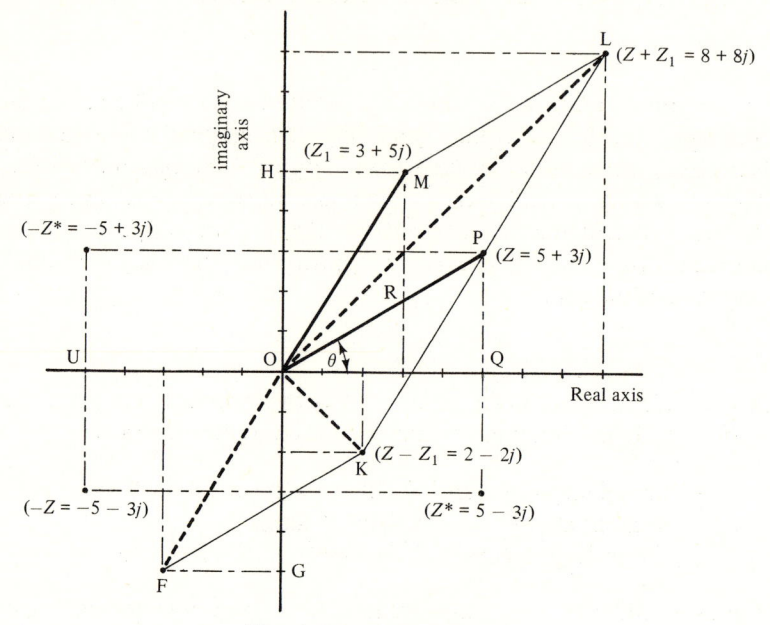

Fig. A.1 Argand diagram

If a complex number $Z = x + jy$, then the symbols $\mathscr{R}e$ and $\mathscr{I}m$ are used to specify the real and imaginary parts:

$$\text{Real part of } Z = \mathscr{R}e(Z) = x = R\cos\theta$$
$$\text{Imaginary part of } Z = \mathscr{I}m(Z) = y = R\sin\theta \quad\quad (A.5)$$

The complex conjugate of Z, written Z^*, has the same real part as Z, but the negative of the imaginary part:

$$\begin{aligned} Z &= x + jy & Z^* &= x - jy \\ &= R(\cos\theta + j\sin\theta) & &= R(\cos\theta - j\sin\theta) \end{aligned} \quad (A.6)$$

Complex numbers may be added or subtracted by adding/subtracting the real parts and the imaginary parts. For example, if $Z = 5 + 3j$ (point P) and $Z_1 = 3 + 5j$ (point M) then $Z + Z_1 = 8 + 8j$ (point L) and $Z - Z_1 = 2 - 2j$ (point K). As with ordinary vectors, this is just a parallelogram (OPLM) rule. In the case of subtraction one finds $-Z_1$ (point F) and adds this to Z to give the resultant at point K.

It is evident from the Argand diagram that if two complex numbers are equal:

$$A + jB = C + jD \quad \text{then} \quad A = C \quad \text{and} \quad B = D \quad\quad (A.7)$$

A very remarkable relation, known as Euler's formula and which makes complex numbers of such particular use in electric circuit analysis, connects exponential and trigonometric functions, Eq. (A.8). The infinite series expansions for $\sin \theta$, $\cos \theta$, and $e^{j\theta}$ are:

$$\sin \theta = \theta - \frac{\theta^3}{3} + \frac{\theta^5}{5} - \frac{\theta^7}{7} + \cdots$$

$$\cos \theta = 1 - \frac{\theta^2}{2} + \frac{\theta^4}{4} - \frac{\theta^6}{6} + \cdots \quad \text{(A.8)}$$

$$e^{j\theta} = 1 + j\theta + \frac{(j\theta)^2}{2} + \frac{(j\theta)^3}{3} + \frac{(j\theta)^4}{4} + \cdots$$

$$= \left(1 - \frac{\theta^2}{2} + \frac{\theta^4}{4} - \frac{\theta^6}{6} + \cdots\right) + j\left(\theta - \frac{\theta^3}{3} + \frac{\theta^5}{5} - \frac{\theta^7}{7} + \cdots\right)$$

$$= \cos \theta + j \sin \theta$$

Conversely, we have:

$$\cos \theta = \frac{e^{j\theta} + e^{-j\theta}}{2}, \quad \sin \theta = \frac{e^{j\theta} - e^{-j\theta}}{2j}$$

$$\cos j\theta \equiv \cosh \theta = \frac{e^{\theta} + e^{-\theta}}{2} \quad \text{(hyperbolic cosine)} \quad \text{(A.9)}$$

$$\sin j\theta \equiv \sinh \theta = j\left(\frac{e^{\theta} - e^{-\theta}}{2}\right) \quad \text{(hyperbolic sine)}$$

Any complex number can now be written in exponential rather than trigonometrical terms:

$$Z = R(\cos \theta + j \sin \theta) = R\, e^{j\theta}$$
$$Z^* = R(\cos \theta - j \sin \theta) = R\, e^{-j\theta}$$
$$Z^n = R^n\, e^{jn\theta} = R^n(\cos n\theta + j \sin n\theta) \quad \text{(A.10)}$$
$$\text{(De Moivre's theorem)}$$
$$|Z| = R = (ZZ^*)^{1/2}$$

We can use this representation to carry out division and multiplication of complex numbers:

$$Z' = A + jB = R_1\, e^{j\theta_1}, \quad Z'' = C + jD = R_2\, e^{j\theta_2}$$
$$Z = Z'.Z'' = (A+jB)(C+jD) = R_1 R_2\, e^{j(\theta_1 + \theta_2)}$$

i.e., modulus of product = product of moduli:

$$|Z| = |Z'.Z''| = |Z'|.|Z''| \quad \text{(A.11)}$$

and argument of product = sum of arguments:

$$\text{Arg } Z = \text{Arg}(Z'.Z'') = \text{Arg } Z' + \text{Arg } Z''$$

Similarly, for division:

$$Z = \frac{Z'}{Z''} = \frac{(A+jB)}{(C+jD)} = \frac{R_1}{R_2} e^{j(\theta_1 - \theta_2)}$$

i.e., modulus of quotient = quotient of moduli:

$$|Z| = \left|\frac{Z'}{Z''}\right| = \frac{|Z'|}{|Z''|} \tag{A.12}$$

and argument of quotient = difference of arguments:

$$\text{Arg } Z = \text{Arg}\left(\frac{Z'}{Z''}\right) = \text{Arg } Z' - \text{Arg } Z''$$

Author index

This index only lists authors directly named in the text or those whose work has been used to a significant extent in writing this book. It does not include all the authors referenced in the text or those only appearing in the reference collections.

Alfke P, 243
Amsel G, 424
Arecchi F T, 392
Avery L R, 197

Babbs R S, 328
Baldini A, 134, 136
Barelli A E, 381
Barnes F A, 376
Becciolini B, 188, 191
Bergh A A, 396
Betts J A, 286
Biard J R, 381
Bijlsma N R, 342, 343, 345, 346, 348
Bilotti A, 275
Birman P, 303, 308, 309, 315
Bladowski R, 47, 48
Blume R J, 286
Bode H W, 15
Bonnet G, 424
Borlase W H, 151, 153, 155
Bosshard R, 424
Botos B, 330, 345, 346
Breece H T, 314
Brown R G, 173, 176, 177, 179
Bruck D B, 285
Bruder H, 361, 362
Buczynski R J, 361
Budek J, 361
Bunze V, 22
Burr-Brown, 162, 163, 164
Burwell P, 342, 343, 345, 346, 348
Burwen R S, 137, 269

Camenzind H R, 47, 196, 197, 278, 279
Campbell L R, 198
Capella D, 350, 351, 352
Carlson F M, 352
Cath P G, 184, 187
Champney D C, 33
Chestnut H, 173, 174
Cholet J, 155
Cini C, 317, 319
Clayton G B, 154, 155
Cleary J F, 248, 249, 357

Conant R, 93, 108
Conradi J, 381
Cowan W T, 234
Cowles L G, 170
Crawford R H, 248
Cutler P, 9

Dale R, 299, 301
D'Alton L B, 72
Dance J B, 383
David E, 153, 155
Dawnay J C G, 42, 43
Dayal M, 299, 301
D'Azzo J, 120, 173, 179
Dean K J, 39, 43, 45
Dean P J, 396
Dean R T, 248
Deardorff J E, 425
Delaney C F G, 234, 237, 260
Demrow R I, 30, 150, 151
DeRoy B E, 179
Diamantides N D, 99
Dixon G, 285
Dobkin R C, 108, 111
Dudley R L, 234, 237

Earls J C, 231, 232
Edwin G, 124
EG&G, 380, 382, 383
EMI, 385, 386, 388
Ernst R R, 424
Evans E G, 342, 343, 345, 346, 348
Evans J P, 326, 327, 328

Fairweather D, 249
Farrer W, 171, 173
Faulkner E A, 4, 9, 34, 35, 42, 43, 45, 120, 124, 143, 146
Foord R, 392
Frederiksen T M, 198, 200
Fullagar D, 353

Galloway J H, 361, 362
Gardner F M, 278, 279, 280, 281, 282
Gatti E, 392

Gazin J F, 353
Gedcke D A, 267
General Electric, 396
Ghausi M S, 159, 170, 239, 241, 402
Gibbons J F, 153, 154, 155
Gilbert B, 269, 270, 272
Girling E J, 165, 170, 172
Givens S, 353
Gliksman R, 322
Goldberg E A, 79
Good E F, 165, 170, 172, 231
Goodyear C C, 286
Graeme J G, 134, 402
Granieri G J, 363
Gray P E, 27, 120, 124
Grebene A B, 275, 278, 279
Gronner A D, 38, 39, 40, 43, 45, 355
Gutzwiller F W, 302, 355, 356, 357, 359, 360, 361, 363

Halkias C C, 343, 345, 346, 347, 348
Hall G, 361
Hall M W G, 23
Hamilton T D S, 96, 303
Hamstra R H, 381, 382
Hardcastle I, 191, 192
Heflin E H, 234
Henry T, 306
Hewlett-Packard, 303, 306, 308, 309, 312, 380, 396
Hoft D, 96
Holbrook J G, 51, 59, 100
Horn H S, 153, 154, 155
Houpis C, 120, 173, 179
Howard W M, 198, 200
Howell E K, 361
Huehne K, 140
Huelsman L P, 134, 167, 168
Hunter L P, 47, 48, 49

Jenkins J O M, 350, 351, 353
Johnson K M, 381
Jones R, 392

Kasser R, 145
Keen M J, 316
Keithley J F, 188
Kerwin W J, 167, 168
Key E L, 165
Kittel C, 32
Klein M V, 376
Korn G A, 269
Korn S R, 400
Korn T M, 269
Krabbe H, 151

Lamden R J, 172
Land P L, 386
Larsen I, 243
Lee Y W, 424, 425, 427
Locher R E, 400
Lozier G S, 322
Lush H J, 386

McCullough W, 31
McDonald W J, 267
McIntyre R J, 381
McRoberts L, 345, 346
Mansfield P, 286
Marzetta L A, 72
Mathews P J D, 72
Matkowski Z, 328
Mattera L, 169
Mayer R W, 173, 174
Maytum M, 321
Millman J, 9, 20, 36, 38, 39, 40, 42, 238, 239, 240, 248, 249, 260, 343, 345, 346, 347, 348
Mills T B, 278, 279
Mitra S K, 158, 165
Morehouse C K, 322
Murari B, 134, 136, 193

Nash G, 279
Nelson C, 246
Newcomb R W, 167, 168
Newmire L J, 357
Nielsen E G, 143, 144
Norris B, 191, 248, 321, 377, 396
Nyquist H, 124

Oliver C J, 391, 392
Olsen D E, 160
O'Neill W, 235
Owen R E, 231

Pamplin B F, 248
Paterson W L, 153
Peabody A M, 184, 187
Pecchio S, 312
Perkinson J C, 306
Pierce W C, 306
Pike E R, 391, 392
Pouliot F, 154, 155

Racino R N, 328
Raines J A, 381
RCA, 188, 189, 191, 192, 355, 357, 359, 362, 385, 387, 388, 390, 391
Reichert J, 285, 286
Reif F, 32
Renschler E, 269
Rex R L, 419, 429
Richards R C, 249
Ritchie C C, 234
Roberts G T, 419, 429
Robinson F N H, 32, 145
Roddam T, 124
Romano A, 193
Rose M J, 355, 359, 361
Roulston J F, 278
Ruehs R G, 191
Rupra K, 319, 320
Russell H T, 400

Sah C T, 36
Sallen R P, 165
Schade O H, 299, 301
Schaeffer L, 195

Scott H H, 170
Searle C L, 27, 120, 124
SGS-Fairchild, 260, 261, 262, 263, 264, 265
Shaufield W N, 381
Sheingold D H, 70, 73, 149, 150, 154, 155, 269
Sherwin J S, 330, 346, 347
Signetics, 278, 279, 282
Skilling J K, 138, 140
Sleeth R S, 198, 200
Smith J I, 73, 151, 306
Smith K L, 277
Smith L, 70, 73, 149, 150
Solomon J E, 202
Sona A, 392
Sowan F A, 376
Stata R, 70, 73, 87, 93, 103, 108
Stevens M, 352
Strange N, 345
Strauss L, 229, 230, 260
Syms B R, 43, 45

Tarmy R, 170
Taub H, 9, 20, 36, 38, 39, 40, 42, 238, 239, 240, 248, 249, 260
Thaler G J, 173, 176, 177, 179
Thomas L C, 169
Thomason J G, 120, 124
Tobey G E, 134, 260
Todd C D, 326, 329
Tow J, 169
Townsend J, 285, 286

Trimble C R, 419, 424, 425
Tucker E W, 322, 325
Tuley J H, 328
Turner C R, 40

Unvala B A, 299, 301
Usher M J, 36

van der Ziel A, 143, 144
Viterbi A, 279, 282

Waidelich D L, 299, 301
Walters C K, 328
Ware D, 286
Waterman G, 361, 362
Waterman P, 328
Watson F B, 145
Watson J, 330, 342, 345, 346, 347
Wendland P, 381, 382
White G, 171
Widlar R J, 319
Williams P, 229
Wittlinger H A, 48, 197, 198
Wojslawowicz J E, 361
Wood A, 352
Wright M, 314
Wunderman I, 376, 400

Yonushka J V, 362
Young B W, 234

Subject index

Absolute maximum values, 102–103
a.c. logarithmic amplifier, 155–158
Acquisition time, 284
Active filter, 158–173
    biquad, 167–170
    infinite gain, multiple feedback loop, 163–164
    infinite gain, single feedback loop, 160–163
    low gain, controlled source, 164–166
    multiple amplifier, 166–170
    notch, 172–173
    pole-zero configurations, 159
    state variable, 167, 169, 170
    transfer functions, 159
    twin-tee, 170 173
    type comparison, 160
    universal, 172, 173
Active load, 49
Active zener, 49–50
Adder, 82, 83, 85–86
    subtracter, 85–87
Admittance, 7
Aliasing, 287
Alkaline manganese cell, 322, 323
All-pass filter, 173
Alpha, 41
Amplifier:
    a.c. logarithmic, 155–158
    active filter, 158–173
    antilog, 274
    audio, 188–195
    bandpass, 89
    booster, 153, 202
    buffer, 193
    charge, 100–102
    chopper, 78–79, 200
    chopper stabilized, 78–79, 200
    class A, 188–189
    class AB, 188–189
    class B, 188–189, 195
    class C, 188
    class D, 188–189, 196
    common-source, 347
    Darlington, 190–191
    d.c., 78–81
    difference, 85
    differential, 30–31, 76, 83, 150–153, 200–201, 203
    differential in-differential out (DIDO), 150, 151, 204
    electrometer, 181–188
    exponential, 274
    feedback, 68–70
    field-effect, 345–349
    filter, (see Active filter)
    follower, 82, 87
    high input resistance, 181–188
    IC characteristics, 102–113
    IC power, 193–195
    ideal operational, 70–71
    instrumentation, 150–153
    integrator (see Integrator)
    inverting, 82
    logarithmic, 153–158
    low drift, 200–201
    low-noise, 143–150
    low-pass, 15–16, 18, 36, 421
    micropower, 198
    non-inverting, 84–85
    Norton, 198–200
    operational, 68–70
    parametric, 80–81
    power, 188–197
    programmable, 198
    protection, 112–113
    pulse, 201
    servo, 195–197
    settling time, 19, 202
    square wave testing, 137–138. 140
    summing, 82, 83, 85–86
    temperature stabilized, 200
    transconductance, 197–198
    transient response, 123, 138–141
    transimpedance, 86–87, 382, 387
    varactor bridge, 80–81
    video, 201, 204
    wide band, 201–204
Amplitude:
    bounce, 231
    error, 18
    limiter, 421
    modulated waveform, 276–277
    modulator, 276–277
    stabilization, 231–232
Analogue:
    division, 272–273
    gates, 353–355
        feedthrough, 354
        multiplex, 355
        types, 352
    multiplier, 272–274
Angular acceleration, 175

Anode, 385
Anticipation, 178
Antilogarithmic amplifier, 274
Aperiodic response, 61
Aperture time, 285
Argand diagram, 447–448
Argument, 5, 8, 447, 449, 450
Astable multivibrator, 239, 240, 241
Asymmetric trigger diode, 362
Asymptotic slope, 16, 18
Attenuator, 13
   compensated, 22–23
Audio amplifier, 188–195
Avalanche:
   breakdown, 39–41
   diode, 326
   multiplication, 381
   photodiode, 381–382
      breakdown in, 382
      dual, 382
      guard ring, 381
      multiplication factor, 381, 382
      multiplication in, 381–382
      noise in, 381–382
      time response, 382
   rectifier, 300

Backlash, 177
Balanced modulator, 277
Ballast resistor, 398, 399
Band-pass filter, 163, 164, 166, 169, 421
Band-stop network, 171–173
Bandwidth, 18–19
   closed-loop, 72, 79, 135, 136–137
   full-power, 201
   large signal, 106, 202
   noise, 36, 422
   pulse, 19–21
   small signal, 201, 202
   three dB, 18–19
   two-lag circuit, 123
   unity-gain, 43, 81, 106, 134, 203
Base spreading resistance, 44
Batteries (see Cells)
Beta, 41, 43, 44, 45, 71–73
   cut-off frequency, 43
   degradation, 39
Bias current, 76, 107, 183, 266
Bidirectional diode thyristor, 358, 361
Bilateral trigger diode, 357, 358, 361
Binomial expansion, 129
Bipolar transistor, 39–46
   input resistance, 144
   noise figure, 144
      variation with frequency, 145
   noise in, 143–145
   optimum source resistance, 144
Biquadratic function, 167–168
Bistable, 123
Black body, 32, 376–378, 394
Blue noise, 186
Bode plot, 15, 120, 125–128
Boltzmann constant, 32

Bootstrap, 87, 348
Bounds, 89–90
Boxcar detector, 419, 424, 427
Break-before-make switch, 355
Breakdown:
   avalanche, 39–41
   LED, 397
   transistor, 39–41
Bridge:
   discrimination in, 230
   half-controlled, 361
   Meacham, 250
   rectifier, 297, 298
   regulator as, 304
   varactor, 80–81
   Wien, 59–61, 229–231
Bridged tee, 160
Buffer amplifier, 193
Butterworth response, 159, 162
Bypass capacitor, 29–30

Cadmium selenide (CdSe), 383, 384
Cadmium sulphide (CdS), 383, 384
Capacitance meter, 239
Capacitor:
   bypass, 29–30
   ceramic, 30
   compensation, 203
   electrolytic, 30, 243, 245, 300–301
   filter, 300–301
   hold, 283
   impedance, 6
   microphone, 101
   polystyrene, 182
   speed-up, 241
   tantalum, 30
   timing, 243, 245, 246, 248
Capture range, 281
Carrier:
   majority, 343
   minority, 38, 42, 343
   mobility, 346
   signal, 275, 420
   suppression, 276
CdS, 383, 384
CdSe, 383, 384
Cells, 322–325
   alkaline manganese, 322, 323
   charging of, 324–325
   dry, 322
   lead acid, 323
   Lecanché, 322, 323
   mercury, 322, 323
   metair, 323
   nickel-cadmium, 322, 323
   primary, 322–323
   reference, 325
   secondary, 322, 323–325
   standard, 323, 325
   Weston, 325, 329
Centre-tap rectifier, 297, 299
Channel conductance, 342–343
Channeltron, 393

Characteristic impedance, 25
Charge-sensitive amplifier, 100–102
Chebychev response, 159
Chopper, 343
   amplifier, 78–79, 200
   damping circuit, 21–22
   drive, 353
   mechanical, 196, 401
   optical, 196, 398
   series, 352–353
   series-shunt, 352–353
   shunt, 352–353
CIE photopic response, 375, 376
Class A amplifier, 188–189
Class AB stage, 188–189
Class B, 188–189, 195
Class C amplifier, 188
Class D, 188–189, 196–197
   amplifier, 196–197
   servo, 196–197
Closed-loop gain, 72
Coaxial cable, 25–26
   characteristic impedance, 25
   matching of, 25–26
   propagation delay in, 25
   propagation velocity, 25
Coherent:
   detector, 419, 420–424
   frequency division, 279
   frequency multiplication, 279
Comb filter, 425
Common base, 144–145
Common collector, 144–145
Common emitter, 144–145
Common-mode:
   gain, 151
   interference, 30–31
   rejection ratio (CMRR), 31, 104–105, 111–112
   resistances, 84
   signals, 84, 150
   voltage limits, 103, 263, 273, 306, 307
Common-source amplifier, 347
Comparator, 260–266, 287
   dual, 264–265
   hysteresis in, 261–263
   IC, 263–266
   overdrive, 263, 264
   positive feedback in, 261–263
   strobe, 266
   transfer curve, 262–263
   zero crossing, 261
Compensated attenuator, 22–23
Compensation:
   feedforward, 135–136
   frequency, 81–82, 125–128
   Miller, 128, 132–134
   –12 dB/octave amplifier, 137–138
   phase, 128–138
   RC shunt, 128–132
   temperature, 154, 155, 318–319, 326, 328–329, 346, 382
Complementary:
   transistors, 46
   unijunction, 249

Complex:
   conjugate, 448
   frequency, 52
   number, 447–450
   roots, 56
   zeros, 160
Conditional stability, 125
Conduction:
   angle, 302, 360
   band, 378
Constant-current:
   source, 348
   stage, 47–48
Constant current-constant voltage regulator, 308–309
Constant fraction discriminator, 267–268
Controlled source, 164–165
Convolution, 33, 425
   theorem, 425, 429
Corner frequency, 143
Correlation, 419, 427–429
   auto, 419, 427–428
   cross, 419, 427–429
Coulomb friction, 177
Counting time, optimum, 392
Critical damping, 55, 122
Crossover distortion, 189
Crystal oscillator, 249–251
Current:
   bias, 76, 107, 183, 266
   feedback, 184
   foldback, 314–315, 316
   gain, 41–43
   generator, 379
   hogging, 40
   limiting, 314, 316
   mirror, 48, 197–198, 199, 318
   offset, 108–110, 263
   regulator, 305–308, 316, 319
   regulator diode, 329–330
      CL2210/4710, 330
      dynamic resistance, 330
      IN5283/5314, 330
      output conductance, 330
   sink, 198, 246
   source, 197, 198, 246, 382, 387, 402
   stabilizer, (see regulator)
Current-controlled negative resistance, 357
Current-to-voltage converter, 86–87, 184, 382, 387, 402

Damped oscillation, 96, 139–140, 176
Damping, 9
   critical, 55
   factor, 123, 281
   over, 176
   ratio (zeta), 140, 176, 177, 178
   under, 140, 176
Darlington pair, 190–191
d.c. amplifier, 78–81
Decibel, 1–4
Delay line clipping, 202
Delay time, 25
Demodulation, 274, 279

DeMoivre's theorem, 449
Depletion-mode FET, 343–344
Derating curve, 41
Derivative, 423
   control, 177–178
   second, 423
Detectivity, 380
Detector:
   coherent, 419, 420–424
   integrating light, 403
   lock, 282
   lock-in, 286, 392, 419, 420–424
   optical, 267
   particle (GeLi), 267
   peak, 287
   phase-sensitive, (see Lock-in)
   photo, power amplifier, 403
   photoconductor, 315, 363
   photodiode, 377, 378–380
   photomultiplier, 267
   synchronous, 196
   zero-crossing, 267
Diac, 358
DIDO amplifier, 150, 151, 169–170
Dielectric:
   absorption, 182
   ceramic, 182
   glass, 182
   glass-epoxy, 182
   leakage, 30, 182, 284
   mylar, 182
   nylon, 182
   polarization, 183
   polycarbonate, 182
   polyethylene, 182
   polypropylene, 182
   polystyrene, 182
   properties, 182
   PTFE, 182
   PVC, 182
   quartz, 182
   sapphire, 182
   silicone resins, 182
   soakage, 183
   volume resistance of, 182
   water absorption, 182
Difference amplifier, 85
Difference of slopes, 126–127
Differential, 423
   gain, 151
   input resistance, 151, 183
   input voltage, 103, 263
   output, 150–151
Differential amplifier, 30–31
Differential-to-single-ended converter, 49
Differentiator, 89, 94–100, 125, 243
   damping, 97–98
   finite bandwidth effect, 96–98
   noise, 95
   phase shift, 128
   ramp response, 96–98
   stability, 97, 126
   transient oscillation, 96–98
   two amplifier, 99–100

Diffusion potential, 346
Digital waveform synthesis, 239
Diode:
   asymmetric trigger, 362
   avalanche, 325, 326
   avalanche photo, 381–382
   avalanche rectifier, 300
   bilateral trigger, 357, 358, 361
   breakdown, 37
   bridge switch, 284
   capacity of, 38
   characteristic voltage, 36
   current regulator, 325, 329–330
   cut-in voltage, 38
   duo, 380
   dynamic resistance, 38
   equation, 36
   flywheel, 361
   forward voltage, 38
   four layer, (see Thyristor)
   germanium, 36–38
   hot carrier, 38–39
   incremental resistance, 38
   junction, 36–39
   leakage current, 37
   light emitting, 394, 396–397, 399
   logarithmic, 39
   metal-semiconductor, 38–39
   1N4148, 38
   1N914, 38
   photo, 377, 378–380
   PN, 36–39
   pump, 237
   rectifier, 299–300
   reference, 328–329
   reverse recovery time, 38
   reverse saturation current, 37
   Schottky, 38–39
   signal, 38–39
   silicon, 36–38
   snap-off, 268
   stabistor, 325, 328
   temperature effects, 38
   trans, 39
   transistor as, 39
   tunnel, 249
   voltage regulator, 325–328
   waveform shaper, 233–234
   Zener, 325–328
Discriminator, 266–268, 392
   amplitude dependent gain and risetime, 268
   constant fraction, (CFPH), 267–268
   crossover pickoff, 267
   leading edge, 267
   pulse pile-up, 268
   slope reversal, 268
   strobed, 264, 266
   time delay, 267
   timing walk, 267
   window, 266
   zero-crossing, 267
Distortion, 74
   crossover, 189
Divider, analogue, 272–273

Dominant pole, 138
Double differentiation, 202
Double-diffused transistor, 46
Drain, 342
Droop, 21, 201
Dry cell, 322
Dual comparator, 264–265
Dual power supply, 311
Duo diode, 380
Dynode, 385, 386

Earthing, 28–30
Electrolytic capacitor, 30, 300–301
    leakage current, 301
    ripple current, 301
    temperature effects, 301
    transient surge voltage, 301
Electrometer:
    ammeter, 183–187
    amplifier, 181–188
    vibrating reed, 184, 188
    vibrating capacitor, 184, 188
Electrometer devices:
    comparison of, 184
    noise in, 184, 186
Electron-hole pair, 378, 383
Electrostatic pickup, 30
Electrostatic screen, 298
Emitter:
    coupled multivibrator, 240–241
    follower, 87
    resistor, 13, 47
Enhancement-mode FET, 343
Epibase transistor, 46
Equation of motion, 175
Equivalent circuit:
    FET, 346–347
    hybrid, 42–43
    hybrid-pi, 44–45
    Miller compensation, 132
    noisy bipolar transistor, 143
    offsets, 107–110
    oscilloscope probe, 22–23
    photodiode, 379–380
    RC shunt compensation, 129
    series-parallel, 14
    tee, 41
    thyristor, 355–356
    transistor, 41–45
    unijunction transistor, 248
Error:
    aperture, 285
    feedback, 71
Euler's theorem, 449
Excitation function, 51
Exponential amplifier, 274
Eye spectral sensitivity, 375

Fabry-Pérot, étalon, 180
Fault protection, 313–315
Feedback, 26–28
    amplifier, 70–75
    derivative, 177–178
    error, 72
    factor, 71, 73
    fraction, 71
    loop, 27
    Miller, 28
    negative, 26–28
    node, 27
    positive, 27, 123, 239, 261, 262, 263, 266, 273, 315, 321, 355–356
    topology, 27
    zero, 160–161, 170
Feedforward, 174, 203
    compensation, 135–136
Field-effect transistor (FET), 342–349
    amplifier, 346
    biasing, 346
    bipolar combination, 348–349
    breakdown, 343, 349
    current regulator diode, 329–330
    depletion mode, 343
    depletion region, 342
    dual, 348, 349
    enhancement mode, 343
    equivalent circuit, 346–347
    gate-channel breakdown, 343, 349
    gate leakage current, 145
    input resistance, 347
    insulated gate (IGFET), 343
    junction (JFET), 342, 343, 380
    load lines, 346
    low noise, 145–146
    metal-oxide-silicon (MOS), 343, 349
    N-channel depletion IGFET, 344
    N-channel enhancement IGFET, 344
    N-channel JFET, 342, 344
    noise figure, 146
    ohmic region, 342, 343
    optimum source resistance, 146
    output conductance, 343, 345
    output resistance, 347
    P-channel depletion IGFET, 344
    P-channel enhancement IGFET, 344
    P-channel JFET, 344
    pentode region, 343
    photo, 380–381
    pinch-off, 342, 343, 345
    power, 195
    protection, 349
    source follower, 347–348
    temperature effects, 343, 348
    threshold voltage, 343
    transconductance, 343, 345, 351
    triode region, 343
    zero temperature coefficient biasing, 346
Filter:
    active, 158–173
    all-pass, 173
    band-pass, 163, 164, 166, 169, 421
        response time, 420
    band-stop, 171–173
    comb, 419, 425
    high-pass, 16, 162, 164, 165, 169
    integrating, 160
    lag, 280

lag-lead, 280
low-pass, 15–16, 18, 36, 161, 164, 165, 169, 278, 421
notch, 172–173
second order, 172
smoothing, 300–301
voltage tunable, 274
Final value theorem, 55–56
Firing angle, 360
Flicker noise, 33, 146
Flip-flip, 241
Flip-flop, 61, 240
Flop-flop, 123, 240, 424
Flywheel diode, 361
Focused photomultiplier, 385, 393
Follower, 87, 347–348
Forced response, 55
Fourier:
  comb filter, 419, 425
  components, 421
  integral, 425
  series, 52, 421
  transform, 52, 426
Four-layer devices, 355-356
Four-quadrant multiplier, 269–272
Frequency:
  beta cut-off, 43
  carrier, 422, 423
  compensation, (see Phase)
  complex, 52
  corner, 19, 143
  divider, 423
  domain, 52
  doubling, 276
  meter, 238
  modulation, 235
  multiplier, 276
  negative, 124
  response, 14–18, 81–82
    large signal, 106
    −6 dB/octave, 15–18
    −12 dB/octave, 136–138
    small signal, 106
    and stability, 81–82
  sweep, 235
  transition, 43
  unity-gain cut-off, 106, 134, 203
Frequency-to-voltage converter, 238–239
Frictional force, 175
Full-power bandwidth, 106, 203
Full-wave rectifier, 297, 301
Function:
  biquadratic, 167–168
  excitation, 51
  exponential, 449
  generator, 232–239
  IC types, 234
  Lorentzian, 8
  phase locking, 237
  response, 51
  single cycle, 237
  tanh, 275
  transfer, 51
  trigonometric, 449

unit impulse, 52
unit step, 52

Gain, 1–4
  closed-loop, 72
  common-mode, 151
  differential, 151
  margin, 126
  measurement, 104
  noise, 73, 126
  non-linear, 181
  open-loop, 71
  operational amplifier, 70–75
  peaking, 122–123, 138–140
  power, 1–4
  proportional, 181
  of two pole system, normalized, 138–140
  voltage, 2–4
Gain-bandwidth, 43
Galvanometer, 184
Gas discharge lamps, 397–399
Gate:
  current mode, 354
  linear, 353–355
  feedthrough, 354
  resistance modulation, 353
  sampling, 284
Geometric series, 426
Glow diode, 398–399
Ground loops, 29–30
Grounding, 28–30
Guard circuits, 30–31
Guard ring, 381
Guarding, 30–31, 182

Half-wave rectifier, 297, 299
Hall-effect devices, 196
Harmonic distortion, 230
High input resistance:
  amplifier, 183
    characteristics of devices, 184
High-pass filter, 16, 162, 164, 165, 169
Holding current, 357
Hole storage, 300, 321
Hot carrier diode, 38–39
Howland circuit, 307
h-parameter, 43
Hybrid parameters, 43
Hybrid-pi equivalent circuit, 44–45
Hysteresis, 362
  comparator, 261–263, 267
  Schmitt, 241

IGFET, 343
Imaginary number, 447
Imaginary part, 447, 448
Impedance, 5–7
  matching, 23–26
Impulse response, 429
Inductor, 6–9, 320, 321
  toroidal, 321
Initial value theorem, 55–56

459

Input:
  capacity, 105
  current, 76, 107, 183, 266
  impedance, 76, 105
    measurement, 105
    closed loop, 74
    common-mode, 84
    inverting amplifier, 83
    non-inverting amplifier, 84
  offset current, 108–110, 263
  offset voltage, 85, 107–112, 183, 201, 266, 273
  resistance, 76, 105
Instrumentation amplifier, 150–153
Insulated-gate FET, 343
Integral control, 178–180, 279
Integrated circuit:
  package pin numbering, 69–70
  types:
    AD301, 80
    AD509, 202
    AD520, 151–153
    AD530, 269, 271, 272
    AM26123, 242
    AM685, 265
    AM686, 265
    BZX47, 328, 329
    CA3048, 149
    CA3059, 363
    CA3060, 197–198
    CA3078, 198
    CA3080, 197
    CA3094T, 198
    CA3099E, 265
    CA3100, 202
    CA6741T, 33
    CD4047, 242
    CMP-01CY, 265
    HA2530, 202
    HA2535, 202
    H117, 242
    LH0021, 193
    LH0024C, 202
    LH0032C, 202
    LH0033C, 193, 202
    LH0041, 193
    LH0061, 202
    LH0063C, 193, 202
    LM103, 328
    LM301, 149
    LM307, 149
    LM309, 317
    LM311, 265
    LM318, 202
    LM320, 317
    LM322, 242, 243, 246–247
    LM323, 317
    LM339, 265
    LM340, 317
    LM379, 193
    LM381, 149
    LM3900, 169, 198–200
    LM4250, 198
    L036, 316, 317–319
    L115, 202
    L141, 135
    L144, 169, 198
    L148, 135
    MC1303, 149
    MC1438R, 193
    MC14528, 242
    MC1463, 317
    MC1469, 317
    MC1494, 269, 271, 272
    MC1495, 269, 271
    MC2870CR, 193
    MC3401, 169
    MC7900, 317
    MFC4050, 193
    MFC8020A, 193
    MIC74123A, 242
    μA710, 263, 264, 265
    μA711, 264, 265, 266
    μA723, 316–318
    μA725, 148, 149
    μA733, 158, 202
    μA734, 265
    μA739, 148, 149
    μA741, 76–77, 97, 102, 128, 132, 135, 136, 148, 150, 158, 164
    μA750, 265
    μA760, 265
    μA776, 148, 149, 198, 238
    μA78N00, 317
    μA7800, 317
    μA791C, 193
    μA795, 271
    MM74C123, 242
    NE501A, 202
    NE526, 265
    NE529, 265
    NE540, 193
    NE555V, 242
    NE566V, 234
    N8T20B, 242
    SG3502, 317
    SL415A, 193
    SL541C, 202
    SL550, 202
    SN15342, 242
    SN72720, 264
    SN72810, 265
    SN72820, 265
    SN74S124, 234
    SN74121, 242
    SN74122, 242
    SN74123, 242
    SN74221, 242
    SN7510, 202
    SN76008, 193
    SN76502, 156–158
    TAA320, 349
    TBA231, 149
    TBA625, 318
    TBA810S, 193
    TBA940, 193
    TDA2020, 193–195
    XRS200, 234
    XR2206, 234

XR2307, 234
XR-320, 242
342CJ, 242
3507, 202
3553, 193
3571, 193
3572, 193
8007, 149
8038, 234, 235, 236
821, 193
822, 193
825, 202
96L02, 242, 244, 245, 246
96S02, 245, 246
9600, 242
9602, 242–245
9603, 242
Integrating filter, 160
Integrating light detector, 403
Integrator, 87–94, 99, 125, 160, 231, 232, 239, 266, 421
   a.c., 89
   augmented, 93
   drift rate, 93–94
   finite bandwidth error, 90–92
   finite gain error, 92–93
   Howland, 307
   offset, 93–94
   operational, 87–94
   phase shift, 128
   stability, 126
   summing, 88–89
Interference, 302, 321, 362–363
Intermodulation, 422
Intrinsic standoff ratio, 248
Inverter, 321
Isolator, photon coupled, 399–402

Johnson noise, 31–32
$j\omega$ axis, 57
j operator, 448
Junction capacitance, 38, 101
Junction:
   diode, 36–39
   summing, 83, 86
Junction-gate FET, 342, 343, 380

Kirchoff's laws, 11–12

Lag network, 15
Lag-lead network, 17
Lamps, 394–399
   gas discharge, 397–399
   mercury arc, 399
   neon, 196, 397–399
   tungsten, 315, 378, 394–395
      current surge, 394–395
   xenon arc, 399
Laplace:
   inverse transform, 52
   theorems, 55–56
   transform pairs, 53
   transforms, 51–61
      applications of, 58–61

Large-signal bandwidth, 106, 202
LASCR (Light activated SCR), 356, 359, 403
Latching current, 357
Latch-up, 77, 105, 273, 274
Lateral PNP, 50, 135
Leading-edge discriminator, 267
Lead-lag network, 17
Lead network, 16
Leakage current, 30
Lechlanché cell, 322, 323
Left half-plane (LHP), 121
Lifetime, 383
Light-activated silicon controlled rectifier (LASCR), 356, 359, 403
Light blinker, 243
Light-emitting diode (LED), 394, 396–397, 399
   hp 5082-4484, 328
   voltage sensing, 402
Light units, 375–376
Limiter, 261
Line regulation, 305
Linear gate, 353–355
Linear velocity drive, 180
Load:
   active, 49
   regulation, 304
   torque, 175, 177–179
Locked oscillator, 231
Lock-in detection, 286, 392, 419, 420–424
   derivative output, 422–423
   digital, 424
   phase shift in, 421
   prefilter, 421, 422
   second derivative output, 423
   S/N ratio, 420–422
Lock range, 281
Logarithmic amplifier, 153–158, 274
   a.c., 155–158
   bandwidth, 155
   slewing rate, 155
   stability, 154–155
Loop-gain, 71, 120–121, 123–125, 262–263
Loop phase shift, 127
Loops, 29–30
Lorentzian function, 8
Low-drift amplifier, 200–201
Low-noise:
   amplifier, 143–150
   design, 146–149
   ICs, 149–150
   transistor, 143–146
Low-pass amplifier, 161, 164, 165, 169, 278
Luminous, 376

Majority carriers, 343
Mark-space ratio, 21, 241, 319, 321, 363
Matched transistors, 47, 48, 150, 154
Matching, 23–26
   coaxial cable, 25–26
   power, 23–25
   transformer, 24–26
Maximally flat response, 162
Meacham bridge, 250

Mercury:
  arc, 399
  cell, 322, 323
Mesh analysis, 11–12
Metal-oxide silicon transistor (MOST), 145, 343
Micropower amplifier, 198
Miller:
  compensation, 132–134
  effect, 28, 380, 401
Millman theorem, 11
Minimum phase-shift network, 58
Minority carrier, 38, 42, 343
Modulation, 274
  degree, 277
Modulator, 274–278
  amplitude, 276–277
  double balanced, 277
    noise in, 277–278
  frequency, 235
  pulse-width, 196–197, 320–321
Modulus, 5, 447, 449, 450
Moment of inertia, 175
Monostable multivibrator, 233, 240, 241
  IC types, 242
  lockout, 241–242
  retriggerable, 241–242, 243
  timing components for, 243, 245–246
  timing equation, 245
Monotonic response, 56
Motor:
  brushless d.c., 195–196
  servo, 195–197
  two-phase, 195
Motorboating, 125
Multiple collector, 48
Multiplication, 268, 275
Multiplier, 268–274, 421, 423
  analogue, 272–274
  four quadrant, 269–272
  variable transconductance, 269–272
Multivibrator, 239–247, 266
  astable, 239, 240, 241
  bistable, 239, 240
  emitter-coupled, 240–241
  monostable, 239, 240, 241
  retriggerable, 241–242, 243
  Schmitt trigger, 239, 240, 241, 243
  triggering, 240–241
Music power, 192

N-channel depletion IGFET, 344
N-channel enhancement IGFET, 344
N-channel JFET, 342–344
Negative feedback, 26–28
Negative frequency, 56
Negative resistance, 248, 356, 399
  current controlled, 248
  oscillator, 248–249
  voltage controlled, 249
Negative temperature coefficient resistor, (see Thermistor)
Neon discharge, 397–399
Nichols' chart, 203
Nickel-cadmium cell, 322, 323

Nodal analysis, 11–12
Node, 12
Noise, 31–36, 143–150, 419–420
  bandwidth, 36, 422
  bipolar transistor, 143–145
  blue, 186
  currents, 32–33, 34, 143–148, 381, 389–392
  equivalent resistances, 34–35, 144–147
  figure, 34–36
  flicker, 33, 146
  gain, 73, 126
  junction FET, 145–146
  Johnson, 31–32, 420
  Nyquist, 32
  $1/f$, 33, 145, 149, 381, 420
  photodiode, 380–381
  photoFET, 381
  photomultiplier, 387, 389, 391
  phototransistor, 381
  pink, 33
  popcorn, 33
  shot, 32–33, 381, 420
  voltages, 32, 33, 34, 143–146
  white, 32, 36, 186, 420, 422
Noise equivalent power (NEP), 380
Noise-in-signal, 389
Non-linear waveform shaping, 233–234
Non-minimum phase networks, 58
Norton:
  amplifier, 198–200
  theorem, 10–11
Notch filter, 172–173
Nyquist:
  diagram, 120, 123–125
  noise, 32
  stability criterion, 124–125

Offset:
  balancing, 110–112
  current, 108–110, 263
  equivalent circuit, 107–110
  voltage, 85, 107–112, 183, 201, 266, 273
Ohm's law, 1, 4
$1/f$ noise, 33, 45, 149
  bipolar transistor corner frequency, 145
One-shot, 241
Open-loop gain, 71
Operational amplifier:
  bandwidth, closed loop, 72, 79, 135, 136–137
  classes of, 75–76
  error factor, 71
  feedback fraction, 71
  gain:
    closed loop, 71
    open loop, 71
    stability, 72
  ideal, 70
  input:
    bias current, 107
    offset current, 107
    offset voltage, 108
  input protection, 112
  input resistance, 74, 84
  inverting, 70

−12 dB/octave, 136–138
low noise, 149–150
non-inverting, 84
output resistance, 73, 74
power, 303
protection, 112–113
741 amplifier, (see IC types)
slew rate, 106–107
summing, 83, 85–86
transconductance, 197–198
types, 75–81
virtual ground, 70, 71
  impedance of, 74
Operational differentiator, 94–100
Operational integrator, 87–94, 99
Operational theorems, 55–56
Optical:
  chopper, 196, 398
  detector, 267, 377
  exitance, 376
  flux, 376
  incidence, 376
  intensity, 376
  isolator, 359
  sterance, 376
Optimum counting time, 392
Optimum source resistance, 35
  bipolar transistor, 144
  JFET transistor, 146
Optocoupler, 359, 399–402
OR circuit, 264, 308
Oscillator:
  amplitude control, 231–232
  astable multivibrator, 239, 240, 241
  crystal, 249–251
  locked, 231
  negative resistance, 239, 248–249
  optically controlled, 403
  phase shift, 230, 232
  quadrature, 231–232
  RC, 229–232
  reference, 420
  relaxation, 239–247
  sinusoidal, 229–232
  two-phase, 231–232
  unijunction, 248–249
  voltage controlled, 278
  Wien, 229–231
Oscilloscope:
  probe, 22–23
  sampling, 286
Output impedance, 73, 74
Output resistance, 73, 105
  closed loop, 73–74
Output stage:
  biasing, 190
  complementary, 189, 191
  efficiency of, 189
  fault protection, 192–193
  integrated circuit, 194
  push-pull, 189
  quasi-complementary, 191
  quiescent current in, 188, 190
  thermal stability, 190, 194–195

Overdamping, 176
Overload protection, 192–195, 313–315
Overshoot, 123, 140, 177

Parabolic waveform, 175, 276
Parallel tee, 160
Parametric amplifier, 80–81
Partial fraction, 56
P-channel depletion IGFET, 344
P-channel enhancement IGFET, 344
P-channel JFET, 344
Peak detector, 287
Peaking, 138–140
  damping ratio, 122–123
Peak-inverse voltage, 297, 299
Phase, 5–7
  compensation, 128–134
  control IC for SCR, 360
  detector, 277, 278
  error, 18, 281
  jitter, 281
  locking, 235, 281
  margin, 126
  response, 14–18
  shift, 5–7, 74, 127, 230, 232, 421
    differentiator, 128
    integrator, 128
    loop, 127
Phase-locked loop, 278–283
  capture range, 281
  capture time, 281
  effect of noise, 282
  filters for, 280
  immediate lock, 281
  lock acquisition range, 281, 282
  lock detector, 282
  lock range, 281
  pull-in, 282
  tracking, 281
Phase-sensitive detector, 164, 286, 419, 421
Photocathode, 385, 386
Photocell, 385
Photoconductor, 315, 363
  time response, 384
  wavelength response, 383
Photodiode, 377, 378–380
  avalanche, 381–382
  capacity, 382
  characteristics, 379
  dark current, 379
  equivalent circuit, 379–380
  load line, 382–383
  noise, 380–381, 383
  photoconductive mode, 378, 380
  photovoltaic mode, 378, 380, 382
  response times, 379, 383
  reverse leakage current, 378
Photoelectric detectors, 376
  spectral response:
    eye, 378
    germanium, 378
    photomultiplier, 388
    silicon, 378
Photoemissive cell, 385

463

Photofet, 380–381
Photometric units, 375–376
Photomultiplier, 267, 377, 384, 385–394
    anode, 385
    bleeder chain, 385, 386, 394
        bypass capacitors, 386
    cathode, 385
    channeltron, 393
    collection efficiency, 386
    cooling, 386, 388–389
    dark current, 387, 388, 389
    dynode, 385, 386
    electron multiplication, 385
    field emission, 387
    focused, 385, 393
    gain, 386
    gain sensitivity, 386
    magnetic effects, 387
    multiplication factor, 386, 390
    noise in, 387, 389, 391
    non-linearity, 386
    photocathode, 385, 386
    quantum efficiency, 387–388, 389
    signal-to-noise ratio, 389–391
    spectral response, 387, 388
    temperature effects, 388
    time response, 385, 393
    unfocused, 385
    venetian blind, 385, 393
    voltage divider for, 385, 386
Photon, 389
Photon (pulse) counting, 387, 389, 391–393, 394
    count rate correction, 392–393
    optimum time, 392
Photon-coupled isolator, 399–402
    current transfer efficiency, 400
    electrical isolation, 399
    linear operation, 402
    speed, 401
    unilateral transfer, 399
Photoresistor, 196, 377, 383–384
    CdS, 383, 384
    CdSe, 383, 384
    CdS.Se, 384
    resistance ratio, 384
    spectral response, 383
    time response, 384
Photo SCR, 356, 359, 403
Photoswitch, 403
Phototransistor, 377, 378, 380–382, 399, 401
    Miller effect in, 380
    noise, 381
    response time, 380
Photovoltaic detector, 377
    open circuit voltage, 378–379
Pick-off, 267
Pick-up, 28–30
Piezoelectric:
    effect, 182
    transducer, 101, 180
Piggy-back regulator, 313
Pile-up, 268
PIN diode, 379, 381
Pinch-off voltage, 342, 343, 345

Pink noise, 33
Planar transistor, 46, 269
Planck:
    constant, 32, 387
    law, 32, 378
PN diode, 36–39
    junction, 378
    junction particle detector, 101
    logarithmic characteristic, 39, 153
PNP transistors, 50
    lateral, 76, 135
    substrate, 50
PNPN devices, 249, 355–362
    characteristics, 357
    loop gain, 355
    operation, 355–356
    triggering, 356, 357, 359
    types, 358
Poisson statistics, 32, 389
Polar coordinates, 447
Pole, 56–58, 120–123
    complex, 122, 160
    dominant, 138
Pole-zero:
    cancellation, 57, 131, 202
    diagram, 56–58, 159
Polynomial, 53, 56, 120
Position servo, 177
Positive feedback, 27, 123, 239, 261, 262, 263, 266, 273, 315, 321, 355–356
Positive zero, 124
Power:
    amplifier, 188–197
        booster, 153
        efficiencies, 189
        protection, 192–193
    driver, 193
    FET, 195
    gain, 1–4
    matching, 23–25
    supply, (see Regulator)
    supply amplifier, 191, 312
    transistor, 45–46
Powers, raising to, 273
Primary cell, 322–323
Probe, 22–23
Programmable amplifier, 198
Programmable unijunction, 357
Programming:
    constant, 303
    resistance, 303, 315
Propagation:
    delay, 25
    velocity, 25
Proportional gain, 181
Proportional error control, 175
Proportional-plus-integral control, 178–180
Proportional servo, 279
Protection circuits, 112–113
Pull-in time, 281
Pulse:
    amplifier, 201
    bandwidth, 19–21
    bipolar, 22

coincidence, 267
droop, 21
pile-up, 201, 268
transformer, 302, 359
Pulse ratemeter, 238
Pulse testing, 137–138, 140
Pulse transformer, 26
Pulse-width modulator, 196–197, 320–321

Q, 7–9, 122–123, 233, 234, 249
of filters, 158, 160, 162, 166, 168–172
and peaking, 140
of two-pole system, 122, 138–139
Quartz crystal, 249
Quadrature oscillator, 231–232
Quasi-complementary output stage, 191

Radiant, 376
Radiometric units, 375–376
Raising to a power, 274
Ramp input, 96, 232, 233
Rate effects, 361
Ratemeter, 238
Ratio to dB conversion, 2–4
Rational function, 53
RC oscillator, 229–232
RC shunt compensation, 128–132
Reactance, 5–6
Real part, 448
Rectifier, 297–302
average current, 299
bridge, 297, 298
BYX50/55, 321
centre tap, 297, 299
diode, 299–300
doubler, 298
fast recovery, 300, 321
forward voltage drop, 297, 300
full-wave, 297, 301
half-wave, 297, 299
1AV/1BV, 299
IN3879, 321
IN4001/7, 38
peak current, 299, 300
peak inverse voltage, 297, 299
reverse avalanche, 300
reverse leakage current, 300
reverse recovery time, 300
ripple voltage, 299
Schottky, 300, 321
silicon controlled, 301–302
smoothing capacitor, 300–301
smoothing filter, 297, 299, 300–301
surge current, 300
three-phase, 299
transformer, 297
voltage multiplying, 298
Reed relay, 352
Reference:
cell, 325
voltage diode, 328–329
Regulation:
line, 305
load, 304

Regulator, 298, 300
as bridge, 304
constant current-constant voltage, 308–309
current, 305–308, 316, 319
dual voltage, 311
Howland current, 306–307
input regulation, 305
integrated circuit, 316–319
low current, 306
master connection, 309
as operational amplifier, 303–304
operational amplifier current, 306
output capacitor, 304
output resistance, 304
parallel connection, 310–311
piggy-back, 313
protection circuits, 313–315
crowbar, 315
current limiting, 314
foldback, 314, 315
lockout, 315
remote sensing, 315
series, 302–305
series connection, 309–310
series element, 300, 302, 319
slave connection, 309
slewing rate, 305
switching, 316, 319–322
tracking, 311–312
transformerless, 321–322
voltage, 302–305
Relaxation oscillator, 239–247
Resistance, 1, 4–5
ballast, 398, 399
base spreading, 44
common mode, 151, 183
copper, temperature coefficient, 305
differential, 151, 183
diode incremental, 38
high value, 183
input, 105
negative, 248, 356, 399
negative temperature coefficient (see Thermistor)
noise equivalent, 34–35
output, 73, 105
photo, 315, 363, 383–384
programming, 303, 306, 315
voltage controlled, 164, 349–352
Resistors:
carbon film, 183
matched film, 201
metal film, 183
metal oxide, 183
photo, 315
silicon, 154
Resonance, 7–9
Response:
aperiodic, 61, 140, 262, 263
Butterworth, 159
Chebychev, 159
forced, 55
free, 55, 57
frequency, 14–18
(continued)

Response: (*continued*)
  impulse, 429
  maximally flat, 159
  monotonic, 56
  −6 dB/octave, 15–18
  −12 dB/octave, 136–138
  oscillatory, 56
  phase, 14–18
  pulse, 18–22
  RC, 14–22
  resonant, 7–9
  square wave, 20–22, 140–141
  step, 19, 20
  transient, 138–141
Reverse current, 300
Richardson law, 388
Right half-plane (RHP), 58, 120, 122, 124, 229
Ring-of-three, 169
Ripple, 299
Rise time, 18–23, 123, 201
Root-locus, 61, 120–123
Root mean square (r.m.s.), 5
Roots of equation, 56, 120–121
  extraction of, 274
Routh-Hurwitz method, 179

Safe operating area, 39–41
Sample-and-hold, 283–287
  aliasing, 287
  aperture time, 285
    stability, 285
  acquisition time, 284
  boxcar integrator, 286
  cascaded, 286
  closed-loop, 285
  delay time, 284, 285
  droop in, 285, 286
  hold time, 285, 286
  IC types, 287
  open-loop, 285
  peak detector, 287
  response speed, 286
  tracking accuracy, 285
Sampling oscilloscope, 286
Sampling theorem, 286–287, 424
Sampling time, 284
Saturation voltage, 42
Sawtooth wave, 232, 233
Schmitt trigger, 239, 240, 241, 246, 400, 401
Schottky diode, 38–39
Second breakdown, 40
Secondary cell, 322, 323–325
Secondary electrons, 386
Selectivity, 230
Semiconductor particle detector, 101
Series chopper, 352–353
Series feedback, 27
Series-parallel equivalent circuit, 14
Series regulator, 302–303
Series-shunt chopper, 352–353
Servo, 27–28, 173–181
  a.c., 197
  amplifier, 173, 195–197
  anticipation, 178

backlash, 177
class D, 196–197
controller, 174, 177, 180–181
controlled output, 174
damping, 176
derivative, 177
equation of motion, 175
error, 174
  proportional, 175
  steady state, 174
integral, 178
motor, 195–197
overshoot, 177
proportional, 173, 175, 363
regulating, 302
set input, 174
settling, 177
three-term, 180–181
  optimization, 181
transient response, 175, 176
type, 0, 1, 2, 174
velocity, 180
velocity lag, 177, 178
Set input, 174
Settling time, 19, 177, 202
  duration, 103
Shaping networks, 233–234
Short-circuit protection, 192–193, 313–315
Shot noise, 32–33, 381, 420
Shunt chopper, 352–353
Shunt compensation, 128–132
Shunt feedback, 27
Side bands, 277
σ axis, 57, 59
Signal:
  averaging, 419, 424–427
    in frequency domain, 425–427
    in time domain, 424–425
    S/N improvement, 424–425
  carrier, 275
  digitizing, 283
  diode, 38
  modulating, 275
Signal-to-noise ratio, 34–36, 74, 381, 420
Silicon bilateral switch, 358
Silicon controlled rectifier (SCR), 301–302, 315, 355, 357–361, 400
  conduction angle, 302, 360
  firing angle, 360
  full-wave phase control, 302, 360–361
  half-controlled bridge, 361
  holding current, 357
  latching current, 357
  light activated, 359
  leakage current, 355
  load line, 357–359
  phase control, 359–361
  photo, 356, 359, 403
  positive feedback in, 355–356
  rate effects, 361
  reactive loads, 361
  snubber, 361
  trigger pulse, 301, 357, 359
  turn-on time, 357

Silicon:
   controlled switch, 358
   resistor, 154
   unilateral switch, 358, 361
Single-diffused transistor, 46
   epitaxial base, 46
Sinusoidal oscillator, 229–232
Slewing rate, 106–107, 137, 203, 238, 284
   bipolar transistor, 203
   FET transistor, 203
Slope-reversal discriminator, 268
Snap-off diode, 268
Snubber circuits, 361
Solar cell, 380
Source follower, 347–348
Square wave, 5, 232, 275
Squaring, 273
Square-root extraction, 274
Stability:
   amplitude, 231–232
   conditional, 125
   of feedback systems, 120–138
   thermal, 190, 343
   unconditional, 122
Stabilizer, (see Regulator)
Stabistor, 325, 328
   EVR1, 328
   MR2361, 328
Staircase generator, 237
Standard cell, 323, 325
Star-delta transformation, 12–14
State-variable synthesis, 167–168
Steady-state error, 174
Step:
   input, 52, 91, 174
   response, 19, 20
Strobe, 264, 266, 286
Strobed discriminator, 264, 266
Substrate PNP, 50
Summing, 82, 83, 85–86
   junction, 83, 86
   operational amplifier, 83, 85–86
Super beta, 183
Superposition theorem, 9–10, 13
Supply-voltage:
   limits, 103
   rejection ratio, 106
Suppressed-carrier modulation, 276
Susceptance, 7
Switch:
   analogue gate, 352
   bipolar, 352
   bounce, 352
   break-before-make, 355
   chopper, 352–353
   diode bridge, 284
   distortion in, 352
   drivers for, 353
   feedthrough, 284, 352, 354
   FET, 352
   ideal, 352
   light activated, 403
   low level, 343
   multiplex, 355

   offset in, 284
   photo, 403
   reed, 352
   sampling, 283, 284
   silicon bilateral, 358
   silicon controlled, 358
   silicon unilateral, 358, 361
   type comparison, 354
Switching regulator, 316, 319–322
   efficiency, 321
   series, 319–321
   transformerless, 319, 321–322
Synchronous detector, 164, 286, 419, 421

Tachogenerator, 360
Tachometer, 177, 243
Tantalum capacitor, 30
Taylor series, 423
Tee-pi transformation, 12–14
Temperature, 32
   coefficient:
      copper resistivity, 305
      differential amplifier, 201
      diode leakage current, 38
      PN junction voltage, 38, 318
      standard cells, 323, 325
      zener voltage, 318, 326, 328, 329
   compensation, 154, 155, 318–319, 326, 328–329, [346, 382
   drift, 75, 78, 200–201, 346
   stabilized amplifier, 200
Theorems:
   convolution, 56
   DeMoivre, 449
   Euler, 449
   final value, 55–56, 174
   initial value, 55–56
   Kirchoff, 11–12
   Laplace, 55–56
   Millman, 11
   network, 9–14
   Norton, 10–11
   operational, 55–56
   sampling, 286–287, 424
   shifting, 56
   superposition, 9–10
   Thévenin, 10
Thermal gradients, 194
Thermal runaway, 343
Thermal shutdown, 193, 194–195
Thermistor, 154, 155, 229, 231, 315, 360, 363
Thermocouple, 200
Thermojunction, 200
Thévenin's theorem, 10
Three-phase rectifier, 299
Three-pole system, 123, 179
Three-term controller, 180–181
   adjustment of, 181
Threshold voltage, 343
Thyristor, 355–362
   avalanche breakdown, 356
   equivalent circuit, 355–356
   holding current, 356
   latching current, 356
   light activated, 403

Time:
  aperture, 285
  delay, 25
  rise, 18–23
  settling, 19, 177, 202
  walk, 267
Time constant, 18–21
Timer, 242–243, 246–247
  IC types, 242
  lockout, 246
Timing capacitor, 243, 245, 246, 248
Toroidal transformer, 25, 299
Torque, 175
Track-hold, 283
Tracking filter, 279
Transconductance, 43–45, 197, 198, 272
Transconductance amplifier, 197–198
Transdiode, 153–155
Transfer function, 51
Transform:
  Fourier, 52
  Laplace, 51–61
  star-delta, 12–14
  tee-pi, 12–14
Transformer:
  broad band, 26
  electrostatic screen, 298
  matching, 24–26
  pulse, 26, 302
  toroidal, 25, 299
Transformerless regulator, 321–322
Transient response, 123, 138–141
Transimpedance amplifier, 86–87, 382, 387
Transistor, 39–46
  application of types, 45–46
  base spreading resistance, 44
  bipolar, 39–46
  breakdown, 39–41
    first, 40
    second, 40
  complementary, 46
  current gain, 41–43
  current hogging, 40
  Darlington, 190–191
  derating, 41
  double diffused, 46
  dual, 200
  epibase, 46
  equivalent circuits, 41–45
    hybrid, 42–43
    hybrid-pi, 44–45
    tee, 41
  field effect, 342–349
  gain-bandwidth product, 43
  input resistance, 41–45
  lateral PNP, 50, 76
  low noise, 143–146
  matched, 47, 48, 150, 154
  maximum safe area of operation, 40–41
  noise in, 143–146
  parameters, 39–46
  parameters, prediction of, 43–45
  photo, 377, 378, 380–382, 399, 401
  planar, 46, 269

  power, comparison of, 45–46
  ratings, 39–41
  saturation, 42
  secondary breakdown, 40
  single diffused, 46
  single diffused epitaxial base, 46
  super beta, 183
  transconductance, 43–45
  transition frequency, 43
  triple diffused, 46
  unibase, 46
  unijunction, 248–249, 357
  vertical PNP, 50
  voltage mode, 45
Transition frequency, 43
Triac, 360, 361–362, 400
  commutation, 361
  conduction angle, 362
  phase control, 361–362
  triggering, 361
  turn-off, 361
Triangular wave, 5
Triboelectric effect, 182
Trigger diac, 357, 358
Triple-diffused transistor, 46
TTL, 242, 243
Tunnel diode, 249
Twin-tee, 160
  response curves, 171
Two-integrator loop, 169, 231–232
Two-phase motor, 195
Two-phase oscillator, 231–232

Unconditional stability, 122
Underdamping, 140, 176
Undershoot, 21, 201
Unibase transistor, 46
Unijunction transistor, 248–249, 357
  complementary, 249
  intrinsic standoff ratio, 248
  load lines, 248
  oscillator, 248–249
  peak current, 249
  programmable, 249, 357
  valley current, 248
Unilateral switch, 361
Unipolar devices, 343
Unity-gain bandwidth, 43, 81, 106, 134, 203
Unity-gain cut-off frequency, 43, 81, 106, 134, 203
Univibrator, 239, 240–241

Valence band, 378
Valley current, 248
Varactor, 80–81
  bridge amplifier, 80
Variable transconductance multiplier, 269–272
Variable zener, 49–50, 190
Velocity lag, 177, 178
Velocity servo, 180
Venetian blind photomultiplier, 385, 393,
Vertical PNP transistor, 50
Vibrating capacitor electrometer, 184, 188
Vibrating reed electrometer, 184, 188

Video amplifier, 201
Virtual ground, 70–71, 74, 83, 261, 263
   differential, 272
Visible spectral region, 376
Voltage:
   controlled:
      attenuator, 351
      distortion in, 352
      function generator, 274
      gain element, 274
      incremental conductance, 351
      linearity, 351–352
      normalized resistance variation, 351
      offset voltage, 350
      oscillator (VCO), 278
      resistor, 164, 349–352
      switch, 349, 352–355
      voltage source (VCVS), 165
   doubler, 298
   follower, 82, 87
   to-frequency converter, 239
   gain, 2–4
   multiplying rectifier, 298
   reference diode, 328–329
   regulator, (see Regulator)
      diode, 325–328
      glow diode, 399
      switching, 316, 319–322
   sensing LED, 402
   source, 10
   stabilizer, (see Regulator)
   tunable filter, 274

Waveform:
   amplitude modulated, 276
      suppressed carrier, 276
   aperiodic, 123
   digital synthesis, 239
   diode shaper, 233–234
      distortion, 234
   frequency modulated, 235
   hyperbolic, 273
   non-linear shaping, 233–234
   parabolic, 175, 276
   pulse, 232, 248
   ramp, 96, 232, 233
   sawtooth, 232, 233
   shaping, 235
   sinusoidal, 18, 232, 233, 234
   square, 5, 232, 275
   staircase, 237
   triangular, 5, 232, 234
White noise, 32, 36
Wideband amplifier, 201–204
Wien bridge, 59–61, 229–231
   selectivity of, 230
   stability factor, 230
Wien oscillator, 229–231
   amplitude stabilization of, 231
Wien law, 378
Window discriminator, 266

Xenon arc, 399
X-Y recorder, 196

y-parameters, 43, 345

Zero, 56–58, 124
   complex, 160
   positive, 124
Zero-crossing detector, 267
Zero-current switching, 364
Zero-voltage switching, 362–364
   IC's for, 363
   for triac, 364
Zener diode, 300, 386
   active, 49–50
   breakdown, 326
      time, 328
   capacity, 328
   dynamic resistance, 327
   noise in, 328
   reference, 328–329
   regulator, 327
   stabistor, 325, 328
   temperature coefficient, 326
   variable, 49–50
Zeta (damping ratio), 140, 176, 177, 178